SO-BBZ-802

Intermediate Algebra

Eighth Edition

Irving Drooyan
Los Angeles Pierce College (Emeritus)

Katherine Franklin Yoshiwara
Los Angeles Pierce College

THOMSON
™
BROOKS/COLE

Australia · Canada · Mexico · Singapore · Spain · United Kingdom · United States

Intermediate Algebra, Eighth Edition
Irving Drooyan/Katherine Franklin Yoshiwara

Custom Editor:
John Horvath

Project Development Editor:
Lisa Sizemore

Marketing Coordinator:
Sara Mercurio

Production/Manufacturing Supervisor:
Donna M. Brown

Project Coordinator:
Terri Daley

Pre-Media Services Supervisor:
Dan Plofchan

Rights and Permissions Specialist:
Bahman Naraghi

Senior Prepress Specialist:
Joel Brennecke

Cover Design:
Krista Pierson

Cover Image:
© Getty Images

Printer:
RR Donnelley

© 2006 Brooks/Cole, a part of the Thomson Corporation. Thomson, the Star logo and Brooks/Cole are trademarks used herein under license.

ALL RIGHTS RESERVED. No part of this work covered by the copyright hereon may be reproduced or used in any form or by any means — graphic, electronic, or mechanical, including photocopying, recording, taping, Web distribution or information storage and retrieval systems — without the written permission of the publisher.

Printed in the United States of America
1 2 3 4 5 6 7 8 9 10 11 12 13 14 08 07 06 05

For information about our products, contact us at:
Thomson Learning Academic Resource Center
(800) 423-0563

For permission to use material from this text or product, submit a request online at **http://www.thomsonrights.com**. Any additional questions about permissions can be submitted by email to **thomsonrights@thomson.com**.

The Adaptable Courseware Program consists of products and additions to existing Wadsworth products that are produced from camera-ready copy. Peer review, class testing, and accuracy are primarily the responsibility of the author(s).

Student Edition: ISBN 0-495-07828-X

Thomson Custom Solutions
5191 Natorp Boulevard
Mason, OH 45040
www.thomsoncustom.com

Thomson Higher Education
10 Davis Drive
Belmont, CA 94002-3098
USA

Asia (Including India):
Thomson Learning
60 Albert Street, #15-01
Albert Complex
Singapore 189969
Tel 65 336-6411
Fax 65 336-7411

Australia/New Zealand:
Thomson Learning Australia
102 Dodds Street
Southbank, Victoria 3006
Australia

Latin America:
Thomson Learning
Seneca 53
Colonia Polano
11560 Mexico, D.F., Mexico
Tel (525) 281-2906
Fax (525) 281-2656

Canada:
Thomson Nelson
1120 Birchmount Road
Toronto, Ontario
Canada M1K 5G4
Tel (416) 752-9100
Fax (416) 752-8102

UK/Europe/Middle East/Africa:
Thomson Learning
High Holborn House
50-51 Bedford Row
London, WC1R 4L$
United Kingdom
Tel 44 (020) 7067-2500
Fax 44 (020) 7067-2600

Spain (Includes Portugal):
Thomson Paraninfo
Calle Magallanes 25
28015 Madrid
España
Tel 34 (0)91 446-3350
Fax 34 (0)91 445-6218

ALLEGHENY CAMPUS BOOKSTORE
821 RIDGE AVE
PITTSBURGH, PA 15212
412-237-2532

ALL SALES FINAL

03-May-06   11:12 AM
Clerk: donna Register # 1

Trans. #158655
    * - Non Taxable Items

PITTMAN, WILLIAM
 Customer ID: 127852

049507828X   1 $69.50 $69.50*
  INTERMEDIATE ALGEBRA CUSTOM (05
Total Items: 1

                Sub-Total: $69.50
                    Total: $69.50
            Total Tendered: $69.50
               Change Due: $0.00

Payment Via:
    VISA/MC $69.50
    XXXXXXXXXXXX4873

            Thank You

Real Numbers

Real numbers
- Rational numbers · Irrational numbers
- Integers · Nonintegers
- Negative integers · Whole numbers
- Zero · Natural numbers

$-a = -1 \cdot a$

$|a| = \begin{cases} a & \text{if } a \geq 0 \\ -a & \text{if } a < 0 \end{cases}$

Some Properties of Real Numbers

$\left.\begin{array}{l} a + b = b + a \\ a \cdot b = b \cdot a \end{array}\right\}$ Commutative properties

$\left.\begin{array}{l} (a + b) + c = a + (b + c) \\ (a \cdot b) \cdot c = a \cdot (b \cdot c) \end{array}\right\}$ Associative properties

$\left.\begin{array}{l} a + 0 = a \\ a \cdot 1 = a \end{array}\right\}$ Identity properties

$a + (-a) = 0$ Negative (or additive-inverse) property

$a \cdot \dfrac{1}{a} = 1 \quad (a \neq 0)$ Reciprocal (or multiplicative inverse) property

$a \cdot 0 = 0$

$-(-a) = a$

Special Products and Factors

$$(x + a)(x + b) = x^2 + (a + b)x + ab$$
$$(x + a)^2 = x^2 + 2ax + a^2$$
$$(x - a)^2 = x^2 - 2ax + a^2$$
$$(x + a)(x - a) = x^2 - a^2$$
$$(x + a)(x^2 - ax + a^2) = x^3 + a^3$$
$$(x - a)(x^2 + ax + a^2) = x^3 + a^3$$

Properties of Fractions

(Denominators do not equal zero.)

$\dfrac{a}{b} = \dfrac{a \cdot c}{b \cdot c}$ Fundamental principle of fractions

$\dfrac{-a}{b} = \dfrac{a}{-b} = -\dfrac{a}{b} = -\dfrac{-a}{-b}$

$\dfrac{a}{b} = \dfrac{-a}{-b} = -\dfrac{a}{-b} = -\dfrac{-a}{b}$

$\dfrac{a}{c} + \dfrac{b}{c} = \dfrac{a + b}{c}; \quad \dfrac{a}{c} - \dfrac{b}{c} = \dfrac{a - b}{c}$

$\dfrac{a}{b} \cdot \dfrac{c}{d} = \dfrac{a \cdot c}{b \cdot d}; \quad \dfrac{a}{b} \div \dfrac{c}{d} = \dfrac{a \cdot d}{b \cdot c}$

Powers

For n a natural number

$a^n = a \cdot a \cdot a \cdots a \quad (n \text{ factors})$

$a^0 = 1 \quad (a \neq 0)$

$a^{-n} = \dfrac{1}{a^n} \quad (a \neq 0)$

$(a^{1/n})^n = a \quad$ (if n is even, $a > 0$, and $a^{1/n} > 0$)

$a^{m/n} = (a^m)^{1/n} = (a^{1/n})^m \quad (a > 0)$

Laws of Exponents

I $a^m \cdot a^n = a^{m+n}$

II $\dfrac{a^m}{a^n} = a^{m-n} = \dfrac{1}{a^{n-m}} \quad (a \neq 0)$

III $(a^m)^n = a^{mn}$

IV $(ab)^m = a^m b^m$

V $\left(\dfrac{a}{b}\right)^m = \dfrac{a^m}{b^m} \quad (b \neq 0)$

Roots

$a^{1/n} = \sqrt[n]{a} \quad$ (if n is even, $a > 0$, and $\sqrt[n]{a} > 0$)

$\sqrt[n]{a^n} = |a| \quad$ for n even

$\sqrt[n]{a^n} = a \quad$ for n odd

$a^{m/n} = \sqrt[n]{a^m} = (\sqrt[n]{a})^m \quad (a > 0)$

I $\quad \sqrt[n]{ab} = \sqrt[n]{a}\sqrt[n]{b} \quad (a > 0, b > 0)$

II $\quad \sqrt[n]{\dfrac{a}{b}} = \dfrac{\sqrt[n]{a}}{\sqrt[n]{b}} \quad (a > 0, b > 0)$

III $\quad \sqrt[cn]{a^{cm}} = \sqrt[n]{a^m} \quad (a > 0)$

Complex Numbers

For $b > 0$, $\quad (\sqrt{-b})^2 = -b$

$i = \sqrt{-1}; \quad i^2 = -1$

$\sqrt{-b} = \sqrt{-1}\sqrt{b} = i\sqrt{b}$

Complex numbers: $a + bi$

$(b = 0) \qquad\qquad\qquad (b \neq 0)$

Real numbers: $a + bi = a$
Imaginary numbers: $a + bi \quad (a = 0)$
Pure imaginary numbers: $a + bi = bi$

Nonlinear Equations

$ab = 0 \quad$ if a equals zero, b equals zero, or a and b equal zero

$x^2 = c \quad$ is equivalent to

$$x = \sqrt{c} \quad \text{or} \quad x = -\sqrt{c}$$

$ax^2 + bx + c = 0 \quad$ is equivalent to

$$x = \frac{-b \pm \sqrt{b^2 - 4ac}}{2a}$$

For n a natural number, the solution set of

$$[P(x)]^n = [Q(x)]^n$$

contains all the solutions of

$$P(x) = Q(x).$$

Linear Equations in Two Variables

Distance: $\qquad d = \sqrt{(x_2 - x_1)^2 + (y_2 - y_1)^2}$

Slope: $\qquad m = \dfrac{y_2 - y_1}{x_2 - x_1} \quad (x_1 \neq x_2)$

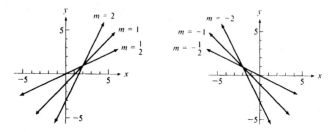

Two line segments with slopes m_1 and m_2 are:

$$\text{parallel if} \quad m_1 = m_2$$
$$\text{perpendicular if} \quad m_1 m_2 = -1$$

Forms of linear equations:

$ax + by + c = 0$	Standard form
$y - y_1 = m(x - x_1)$	Point-slope form
$y = mx + b$	Slope-intercept form
$\dfrac{x}{a} + \dfrac{y}{b} = 1$	Intercept form

Logarithmic Functions

The logarithmic function

$$x = b^y \quad \text{or} \quad y = \log_b x \quad (x > 0)$$

is the inverse of the exponential function

$$y = b^x \quad (y > 0)$$

Laws of Logarithms

I $\quad \log_b(x_1 x_2) = \log_b x_1 + \log_b x_2$

II $\quad \log_b \dfrac{x_2}{x_1} = \log_b x_2 - \log_b x_1$

III $\quad \log_b x^p = p \log_b x$

$$\ln x = \log_e x = \frac{\log_{10} x}{\log_{10} e}$$

$$= 2.303 \log_{10} x$$

(continued on back endpapers)

Contents

Preface

Intermediate Algebra, Eighth Edition, is designed for a standard intermediate algebra course for college students who need to prepare for further study in mathematics or statistics and who require a brief review of elementary algebra. This text covers the essential intermediate algebra topics and presents them in a direct, no-nonsense manner that students and instructors alike have appreciated over the years.

When preparing this edition of *Intermediate Algebra*, we made every effort to maintain the time-tested features that contributed to the success of previous editions, while incorporating improvements recommended by reviewers and professional organizations such as the American Mathematical Association of Two Year Colleges and the National Council of Teachers of Mathematics. By carefully integrating new elements into our proven pedagogical approach, we believe we have created a better tool for learning and teaching.

Goals and Features of the Eighth Edition

We understand that instructors and students need to cover a wide range of topics in a limited time. One of our principal goals in this revision was to better facilitate the coverage of review materials and to promote flexibility in topic coverage. To this end, we have implemented several key revision and reorganizations that will help instructors and students get to the core topics of intermediate algebra—modeling, functions, and graphs—more quickly.

To facilitate the coverage of review materials, we have revised Chapters 1 through 4 to provide a fast-paced review of topics ususally covered in elementary algebra; only basic topics that provide a foundation for the following chapters are included. Detailed annotations have been added to the examples, and exercise sets have been revised to make these early chapters student friendly and accessible. This approach will help students progress comfortably and stay motivated as they move through the review of basic skills and mathematical modeling. If students have successfully completed an elementary algebra course recently, Chapters 1 through 4 can be covered by treating several sections in one class period or by limiting assignments to selected sections and to the chapter sumaries and review exercises at the end of each chapter.

Some topics that are not prerequisites for the core topics of modeling, functions, and graphs have been moved to later chapters in the eighth edition. In particular, inequalities are now treated in Chapter 12. Instructors who prefer to cover linear inequalities earlier with linear equations can use sections of Chapter 12 together with related treatments of equalities in earlier chapters.

To provide instructors with more flexibility in selecting topics, we now treat functions—including linear, quadratic, exponential, and logarithmic functions—earlier in Chapters 8 and 9. The chapters that follow are independent of each other. To meet course objectives and time limitations, therefore, any of these chapters can be omitted without loss of continuity.

Additional Changes in the Eighth Edition

The following additional changes have been made in this edition based on recommendations from users of the text and other reviewers:

- More attention has been given to problem solving and graphing.
- Section 7.5, a new section on applications of linear equations and their graphs, has been added to Chapter 7 "Equations in Two Variables."
- Introduced earlier in this edition (Section 8.3) are quadratic functions, with new treatment of graphing and emphasis on modeling.
- Section 8.4 on exponential functions includes new material on exponential growth and exponential decay models.
- New exercises in other sections of Chapters 7 and 8 also require modeling methods.
- All central conics are now treated together in Section 11.1, thereby allowing instructors, who are usually under some time constraints toward the end of the semester, to cover the material in a single class period.
- At the request of some reviewers and users of the earlier edition, Chapter 13, entitled "Sequences and Series," has been added.
- Geometric topics have been added to several sections as applications of algebraic properties. These topics provide material for modeling that is practical and usually interesting to students. In addition, integrating of topics, particularly geometric topics, is strongly recommended by the professional organizations.
- To provide greater variety, exercise sets now include a group entitled Miscellaneous Exercises. These exercises are often more challenging than the basic exercises that are referenced to examples in the text.
- Cumulative Exercises, which are included at the end of each chapter, beginning with Chapter 2, provide a wide variety of exercises and word problems so students can continually test their mastery of material covered earlier. These exercises also remind students that topics studied are interconnected parts of a whole, not isolated units.
- More attention has been given to material that provides appropriate opportunities for calculator use. Specifically, a new section on decimal approximations of irrational numbers that requires the use of scientific calculators has been added to Chapter 5, "Exponents, Roots and Radicals." Section 5.3 provides treatment concerning the use of a scientific calculator for scientific notation, and Section 5.6 covers calculator treatment of rational exponents. (Note

that material requiring the use of a calculator is not a prerequisite for any topics that follow in the text and can be omitted.)

A Comment on Calculators

Calculators are useful tools in mathematics. By giving additional coverage to those topics suitable to calculator use, we hope to help students learn how and when to use their calculators wisely.

A simple four-function calculator will be helpful for decimal computations, which occur in evaluating formulas and solving word problems. Students will certainly be familiar with the simple calculator operations for these computations.

Applications that require a scientific calculator (or the corresponding operations on a graphing calculator) are optional. As we have noted, Section 5.3 includes a calculator treatment of scientific notation and Section 5.6 covers a calculator treatment of rational exponents. Section 8.4 also includes a calculator approach to powers; and Section 9.4 provides a calculator treatment of logarithms, which can be used in place of Section 9.3, where tables are used.

Key strokes are shown when scientific calculators are used, thereby helping students to master this tool while they study mathematics. Although no examples or exercises are formally designated as intended for graphing calculators, the increased emphasis on graphing in this edition does offer opportunities for their use.

Special Features

- Each chapter concludes with a Chapter Summary. These summaries are highlighted for easy identification.
- Review Exercises are included at the end of each chapter and provide students with practice for tests.
- Cumulative Exercises are included at the end of each chapter, beginning with Chapter 2.
- Calculator exercises are identified by a ▣ icon.
- Important concepts are boxed so that they are easily identifiable.
- Common Errors are highlighted so that students learn to recognize and avoid common mistakes.
- Subheads are used to highlight the major topics in each section.
- The answer section includes answers to all odd-numbered exercises in each section and answers to all chapter review and cumulative review exercises. Answers for word problems include appropriate mathematical models.
- For easy reference important mathematical properties are provided on the front and back endpapers.
- A list of mathematical symbols, referenced to appropriate sections of the text, follows the preface.
- Tables for e^x and $\ln x$, as well as the traditional $\log x$ table, are included for students using tables.

Design

The design and page layout of a text should support the pedagogical goals. Our goal in the eighth edition was to present the core topics of intermediate algebra in a direct, clear, and effective manner. Consequently, the text has been designed to have a clean straightforward appearance, which we hope will help students to stay focused on the important concepts.

Ancillaries

- A **Student's Solutions Manual**, containing detailed solutions to all even-numbered exercises, is available for purchase by students.
- **Test Items**, available free to adopters, contains two multiple-choice and two fill-in tests per chapter, plus two forms of the final exam.
- **EXPTest** and **ExamBuilder**, computerized testing programs in DOS and Macintosh formats, are also available free to adopters. Users can edit and scramble test items or create their own.

Acknowledgments

We benefited greatly from the comments and suggestions of the many instructors who reviewed drafts of the eighth edition manuscript. They include:

Thomas Arbutiski
Community College of Allegheny County

Robert J. Biagini-Komas
College of San Mateo

Sharon Rose Butler-Davis
Pikes Peak Community College

Curtis L. Card
Black Hills State University

Michael K. Fikar
Long Island University

Joseph J. Friederichs
Dawson Community College

Dauhrice K. Gibson
Gulf Coast Community College

Stephen C. Hennagin
Ouachita Baptist University

J. C. Holton
Carl Albert State College

Louise Hoover
Clark College

Nancy Long
Trinity Valley Community College

Judy McInerney
Sandhills Community College

Arumugam Muhundan
Manatee Community College

Robert Piearcy
Carl Albert State College

Jack W. Rotman
Lansing Community College

Minnie W. Shuler
Gulf Coast Community College

Charles E. Smith
Roane State Community College

Brian K. Wells
Chadron State College

We especially want to acknowledge the memory of William Wooton, our co-author on previous editions. In his prolific work over thirty years, he made a significant contribution to the present precalculus mathematics curriculum. Bill was an inspirational coauthor and a good friend.

Irving Drooyan
Katherine Franklin Yoshiwara

Symbols

The section where the symbol is first used is shown in brackets.

$\{a, b\}$ the set whose elements (or members) are a and b [1.1]

A, B, C, etc.   names of sets   [1.1]

$\varnothing$ null set or empty set   [1.1]

N set of natural numbers   [1.1]

W set of whole numbers   [1.1]

J set of integers   [1.1]

Q set of rational numbers   [1.1]

H set of irrational numbers   [1.1]

R set of real numbers   [1.1]

$<$ is less than   [1.1]

$\leq$ is less than or equal to   [1.1]

$>$ is greater than   [1.1]

$\geq$ is greater than or equal to   [1.1]

$|a|$ absolute value of a [1.2]

a^n nth power of a or a to the nth power   [2.1]

$P(x), Q(z)$, etc. P of x, Q of z, etc.; polynomials   [2.1]

a^0 equals 1   [5.2]

a^{-n} $\dfrac{1}{a^n}(a \neq 0)$ [5.2]

$a^{1/n}$ nth root of a [5.4]

$\sqrt[n]{a}$ nth root of a [5.5]

C set of complex numbers   [5.9]

i imaginary unit   [5.9]

$\sqrt{-b}$ $i\sqrt{b}\,(b > 0)$ [5.9]

$a + bi$ complex number   [5.9]

$\pm$ plus or minus   [6.2]

(x, y) ordered pairs of numbers; first component is x and second component is y [7.1]

$f, g,$ etc.   names of functions   [8.1]

$f(x),$ etc. f of x, or the value of f at x [8.1]

f^{-1} f inverse or the inverse of f [8.5]

$\log_b x$ logarithm to the base b of x [9.1]

$\text{antilog}_b x$ antilogarithm to the base b of x [9.3]

$\ln x$ logarithm to the base e of x [9.3]

$\begin{vmatrix} a_1 & b_1 \\ a_2 & b_2 \end{vmatrix}$ second-order determinant   [10.3]

$\begin{vmatrix} a_1 & b_1 & c_1 \\ a_2 & b_2 & c_2 \\ a_3 & b_3 & c_3 \end{vmatrix}$ third-order determinant   [10.4]

$\begin{bmatrix} a_1 & b_1 \\ a_2 & b_2 \end{bmatrix}$ second-order matrix   [10.5]

$\begin{bmatrix} a_1 & b_1 & c_1 \\ a_2 & b_2 & c_2 \\ a_3 & b_3 & c_3 \end{bmatrix}$ third-order matrix   [10.5]

$\{x1 \ldots\}$ set of all x such that ...   [12.2]

$\cap$ the intersection of   [12.2]

$\cup$ the union of   [12.2]

$(\;)$ open interval   [12.2]

$[\;]$ closed interval   [12.2]

s_n nth term of a sequence   [13.1]

S_n sum of n terms of a sequence   [13.1]

$\sum$ the sum   [13.1]

S_∞ infinite sum   [13.1]

$n!$ n factorial or factorial n [13.5]

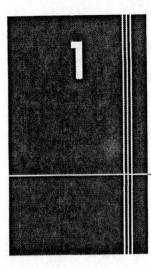

REVIEW OF THE REAL NUMBERS

We will start our study of intermediate algebra in this chapter by reviewing properties of numbers and mathematical notation that are usually introduced in elementary algebra courses. You may remember some of this material from your previous work in algebra.

1.1 DEFINITIONS; EQUALITY AND ORDER

Number Relationships

In this book we are going to be concerned primarily with the following numbers:

▲ The **natural numbers**, also called **counting numbers**, consist of the numbers 1, 2, 3, ..., where the three dots mean "and so on."

▲ The **whole numbers** consist of the natural numbers and zero. Included are such numbers as 5, 110, and 0.

▲ The **integers** consist of the natural numbers, their negatives, and zero. Included are such numbers as -7, -3, 0, 5, and 11.

▲ The **rational numbers** are integers or quotients a/b, where a and b are integers and b does not equal zero. Included are such elements as $-\frac{3}{4}$, $\frac{2}{3}$, 3, and -6. All rational numbers can be written as terminating or repeating decimals. For example, $-\frac{3}{4}$ is equivalent to the terminating decimal -0.75, and $\frac{2}{3}$ is equivalent to the repeating decimal $0.666\ldots$.

▲ The **irrational numbers** are numbers with decimal representations that are nonterminating and nonrepeating. An irrational number *cannot* be represented in the form a/b, where a and b are integers. Included are such elements as $\sqrt{15}$, $-\sqrt{7}$, and π.

▲ The **real numbers** consist of all rational and irrational numbers.

Sets and Symbols

A **set** is a well-defined collection of objects. In algebra we work primarily with collections, or sets, of numbers. Each item in a set is called an **element** or a **member** of the set. For example, the numbers 1, 2, 3,... are the elements of a set we call the set of natural numbers. Because the natural numbers never end—we can never reach a *last* number—we refer to this set as an **infinite set**. A set whose elements can be counted is called a **finite set**.

We indicate sets by means of capital letters, such as *A*, *I*, or *R*, or by means of braces, { }, used together with words or symbols.

EXAMPLE 1

a. {natural numbers less than 4} is read "the set whose elements are natural numbers less than 4."

b. If   *A* = {natural numbers less than 7},   then   *A* = {1, 2, 3, 4, 5, 6}.   The set *A* is a finite set.

c. If   *B* = {natural numbers greater than 7},   then   *B* = {8, 9,...}.   The set *B* is an infinite set.

We can see how the different sets of numbers relate to one another from the diagram in Figure 1.1. Notice how all natural numbers also belong to the set of whole numbers; how all whole numbers also belong to the integers; how all integers are included in the rational numbers; and how all rational and irrational numbers are also real numbers. *Note*: The symbols *R*, *Q*, *H*, *J*, *W*, and *N* can be used to name these sets of numbers as shown in Figure 1.1.

Variables and Constants

When we want to indicate an unspecified number, we use a lowercase letter, such as *a*, *b*, *c*, *x*, *y*, or *z*. Such symbols are called **variables**. A symbol used to denote a specific number is called a **constant**; one example is π.

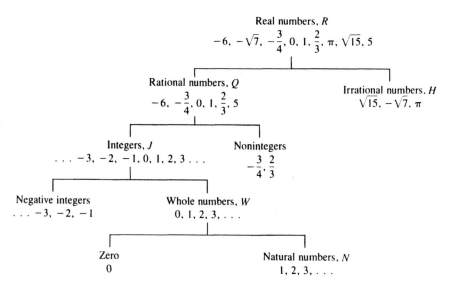

Figure 1.1

Null Set

It is sometimes convenient to consider a set with no members. We call such a set containing no members the **empty set** or **null set**, and we regard it as a finite set. The empty set is denoted by ∅ or { }. Note that the symbol ∅ (read "the empty set") is *not* enclosed by braces.

E X A M P L E 2

a. {odd numbers exactly divisible by 2} = $\varnothing$

b. {natural numbers less than 1} = $\varnothing$

COMMON ERROR

$$\{natural\ numbers\ less\ than\ 1\} = \{\varnothing\}$$

is incorrect. The expression $\{\varnothing\}$ *does not represent the empty set because it contains an element, namely the empty set* $\varnothing$.

Properties of Equality

In mathematics we assume that certain properties of numbers are always valid. The words *property*, *law*, and *principle* are sometimes used to denote assumptions. In this book we use, in each situation, the word we believe to be the one most frequently encountered. The first such assumptions to be considered concern equality.

An **equality**, or an "is equal to" assertion, is a mathematical statement that *two symbols, or groups of symbols, are names for the same number.* A number has an infinite variety of names. Thus, 3, $\frac{6}{2}$, $4 - 1$, and $2 + 1$ are all names for the same number; hence, the equality

$$4 - 1 = 2 + 1$$

is a statement that "$4 - 1$" and "$2 + 1$" are different names for the same number.

We shall assume that the "is equal to" ($=$) relationship has the following properties.

If $a = b$, *then* $b = a$.	**Symmetric property**
If $a = b$ *and* $b = c$, *then* $a = c$.	**Transitive property**
If $a = b$, *then b may be replaced by a or a by b in any statement without altering the truthfulness of the statement.*	**Substitution property**

E X A M P L E 3

a. Symmetric property: If $t = 8$, then $8 = t$.

b. Transitive property: If $x + 2 = y$ and $y = 3$, then $x + 2 = 3$.

c. Substitution property: If $x = 5$ and $x + y = 2$, then $5 + y = 2$.

We refer to the symbol (or the number it names) to the left of an equals sign as the *left-hand member* or simply, the *left side*, and that to the right as the *right-hand member* or simply, the *right side*, of the equality.

Order Relationships

The relationship that establishes the order between b and a is called an **inequality**. In symbols, we write

$$b < a, \quad \text{which is read} \quad \text{"}b\text{ is less than }a\text{"}$$

or

$$a > b, \quad \text{which is read} \quad \text{"}a\text{ is greater than }b\text{"}$$

Furthermore, two conditions such as $a < b$ and $b < c$ can be written as the continued inequality $a < b < c$, which is read "a is less than b and b is less than c" or simply "b is between a and c."

It is also possible to combine the concepts of equality and inequality and write two statements at once:

$\leqslant$ is read   "is less than or equal to";

$\geqslant$ is read   "is greater than or equal to"

EXAMPLE 4

a. $y \leqslant 10$ is read "y is less than or equal to 10."

b. $x \geqslant 8$ is read "x is greater than or equal to 8."

c. $-2 < x \leqslant 5$ is read "-2 is less than x and x is less than or equal to 5" or "x is between -2 and 5 or is equal to 5."

Number Lines

For each real number there corresponds one and only one point on a line, and vice versa. Hence, a geometric line can be used to visualize relationships between real numbers. For example, to represent 1, 3, and 5 on a line, we scale a straight line in convenient units, with increasing positive direction indicated by an arrow, and mark the required points with dots on the line. This kind of line is called a **number line**, and this particular number line is shown in Figure 1.2. The real numbers corresponding to points on the number line are called the **coordinates** of the points, and the points are called the **graphs** of the numbers.

Figure 1.2

Positive numbers are associated with the points on the line to the *right* of a point called the **origin** (labeled 0); negative numbers are associated with the points on the line to the *left* of the origin. The number 0 is neither positive nor negative; it serves as a point of separation for the positive and negative numbers.

EXAMPLE 5

a. $\{-4, -\frac{1}{2}, 3, 5\}$;   graph:

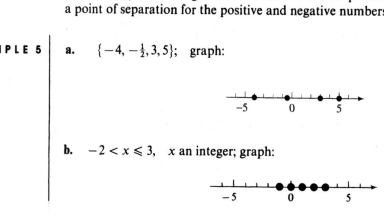

b. $-2 < x \leqslant 3$, x an integer; graph:

Certain algebraic statements concerning the order of real numbers can be interpreted geometrically. We list some of the more common correspondences in Table 1.1, where in each case a, b, and c are real numbers.

Table 1.1

Algebraic Statement	Geometric Statement	
1. $a > 0$; a is positive	1. The graph of a lies to the right of the origin.	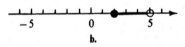
2. $a < 0$; a is negative	2. The graph of a lies to the left of the origin.	
3. $a > b$	3. The graph of a lies to the right of the graph of b.	
4. $a < b$	4. The graph of a lies to the left of the graph of b.	
5. $a < c < b$	5. The graph of c is to the right of the graph of a and to the left of the graph of b (c lies between a and b).	

Graphs of Real Numbers

Number lines can be used to display infinite sets of points as well as finite sets. For example, Figure 1.3a is the graph of the *integers* greater than or equal to 2 *and* less than 5. The graph consists of three points. Figure 1.3b is the graph of *real numbers* greater than or equal to 2 and less than 5. The graph is an *infinite set of points*. The closed dot on the left end of the shaded portion of the graph in Figure 1.3b indicates that the endpoint is part of the graph, while the open dot on the right end indicates that the endpoint is not in the graph.

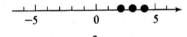

Figure 1.3

The set of numbers whose graph is shown in Figure 1.3a can be described by

$$2 \leqslant x < 5 \qquad \text{where } x \text{ is an integer}$$

(read "x is greater than or equal to 2 and less than 5, where x is an integer"). Similarly, the set of numbers whose graph is shown in Figure 1.3b can be described by

$$2 \leqslant x < 5 \qquad \text{where } x \text{ is a real number}$$

If the replacements for a variable are not specified, as in the next example, we assume that they are real numbers.

EXAMPLE 6

a. $x \geqslant -2$; graph:

b. $30 \leqslant y < 40$; graph:

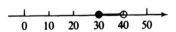

EXERCISE SET 1.1

▲ *Refer to Figure 1.1 as necessary.*

▲ *Specify each set by listing the members. See Example 1.*

1. {natural numbers between 2 and 6}
2. {integers between -3 and 4}
3. {first three whole numbers}
4. {first three natural numbers}
5. {natural numbers greater than 4}
6. {integers less than 2}
7. {odd natural numbers between 4 and 10}
8. {even integers between -7 and -1}

▲ *State whether the given set is finite or infinite.*

9. {whole numbers less than 10,000}
10. {integers less than 10,000}
11. {integers between -3 and 4}
12. {integers greater than -4}
13. {rational numbers between -1 and 0}
14. {rational numbers between 0 and 1}

▲ *Replace each question mark to make the given statement an application of the given property. See Example 3.*

15. If $r = 6$ and $r - 3 = t$, then $\underline{?} - 3 = t$; substitution property.
16. If $4 = x$ and $x = y$, then $\underline{?} = \underline{?}$; transitive property.
17. If $y = x - 2$ then $x - 2 = \underline{?}$; symmetric property.
18. If $a = c$ and $c = 4$, then $\underline{?} = 4$; transitive property.
19. If $r = n$ and $n + 6 = 8$, then $\underline{?} + 6 = 8$; substitution property.
20. If $t = 4$ and $5 \cdot t = 6s$, then $5 \cdot \underline{?} = 6s$; substitution property.

▲ *Express each relation using symbols. See Example 4.*

21. 8 is greater than 5.
22. -5 is greater than -8.
23. -6 is less than -4.
24. -3 is less than 4.
25. $x + 1$ is negative.
26. $x - 3$ is positive.
27. $x - 4$ is nonpositive.

28. $x + 2$ is nonnegative.
29. y is between -2 and 3.
30. y is between -4 and 0.
31. x is greater than or equal to 1 and less than 7.
32. $3t$ is greater than or equal to 0 and less than or equal to 4.

▲ *Replace each question mark with an appropriate order symbol to form a true statement.*

33. $-2 \, ? \, 8$
34. $3 \, ? \, 6$
35. $-7 \, ? \, -13$
36. $0 \, ? \, -5$
37. $1\frac{1}{2} \, ? \, \frac{3}{2}$
38. $3 \, ? \, \frac{6}{2}$
39. $3 \, ? \, 0 \, ? \, -4$
40. $-5 \, ? \, -2 \, ? \, 0$

▲ *Graph each inequality on a separate number line. See Example 5.*

41. $x > 2$, x an integer
42. $x < -3$, x an integer
43. $-1 \leqslant x < 6$, x an integer
44. $-5 < x \leqslant -1$, x an integer

▲ *Graph each inequality on a separate number line. Variables are real numbers. See Example 6.*

45. $x \geqslant -5$
46. $3 < y \leqslant 7$
47. $t < -3$
48. $s \leqslant 8$
49. $-5 \leqslant x \leqslant -3$
50. $-5 \leqslant y < 10$

Miscellaneous Exercises

▲ *List the members in each of the following sets that are elements of* $\left\{-5, -\sqrt{15}, -3.44, -\frac{2}{3}, 0, \frac{1}{5}, \frac{7}{3}, 6.1, 8\right\}$.

51. {whole numbers}
52. {natural numbers}
53. {irrational numbers}
54. {rational numbers}
55. {negative real numbers}
56. {real numbers}
57. What symbols are used to denote a set with no members?
58. If $s > t$ and $t \geqslant u$, express the relationship between s and u.
59. Use symbols to express that x is nonnegative.
60. Use symbols to express that the graph of x lies to the right of the graph of y.

1.2 | PROPERTIES FOR BASIC OPERATIONS

Properties for Addition and Multiplication

The following properties of addition and multiplication provide the foundation for all our work on operations of real numbers.

If a, b, and c are real numbers:

$a + b = b + a$	**Commutative property of addition**
$(a + b) + c = a + (b + c)$	**Associative property of addition**
$ab = ba$	**Commutative property of multiplication**
$(ab)c = a(bc)$	**Associative property of multiplication**
$a(b + c) = (ab) + (ac)$	**Distributive property**
$a + 0 = a$ _and_ $0 + a = a$	**Identity element for addition**
$a \cdot 1 = a$ _and_ $1 \cdot a = a$	**Identity element for multiplication**
$a + (-a) = 0$ _and_ $(-a) + a = 0$	**Additive-inverse property**
$a\left(\dfrac{1}{a}\right) = 1$ _and_ $\left(\dfrac{1}{a}\right)a = 1,$	**Multiplicative-inverse property**

where $a \neq 0$

The multiplicative-inverse of a nonzero number is called the **reciprocal** of the number.

Parentheses are used in some of the preceding properties to indicate an order of operations; operations enclosed in parnetheses are performed before any others. Note that the distributive property is the only one of the properties that involves the operation of addition _and_ the operation of multiplication.

EXAMPLE 1

		For Addition	For Multiplication
a.	Communicative property:	$3 + 4 = 4 + 3$	$3 \cdot 4 = 4 \cdot 3$
b.	Associative property:	$(2 + 3) + 4 = 2 + (3 + 4)$	$(2 \cdot 3) \cdot 4 = 2 \cdot (3 \cdot 4)$
c.	Identity element:	$3 + 0 = 3$	$3 \cdot 1 = 3$
d.	Inverse property:	$3 + (-3) = 0$	$3\left(\dfrac{1}{3}\right) = 1$
e.	Distributive property:	$3(4 + 5) = 3(4) + 3(5)$	

The following properties are logical consequences of the properties listed above. To simplify the statement of these properties, we make the following assumption:

▲   *In any expression or equation involving variables in this book, unless otherwise stated, the variables will represent real numbers.*

If **a = b,**   *then*

$$a + c = b + c. \qquad \textbf{Addition property of equality}$$

If **a = b,**   *then*

$$ac = bc. \qquad \textbf{Multiplication property of equality}$$

EXAMPLE 2   **a.** If $x = y$,   then $x + 3 = y + 3$ and $5x = 5y$.

b. If $x + y = z$,   then $x + y + (-y) = z + (-y)$.

c. If $\dfrac{x + y}{4} = z$,   then $4\left(\dfrac{x + y}{4}\right) = 4z$.

Two other important properties detail the role of 0 in a product and assert a property of negatives.

$$a \cdot 0 = 0 \qquad \textbf{Zero-factor property}$$

EXAMPLE 3   **a.** $3 \cdot 0 = 0$ **b.** $-8 \cdot 0 = 0$ **c.** $0 \cdot 0 = 0$

The following property expresses the fact that *the opposite of the opposite of a number is the number itself.*

$$-(-a) = a$$

Thus, the additive-inverse of $-a$ is a itself.

EXAMPLE 4   **a.** $-(-8) = 8$ **b.** $-[-(-6)] = -[6] = -6$

We read -8 as "negative 8" and $-(-8)$ as "the *opposite* of negative 8." We will also read $-a$ as "the *opposite* of a."

Absolute Value of a Number   Sometimes we wish to consider only the nonnegative member of a pair of numbers a and $-a$. For example, since the graphs of $-a$ and a are each located the same distance from the origin, when we wish to refer simply to this distance and not to its direction to the left or right of 0, we can use the notation $|a|$ (read "the absolute value of a"). For example, in Figure 1.4, observe that although $+6$ and -6 lie on opposite sides of 0 on the number line, each of the two numbers is the same distance (six units) from 0. The positive number 6 is the absolute value of $+6$ and of -6.

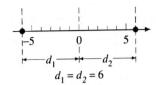

Figure 1.4 $d_1 = d_2 = 6$

Absolute value is defined more formally as follows:

$$|a| = \begin{cases} a, & \text{if } a \geq 0 \\ -a, & \text{if } a < 0 \end{cases}$$

From this definition, $|a|$ is always nonnegative.

EXAMPLE 5

a. $|3| = 3$

b. $|0| = 0$

c. $|-3| = -(-3) = 3$

d. If $x < 0$, then $|x| = -x$.
— positive
— negative

e. $-|-3| = -(3) = -3$

Sums of Real Numbers

Addition is an operation that associates with each pair of real numbers a and b a third real number $a + b$, called the **sum** of a and b. The familiar laws of signs for sums follow from the properties of real numbers.

> *The sum of two positive numbers is positive.*

EXAMPLE 6

a. $28 + 73 = +101$.

b. If $x > 0$, then $x + 5 > 0$.

c. If $x > 0$ and $y > 5$, then $x + y > 0$.

> *The sum of two negative numbers is the opposite of the sum of their absolute values.*

EXAMPLE 7

a. $(-3) + (-5) = -(|-3| + |-5|)$
$= -(3 + 5)$
$= -8$

b. $(-18) + (-6) = -(|-18| + |-6|)$
$= -(18 + 6)$
$= -24$

> *The sum of a positive number and a negative number is equal to the nonnegative difference of their absolute values preceded by the sign of the number with the greater absolute value.*

EXAMPLE 8

a. $8 + (-6) = \overset{\text{Difference of absolute values}}{\overline{8 - |-6|}}$

$= \underset{\text{Positive, because } |8| > |-6|}{2}$

b. $5 + (-7) = -\overset{\text{Difference of absolute values}}{\overline{(|-7| - 5)}}$

$\underset{\text{Negative, because } |-7| > |5|}{}$

$= -(7 - 5)$

$= -2$

c. $-12 + 10 = -\overset{\text{Difference of absolute values}}{\overline{(|-12| - 10)}}$

$\underset{\text{Negative, because } |-12| > |10|}{}$

$= -(12 - 10)$

$= -2$

Differences of Real Numbers   In algebra it is useful to write the **difference** of two numbers in terms of a sum. Note that

$$7 - 2 = 5 \quad \text{and} \quad 7 + (-2) = 5$$

and that

$$2 - 7 = -5 \quad \text{and} \quad 2 + (-7) = -5$$

These examples suggest the following:

> *The difference of b subtracted from a equals the sum of a and* $-b$:
>
> $$a - b = a + (-b)$$

EXAMPLE 9

a. $8 - (-3) = \overset{\text{Change the sign and add.}}{8 + (3)}$

$= 11$

b. $(-7) - (4) = \overset{\text{Change the sign of 4 and add.}}{(-7) + (-4)}$

$= -11$

c. $(-5) - (-2) = \overset{\text{Change the sign and add.}}{(-5) + (2)}$

$= -3$

d. $3 - 8 = \overset{\text{Change the sign of 8 and add.}}{3 + (-8)}$

$= -5$

Three Uses of the Minus Sign

Since we have seen that the difference $a - b$ is given by $a + (-b)$, we may consider the symbols $a - b$ as representing either the difference of a and b or, preferably, the sum of a and $(-b)$. Note that we have now used the sign $+$ in two ways and the sign $-$ in three ways. We have used these signs to denote positive and negative numbers and as signs of operation to indicate the sum or difference of two numbers; we also have used the sign $-$ to indicate the "opposite" of a number. For example,

-3; the sign denotes a negative integer.

$7 - 3$; the sign shows the operation of subtraction in which $+3$ is subtracted from $+7$.

$-a$; the sign denotes the "opposite" of a. If a is positive, then $-a$ is negative. If a is negative, then $-a$ is positive.

In discussing the results of operations, it is convenient to use the term **basic numeral**. For example, whereas the numeral "3 + 5" names the sum of the real numbers 3 and 5, we shall refer to "8" as the basic numeral for this number. Similarly, the basic numeral for "2 − 8" is "−6".

EXAMPLE 10

Write each expression as a basic numeral.

a. $5 - 7 + (-3)$
  $= -2 + (-3)$
  $= -5$

b. $-6 + 2 - 5$
  $= -4 - 5$
  $= -9$

Product of Real Numbers

Multiplication is an operation that associates with each pair of numbers a and b a third number $a \cdot b$, also written $(a)(b)$ or ab. The number ab is called the **product** of the **factors** a and b.

As a consequence of properties of the real numbers, we have the following laws of signs for products:

> *The product of two numbers with like signs is positive; the product of two numbers with unlike signs is negative.*

We express this fact in symbols as follows:

> If $a, b > 0$:
> $$(a)(b) = ab, \qquad a(-b) = -ab,$$
> $$(-a)(b) = -ab, \qquad \text{and} \qquad (-a)(-b) = ab.$$

EXAMPLE 11

a. $(3)(-2) = -6$

b. $(-3)(-2) = 6$

c. $(-2)(3) = -6$

d. $(3)(2) = 6$

e. $(-1)(3) = -3$

f. $(-1)(-3) = 3$

In general,

$$-1 \cdot a = -(1 \cdot a) = -a$$

Since each *pair* of negative factors yields a positive product, we have the following guideline.

If a product contains

1. *an even number of negative factors, then the product is positive;*
2. *an odd number of negative factors, then the product is negative.*

E X A M P L E 1 2

a. $(-3)(2)(-4)(5)$ ⎯ Two negative factors
$$= (-3)(-4)(2)(5)$$
$$= 12 \cdot 10 = 120$$
  ⎯ Product is positive.

b. $(-1)(-5)(3)(-2)(6)$ ⎯ Three negative factors
$$= (-1)(-5)(-2)(3)(6)$$
$$= -10 \cdot 18 = -180$$
  ⎯ Product is negative.

Quotients of Real Numbers   We can define the *quotient* of two real numbers in terms of multiplication.

---

*The **quotient** of two numbers a and b is the unique number q,*

$$\frac{a}{b} = q, \qquad such\ that \quad bq = a$$

E X A M P L E 1 3

a. $\dfrac{6}{2} = 3$ because $2 \cdot 3 = 6.$

b. $\dfrac{-6}{-2} = 3$ because $(-2)(3) = -6.$

c. $\dfrac{-6}{2} = -3$ because $2(-3) = -6.$

d. $\dfrac{6}{-2} = -3$ because $(-2)(-3) = 6.$

The quotient a/b of two numbers must be consistent with the laws of signs for the product of two signed numbers. Therefore, if a and b are both positive or both negative, a/b is positive, as in Examples 13a and b. If a and b have opposite signs, a/b is negative, as in Examples 13c and d.

When a fraction bar is used to indicate that one algebraic expression is to be divided by another, the dividend is the **numerator** and the divisor is the **denominator**. The denominator of a/b is restricted to nonzero numbers; for if b is 0 and a is not 0, then there exists no q such that

$$0 \cdot q = a$$

Again, if b is 0 and a is 0, then for any q

$$0 \cdot q = 0$$

and the quotient is not unique. Thus:

▲ *Division by zero is not defined.*

EXAMPLE 14   **a.** $\dfrac{-5}{0}$ is not defined.   **b.** $\dfrac{1}{x-2}$ is not defined for $x = 2$ because $(2) - 2 = 0$.

Sometimes it is useful to write a quotient as a product. We express the relationship as follows:

$$\frac{a}{b} = a\left(\frac{1}{b}\right) \qquad (b \neq 0)$$

EXAMPLE 15   **a.** $\dfrac{2}{3} = 2\left(\dfrac{1}{3}\right)$ **b.** $\dfrac{a}{3b} = a\left(\dfrac{1}{3b}\right)$ $(b \neq 0)$ **c.** $\dfrac{x}{y-x} = x\left(\dfrac{1}{y-x}\right)$ $(y \neq x)$

Alternatively, we can write products as quotients. For example,

$$3\left(\frac{1}{5}\right) = \frac{3}{5}, \qquad 2 \cdot \frac{3}{7} = \frac{2 \cdot 3}{7}, \qquad \text{and} \qquad \frac{1}{2} \cdot 3x = \frac{3x}{2}$$

Note how this definition of a quotient along with the associative law of multiplication can be used to simplify some products.

EXAMPLE 16   **a.** $\dfrac{1}{2} \cdot 2x = \left(\dfrac{1}{2} \cdot 2\right)x$ **b.** $\dfrac{1}{3} \cdot 3y = \left(\dfrac{1}{3} \cdot 3\right)y$

                    $= x$ $= y$

‖ EXERCISE SET 1.2

▲ *In Problems 1–16, replace each question mark to make the given statement an application of the given property. See Examples 1, 2, and 3.*

1. $12 + x = x +$?; commutative property of addition

2. $(2m)n = 2($?$)$; associative property of multiplication

3. $3(x + y) = 3x +$?; distributive property

4. $(2 + z) + 3 = 2 + ($?$)$; associative property of addition

5. $4 \cdot t =$?; commutative property of multiplication

6. $7 +$? $= 0$; additive-inverse property

7. $3 \cdot \dfrac{1}{3} =$?; multiplicative-inverse property

8. $m + \underline{?} = m$; identity element for addition

9. $r \cdot \underline{?} = r$; identity element for multiplication

10. $r + (s + 2) = (s + 2) + \underline{?}$; commutative property of addition

11. $3(x + y) = \underline{?} + \underline{?}$; distributive property

12. $6 \cdot \dfrac{1}{6} = \underline{?}$; commutative property of multiplication

13. If $z = 4$, then $z + 5 = 4 + \underline{?}$; additive property of equality

14. $(x + y) + z = x + \underline{?}$; associative property of addition

15. If $x = 6$, then $-3x = \underline{?} \cdot 6$; multiplicative property of equality

16. $15 \cdot \underline{?} = 0$; zero-factor property

▲ *Simplify each expression. See Example 4.*

17. $-(-3)$

18. $-[-(-7)]$

19. $-[-(-x)]$

20. $-[-(x + 2)]$

▲ *Rewrite each expression without using absolute-value notation. See Example 5.*

21. $|-3|$

22. $|-7|$

23. $|4|$

24. $|6|$

25. $-|-2|$

26. $-|-4|$

27. $-|5|$

28. $-|7|$

29. $|x|$

30. $|-x|$

▲ *Write each sum or difference using a basic numeral. See Examples 6–10.*

31. $4 + 7$

32. $6 + 9$

33. $-2 + 8$

34. $-5 + 7$

35. $6 + (-3)$

36. $5 + (-10)$

37. $-2 + (-5)$

38. $-6 + (-6)$

39. $8 - 3$

40. $6 - 1$

41. $4 - 7$

42. $8 - 14$

43. $-2 - 7$

44. $-5 - 11$

45. $4 - (-2)$

46. $8 - (-4)$

47. $-2 - (-4)$

48. $-8 - (-5)$

49. $6 - 2 + 7$

50. $8 + 3 - 5$

51. $(6 - 5) - 11$

52. $(3 - 7) - 1$

53. $(6 - 1 + 8) - 3$

54. $4 - (6 + 2 - 11)$

55. $(7 - 2) + (-3 + 1)$

56. $(5 - 9) + (4 - 2)$

57. $(3 - 5 + 4) - (8 - 13)$

58. $(38 - 25) + (13 - 17 - 2)$

▲ *Write each product as a basic numeral. See Examples 11 and 12.*

59. $(4)(-3)$

60. $(-5)(3)$

61. $(-2)(-6)$

62. $(-8)(-5)$

63. $(3)(-2)(-4)$

64. $(-5)(2)(-3)$

65. $(5)(-1)(4)$

66. $(2)(-2)(6)$

67. $(2)(3)(-1)(-4)$

68. $(5)(-2)(-1)(6)$

69. $(4)(0)(-2)(3)$

70. $(-6)(0)(2)(3)$

71. $-2(3 \cdot 4)$

72. $-2(2 \cdot 6)$

▲ *Write each quotient as a basic numeral, or state if undefined. See Examples 13 and 14.*

73. $\dfrac{-16}{4}$

74. $\dfrac{-32}{8}$

75. $\dfrac{39}{-3}$

76. $\dfrac{45}{-15}$

77. $\dfrac{-27}{-9}$

78. $\dfrac{-54}{-6}$

79. $\dfrac{0}{-7}$

80. $\dfrac{0}{-12}$

81. $\dfrac{-5}{0}$

82. $\dfrac{-27}{0}$

83. $-\left(\dfrac{-8}{2}\right)$

84. $-\left(\dfrac{-12}{-3}\right)$

▲ *Rewrite each quotient as a product in which one factor is a natural number and the other factor is the reciprocal (multiplicative inverse) of a natural number. See Example 15.*

85. $\dfrac{7}{8}$

86. $\dfrac{27}{7}$

87. $\dfrac{3}{8}$

88. $\dfrac{9}{17}$

▲ *Rewrite each product as a quotient and simplify if possible. See Examples 15 and 16.*

89. $3\left(\dfrac{1}{2}\right)$

90. $8\left(\dfrac{1}{3}\right)$

91. $3\left(\dfrac{x}{y}\right)$

92. $\left(\dfrac{2}{z}\right)x$

93. $\dfrac{1}{4} \cdot 4x$

94. $\dfrac{1}{5} \cdot 5y$

95. $\dfrac{1}{2} \cdot 2(x + y)$

96. $\dfrac{1}{3} \cdot 3(x - y)$

Miscellaneous Exercises

97. For what values of a and b is

    a. $a + b > 0$?
    b. $a - b > 0$?

98. For what values of a and b is

    a. $\dfrac{a}{b} = 0$?
    b. $\dfrac{a}{b} > 0$?
    c. $\dfrac{a}{b} < 0$?

99. If $a < 0$, is $-(-a)$ positive or negative?

100. For what values of a is the product $-a(-a)(-a)$ positive?

101. If $a < 0$ and $b > 0$, is $-ab$ positive or negative?

102. If $a > 0$ and $b < 0$, is $-\dfrac{-a}{b}$ positive or negative?

103. For what values of x is $|x| = x$? For what values of x is $|x| = -x$?

104. For what values of x is $|x - 2| = x - 2$?

1.3 | ORDER OF OPERATIONS

Using the associative properties of addition and of multiplication, we obtain the same sum or product regardless of the way that we group terms of a sum or factors of a product. However, if two or more operations are involved in an algebraic expression, we can possibly obtain different results depending on the order in which the operations are performed. For example, the expression $2 + 3 \cdot 5$ might be interpreted two ways. We might see it as meaning

$$(2 + 3) \cdot 5 \quad \text{or} \quad 2 + (3 \cdot 5)$$

in which case the result is either

$$5 \cdot 5 = 25 \quad \text{or} \quad 2 + 15 = 17$$

To avoid such confusion, we make certain agreements about the order of performing operations.

Order of Operations

1. First, any expression within a symbol of inclusion (parentheses, brackets, fraction bars, etc.) is simplified.
2. Next, multiplications and divisions are performed as encountered in order from left to right.
3. Last, additions and subtractions are performed in order from left to right.

Thus, in the example above, $2 + 3 \cdot 5$, we first multiply and then add to get

$$2 + 15 = 17$$

EXAMPLE 1

a. $3(2 + 7) - 3(-4)$ Simplify (2 + 7) within parentheses.

$= 3(9) - 3(-4)$ Multiply.

$= 27 - (-12)$ Subtract: change the sign of -12, and add.

$= 27 + 12$

$= 39$

b. $\dfrac{6 + (-15)}{-3} + \dfrac{5}{4 - (-1)}$ Simplify $6 + (-15)$ above the fraction bar and $4 - (-1)$ below the fraction bar.

$= \dfrac{-9}{-3} + \dfrac{5}{5}$ Simplify each quotient.

$= 3 + 1$ Add.

$= 4$

c. $\dfrac{-4-8}{-4} + 2(8-3)$ Simplify $-4-8$ above the fraction bar and $8-3$ in parentheses.

$\quad = \dfrac{-12}{-4} + 2(5)$ Simplify quotient.

$\quad = 3 + 2(5)$ Multiply.

$\quad = 3 + 10$ Add.

$\quad = 13$

COMMON ERROR   *Note that in Example 1c,* $3 + 2 \cdot 5 \neq (3 + 2) \cdot 5.$

Numerical Evaluation   The process of substituting given numbers for variables and simplifying the arithmetic expression (according to the agreed order of operations) is called **numerical evaluation**.

EXAMPLE 2

a. Evaluating $a + (n-1)d$ for $a = 2$, $n = 5$, and $d = -3$, we obtain

$$a + (n-1)d = (2) + [(5) - 1)](-3)   \text{Simplify } [(5) - 1].$$
$$= 2 + 4(-3)   \text{Multiply.}$$
$$= 2 + (-12) = -10   \text{Add.}$$

b. Evaluating $P + Prt$, for $P = 2000$, $r = 0.08$, and $t = 6$, we obtain

$$P + Prt = (2000) + (2000)(0.08)(6)   \text{Multiply.}$$
$$= 2000 + 960 = 2960   \text{Add.}$$

You may find it helpful to enclose in parentheses each number substituted as shown in the above solutions.

EXERCISE SET 1.3

▲ *Write each expression as a basic numeral.*
See Example 1.

1. $4 + 4 \cdot 4$

2. $7 - 6 \cdot 2$

3. $4(-1) + 2 \cdot 2$

4. $6 \cdot 3 + (-2)(5)$

5. $-2 \cdot (4 + 6) + 3$

6. $5(6 - 12) + 7$

7. $2 - 3(6 - 1)$

8. $4 - 7(8 + 2)$

9. $\dfrac{7 + (-5)}{2} - 3$

10. $\dfrac{12}{8 - 2} - 5$

11. $\dfrac{3(6 - 8)}{-2} - \dfrac{6}{-2}$

12. $\dfrac{5(3 - 5)}{2} - \dfrac{18}{-3}$

13. $6[3 - 2(4 + 1)] - 2$

14. $6[5 - 3(1 - 4)] + 3$

15. $(4 - 3)[2 + 3(2 - 1)]$

16. $(8 - 6)[5 + 7(2 - 3)]$

17. $64 \div [8(4 - 2[3 + 1])]$

18. $27 \div (3[9 - 3(4 - 2)])$

19. $5[3 + (8 - 1)] \div (-25)$

20. $-3[-2 + (6 - 1)] \div [18 \div (-2)]$

21. $[-3(8 - 2) + 3] \cdot [24 \div (2 - 8)]$

22. $[-2 + 3(5 - 8)] \cdot [-15 \div (5 - 2)]$

23. $\left[\dfrac{7 - (-3)}{5 - 3}\right]\left[\dfrac{4 + (-8)}{3 - 5}\right]$

24. $\left[\dfrac{12 + (-2)}{3 + (-8)}\right]\left[\dfrac{6 + (-15)}{8 - 5}\right]$

25. $\left(3 - 2\left[\dfrac{5 - (-4)}{2 + 1} - \dfrac{6}{3}\right]\right) + 1$

26. $\left(7 + 3\left[\dfrac{6 + (-18)}{4 + 2}\right] - 5\right) + 3$

27. $\dfrac{8 - 6\left(\dfrac{5+3}{4-8}\right) - 3}{-2 + 4\left(\dfrac{6-3}{1-4}\right) + 6}$

28. $\dfrac{12 + 3\left(\dfrac{12-20}{3-1}\right) - 1}{-8 + 6\left(\dfrac{12-30}{2-5}\right) + 1}$

29. $\dfrac{3(3+2) - 3\cdot 3 + 2}{3\cdot 2 + 2(2-1)}$

30. $\dfrac{6 - 2\left(\dfrac{4+6}{5}\right) + 8}{3 - 3\cdot 2 + 8}$

31. $\dfrac{3|-3| - |-5|}{|-2|} - \dfrac{|-6|}{3}$

32. $\dfrac{2|5-8|}{|-3|} - \dfrac{|-4| + 2}{|-2|}$

▲ *Evaluate each expression for the given values of the variables. See Example 2.*

33. $\dfrac{5(F - 32)}{9}$; $F = 212$

34. $\dfrac{R + r}{r}$; $R = 12$ and $r = 2$

35. $\dfrac{E - e}{R}$; $E = 18$, $e = 2$, and $R = 4$

36. $\dfrac{a - rs_n}{1 - r}$; $r = 2$, $s_n = 12$, and $a = 4$

37. $P + Prt$; $P = 1000$, $r = 0.04$, and $t = 2$

38. $R_0(1 + at)$; $R_0 = 2.5$, $a = 0.05$, and $t = 20$

Miscellaneous Exercises

39. If P dollars is invested at simple rate r, then the amount of money that is accumulated after t years is given by $P + Prt$. Determine the amount accumulated if \$800 is invested at 9% ($r = 0.09$) for 3 years.

40. The net resistance of an electric circuit is given by $\dfrac{rR}{r + R}$, where r and R are two resistors in the circuit. Determine the net resistance if r and R are 10 and 20 ohms, respectively.

▲ *Evaluate each of the following expressions (to the nearest tenth) for the volumes and surface areas of some common solids. Use the approximation 3.14 for* π.*

41. **a.** Volume of a sphere: $\dfrac{4}{3}\pi r^3$, for $r = 1.2$ meters

  b. Surface area of a sphere: $4\pi r^2$, for $r = 0.7$ centimeter

42. **a.** Volume of a rectangular prism (or box): lwh, for $l = 12.3$ inches, $w = 4$ inches, and $h = 7.3$ inches

  b. Surface area of a box: $2lw + 2lh + 2wh$, for $l = 6.2$ feet, $w = 5.8$ feet, and $h = 2.6$ feet

43. **a.** Volume of a right circular cylinder: $\pi r^2 h$, for $r = 6$ meters and $h = 23.2$ meters

  b. Surface area of a right circular cylinder: $2\pi r^2 + 2\pi rh$, for $r = 15.3$ inches and $h = 4.5$ inches

44. **a.** Volume of a right circular cone: $\dfrac{1}{3}\pi r^2 h$, for $r = 4.6$ feet and $h = 8.1$ feet

  b. Surface area of a right circular cone $\pi r^2 + \pi rs$, for $r = 16$ centimeters and $s = 42$ centimeters

Exercise 41

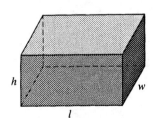

Exercise 42

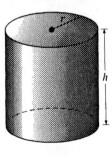

Exercise 43

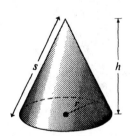

Exercise 44

---

*Additional properties of geometric figures are given in Appendix E.

CHAPTER SUMMARY

[1.1] A **set** is a collection of objects. The items in the collection are the **members**, or **elements**, of the set. **Natural numbers, whole numbers, integers, rational numbers,** and **irrational numbers** are all **real numbers** (see Figure 1.1).

A **variable** is a symbol used to represent an unspecified element of a given set. A symbol used to denote a single element is called a **constant**.

The **equality** (=) and **order** (<, >) relations in the set of real numbers are governed by the properties on pages 3 and 4. Order relationships between real numbers can be pictured on a **number line**.

[1.2] The operations of addition and multiplication are governed by the properties on page 7. These properties follow:

$$\text{If } a = b, \quad \text{then } a + c = b + c \quad \text{and} \quad ac = bc.$$
$$a \cdot 0 = 0,$$
$$-(-a) = a$$

The **absolute value** of a number a is defined by

$$|a| = \begin{cases} a, & \text{if } a \geq 0, \\ -a, & \text{if } a < 0 \end{cases}$$

The sum of two positive numbers is positive; the sum of two negative numbers is negative; and the sum of a positive number and a negative number is equal to the nonnegative difference of their absolute values preceded by the sign of the number with the greater absolute value.

The difference $a - b$ of two numbers is equal to the sum of a and the additive inverse of b:

$$a - b = a + (-b)$$

The product of two positive numbers or two negative numbers is positive; the product of a positive number and a negative number is negative.

The quotient of two numbers a/b, with $b \neq 0$, is equal to the number q, such that $b \cdot q = a$. Alternatively,

$$\frac{a}{b} = a\left(\frac{1}{b}\right)$$

Division by 0 is not defined.

[1.3] Operations are performed in the following order:

1. First, any expression within a symbol of inclusion (parentheses, brackets, fraction bars, etc.) is simplified.

2. Next, multiplications and divisions are performed as encountered in order from left to right.

3. Last, additions and subtractions are performed in order from left to right.

REVIEW EXERCISES

[1.1]

▲ Let $A = \left\{ -3, -2.55, -\sqrt{2}, -\frac{3}{5}, 0, 1, 5.55\ldots, \frac{13}{2} \right\}$.

1. List the members in set A that are integers.
2. List the members in set A that are whole numbers.
3. Use symbols to show the relationship between a and c if $a < b$ and $b < c$.
4. Use symbols to show that a is equal to or less than 7.
5. Use symbols to show that b is between a and c.
6. Express the relation "y is greater than or equal to 6" using symbols.
7. Graph $-4 \leqslant x < 5$, x an integer.
8. Graph $-4 \leqslant x < 5$, x a real number.

[1.2]

9. By the commutative property of addition, $x + 2 = \underline{?} + \underline{?}$.
10. By the addition property of equality, if $z = 18$, then $z + t = \underline{?}$.
11. By the multiplicative-inverse property, $3 \cdot \underline{?} = 1$.
12. By the identity property for multiplication, $7 \cdot \underline{?} = 7$.

▲ Write each sum or difference as a basic numeral.

13. a. $2(-4) + 8$ b. $5 - (-6) - 3$
14. a. $3 - |6| - |-3|$ b. $2 + |6 - 12| - |3|$

▲ Write each product as a basic numeral.

15. a. $3(-2)(6)$ b. $-3(-6)(0)$
    c. $7(-3)(-1)$ d. $-1(-2)(-3)(-4)$
16. a. $-3(-3)(-3)$ b. $4(-6)(0)(-1)$
    c. $4(-2)(-1)(3)$ d. $-(6)(2)(-2)(3)$

▲ Write each quotient as a basic numeral.

17. a. $\dfrac{-24}{-2}$ b. $\dfrac{0}{-3}$ c. $\dfrac{-16}{2}$ d. $\dfrac{32}{-4}$

▲ Express each quotient as a product.

18. a. $\dfrac{-7}{5}$ b. $\dfrac{24}{7}$ c. $-\dfrac{4}{5}$ d. $\dfrac{8}{3}$

▲ Express each product as a quotient.

19. a. $\dfrac{2}{3} \cdot x$ b. $\dfrac{3}{4} \cdot y$ c. $x \cdot \dfrac{1}{3}$ d. $y \cdot \dfrac{1}{4}$

▲ Perform the indicated operations.

20. a. $-5 + (-6)$ b. $-9 - 3$
    c. $-9 \div 3$ d. $-8(-6)$
21. a. $-63 \div (-9)$ b. $-6(4)$
    c. $-8 + 12$ d. $20 - (-6)$
22. a. $-7 - 14$ b. $-14 \div (-7)$
    c. $0 + (-4)$ d. $6(-6)$
23. a. $\dfrac{-6}{2}$ b. $\dfrac{14}{-7}$
    c. $-4 + (-7)$ d. $4 - (-7)$

[1.3]

▲ Write each expression as a basic numeral.

24. a. $5 - \dfrac{3+9}{6}$ b. $\dfrac{6 + 2 \cdot 3}{10 - 4 \cdot 2}$
25. a. $\dfrac{6 \cdot 8 \div 4 - 2}{7 - 5}$ b. $\dfrac{6 - 4 \cdot 3 + 2}{4 - 4 \cdot 2}$
26. a. $(4 - 2)[3 + (6 - 2)] + 2$
    b. $(8 + 1)[4 - (8 - 3)] - 2$

▲ Evaluate each algebraic expression for the given values of the variables.

27. $\dfrac{E - e}{R}$; $E = 18$, $e = 2$, and $R = 4$
28. $\dfrac{a - 4s}{1 - r}$; $r = 2$, $s = 12$, and $a = 4$
29. $P + Prt$; $P = 1000$, $r = 0.04$, and $t = 2$
30. $R(1 + at)$; $R = 2.5$, $a = 0.05$, and $t = 20$

▲ Simplify each expression.

31. $\left[\dfrac{4 - (-2)}{-3} \right] - 2[8 - 3 \cdot 4]$
32. $2\left[4 - \dfrac{2 - (-6)}{4} \right] - 5\left[3 - \dfrac{6 \cdot 3}{-4 - 2} \right]$
33. $\dfrac{3|-2| - (-4)}{|-5|} - \dfrac{|-4| - 4}{|-3|}$
34. $\dfrac{2|4 - 6| - |6 - 4|}{|4 - 6|} + 2[|5 - 6| - 3]$

2

BASIC POLYNOMIALS AND EQUATIONS

In Chapter 1 we used the term *algebraic expression* or simply *expression* for any meaningful collection of numerals, variables, and signs of operations. In this chapter we will first consider a particular kind of algebraic expression called a *polynomial*. We will then develop methods to solve equations that involve these expressions and construct polynomial equations as mathematical models to help us solve word problems.

2.1 DEFINITIONS

In Chapter 1 we saw that the product of two numbers a and b is expressed by ab. Sometimes, to avoid any possible confusion, we used a centered dot to indicate multiplication; for example, $a \cdot b$, $x \cdot y$, $2 \cdot 3$. In other cases we used parentheses around one or both of the symbols, as in $(2)(3)$, $2(3)$, and $(x)(x)$.

Powers   If the factors in a product are identical, the number of such factors is indicated by means of a natural-number superscript called an **exponent**. Thus, in the expression 3^4, which denotes $3 \cdot 3 \cdot 3 \cdot 3$, the exponent is 4. The expression 3^4 is called a **power**, and the number 3 is called the **base** of the power. In general, a power is defined as follows:

> *If n is a natural number,*
>
> $$a^n = a \cdot a \cdot a \cdot \cdots \cdot a \qquad (n \ factors)$$

For example,

$$x^2 = x \cdot x, \qquad y^3 = y \cdot y \cdot y, \qquad \text{and} \qquad z^5 = z \cdot z \cdot z \cdot z \cdot z$$

If no exponent appears on a variable, as in y for example, the exponent 1 is assumed. Thus, $y = y^1$.

Terms of an Expression

In an expression of the form $A + B + C + \cdots$, A, B, and C are called **terms** of the expression.

EXAMPLE 1

a. $3x + 4yz$ contains two terms; the first term, $3x$, contains two factors, and the second term, $4yz$, contains three factors.

b. $3(x + 4y^2)$ contains only one term; however, the factor $x + 4y^2$ contains two terms.

Differences as Sums

From the discussion on page 10 we know that $a - b$ is equal to $a + (-b)$. Thus,

$$2x^2 - 3y = 2x^2 + (-3y)$$

consists of the terms $2x^2$ and $-3y$, and

$$3(x + 4y^2) - 2x^3y - y^3 = 3(x + 4y^2) + (-2x^3y) + (-y^3)$$

consists of the terms $3(x + 4y^2)$, $-2x^3y$, and $-y^3$.

▲ *In our work it will be helpful to view any difference as a sum.*

Coefficient

Any factor or group of factors in a term is said to be the **coefficient** of the product of the remaining factors in the term. Thus, in the term $3xyz$ the product $3x$ is the coefficient of yz; y is the coefficient of $3xz$; 3 is the coefficient of xyz; and so on. Hereafter, the word "coefficient" will refer to a number unless otherwise indicated. For example, the coefficient of the term $4xy$ is 4; the coefficient of $-2a^2b$ is -2. The term **numerical coefficient** is sometimes used to emphasize this point. If no coefficient appears in a term, the coefficient is understood to be 1. Thus, x is viewed as $1x$.

EXAMPLE 2

a. In the expression $3x^2 - 5x$, the coefficient of x^2 is 3 and the coefficient of x is -5.

b. In the expression $x^2 - y$, the coefficient of x^2 is 1 and the coefficient of y is -1.

c. The terms of $2x^3 - xy + y^2$ are $2x^3$, $-xy$, and y^2 with coefficients of 2, -1, and 1, respectively.

Names for Algebraic Expressions

An algebraic expression of the form cx^n, where c is a constant and n is a *whole number*, or a product of such expressions is called a **monomial**. Constants are also monomials. For example,

$$y^3, \quad -3x^4, \quad 2x^2y^3, \quad \text{and} \quad 7$$

are monomials. A **polynomial** is an algebraic expression that contains only terms that are monomials. Thus,

$$x^2, \qquad \frac{1}{5}x - 2, \qquad 3x^2 - 2x + 1, \qquad \text{and} \qquad x^3 - 2x^2 + 1$$

are polynomials. On the other hand,

$$x^2 + \frac{1}{x} \qquad \text{and} \qquad y - \sqrt{y}$$

are not polynomials because $\frac{1}{x}$ and $\sqrt{y}$ are not monomials. If the polynomial contains two or three terms, we refer to it as a **binomial** or a **trinomial**, respectively. Polynomials with four or more terms do not have special names.

EXAMPLE 3

a. $3, 5x^3$, and $x^2 y$ are monomials.

b. $x + y$, $2x^2 - 3x$, and $4x + 3y$ are binomials.

c. $4x + 3y + 2z$, $x^2 + 2x + 1$, and $5xy + 2x - 3y$ are trinomials.

The **degree** of a monomial in one variable is given by the exponent on the variable. Thus, $3x^4$ is of fourth degree, and $7x^5$ is of fifth degree. The degree of a polynomial in one variable is the same as the degree of its term of largest degree.

EXAMPLE 4

a. $3x^2 + 2x + 1$ is a second-degree polynomial.

b. $x^5 - x - 1$ is a fifth-degree polynomial.

c. $2x - 3$ is a first-degree polynomial.

Order of Operations   We now revise the agreement that was made in Section 1.3 concerning the order in which operations are to be performed in order to accommodate powers. As before, we first simplify expressions within parentheses. Next we compute powers and then continue with our order of operations.

EXAMPLE 5

a. $5 + 3 \cdot 4^2$ **Simplify power.**

  $= 5 + 3 \cdot 16$ **Multiply.**

  $= 5 + 48 = 53$ **Add.**

b. $5 + (3 \cdot 4)^2$ **Simplify base (3 · 4).**

  $= 5 + 12^2$ **Simplify powers.**

  $= 5 + 144 = 149$ **Add.**

Particular care should be taken in evaluating powers that involve negative signs. For example, note that

$$(-2)^2 = (-2)(-2) = 4$$

and that

$$-2^2 = -(2)^2 = -(2)(2) = -4$$

Thus, $(-2)^2 \neq -2^2$. In general $(-x)^2 \neq -x^2$ for all $x \neq 0$.

We can now numerically evaluate algebraic expressions involving powers by simply following the appropriate order of operations.

EXAMPLE 6

Given $x = 3$ and $y = -2$:

a. $2xy - y^2 = 2(3)(-2) - (-2)^2$

$$= -12 - 4$$
$$= -16$$

b. $\dfrac{x^2 - y}{3x + 2} + x(-y) = \dfrac{(3)^2 - (-2)}{3(3) + 2} + 3[-(-2)]$

$$= \dfrac{9 + 2}{9 + 2} + 3(2)$$

$$= \dfrac{11}{11} + 6 = 1 + 6 = 7$$

Names for Polynomials

Polynomials are frequently represented by symbols such as

$$P(x), \qquad D(y), \qquad \text{and} \qquad Q(z)$$

where the symbol in parentheses designates the variable. The symbols are read "P of x," "D of y," and "Q of z," respectively. For example, we might write

$$P(x) = x^2 - 2x + 1$$
$$D(y) = y^6 - 2y^2 + 3y - 2$$
$$Q(z) = 8z^4 + 3z^3 - 2z^2 + z - 1$$

The notation $P(x)$ can be used to denote values of the polynomial for specific values of x. Thus, $P(2)$ represents the value of the polynomial $P(x)$ when x is replaced by 2.

EXAMPLE 7

If $P(x) = x^2 - 2x + 1$, then

$$P(2) = (2)^2 - 2(2) + 1 = 1$$
$$P(3) = (3)^2 - 2(3) + 1 = 4$$
$$P(-4) = (-4)^2 - 2(-4) + 1 = 25$$

EXERCISE SET 2.1

▲ *Identify each polynomial as a monomial, binomial, or trinomial. Give the degree of the polynomial and name the coefficient of each nonconstant term. See Examples 1 to 4.*

1. $2x^3 - x^2$

3. $5n^4$

2. $x^2 - 2x + 1$

4. $3n + 1$

5. $3r^2 - r + 2$

7. $y^3 - 2y^2 - y$

6. r^3

8. $3y^2 + 1$

▲ *Simplify. See Example 5.*

9. -5^2

11. $(-3)^2$

10. $(-5)^2$

12. -3^2

13. $4^2 - 2 \cdot 3^2$

14. $4^2 - (2 \cdot 3)^2$

15. $\dfrac{4 \cdot 2^3}{16} + 3 \cdot 4^2$

16. $\dfrac{4 \cdot 3^2}{6} + (3 \cdot 4)^2$

17. $\dfrac{3^2 - 5}{6 - 2^2} - \dfrac{6^2}{3^2}$

18. $\dfrac{3^2 \cdot 2^2}{4 - 1} + \dfrac{(-3)(2)^3}{6}$

19. $\dfrac{(-5)^2 - 3^2}{4 - 6} + \dfrac{(-3)^2}{2 + 1}$

20. $\dfrac{7^2 - 6^2}{10 + 3} - \dfrac{8^2 \cdot (-2)}{(-4)^2}$

▲ *Given* $x = 3$ *and* $y = -2$, *evaluate each expression. See Example 6.*

21. $3x + y$

22. $x - y^2$

23. $x^2 - 2y$

24. $(x + 2y)^2$

25. $x^2 - y^2$

26. $(3y)^2 - 3x$

27. $\dfrac{4x}{y} - xy$

28. $\dfrac{-xy^2}{6} + 2xy$

29. $\dfrac{(x - y)^2}{-5} + \dfrac{(xy)^2}{6}$

30. $(x + y)^2 + (x - y)^2$

▲ *Evaluate each expression for the given values of the variables.*

31. $\dfrac{1}{2}gt^2$; $g = 32$ and $t = 2$

32. $\dfrac{1}{2}gt^2 - 12t$; $g = 32$ and $t = 3$

33. $\dfrac{Mv^2}{g}$; $M = 64$, $v = 2$, and $g = 32$

34. $\dfrac{32(V - v)^2}{g}$; $V = 12$, $v = 4$, and $g = 32$

35. ar^{n-1}; $a = 2$, $r = 3$, and $n = 4$

36. $\dfrac{a - ar^n}{1 - r}$; $a = 4$, $r = 2$, and $n = 3$

▲ *Find the values of each expression for the specified values of the variable. See Example 7.*

37. If $P(x) = x^3 - 3x^2 + x + 1$, find $P(2)$ and $P(-2)$.

38. If $P(x) = 2x^3 + x^2 - 3x + 4$, find $P(3)$ and $P(-3)$.

39. If $D(x) = 3x^2 - 16x + 16$, find $D(2)$ and $D(0)$.

40. If $D(x) = 11x^2 - 6x + 1$, find $D(4)$ and $D(0)$.

Miscellaneous Exercises

▲ *In the following exercises,*

$$P(x) = x^2 - 3x + 1, \qquad Q(x) = 2x^3 - 4, \qquad \text{and}$$
$$R(x) = 2x^2 + 4x + 2$$

41. Which polynomial is a binomial?

42. What is the degree of $P(x)$?

43. What is the coefficient of the first-degree term of $P(x)$?

44. What is the constant term in $P(x)$?

45. What is the degree of $Q(x)$?

46. Find $P(3)$ and $Q(-1)$.

47. Find $Q(2)$ and $R(0)$.

48. Find $P(2) + Q(1) \cdot R(-1)$.

49. Find $Q(1) - P(0) \cdot R(-3)$.

50. Find $P(0) \cdot Q(1) \cdot R(2)$.

2.2 | SUMS AND DIFFERENCES

Rewriting Sums   We can use the distributive property in the form

$$ba + ca = (b + c)a$$

to rewrite sums such as

$$2x + 3x, \qquad 5y + 3y + 6y, \qquad \text{and} \qquad 3x + 2y + x + 3y$$

EXAMPLE 1   By the distributive property:

a. $2x + 3x = (2 + 3)x$

$\qquad = 5x$

b. $5y + 3y + 6y = (5 + 3 + 6)y$

$\qquad\qquad = 14y$

By the associative and distributive properties:

c. $3x + 2y + x + 3y = 3x + x + 2y + 3y$

$\qquad\qquad\qquad = (3 + 1)x + (2 + 3)y$

$\qquad\qquad\qquad = 4x + 5y$

Equivalent Expressions

Terms that differ at most in their numerical coefficients are called **like terms**. When we apply the distributive property to like terms, as in the preceding examples, we are *combining like terms*. The expression obtained from combining like terms represents the same number as the original expression for all values of the variables involved.

Expressions that represent (or name) *the same number for all values of the variables* are called **equivalent expressions**. Thus, in the preceding examples we obtained equivalent expressions when we simplified each polynomial.

We can show that two expressions are *not* equivalent simply by finding replacement(s) for the variable(s) for which the two expressions have different values. For example, we can show that

$$-(xy)^2 \text{ is not equivalent to } -xy^2$$

by substituting numbers for x and y. Let us try **2** for x and **3** for y. Thus,

$$-(xy)^2 = -(2 \cdot 3)^2 = -6^2 = -36$$

and

$$-xy^2 = -2 \cdot 3^2 = -2 \cdot 9 = -18$$

Hence, $-(xy)^2 \neq -xy^2$. We have used what is known as a **counterexample** to show that the two expressions are not equivalent.

Rewriting Differences

In the discussion on page 21 we noted that the signs in any polynomial are viewed as indications of positive or negative coefficients, and the operations involved are understood to be addition.

E X A M P L E 2

a. $3x - 5x + 4x$ Add $-5x$.

$= 3x + (-5x) + 4x$ **Add coefficients.**

$= (3 - 5 + 4)x$

$= 2x$

b. $3x^2 + 2y^2 - x^2 + y^2$ Add $-x^2$.

$= 3x^2 + (-x^2) + 2y^2 + y^2$ **Add coefficients of like terms.**

$= [3 + (-1)]x^2 + (2 + 1)y^2$

$= 2x^2 + 3y^2$

We can write an expression such as $a + (b + c)$ without using parentheses as $a + b + c$. However, for an expression such as

$$a - (b + c)$$

in which the parentheses are preceded by a negative sign, we add the opposite of each term inside the parentheses. Thus,

$$a - (b + c) = a + [-b - c]$$
$$= a - b - c$$

> *An expression in parentheses preceded by a minus sign can be written equivalently without parentheses by replacing each term within the parentheses with its opposite.*

EXAMPLE 3

a. $(x^2 + 2x) - (2x^2 - 3x)$ Change signs of $2x^2$ and $-3x$, and add.

$= x^2 + 2x + (-2x^2 + 3x)$
$= x^2 + 2x - 2x^2 + 3x$
$= -x^2 + 5x$

b. $(5x^2 - 2) - (2x^2 - 4x + 3)$ Change signs of $2x^2$, $-4x$, and 3, and add.

$= 5x^2 - 2 + (-2x^2 + 4x - 3)$
$= 5x^2 - 2 - 2x^2 + 4x - 3$
$= 3x^2 + 4x - 5$

COMMON ERROR   *Note that in Example 3a,* $-(2x^2 - 3x) \neq -2x^2 - 3x.$

Sums and differences can also be obtained in vertical form, with like terms vertically aligned. For example, the sum

$$(2x^2 - 3x + 1) + (-x + 3) + (x^2 + 5x - 2)$$

can be obtained by writing the sum in a vertical arrangement in which like terms are aligned:

$$
\begin{array}{r}
2x^2 - 3x + 1 \\
- x + 3 \\
\underline{x^2 + 5x - 2} \\
3x^2 + x + 2
\end{array}
$$

If a difference is written in vertical form, we can simply replace each term in the subtrahend with its negative and then add. For example, the difference

$$
\begin{array}{r}
3t^2 - 4t + 3 \\
\underline{(-) \ -5t^2 + 2t - 2}
\end{array}
$$
  can be written as the sum
$$
\begin{array}{r}
3t^2 - 4t + 3 \\
\underline{(+) \ 5t^2 - 2t + 2} \\
8t^2 - 6t + 5
\end{array}
$$

Simplifying Expressions   The rewriting of a polynomial by combining like terms is part of a process called **simplifying** the polynomial, since the result is a polynomial with fewer terms than the original. If a polynomial contains no like terms or grouping symbols, we say that the polynomial is in simple form.

When simplifying expressions where grouping devices occur within grouping devices, a great deal of difficulty can be avoided by removing the inner devices first and working outward. Furthermore, it is usually helpful to simplify an expression inside a grouping device before removing the parentheses or brackets.

We use the definition of a difference to write expressions of the form

$$a - (b + c) \quad \text{and} \quad a - (b - c)$$

without parentheses as

$$a - b - c \quad \text{and} \quad a - b + c$$

EXAMPLE 4

a. $3x - [2 - (3x + 1)]$ First express $-(3x + 1)$ as $-3x - 1$.

   $= 3x - [2 - 3x - 1]$ Simplify expression inside brackets.

   $= 3x - [1 - 3x]$ Express $-[1 - 3x]$ as $-1 + 3x$.

   $= 3x - 1 + 3x$ Simplify.

   $= 6x - 1$

b. $x^2 - [3x - (x^2 - 2)]$ First express $-(x^2 - 2)$ as $-x^2 + 2$.

   $= x^2 - [3x - x^2 + 2]$ Express $-[3x - x^2 + 2]$ as $-3x + x^2 - 2$.

   $= x^2 - 3x + x^2 - 2$ Simplify.

   $= 2x^2 - 3x - 2$

The distributive property frequently plays a role in the simplification of expressions involving grouping devices. For example, we can begin to simplify

$$2[x - 3y + 3(y - x)] - 2(2x + y)$$

by applying the distributive property to $3(y - x)$, that is, to the *inner* set of parentheses, and then combining like terms.

EXAMPLE 5

$$2[x - 3y + \overline{3(y - x)}] - 2(2x + y) = 2[x - 3y + \overline{3y - 3x}] - 2(2x + y)$$

$$= 2[-2x] - 2(2x + y)$$

$$= -4x - 4x - 2y$$

$$= -8x - 2y$$

EXAMPLE 6

a. $3[2x - (x - 2) + 3]$ Write $-(x - 2)$ as $-x + 2$.

   $= 3[2x - x + 2 + 3]$ Combine like terms.

   $= 3[x + 5]$ Apply distributive law.

   $= 3x + 15$

b. $4[x - (x^2 + 4x + 4) + 4]$ Write $-(x^2 + 4x + 4)$ as $-x^2 - 4x - 4$.

   $= 4[x - x^2 - 4x - 4 + 4]$ Combine like terms.

   $= 4[-x^2 - 3x]$ Apply distributive law.

   $= -4x^2 - 12x$

$\| \|$ E X E R C I S E S E T 2.2

▲ *Write each expression in simplest form. See Examples 1, 2, and 3.*

1. $3x^2 + 4x^2$

2. $7x^3 - 3x^3$

3. $-6y^2 + 3y^2$

4. $-5y^2 - 6y^2$

5. $8z^2 - 8z^2 + z^2$

6. $-6z^3 + 6z^2 - z^2$

7. $3x^2y + 4x^2y - 2x$

8. $6xy^2 - 4xy^2 + 3y$

9. $3r^2 + (3r^2 + 4r)$

10. $r^2 - (2r^2 + r)$

11. $(s^2 - s) - 3s$

12. $(s^2 + s) - 3s^2$

13. $(2t^2 + 3t - 1) - (t^2 + t)$

14. $(t^2 - 4t + 1) - (2t^2 - 2)$

15. $(u^2 - 3u - 2) - (3u^2 - 2u + 1)$

16. $(2u^2 + 4u + 2) - (u^2 - 4u - 1)$

17. $(2x^2 - 3x + 5) - (3x^2 + x - 2)$

18. $(4y^2 - 3y - 7) - (6y^2 - y + 2)$

19. $(4t^3 - 3t^2 + 2t - 1) - (5t^3 + t^2 + t - 2)$

20. $(4s^3 - 3s^2 + 2s - 1) - (s^3 - s^2 + 2s - 1)$

21. $(4a^2 + 6a - 7) - (a^2 + 5a + 2) + (-2a^2 - 7a + 6)$

22. $(7c^2 - 10c + 8) - (8c + 11) + (-6c^2 - 3c - 2)$

23. $(4x^2y - 3xy + xy^2) - (-5x^2y + xy - 2xy^2) - (x^2y - 3xy)$

24. $(m^2n^2 - 2mn + 7) - (-2m^2n^2 + mn - 3) - (3m^2n^2 - 4mn + 2)$

▲ *Simplify. See Examples 4, 5, and 6.*

25. $y - [2y + (y + 1)]$

26. $3a + [2a - (a + 4)]$

27. $3 - [2x - (x + 1) + 2]$

28. $5 - [3y + (y - 4) - 1]$

29. $(3x + 2) - [x + (2 + x) + 1]$

30. $-(x - 3) + [2x - (3 + x) - 2]$

31. $[x^2 - (2x + 3)] - [2x^2 + (x - 2)]$

32. $[2y^2 - (4 - y)] + [y^2 - (2 + y)]$

33. $3y - (2x - y) - (y - [2x - (y - 2x)] + 3y)$

34. $[x - (y + x)] - (2x - [3x - (x - y)] + y)$

35. $[x - (3x + 2)] - (2x - [x - (4 + x)] - 1)$

36. $-(2y - [2y - 4y + (y - 2)] + 1) + [2y - (4 - y) + 1]$

37. $2[a - (a - 1) + 2]$

38. $3[2a - (a + 1) + 3]$

39. $a[a - (2a + 3) - (a - 1)]$

40. $-2a[3a + (a - 3) - (2a + 1)]$

41. $-[a - 3(a + 1) - (2a + 1)]$

42. $-[(a + 1) - 2(3a - 1) + 4]$

43. $2(a - [a - 2(a + 1) + 1] + 1)$

44. $-4(4 - [3 - 2(a - 1) + a] + a)$

45. $-x(x - 3[2x - 3(x + 1)] + 2)$

46. $x(4 - 2[3 - 4(x + 1)] - x)$

Miscellaneous Exercises

47. Subtract $4x^2 - 3x + 2$ from the sum of $x^2 - 2x + 3$ and $x^2 - 4$.

48. Subtract $2t^2 + 3t - 1$ from the sum of $2t^2 - 3t + 5$ and $t^2 + t + 2$.

49. Subtract the sum of $2b^2 - 3b + 2$ and $b^2 + b - 5$ from $4b^2 + b - 2$.

50. Subtract the sum of $7c^2 + 3c - 2$ and $3 - c - 5c^2$ from $2c^2 + 3c + 1$.

▲ *Given that $P(x) = x - 1$, $Q(x) = x^2 + 1$, and $R(x) = x^2 - x + 1$, write each expression in terms of x and simplify.*

51. $P(x) + Q(x) - R(x)$

52. $P(x) - Q(x) + R(x)$

53. $R(x) - [Q(x) - P(x)]$

54. $Q(x) - [R(x) + P(x)]$

55. $Q(x) - [R(x) - P(x)]$

56. $P(x) - [R(x) - Q(x)]$

57. $R(x) + [P(x) - Q(x)]$

58. $Q(x) + [R(x) - P(x)]$

59. Show by a counterexample that $-(x + 1)$ is not equivalent to $-x + 1$.

60. Show by a counterexample that $-(x - y)$ is not equivalent to $-x - y$.

2.3 | **SOLVING LINEAR EQUATIONS**

The development of skills that are used to solve applications, commonly called word problems, is an important aim in algebra. There are two distinct skills involved that we will consider. One skill involves writing equations that are mathematical models for conditions stated in the word problems. The second skill involves solving the equations.

We will first review properties and procedures that are used to solve equations that involve first-degree polynomials. Such equations are called **linear equations**.

Equivalent Equations

Any number that satisfies an equation is called a **solution** of the equation, and the set of all solutions is called the solution set. The process of finding solution sets of equations involves generating equations that have the same solution set. Equations that have identical solution sets are called **equivalent equations**. For example,

$$5x - 4 = 16$$
$$5x = 20$$

and

$$x = 4$$

are equivalent equations because {4} is the solution set of each.

Simplifying Members of an Equation

There are several properties that enable us to form equivalent equations. One way is to simplify a member of an equation by writing the sum or difference of two or more terms as a single term. For example, the solution of the equation $9x - 8x = 12$ becomes evident when it is written in the equivalent form $x = 12$. Another way is to remove parentheses, for example, changing $3(2x - 3) = 9$ to $6x - 9 = 9$.

Addition and Multiplication Laws

One more way to generate equivalent equations follows from the equality properties of real numbers that were introduced in Section 1.2.

If $a = b$, then

$$a + c = b + c \qquad \text{**Addition property of equality**}$$

If $a = b$, then

$$ac = bc \qquad \text{**Multiplication property of equality**}$$

Applying these properties to algebraic expressions, we have the following more general properties:

---

1. *The addition of the same expression to each member of an equation produces an equivalent equation.*
2. *The multiplication of each member of an equation by the same nonzero number produces an equivalent equation.*

Any application of these properties always produces an equivalent equation.

Because subtraction can be defined in terms of addition and division can be defined in terms of multiplication, these properties also apply to subtraction and division, respectively.

The application of Properties 1 and 2 above enables us to transform an equation whose solution may not be obvious, through a series of equivalent equations, until we obtain an equation that has an obvious solution. If necessary, we may obtain an equation in which the variable with coefficient of 1 stands alone as one member.

EXAMPLE 1

To solve

$$3x + 5 = 11$$

we first add -5, the additive inverse of 5, to each member to obtain

$$3x + 5 + (-5) = 11 + (-5)$$
$$3x = 6$$

Now, by inspection, we can readily determine that 2 is the solution. However, if necessary, we can multiply each member by $\frac{1}{3}$, the multiplicative inverse of 3, in order to obtain the variable x with a coefficient of 1. Alternatively, we can divide each member by 3. Thus,

$$\frac{3x}{3} = \frac{6}{3}$$
$$x = 2$$

In either case the solution set is {2}.

We can always determine whether an apparent solution of an equation is really a solution by substituting it into the original equation and verifying that the resulting statement is true. If each of the equations in a sequence is simply obtained by means of an application of Properties 1 and 2, the sole purpose for such a check is to detect arithmetic errors.

Let us consider several other examples.

EXAMPLE 2

To solve

$$3y - 7 = y + 5$$

we first add $-y$ and $+7$ to each member, where $-y$ is the additive inverse of y and $+7$ is the additive inverse of -7, to obtain

$$3y - 7 + (-y) + 7 = y + 5 + (-y) + 7$$
$$3y - y = 5 + 7$$
$$2y = 12$$

We now have an equation in which one member includes only terms containing the variable and the other member includes only constants. By inspection, we can determine that 6 is the solution. Alternatively, we can multiply each member by $\frac{1}{2}$, or divide by 2, to obtain the variable y with a coefficient of 1. Thus,

$$\frac{1}{2}(2y) = \frac{1}{2}(12)$$
$$y = 6$$

The solution set is {6}.

By first adding $-y$ and $+7$ to each member of $3y - 7 = y + 5$ in the above example, we obtained the equivalent equation $2y = 12$, with a positive coefficient for y. Note that if we add $-3y$ and -5 to each member, we obtain $-12 = -2y$, which has the same solution set.

Equations Containing Parentheses

In solving an equation that contains grouping symbols, it may be necessary to use the distributive property to simplify one or both members.

E X A M P L E 3

$3(x + 2) - 2(x + 1) = 8$ **Apply distributive property.**

$3x + 6 - 2x - 2 = 8$ **Simplify left side.**

$x + 4 = 8$ **Add −4 to each side.**

$x = 4$

Hence, the solution set is $\{4\}$.

E X A M P L E 4

$2(x^2 - 6x + 9) - 2x^2 = 9$ **Apply distributive property.**

$2x^2 - 12x + 18 - 2x^2 = 9$ **Simplify left side.**

$-12x + 18 = 9$ **Add −18 to each side.**

$-12x = -9$ **Divide each side by −12.**

$x = \dfrac{-9}{-12} = \dfrac{9}{12} = \dfrac{3}{4}$

Hence, the solution set is $\{3/4\}$.

Sometimes grouping symbols are nested within a second set of grouping symbols, and we have to apply the distributive law more than once.

E X A M P L E 5

$4[x - 3(x + 2) - 4] = 3$ **Express** $-3(x + 2)$ **as** $-3x - 6$.

$4[x - 3x - 6 - 4] = 3$ **Simplify expression inside brackets.**

$4[-2x - 10] = 3$ **Apply distributive property.**

$-8x - 40 = 3$ **Add 40 to each side.**

$-8x = 43$ **Divide each side by −8.**

$x = -\dfrac{43}{8}$

Hence, the solution set is $\{-43/8\}$.

The procedures that we used to solve equations in the previous examples we can also use to solve equations that involve decimals.

E X A M P L E 6

$0.10(x - 2) + 0.20(x + 3) = 2.50$ **Apply distributive property.**

$0.10x - 0.20 + 0.20x + 0.60 = 2.50$ **Simplify left side.**

$0.30x + 0.40 = 2.50$ **Add −0.40 to each side.**

$0.30x = 2.10$ **Divide each side by 0.30.**

$\dfrac{0.30x}{0.30} = \dfrac{2.10}{0.30}$

$x = 7$

The solution set is $\{7\}$.

Working with nondecimal numbers is usually easier. In the preceding example we could first multiply each member of the original equation by 100 to obtain the equation

$$100[0.10(x - 2) + 0.20(x + 3)] = 100(2.50)$$ **Multiply both sides by 100.**
$$0.10(x - 2) + 0.20(x + 3) = 2.50$$

or

$$10(x - 2) + 20(x + 3) = 250$$ **Apply distributive property.**
$$10x - 20 + 20x + 60 = 250$$

and then proceed to solve the equation.

$$30x + 40 = 250$$
$$30x = 210$$
$$x = 7$$

The solution set is the same as in Example 6.

Solving Formulas

Equations that express relationships between quantities (variables) of practical interest are called **formulas**. Formulas arise in business, engineering, physics, and in fact all disciplines in our experience. In particular, you may recall some simple formulas pertaining to geometric figures from previous courses. A list of common geometric formulas is provided in Appendix E.

EXAMPLE 7

The perimeter of a rectangle is given by the formula
$$P = 2l + 2w$$
Find l, given that $P = 38.6$ cm   and $w = 4.1$ cm.

Solution

Substitute the given values for P and w in the formula:

$$38.6 = 2l + 2(4.1)$$ **Add -8.2 to each side.**
$$38.6 - 8.2 = 2l$$ **Simplify left side.**
$$30.4 = 2l$$ **Divide each side by 2.**
$$15.2 = l$$

The solution set of the equation is $\{15.2\}$. Hence, the length of the rectangle is 15.2 centimeters.

Solving Equations for Specified Symbols

An equation containing more than one variable can be solved for one of the variables in terms of the remaining symbols. In general, we apply the properties listed on page 29 until the desired variable stands alone on one side of an equation. The following suggestions may be helpful:

> ### Solving a First-Degree Equation for a Specified Variable
>
> 1. Transform the equation to a form in which all terms containing the specified variable are on one side and all terms not containing that variable are on the other side.
> 2. Combine like terms on each side.
> 3. Divide each side by the coefficient of the specified variable.

EXAMPLE 8

To solve the formula

$$P = 2l + 2w \qquad \text{for } w$$

we first add $-2l$ to each side to obtain

$$P - 2l = 2l + 2w - 2l$$
$$P - 2l = 2w$$

Then we divide each side by 2, the coefficient of w, (or multiply by $\frac{1}{2}$) to get

$$\frac{P - 2l}{2} = w \qquad \text{or} \qquad w = \frac{P - 2l}{2}$$

EXAMPLE 9

To solve the formula

$$S = lw + lh + 2hw \qquad \text{for } w$$

we first obtain

$$S - lh = lw + 2hw$$

in which all terms containing the specified variable w are on one side and all terms not containing w are on the other side. Then we combine the like terms $lw + 2hw$ to obtain

$$S - lh = w(l + 2h)$$

and finally divide each side by $(l + 2h)$, the coefficient of w, to get

$$\frac{S - lh}{l + 2h} = w \qquad \text{or} \qquad w = \frac{S - lh}{l + 2h}$$

The method that we used to solve an equation for one of the variables in terms of other variables and constants is also applicable when the equation contains parentheses. When parentheses are involved, there are usually several ways to proceed that may lead to equations that have different forms. However, they will be equivalent.

EXAMPLE 10

Solve $\quad 2A = h(b + c) \quad$ for b.

Solution (1)

Dividing each side by h, the coefficient of $b + c$, yields

$$\frac{2A}{h} = \frac{h(b + c)}{h}$$

$$\frac{2A}{h} = b + c$$

Adding $-c$ to each side, we get

$$\frac{2A}{h} - c = b \quad \text{or} \quad b = \frac{2A}{h} - c$$

Solution (2) Applying the distributive law on the right-hand side of $2A = h(b + c)$ yields

$$2A = hb + hc$$

Adding $-hc$ to each side, we get

$$2A - hc = hb + hc - hc$$
$$2A - hc = hb$$

Finally, dividing each side by h, the coefficient of b, we get

$$\frac{2A - hc}{h} = b \quad \text{or} \quad b = \frac{2A - hc}{h}$$

In our later work we will develop methods to verify that the different equations obtained are equivalent.

EXERCISE SET 2.3

▲ *Solve each equation. See Examples 1–5.*

1. $3x + 5 = 26$ **2.** $2 + 5x = 37$

3. $4x - 6 = 22$ **4.** $3x - 5 = 7$

5. $y + (y + 140) = 620$ **6.** $y + (y - 160) = 830$

7. $y + (y - 210) + (y - 490) = 7970$

8. $y + (y - 620) + (y - 810) = 8620$

9. $3(z + 2) = 14$ **10.** $2(z - 3) = 15$

11. $3z - (z - 4) = 12$ **12.** $5z - (z + 1) = 14$

13. $2[x - 3(x + 2) - 4] = 6$

14. $3[3x - 2(x - 3) + 1] = 8$

15. $3[4 + 2(x - 3) - x] = 10$

16. $2[1 - 3(x + 1) - 2x] = 12$

17. $-[4 - (y - 2) + 2y] = 0$

18. $-[7 - (y - 3) - 4y] = 0$

19. $-2[y - (y + 1)] = 3(y - 2)$

20. $-3[2y - (y - 2)] = 2(y + 3)$

▲ *Solve each equation. See Example 6.*

21. $0.40(y - 4) = 2.80$ **22.** $0.60(y + 2) = 3.60$

23. $0.25y + 0.10(y + 32) = 11.60$

24. $0.12y + 0.08(y + 10,000) = 12,000$

25. $0.10x + 0.80(20) = 0.50(x + 20)$

26. $0.10x + 0.12(x + 4,000) = 920$

▲ *Solve each formula for the specified variable to the nearest tenth. See Example 7.*

27. $P = 2l + 2w$ for l, given that $w = 5.9$ and $P = 63.4$

28. $A = \frac{1}{2}bh$ for b, given that $A = 27.3$ and $h = 14.7$

29. $A + B + C = 180$ for B, given that $A = 62.1$ and $C = 44.3$

30. $V = lwh$ for w, given that $V = 48.4$, $l = 4.2$, and $h = 6.1$

31. $A = P + Prt$ for t, given that $A = 1320$, $P = 1000$, and $r = 0.08$

32. $A = P + Prt$ for t, given that $A = 2320$, $P = 1000$, and $r = 0.11$

▲ *Solve each formula for the specified variable. See Examples 8–10.*

33. $f = ma$ for m **34.** $pv = k$ for v

35. $I = prt$ for p **36.** $V = lwh$ for h

37. $P = 2l + 2w$ for w **38.** $S = 3\pi d + \pi d$ for d

39. $v = k + gt$ for g **40.** $v = k + gt$ for t

41. $S = 2\pi(r + h)$ for h **42.** $S(1 - r) = a$ for r

43. $l = a + (n - 1)d$ for n

44. $2A = h(b + c)$ for c

45. $A = P(1 + rt)$ for t

46. $S = 2[l(w + h) + wh]$ for l

51. $d = rt$ **a.** for r **b.** for t

52. $i = prt$ **a.** for r **b.** for t

53. $A + B + C = 180$

 a. for A **b.** for C

54. $A = \frac{1}{2}bh$ **a.** for b **b.** for h

55. **a.** Simplify $2[x - (x + 2)] + x$

 b. Solve $2[x - (x + 2)] + x = 0$

56. **a.** Simplify $0.20(y - 5) + 0.30y$

 b. Solve $0.20(y - 5) + 0.30y = 0$

Miscellaneous Exercises

▲ *Solve each equation in 47–54 mentally.*

47. **a.** $x - 4 = 12$ **b.** $-2x = 18$

48. **a.** $2x + 1 = 11$ **b.** $3x - 4 = 8$

49. **a.** $0.1x = 40$ **b.** $-0.1x = 2.0$

50. **a.** $2x + y = 6$ for x in terms of y

 b. $x - y = 4$ for y in terms of x

2.4 | # CONSTRUCTING MATHEMATICAL MODELS; APPLICATIONS

In the next two sections, we will solve a variety of word problems. Some problems require simply translating word sentences into equations and then solving for a specified variable. More practical word problems require the construction of mathematical models, which are often in the form of one or more equations. In this chapter the word problems can be modeled by a single equation.

Translating Sentences

In the first example we translate several simple word sentences into equations in which we have represented a number by x.

EXAMPLE 1
 a. Four more than three times a number is equal to 25.

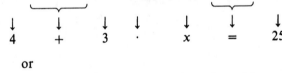

 or

$$4 + 3x = 25$$

 b. Two times the sum of a number and six equals 18.

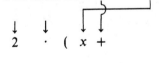

The word "sum" requires symbols of grouping here.

 or

$$2(x + 6) = 18$$

In the above examples the word sentences were simple, and translating each sentence into an equation was direct. Mathematical models often require more insight to construct.

Constructing Mathematical Models

In problems in which the relationship between given quantities and one or more quantities that we wish to find is not evident from a reading of the problem, *we can start the process of constructing a mathematical model by first writing in words the quantity or quantities we want to find.* Then these quantities can be represented by variables (in this section one variable) or by expressions containing the variable. These first two steps will help us write an appropriate equation that describes the condition on the variable stated in the problem.

We first look at several simple examples in which only one quantity is to be found. In each example we proceed in the following order:

1. Represent the unknown quantity using words.
2. Assign a variable to represent the unknown quantity.
3. Write an equation expressing the condition on the variable.
4. Solve the equation.
5. Interpret the solution of the equation in terms of the quantity represented by the variable in Step 2. (Does your answer make sense?)

EXAMPLE 2   Six percent (0.06) of the students in all algebra sections received an "A" grade. How many students were enrolled if nine students received A's?

Solution

Step 1 ⟶   ⟵ Step 2

(Number of students enrolled:) n

Step 3   Write an equation expressing the fact that 0.06 of the number of students enrolled equals 9:

$$0.06n = 9$$

Step 4   Solve the equation:

$$n = \frac{9}{0.06} = 150$$

Step 5   Hence, 150 students are enrolled.

EXAMPLE 3   A camera is on sale at a 25% discount. What was the original cost if the discount is $45?

Solution

Step 1 ⟶   ⟵ Step 2

(Original cost:) c

Step 3   Write an equation expressing the fact that 0.25 of the original cost is $45:

$$0.25c = 45$$

Step 4   Solve the equation:

$$c = \frac{45}{0.25} = 180$$

Step 5   Hence, the original cost is $180.

In each of the above examples, only one quantity was to be found. *If two or more quantities are to be found, separate phrases should be used for each quantity.* After a variable is assigned to represent one of the quantities, the conditions in the problem are used to determine the algebraic expressions involving the variable, which are then assigned to the other quantities.

In our later work we will sometimes use different variables for different quantities; however, at this time we will use one variable.

EXAMPLE 4

A small business calculator sells for $5 less than a scientific model. If the cost to buy both is $41, how much does each cost?

Solution

Step 1   First write *two* word phrases for the quantities to be found.

Step 2   Assign a variable, say C, for the *cost* of the scientific calculator.

Step 2a   Then, because the business calculator costs $5 less than the scientific calculator, the *cost* of the business calculator can be expressed as $C - 5$.

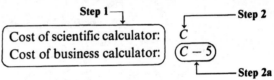

Step 3   Write an equation expressing the fact that the total cost is $41.
$$C + (C - 5) = 41$$

Step 4   Solve the equation. First simplify the left side.

$$2C - 5 = 41 \qquad \text{Add 5 to each side.}$$
$$2C = 46 \qquad \text{Divide each side by 2.}$$
$$C = 23$$

Step 5   Hence, the cost of the scientific calculator is $23, and the cost of the business calculator is $C - 5 = 23 - 5$ or $18.

It is sometimes possible to write more than one equation that would be correct for the conditions of a problem, depending on the quantity to which we assign the variable. In the above example, if we had let C represent the cost of the business calculator, then $C + 5$ would represent the cost of the scientific calculator; and an appropriate equation would be

$$C + (C + 5) = 41$$

The procedure used in Example 4 can also be used when three or more quantities are to be obtained. In the following example we will let the variable represent the *largest* number we wish to obtain and then express each of the other smaller quantities in terms of this variable.

EXAMPLE 5

One thousand sixty students voted to elect a candidate to represent their college at a national convention. One candidate received 60 votes more than a second candidate and 104 votes more than a third candidate. How many votes did each candidate receive?

Solution

Step 1 ────────────────────────────┐   ┌──── Step 2

> Number of votes of winning candidate: x
> Number of votes of second candidate: $x - 60$
> Number of votes of third candidate: $x - 104$

└──── Step 2a

Step 3 Write an equation expressing the fact that there was a total of 1060 votes.

$$x + (x - 60) + (x - 104) = 1060$$

Step 4 Solve the equation. First simplify the left side.

$$3x - 164 = 1060 \qquad \textbf{Add 164 to each side.}$$
$$3x = 1224 \qquad \textbf{Divide each side by 3.}$$
$$x = 408$$

Step 5 Hence, the winning candidate received 408 votes, the second candidate received $x - 60 = 408 - 60$ or 348 votes, and the third candidate received $x - 104 = 408 - 104$ or 304 votes.

Using Formulas and Figures

Sketching the figure or a geometric condition stated in the problem is usually helpful when solving problems involving a geometric figure.

EXAMPLE 6

The vertex angle of an isosceles triangle measures 30° more than the sum of the measures of the other two equal angles. What is the measure of each angle in the triangle?

Solution

Step 1 Express the measure of each angle in a simple phrase.

Step 2 Represent the measure of each base angle by a variable, say x.

Step 2a Represent the measure of the third angle (vertex angle) by $x + x + 30$.

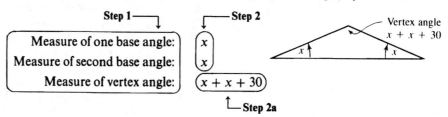

> Measure of one base angle: x
> Measure of second base angle: x
> Measure of vertex angle: $x + x + 30$

Step 3 Write an equation using the fact that the sum of the measures of the angles in any triangle is 180°. (See Appendix E.)

$$(x) + (x) + (2x + 30) = 180$$

Step 4 Solve the equation.

$$4x = 150$$
$$x = 37.5$$

Step 5 Hence, each base angle equals $37\frac{1}{2}°$, and the vertex angle equals

$$x + x + 30 = 37.5 + 37.5 + 30 \quad \text{or} \quad 105°$$

Reason for Step-by-Step Approach

You may at times read a problem and know immediately how to write an equation. Since this is not usually the case, the procedure to construct mathematical models shown in the preceding examples will be helpful. The step-by-step procedure shown may seem overly detailed for these simple examples. However, if you take the simple approach suggested, you will be prepared to use the same procedure when the problems are more difficult and when writing an appropriate equation is not as easy.

You may wish to refer to the following summary of the steps as you proceed to solve the word problems in this and other sections.

Solving Word Problems

Step 1. Read the problem and note particularly what is asked for. *Write a short word phrase to describe each unknown quantity.*

Step 2a. Represent one unknown quantity by a variable.

b. Represent other unknown quantities in terms of this variable. (Where applicable, draw a sketch and label the parts.)

Step 3. Write an equation that involves the variable and is a "model" for the conditions on the variable stated in the problem.

Step 4. Solve the equation.

Step 5. Interpret the solution of the equation in terms of the quantity or quantities that were represented by the variable in Step 2.

EXERCISE SET 2.4

▲ *Write each sentence as an equation using x as the variable. See Example 1.*

1. The sum of three times a number and 5 is 26.
2. Two plus five times a number equals 37.
3. Four times a number less 6 equals 22.
4. Three times a number minus 5 is 7.
5. The sum of two times a number and the number itself equals 21.
6. The sum of three times a number and two times the number equals 40.
7. The sum of an integer and 2, divided by 4, equals 5.
8. An integer less 2, divided by 5, equals 3.

▲ *Solve each problem. Use the five steps suggested on page 36. See Examples 2 and 3 for Problems 9–18.*

9. One year the Dean of Admissions at City College selected 75% of all applicants for the freshman class. How many students applied for entrance if the college selected 600 students?

10. A part-time secretary takes home 80% of her total salary. What is her total salary if she takes home $120 per week?

11. A saleswoman earns a commission of 2% on her sales. How much must she sell to have an income of $300 per week?

12. A company contracts to produce 1200 gears that meet certain specifications. If 3% of the gears manufactured are defective, what is the total number of gears that must be manufactured?

13. Thirty percent of all the students enrolled in a mathematics class are women. How many students are enrolled if there are 12 women in the class?

14. A basketball player made 40% of all his shooting attempts. How many shots did he attempt if he made 8 baskets?

15. A company contracts to manufacture 1710 baseball bats. If 5% of the bats are discarded because of defects, what is the total number of bats that must be manufactured to yield the 1710 bats?

16. A company that manufactures transistors always ships 2% additional transistors over any amount ordered to cover any defective ones that might be included. How many transistors were ordered if 22,400 were shipped?

17. An employer finds that 94% of the employees were present on Monday. If 9 employees were absent, how many employees does the employer have?

18. A computer was on sale for a 40% discount. What was the original cost if the sale price was $384?

▲ *See Examples 4 and 5 for Problems 19–24.*

19. A 24-foot rope is cut into two pieces so that one piece is 6 feet longer than the other. How long is each piece?

20. A 36-foot chain is cut into two pieces so that one piece is twice as long as the other piece. How long is each piece?

21. Six hundred twenty students voted in an election for two candidates for student body president. The winner received 140 more votes than the loser. How many votes did each candidate receive?

22. Eight hundred thirty students voted in an election for student body treasurer. The loser received 160 fewer votes than the winner. How many votes did each candidate receive?

23. Three candidates ran for city council member in an election in which 6560 votes were cast. The winner received 210 more votes than the second candidate and 490 more votes than the third candidate. How many votes did each candidate receive?

24. One candidate in an election received 620 more votes than a second candidate and 810 more votes than a third candidate. How many votes did each candidate receive if 8650 votes were cast?

▲ *See Example 6 for Problems 25–34. (See Appendix E for geometric formulas.)*

25. One angle of a triangle measures two times another angle, and the third angle measures 12° more than the sum of the measures of the other two. Find the measure of each angle.

26. The measure of the smallest angle of a triangle is 25° less than the measure of another angle and 50° less than the measure of the third angle. Find the measure of each angle.

27. One angle of a triangle measures 10° more than another, and the measure of the third angle equals the sum of the measures of the first two angles. Find the measures of each angle.

28. The measure of one angle of a triangle is 20° more than that of another, and the measure of the third angle is six times the measure of the smaller. Find the measures of each angle.

29. The length of each of two equal sides of an isosceles triangle is 15.6 centimeters greater than the length of the third side. Find the length of the three sides to the nearest tenth if the perimeter is 66.8 centimeters.

30. The length of the longest side of a triangle is three times that of the shortest side, and the length of the third side is 72.4 centimeters more than that of the shortest side. Find the length of the three sides to the nearest tenth if the perimeter is 272.8 centimeters.

31. When the length of each side of a square is increased by 5.1 centimeters, the area is increased by 85.7 square centimeters. Find the length of a side of the original square to the nearest tenth.

32. The length of each side of a square is decreased by 6.1 inches. If the area is decreased by 84.3 square inches, find the length of the side of the original square to the nearest tenth.

33. The length of a table tennis table is four feet longer than its width, and its perimeter is 28 feet. Find its dimensions.

34. The length of a tennis court for singles is 24 feet longer than twice its width, and its perimeter is 210 feet. Find its dimensions.

Miscellaneous Exercises

▲ *Solve each problem mentally.*

35. A contractor starts a job with 3800 bricks. After 1200 bricks are used, how many are left?

36. If a press stamps out 18,000 pieces in 9 hours, how many pieces can it stamp out in 1 hour? In 2 hours?

37. A station sells motor oil at 24 quarts for $48.00. Find the cost of 36 quarts.

38. A typist can type 60 words in 1 hour. At that rate, how many words can he type in $1\frac{1}{2}$ hours?

39. Two angles of a triangle are 30° and 70°. What is the measurement of the third angle?

40. The area of a square is 36 centermeters. What is the length of each side? What is the perimeter?

In Section 2.4 the construction of the mathematical models in the form of equations was relatively straightforward. If a word problem is more involved, it is sometimes helpful to summarize information in a tabular form to assist us in constructing a mathematical model.

Value Problems

A basic idea of problems involving coins (or bills) is that the value of a number of coins (or bills) of the same denomination is equal to the product of the value of a single coin (or bill) and the total number of coins (or bills).

$$\begin{bmatrix} \text{value of} \\ n \\ \text{coins} \end{bmatrix} = \begin{bmatrix} \text{value of} \\ \text{each} \\ \text{coin} \end{bmatrix} \times \begin{bmatrix} \text{number} \\ \text{of} \\ \text{coins} \end{bmatrix}$$

For example,

$$\$2.00 = 0.10 \times 20$$

EXAMPLE 1

A collection of coins consisting of dimes and quarters has a value of $11.60. How many dimes and quarters are in the collection if there are 32 more dimes than quarters?

Solution

Step 1 Express the *two* quantities asked for in *two* simple phrases.

Step 2 Represent the number of quarters using a variable, say q.

Step 2a Represent the number of dimes by $q + 32$ (there are 32 more dimes than quarters).

Step 3 A table showing the total value of the quarters and the total value of the dimes will help you construct a mathematical model.

Denomination	Value of 1 Coin	Number of Coins	Value of Coins
Quarters	0.25	q	$0.25q$
Dimes	0.10	$q + 32$	$0.10(q + 32)$

Write an equation relating the value of the quarters and the value of the dimes to the value of the entire collection.

$$\begin{bmatrix} \text{value of} \\ \text{quarters} \end{bmatrix} + \begin{bmatrix} \text{value of} \\ \text{dimes} \end{bmatrix} + \begin{bmatrix} \text{value of} \\ \text{collection} \end{bmatrix}$$

$$0.25q \quad + 0.10(q + 32) + \quad 11.60$$

Step 4 Solve the equation. It may be easier to first multiply each side by 100 to obtain an equivalent equation in which none of the terms contain decimals.

$$25q + 10q + 320 = 1160 \qquad \text{Simplify the left side. Add } -320 \text{ to each side.}$$
$$35q = 840 \qquad \text{Divide each side by 35.}$$
$$q = 24$$

Step 5 Therefore, there are 24 quarters and $24 + 32$ or 56 dimes in the collection.

Interest Problems

Simple interest problems involve the fact that the interest (I) earned during a single year is equal to the amount (A) invested times the annual rate (r) of interest. Thus, $I = Ar$.

EXAMPLE 2

A man has an annual income of $12,000 from two investments. He has $10,000 more invested at 4% than he has invested at 6%. How much does he have invested at each rate?

Solution

Step 1 Express the *two* quantities asked for in *two* simple phrases.

Step 2 Represent the amount invested at 6% using a variable, say A.

Step 2a Represent the amount invested at 4% by $A + 10,000$.

Step 3 A table showing the total interest received on each investment will help you construct the mathematical model.

Investment Rate		Amount Invested	Interest
6%	0.06	A	$0.06A$
4%	0.04	$A + 10,000$	$0.04(A + 10,000)$

Write an equation relating the interest from each investment and the total interest received.

$$\begin{bmatrix} \text{interest from} \\ 6\% \text{ investment} \end{bmatrix} + \begin{bmatrix} \text{interest from} \\ 4\% \text{ investment} \end{bmatrix} = [\text{total interest}]$$
$$0.06A \qquad + 0.04(A + 10,000) = \qquad 12,000$$

Step 4 Solve the equation. First multiply each side by 100.

$$6A + 4(A + 10,000) = 1,200,000 \qquad \text{Apply distributive property.}$$
$$6A + 4A + 40,000 = 1,200,000 \qquad \text{Simplify the left side.}$$
$$10A + 40,000 = 1,200,000 \qquad \text{Add } -40,000 \text{ to each side.}$$
$$10A = 1,160,000 \qquad \text{Divide each side by 10.}$$
$$A = 116,000$$

Step 5   Therefore, $116,000 is invested at 6%, and $116,000 + 10,000$ or $126,000 is invested at 4%.

Mixture Problems

A key to solving mixture problems is to recognize that the amount of a given substance in a mixture is obtained by multiplying the amount of the mixture by the percent (or rate) of the given substance in the mixture.

$$\begin{bmatrix} \text{amount} \\ \text{of} \\ \text{substance} \end{bmatrix} = \begin{bmatrix} \text{fraction} \\ \text{of substance} \\ \text{in mixture} \end{bmatrix} \times \begin{bmatrix} \text{amount} \\ \text{of} \\ \text{mixture} \end{bmatrix}$$

Tables are especially helpful in mixture problems.

EXAMPLE 3

How many liters of a 10% solution of acid should be added to 20 liters of a 60% solution of acid to obtain a 50% solution?

Solution

Step 1   Express the quantity asked for in a simple phrase.

Step 2   Represent the quantity using a variable, say n.

Step 1 ⟶
(Number of liters of 10% solution:) n ⟵ Step 2

Step 3   Set up a table showing the amount of *pure* acid in each solution.

Fraction of Acid in Mixture	Number of Liters	Amount of Acid
0.10	n	$0.10n$
0.60	20	$0.60(20)$
0.50	$n + 20$	$0.50(n + 20)$

A figure may also be helpful. Here, the amount of pure acid in the solution is shaded; the remainder is water.

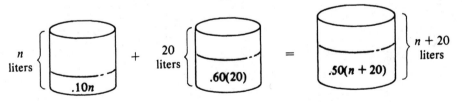

Write an equation relating the amount of *pure* acid.

$$\begin{bmatrix} \text{Amount of} \\ \text{pure acid in} \\ \text{10\% solution} \end{bmatrix} + \begin{bmatrix} \text{Amount of} \\ \text{pure acid in} \\ \text{60\% solution} \end{bmatrix} = \begin{bmatrix} \text{Amount of} \\ \text{pure acid in} \\ \text{50\% solution} \end{bmatrix}$$

$$0.10n \quad + \quad 0.60(20) \quad = \quad 0.50(n + 20)$$

Step 4   Solve the equation. First multiply each side by 100.

$10n + 60(20) = 50(n + 20)$	**Apply distributive property.**
$10n + 1200 = 50n + 1000$	**Add -1200 and $-50n$ to each side.**
$-40n = -200$	**Divide each side by -40.**
$n = 5$	

Step 5   Therefore, 5 liters of a 10% solution are needed.

‖‖ E X E R C I S E   S E T   2.5

▲ *See Example 1 for Problems 1–10.*

1. A collection dimes and quarters has a value of $3.60. There are twice as many dimes as quarters. How many of each kind are there?

2. A collection of nickels and dimes has a value of $4.90. There are 22 more dimes than nickels. How many of each kind are there?

3. A woman who has 12 more quarters than dimes has a total of $12.45 in quarters and dimes. How many of each kind of coin does she have?

4. A savings bank containing $1.75 in dimes, quarters, and nickels contains 3 more dimes than quarters and 3 times as many nickels as dimes. How many coins of each kind are in the bank?

5. On an airplane flight for which first-class fare is $80 and tourist fare is $64 there were 42 passengers. If receipts for the flight totaled $2880, how many first-class and how many tourist passengers were on the flight?

6. An ice cream vendor bought 50 ice cream bars—chocolate-covered bars at 18¢ each and sandwich bars at 15¢ each. If the total cost was $8.10, how many bars of each kind did the vendor purchase?

7. One brand of coffee sells for $1.20 per pound, and a second brand sells for $1.40 per pound. A restaurant buyer paid $28.80 for some of each brand. How many pounds of each brand did he buy if he bought 2 pounds more of the expensive brand than of the less expensive brand?

8. A hardware clerk sold some 12-cent and 16-cent bolts for a total of $7.80. How many of each were sold if there were three times as many 12-cent bolts as there were 16-cent bolts?

9. A theater charged $4.00 for an adult ticket and $2.50 for children under 12 years old. One evening 82 people viewed a movie. If the receipts totaled $310, how many of each kind of ticket were sold?

10. The first-class fare on an airplane flight is $240, and the tourist fare is $150. If 48 passengers paid a total of $8100 for the flight, how many of each ticket were sold?

▲ *See Example 2 for Problems 11–18.*

11. Two investments produce an annual income of $920. One investment earns 4%, and the other earns 6%. How much is invested at each rate if the amount invested at 6% is $4000 more than the amount invested at 4%?

12. An amount of money is invested at 4%, and $3000 more than that amount is invested at 5%. How much is invested at each rate if the total income is $690?

13. An amount of $42,000 is invested, part at 6% and the remainder at 4%. Find the amount invested at each rate if the yearly incomes on the investments are equal.

14. An amount of money is invested at 4%, and twice that amount is invested at 6%. How much is invested at each rate if the total income is $720?

15. A woman has invested $8000, part in a bank at 5% and part in a savings and loan association at 6%. If her annual return is $430, how much has she invested at each rate?

16. A sum of $2400 is split between an investment in a mutual fund paying 7% and one in corporate bonds paying 6%. If the return on the 7% investment exceeds that on the 6% investment by $25 per year, how much is invested at each rate?

17. If $8000 is invested in bonds at 4%, how much additional money must be invested in stocks paying 7% to make the earnings on the total investment 5%?

18. If $6000 is invested in bonds at 4%, how much additional money must be invested in stocks at 6% to earn a return of 5% on the total investment?

▲ *See Example 3 for Problems 19–26.*

19. How many quarts of a 10% solution of acid should be added to 20 quarts of a 40% solution of acid to obtain a 30% solution of acid?

20. How many quarts of a 30% salt solution must be added to 50 quarts of a 10% salt solution to obtain a 25% salt solution?

21. How many ounces of an alloy containing 40% aluminum must be melted with an alloy containing 60% aluminium to obtain 60 ounces of an alloy containing 50% aluminum?

22. How many pounds of an alloy containing 30% copper must be melted with an alloy containing 10% copper to obtain 12 pounds of an alloy containing 25% copper?

23. How many liters of a 30% salt solution must be added to 40 liters of a 12% salt solution to obtain a 20% solution?

24. How many grams of an alloy containing 45% silver must be melted with an alloy containing 60% silver to obtain 40 grams of an alloy containing 48% silver?

25. How much pure alcohol should be added to 12 liters of a 45% solution to obtain a 60% solution?

26. How many liters of a 20% sugar solution should be added to 40 liters of a 32% solution to obtain a 28% solution?

Miscellaneous Exercises

27. When building a house, a contractor allows 3% of the total cost for grading and excavation. How much is allowed for this work if the total cost of the house is $140,000?

28. The length of a rectangle is twice the width. Find the dimensions of the rectangle if the perimeter is 36.6 feet.

29. How many gallons of a 15% salt solution should be added to 80 gallons of a 60% solution to obtain a 55% salt solution?

30. A tool sales person is paid 12% of her sales. What were her total sales for 1 week if she was paid $180?

31. A family has twice as much money invested at 4% as at 6%. How much does the family have invested in each if the yearly income from the investments is $560?

32. A collection of coins consisting of dimes and quarters has a value of $2.95. How many dimes and quarters are in the collection if there are 2 more quarters than dimes?

33. Three pieces, with lengths 1.06, 2.12, and 1.88 inches, are cut from a rod that was 10.00 inches long. If 0.06 inch is wasted on each cut, how much is left of the original rod?

34. A brick mason estimated that 8% of the bricks delivered to a job were broken. If 2800 bricks were delivered, how many bricks can be used?

35. A company sells its used computers. The 1990 models are $120 cheaper than the 1992 models. If it costs $940 to buy one of each, how much does each cost?

36. An automobile radiator contains 8 quarts of a 40% antifreeze solution. How many quarts of this solution should be drained from the radiator and replaced with water if the resulting solution is to be 20% antifreeze?

CHAPTER SUMMARY

[2.1] Expressions of the form a^n, where

$$a^n = aaa \cdots \cdot a \qquad (\textbf{\textit{n}} \textbf{ factors}),$$

are called powers; a is the base and n is the exponent of the power.

Any meaningful collection of numerals, variables, and signs of operation is called an expression. In an expression of the form $A + B + C + \cdots$, A, B, and C are called terms. Any factor or group of factors in a term is the coefficient of the product of the remaining factors.

An algebraic expression of the form cx^n, where c is a constant and n is a whole number, or a product of such expressions, is called a monomial. A polynomial is an algebraic expression that contains only terms that are monomials.

Polynomials of two and three terms are called binomials and trinomials, respectively.

The degree of a monomial in one variable is given by the exponent on the variable. The degree of a polynomial is the degree of its term of highest degree.

Polynomials are represented by symbols such as $P(x)$, $Q(z)$, etc., and the values of these polynomials for some specific value a are represented by $P(a)$, $Q(a)$, etc.

[2.2] Terms that differ only in their numerical coefficients are called like terms. Two expressions that are equal for all real-number replacements of any variable or variables involved are equivalent expressions.

[2.3] A replacement for the variable in an equation that results in a true statement is called a solution of the equation; the set of all solutions is called the solution set.

Equations that have identical solution sets are called equivalent equations. An equation can be solved by generating a sequence of equivalent equations until an equation is obtained that can be solved by inspection.

The equation

$$a = b$$

is equivalent to

$$a + c = b + c, \qquad a - c = b - c$$

$$a \cdot c = b \cdot c \qquad \text{and} \qquad \frac{a}{c} = \frac{b}{c} \qquad (c \neq 0)$$

[2.4–2.5] The first step in a systematic approach to constructing a mathematical model for a word problem is to write *separate word phrases* for each quantity to be found. Then represent one quantity by a variable and represent any other quantities in terms of this variable. (See the suggestions on page 39 for the complete process of solving word problems.)

‖ R E V I E W   E X E R C I S E S

[2.1]

▲ *In Exercises 1 and 2, identify each polynomial as a monomial, binomial, or trinomial. State the degree of the polynomial.*

1. **a.** $2y^3$ **b.** $3x^2 - 2x + 1$

2. **a.** $3x^2 - x^5$ **b.** $5y^4 - y^3 - y^2$

3. Find the value of $\dfrac{2x^2 - 3y}{x - y}$ for $x = -2$ and $y = 3$.

4. Find the value of $x^2 - 2xy^2 - xy + y^4$ for $x = 3$ and $y = -1$.

5. If $P(x) = 2x^2 - 3x - 1$, find

    a. $P(3)$ **b.** $P(-2)$

6. If $Q(x) = x^3 - 2x^2 - x$, find

    a. $Q(-1)$ **b.** $Q(-2)$

[2.2]

▲ *Simplify each expression.*

7. **a.** $(2x - y) - (x - 2y + z)$
    b. $(2x^2 - 3z^2) - (x - 2y) + (z^2 + y)$

8. **a.** $(x - 3y) + (2x + y) - (y - z)$
    b. $(y - 3z) - (x + 2y) - (x + 3z)$

9. **a.** $(x^2 - 2y - z^2) - (3x^2 + 2y + z)$
    b. $(2x - y^2 + z) - (2x^2 + y - z)$

10. **a.** $2x - [x - (x - 3) + 2]$
    b. $x^2 - (x + 1) - [2x^2 + (x - 1)]$

11. **a.** $y^2 + y - [y - (y^2 - 1)]$
    b. $y^2 - [y^2 - (y + 1) - y]$

12. **a.** $z - [z^2 - (z^2 - z) + z]$
    b. $z - (z^2 - 1) - [z - (z^2 + 1)]$

[2.3]

▲ *Solve.*

13. $2x - 6 = 4x - 8$
14. $0.40x = 240$
15. $2(x - 3) + 4(x + 2) = 6$
16. $2x - (x + 3) = 2(x + 1)$
17. $2[2x - (x + 3) + 4] = 12$
18. $-[x - (3x - 2) - 2] = 16$
19. $3[x - 4(2x - 1)] = 4 + x$
20. $2[3 - 2(2x + 3)] = 2(x - 1)$
21. $0.30(y + 2) = 2.10$
22. $0.06y + 0.04(y + 1000) = 60$
23. Solve $3N = 5t - 3c$ for t, given that $N = 10$ and $c = 5$.

24. Solve $C = 10 + 2p - 2t$ for p, given that $C = 38$ and $t = 3$.
25. Solve $l = a + nd - d$ for n.
26. Solve $2s = at + k$ for a.
27. Solve $S = 2\pi(R - r)$ for R.
28. Solve $9C = 5(F - 32)$ for F.

[2.4–2.5]

▲ *Solve each problem. Use the five steps suggested on page 39.*

29. A tennis player made 26% of her first serves in a match. If her first serve was good 52 times, how many times did she serve?

30. A part-time secretary has a take-home pay of $180 per week. What is his total salary if 20% has been deducted for income taxes?

31. Two investments produce an annual interest of $324. An amount of $1000 more is invested at 6% than at 5%. How much is invested at each rate?

32. A postal clerk sells some 2-cent and 29-cent stamps for a total of $3.84. If there are six more 2-cent stamps than 29-cent stamps, how many of each were sold?

33. How many pounds of an alloy containing 60% copper must be melted with an alloy containing 20% copper to obtain 4 pounds of an alloy containing 35% copper?

34. If a car can be rented for $28 per day plus 16¢ per mile, what is the cost of renting a car for 7 days if it is driven 480 miles?

35. Find the net price of a calculator with a list price of $24 if it is discounted 15%.

▲ *The numbers in brackets refer to the sections in which such problems are first considered.*

1. List the members in $\left\{-2.3, 0, \sqrt{3}, \dfrac{4}{3}, \pi\right\}$ that are rational numbers.   **[1.1]**

2. Graph $x > -2$, x a real number.   **[1.1]**

3. Express $\dfrac{x}{7}$ as a product.   **[1.2]**

4. Express $\dfrac{1}{3}(x + y)$ as a quotient.   **[1.2]**

▲ *Write each expression as a basic numeral.*

5. $-6 + |-3| - |-2|$ **[1.2]**

6. $\dfrac{2 - 3 \cdot 2 + 10}{6 - 3 \cdot 4}$ **[1.3]**

7. $\dfrac{3|-2| - |2 - 4|}{|3 - 5|}$ **[1.3]**

8. $\dfrac{-2(-3 + 1) - 2|3 - 5|}{-2|2 - 4|}$ **[1.3]**

9. Evaluate $P + Prt$ for $P = 140$, $r = 0.05$, and $t = 3$.   **[1.3]**

10. Evaluate $R_0(1 + at)$ for $R_0 = 3.5$, $a = 0.04$, and $t = 30$.   **[1.3]**

11. Evaluate $x^2 - 3xy^2 + 2x^2y + y^2$ for $x = -1$ and $y = -2$.   **[2.1]**

12. If $P(x) = x^2 + 1$ and $Q(y) = 2y^2 - 3y$ find $P(-3) - Q(-2)$.   **[2.1]**

▲ *Simplify each expression.*

13. $2y - (x^2 + 3y) - (2x^2 - y)$ **[2.2]**

14. $x^2 - (x^2 - 3xy + y^2) - (2x^2 - xy)$ **[2.2]**

▲ *Solve each equation.*

15. $2[2x - (x - 3)] + 2x = 12$ **[2.3]**

16. $-3(x - 2) + 4(x - 3) = 2x + 2$ **[2.3]**

17. $0.05(y - 3) = 4.50$ **[2.3]**

18. $0.03(y + 5000) + 0.02y = 450$ **[2.3]**

19. Solve $R = R_0(1 + at)$ for R_0 in terms of the other variables.   **[2.3]**

20. Solve $R = R_0(1 + at)$ for t in terms of the other variables.   **[2.3]**

21. Computer A sells for $120 more than Computer B. How much does each computer cost if their total cost is $460?   **[2.4]**

22. One candidate in a student body election for president received 120 votes more than a second candidate and 160 votes more than a third candidate. How many votes did each candidate receive if there were 440 votes cast?   **[2.4]**

23. A hardware clerk sold some 10-cent and 13-cent bolts for a total of $2.58. There were three times as many 10-cent bolts as 13-cent bolts sold. How many of each were sold?   **[2.4]**

24. An amount of $3600 is invested, part at 4% and the remainder at 5%. How much is invested at each rate if the early income on each investment is the same?   **[2.5]**

25. How many quarts of a 20% solution of acid should be added to 10 quarts of a 30% solution to obtain a 25% solution?   **[2.5]**

3

MORE ABOUT POLYNOMIALS

In this chapter we will first see how to multiply polynomials. Then we will consider ways to solve second-degree equations that involve such products and how to solve word problems that can be described by such equations.

3.1 PRODUCTS OF MONOMIALS

Consider the product $a^m a^n$, where m and n are natural numbers. Since

$$a^m = \underbrace{aaa \cdots\cdots a}_{m \text{ factors}} \qquad \text{and} \qquad a^n = \underbrace{aaa \cdots\cdots a}_{n \text{ factors}}$$

it follows that

$$a^m a^n = \overbrace{(aaa \cdots\cdots a)}^{m \text{ factors}} \overbrace{(aaa \cdots\cdots a)}^{n \text{ factors}} = \overbrace{(aaa \cdots\cdots a)}^{m + n \text{ factors}}$$

Hence, we have the following property:

> *For all natural numbers m and n,*
> $$a^m a^n = a^{m+n} \tag{1}$$

We shall refer to this property as the **first law of exponents**. Thus, we can simplify an expression for the product of two natural-number powers of the same base simply by adding the exponents and using the sum as an exponent on the same base.

49

E X A M P L E 1   **a.** $x^2x^3 = x^{2+3}$ **b.** $xx^3x^4 = x^{1+3+4}$ **c.** $y^3y^4y^2 = y^{3+4+2}$
$\qquad = x^5$ $\qquad\qquad = x^8$ $\qquad\qquad = y^9$

We can use the commutative and associative properties of multiplication with the first law of exponents to multiply two or more monomials.

E X A M P L E 2   **a.** $(3x^2y)(2xy^2) = 3 \cdot 2x^2xyy^2$ **b.** $(-2xy^4)(x^2y)(4y^2) = -2 \cdot 4xx^2y^4yy^2$
$\qquad\qquad\qquad = 6x^3y^3$ $\qquad\qquad\qquad\qquad = -8x^3y^7$

Now consider the powers $(a^m)^n$ and $(ab)^n$, where m and n are natural numbers.

$$(a^m)^n = a^m \cdot a^m \cdot a^m \cdots \cdot a^m \qquad n \text{ factors}$$
$$= a^{m+m+m+\cdots+m} \qquad n \text{ terms}$$
$$= a^{mn}$$

and

$$(ab)^n = (ab)(ab)(ab) \cdots \cdot (ab) \qquad n \text{ factors}$$
$$= \overbrace{(a \cdot a \cdots \cdot a)}^{n \text{ factors}} \overbrace{(b \cdot b \cdots \cdot b)}^{n \text{ factors}}$$
$$= a^n b^n$$

Hence, we have the following properties:

For all natural numbers m and n,

$$(a^m)^n = a^{mn} \tag{2}$$

and

$$(ab)^n = a^n b^n \tag{3}$$

We shall refer to these properties as the **second** and **third laws of exponents**, respectively.

E X A M P L E 3   **a.**   From (2),
$$(x^2)^3 = x^6 \qquad \text{and} \qquad (x^5)^2 = x^{10}$$
  b.   From (3),
$$(xy)^3 = x^3y^3 \qquad \text{and} \qquad (3x)^4 = 3^4x^4 = 81x^4$$
  c.   From (2) and (3),
$$(x^2y^3)^3 = x^6y^9 \qquad \text{and} \qquad (2x^3y^2z)^2 = 2^2x^6y^4z^2 = 4x^6y^4z^2$$

We can use the distributive law in conjunction with the laws of exponents to simplify products of polynomials. We first consider the product of a monomial and a binomial.

EXAMPLE 4 | **a.** $a^2b(a^2 + b) = a^4b + a^2b^2$ **b.** $-ab^3(a^3 - b^2) = -a^4b^3 + ab^5$

The associative property of addition can be used to extend the distributive property to cases where the right-hand factor contains more than two terms. Thus,

$$a[b + c + d] = a[(b + c) + d]$$
$$= a(b + c) + ad$$
$$= ab + ac + ad$$
$$a[b + c + d + e] = a([b + c + d] + e)$$
$$= ab + ac + ad + ae \quad \text{etc.}$$

We refer to this as the **generalized distributive property**.

EXAMPLE 5 | **a.** $3x(x + y + z) = 3x(x) + 3x(y) + 3x(z)$
$$= 3x^2 + 3xy + 3xz$$

b. $-2ab^2(3a^2b - ab + 2ab^2)$

$$= (-2ab^2)(3a^2b) + (-2ab^2)(-ab) + (-2ab^2)(2ab^2)$$
$$= -6a^3b^3 + 2a^2b^3 - 4a^2b^4$$

EXERCISE SET 3.1

▲ *Write each product as a polynomial in simplest form. See Examples 1 and 2.*

1. $(7t)(-2t^2)$
2. $(4c^3)(3c)$
3. $(4a^2b)(-10ab^2c)$
4. $(-6r^2s^2)(5rs^3)$
5. $(11x^2yz)(4xy^3z)$
6. $(-8abc)(-b^2c^3)$
7. $2(3x^2y)(x^3y^4)$
8. $-5(ab^3)(-3a^2bc)$
9. $(-r^3)(-r^2s^4)(-2rt^2)$
10. $(-5mn)(2m^2n)(-n^3)$
11. $(y^2z)(-3x^2z^2)(-y^4z)$
12. $(-3xy)(2xz^4)(3x^3y^2z)$
13. $(2rt)(-3r^2t)(-t^2)$
14. $-a^2(ab^2)(2a)(-3b^2)$
15. $-(2x)(x^2)(-3x)$
16. $(-2y^2)(y^2)(y)$
17. $z^3(-2z)(3z)(-1)$
18. $(-t)(2t^2)(-t)(0)$

▲ *Write each expression as a polynomial in simplest form. See Example 3.*

19. $(x^3)^2$
20. $(x^4)^3$
21. $(xy)^4$
22. $(xy)^2$
23. $(y^2z)^3$
24. $(yz^4)^2$
25. $(2xz^2)^3$
26. $(3x^2z)^2$
27. $(2xy^2z)^2$
28. $(3x^2yz^2)^3$
29. $(-2xy^3z)^3$
30. $(-3x^2yz^3)^3$
31. $(x^2y)^2 + (xy)^3$
32. $(2xy^3)^4 + (3xy)^2$
33. $(2xy^2z)^2 - (xyz^2)^2$

34. $(3x^2yz)^3 - (4x^2y^2z^2)^2$
35. $(-xy)^2 - xy^2(xy)^2$
36. $(x^2y)(xy)^2 + (xy^2)^2$
37. $(2x^2y)^2(xy) + (xy^2)$
38. $(xy)^2 + (-x^2y)^2(-xy^2)$
39. $(2xy)^2 - 3x(x^2y)^2 + 4x(xy^2)$
40. $3(x^2y)^2 + x(x^2y) - x^2(x^2y^2)$

▲ *Write each product as a polynomial in simplest form. See Examples 4 and 5.*

41. $xy(x^2y^2 - x^3y)$
42. $x^2y^2(xy^3 + x^2y)$
43. $2rt^2(3r^2t + 2rt^3)$
44. $-3r^2t(rt - r^3t^2)$
45. $a^2b(a^2 - ab + b^2)$
46. $ab^2(a + a^2b^2 + b)$
47. $-xy(2x^2 + x^2y - y)$
48. $-x^2y^2(x - 2xy^2 + y^3)$
49. $r^2t^2(r^3 + 2r^2t^2 - t^3)$
50. $2r^3t^3(r^2 - rt^3 + t^2)$

Miscellaneous Exercises

▲ *Write each expression as a polynomial in simplest form.*

51. $ab^2(a^2 + ab) + a^2b^3$
52. $a^2b(a - ab^2) - a^3b$

53. $ab(ab^2) - a^2(b^3 + b^2)$

54. $ab(a^2b) + b^2(a^3 - a^2)$

55. $a^2(a^2 - ab + b^2) + a(ab^2)$

56. $b^2(a^2 + ab - b^2) - b(ab^2)$

57. $a(a^2 - b^2) + b(a^2 + ab + b^2)$

58. $b(a^2 - b^2) - a(a^2 - ab + b^2)$

59. $abc(ab - bc + ac) + ab(abc + bc^2 - ac^2)$

60. $ac^2(a^2b + ac - b^2c) - a^2b(ac^2 - ab + b^2c)$

3.2 | FACTORING MONOMIALS FROM POLYNOMIALS

In Section 3.1 we used the distributive property to write expressions without parentheses for products of monomials and other polynomials. The reverse of this process is called **factoring**. Before we consider this process for polynomials, we will review the notion of factoring for natural numbers.

Factoring Natural Numbers

If a natural number greater than 1 has no factors that are natural numbers other than itself and 1, it is said to be a **prime number**. Thus, 2, 3, 5, 7, 11, etc., are prime numbers. A natural number greater than 1 that is not a prime number is said to be a **composite number**. Thus, 4, 6, 8, 9, 10, etc., are composite numbers. When a composite number is exhibited as a product of prime factors only, it is said to be completely factored. For example, the complete factorization of 30 is (2)(3)(5), where all the factors are prime numbers.

The terms *composite* and *prime* are used in reference to natural numbers only. Any negative integer can, however, be expressed as the product $(-1)a$, where a is a natural number. Hence, if we refer to the completely factored form of a negative integer, we refer to the product of (-1) and the prime factors of the associated natural number. The composite numbers in this section will be less than 100, and hence the factors can be determined by inspection.

EXAMPLE 1 | **a.** $24 = (2)(2)(2)(3)$ **b.** $-33 = -1(3)(11)$ **c.** 37 is prime

Factoring Polynomials

Now we shall see how the distributive property in the form

$$ax + bx + cx + dx = (a + b + c + d)x$$

furnishes us a means of writing a polynomial as a single term comprised of two or more factors. By the distributive property,

$$3x^2 + 6x = 3x(x + 2)$$

Of course, we can also write

$$3x^2 + 6x = 3(x^2 + 2x)$$

or

$$3x^2 + 6x = 3x^2\left(1 + \frac{2}{x}\right) \qquad (x \neq 0)$$

or any other of an infinite number of such expressions. We are, however, primarily interested in factoring a polynomial into a unique form (except for signs and order of factors) referred to as the completely factored form. A polynomial with integral coefficients is in completely factored form if

1. It is written as a product of polynomials with integral coefficients;
2. No polynomial—other than a monomial—can be further factored.

The restriction that the factors be polynomials means that all the variables involved have exponents from $\{1, 2, 3, \ldots\}$. Restricting the coefficients to integers prohibits such factorizations as

$$x + 3 = 3\left(\frac{1}{3}x + 1\right)$$

Common monomial factors can be factored from a polynomial by first identifying such common factors and then writing the resultant factored expression. For example, observe that the polynomial

$$6x^3 + 9x^2 - 3x$$

contains the monomial $3x$ as a factor of each term. We therefore write

$$6x^3 + 9x^2 - 3x = 3x(\qquad)$$

and insert within the parentheses the appropriate polynomial factor. This factor can be determined by inspection. We ask ourselves for the monomials that multiply $3x$ to yield $6x^3, 9x^2$, and $-3x$. The final result appears as

$$6x^3 + 9x^2 - 3x = 3x(2x^2 + 3x - 1)$$

Checking the Result of Factoring

We can always check the result of factoring an expression by multiplying the factors. In the example above,

$$3x(2x^2 + 3x - 1) = 6x^3 + 9x^2 - 3x$$

EXAMPLE 2

a. $18x^2y - 24xy^2$
    $= 6xy(? - ?)$
    $= 6xy(3x - 4y);$
    because
    $6xy(3x - 4y)$
    $= 18x^2y - 24xy^2$

b. $y(x - 2) + z(x - 2)$
    $= (x - 2)(? + ?)$
    $= (x - 2)(y + z);$
    because
    $(x - 2)(y + z)$
    $= y(x - 2) + z(x - 2)$

c. $2(x + 4)^2 - 2(x + 4)$
    $= 2(x + 4)(? - ?)$
    $= 2(x + 4)(x + 4 - 1)$
    $= 2(x + 4)(x + 3)$

d. $3x(x - 2)^2 + (x - 2)^2$
    $= (x - 2)^2(? + ?)$
    $= (x - 2)^2(3x + 1)$

Notice that complete factorization of monomial factors is not required. Thus, in Example 2a it is not necessary that the factor $6xy$ be written $2 \cdot 3xy$ for the expression to be considered completely factored.

COMMON ERROR   *The factorization of $6xy - x^2$ is not $2 \cdot 3xy - xx$. The complete factorization results in the single term $x(6y - x)$, which consists of two factors.*

Factoring $a - b$ One particularly useful factorization is of the form

$$a - b = (-1)(-a + b)$$
$$= (-1)(b - a)$$
$$= -(b - a)$$

Hence, we have the following important relationship:

$$a - b = -(b - a)$$

That is, $a - b$ and $b - a$ are opposites of each other.

EXAMPLE 3
a. $3x - y = -(y - 3x)$ **b.** $a - 2b = -(2b - a)$

c. $4x - 2y = -2(y - 2x)$ **d.** $6y - 3x = -3(x - 2y)$

EXERCISE SET 3.2

▲ *Express each integer in completely factored form. If the integer is a prime number, so state. See Example 1.*

1.	8	**2.**	26	**3.**	49	**4.**	18
5.	17	**6.**	-16	**7.**	-12	**8.**	23
9.	56	**10.**	65	**11.**	-48	**12.**	-52

▲ *Factor completely. Check by multiplying factors. See Example 2.*

13. $2x + 6$ **14.** $3x - 9$ **15.** $4x^2 + 8x$

16. $3x^2y + 6xy$ **17.** $3x^2 - 3xy + 3x$

18. $x^3 - x^2 + x$ **19.** $24a^2 + 12a - 6$

20. $15r^2s + 18rs^2 - 3rs$ **21.** $2x^4 - 4x^2 + 8x$

22. $3n^4 - 6n^3 + 12n^2$ **23.** $12z^4 + 15z^3 - 9z^2$

24. $2x^2y^2 - 3xy + 5x^2$ **25.** $ay^2 + aby + ab$

26. $x^2y^2z^2 + 2xyz - xz$

27. $3m^2n - 6mn^2 + 12mn$

28. $6x^2y - 9xy^2 + 12x$

29. $15a^2c^2 - 12ac + 6ac^3$

30. $14xy + 21x^2y^2 - 28xyz$

31. $a(a + 3) + b(a + 3)$ **32.** $b(a - 2) + a(a - 2)$

33. $2x(x + 3) - y(x + 3)$ **34.** $y(y - 2) - 3x(y - 2)$

35. $2y(a + b) - x(a + b)$

36. $3x(2a - b) + 4y(2a - b)$

37. $(x + 3) + (x + 3)^2$ **38.** $(x - 6)^2 + (x - 6)$

39. $4(x - 2)^2 - 8(x - 2)$ **40.** $6(x + 1) - 3(x + 1)^2$

41. $x(2x - 1)^2 + (2x - 1)^2$

42. $(2x + 3)^2 + x(2x + 3)^2$

43. $x(x - 5)^2 - x^2(x - 5)$

44. $x^2(x + 3) - x(x + 3)^2$

45. $4(x - 1)(x + 3) + 2(x + 1)(x + 3)$

46. $3(x + 2)(x - 4) + 6(x + 2)(x + 1)$

47. $(x - 1)^2 - (x - 1)(x + 3)$

48. $(x + 2)^2 - (x + 2)(x - 1)$

▲ *Supply the missing factors or terms. See Example 3.*

49. $7 - r = -(? - ?)$ **50.** $3m - 2n = -(? - ?)$

51. $2a - b = -(? - ?)$ **52.** $r^2 - s^2t^2 = -(? - ?)$

53. $-2x + 2 = -2(?)$ **54.** $-6x - 9 = -3(?)$

55. $-ab - ac = ?(b + c)$ **56.** $-a^2 + ab = ?(a - b)$

57. $2x - 1 = -(?)$ **58.** $x^2 - 3 = -(?)$

59. $x - y + z = -(?)$

60. $3x + 3y - 2z = -(?)$

Miscellaneous Exercises

▲ *Factor and simplify each factor.*

61. $x(y + 1) - 2x$ **62.** $2y(x - 1) + 3y$

63. $y(2x - 2) - y(x + 3)$ **64.** $x(3y + 2) - x(y + 3)$

65. $a^2 - a(b + c)$ **66.** $b^2 - b(a - c)$

67. $a(a - b) + a(2a + b)$ **68.** $b(a + b) - b(a - 2b)$

69. $a^2 - a(b + c) + a(a - c)$

70. $b^2 + b(a - c) - b(a + b)$

3.3 **PRODUCTS OF POLYNOMIALS**

In Section 3.1 we used the distributive property to simplify expressions for products of monomials and other polynomials. The distributive property can also be applied to simplify expressions for products of polynomials containing more than one term. For example,

$$(x - y)(3x + 2y) = 3x(x - y) + 2y(x - y) \quad \text{(1)}$$
$$= 3x^2 - 3xy + 2xy - 2y^2 \quad \text{(2)}$$
$$= 3x^2 - xy - 2y^2 \quad \text{(3)}$$

The four products in step (2) can be obtained more directly by writing the products in the following form:

$$(3x + 2y)(x - y) = 3x^2 - 3xy + 2xy - 2y^2$$
$$= 3x^2 - xy - 2y^2$$

This process is sometimes called the "FOIL" method, where "FOIL" represents

the product of the **F**irst terms;
the product of the **O**uter terms;
the product of the **I**nner terms; $(3x + 2y)(x - y)$
the product of the **L**ast terms;

① the product of the **F**irst terms $(3x + 2y)(x - y) \rightarrow 3x^2$

② the product of the **O**uter terms $(3x + 2y)(x - y) \rightarrow -3xy$

③ the product of the **I**nner terms $(3x + 2y)(x - y) \rightarrow +2xy$

④ the product of the **L**ast terms $(3x + 2y)(x - y) \rightarrow -2y^2$

EXAMPLE 1

a.
$$(2x - 1)(x + 3) = 2x^2 + 6x - x - 3$$
$$= 2x^2 + 5x - 3$$

b.
$$(3x + 1)(2x - 1) = 6x^2 - 3x + 2x - 1$$
$$= 6x^2 - x - 1$$

Special Products of Binomials   The following products are special cases of the multiplication of binomials. Although the **FOIL** method can be used to rewrite these products, they occur so frequently that you should learn to recognize them on sight.

$$
\begin{aligned}
\textbf{I.} \quad & (x + a)^2 = (x + a)(x + a) = x^2 + 2ax + a^2 \\
\textbf{II.} \quad & (x - a)^2 = (x - a)(x - a) = x^2 - 2ax + a^2 \\
\textbf{III.} \quad & (x + a)(x - a) = x^2 - a^2
\end{aligned}
$$

COMMON ERROR   *Note that in* I, $(x + a)^2 \neq x^2 + a^2$,   *and in* II, $(x - a)^2 \neq x^2 - a^2$.

E X A M P L E 2

a. $(z - 3)^2$
   $= (z - 3)(z - 3)$
   $= z^2 - 2 \cdot 3z + 3^2$
   $= z^2 - 6z + 9$

b. $(x + 4)^2$
   $= (x + 4)(x + 4)$
   $= x^2 + 2 \cdot 4x + 16$
   $= x^2 + 8x + 16$

c. $(y + 5)(y - 5)$
   $= y^2 - 5^2$
   $= y^2 - 25$

More About Products   The distributive property can also be used to simplify expressions involving products of polynomials containing more than two terms by multiplying each term of one factor by each of the terms in the other factor.

E X A M P L E 3

a. $(x + 2)(x^2 - x + 1) = x(x^2 - x + 1) + 2(x^2 - x + 1)$
   $= x^3 - x^2 + x + 2x^2 - 2x + 2$
   $= x^3 + x^2 - x + 2$

b. $(2x - 3)(x^2 + 2x - 1) = 2x(x^2 + 2x - 1) - 3(x^2 + 2x - 1)$
   $= 2x^3 + 4x^2 - 2x - 3x^2 - 6x + 3$
   $= 2x^3 + x^2 - 8x + 3$

As we noted in Section 2.2, it is best to simplify the inner set of parentheses first when simplifying an expression that contains more than one set of grouping symbols.

E X A M P L E 4

————— **Write product as a polynomial.**

$3[2x - (x + 1)(x - 2)]$
$= 3[2x - (x^2 - x - 2)]$ **Write** $-(x^2 - x - 2)$ **as** $-x^2 + x + 2.$
$= 3[2x - x^2 + x + 2]$ **Collect like terms 2x and x.**
$= 3[-x^2 + 3x + 2]$ **Apply distributive property.**
$= -3x^2 + 9x + 6$

EXERCISE SET 3.3

▲ *Write each expression as a polynomial in simple form. See Examples 1 and 2.*

1. $(x + 3)(x - 3)$ **2.** $(x - 7)(x + 7)$

3. $(n + 2)(n + 8)$ **4.** $(r - 1)(r - 6)$

5. $(r + 5)(r - 2)$ **6.** $(y - 2)(y + 3)$

7. $(y - 6)(y - 1)$ **8.** $(z - 3)(z - 5)$

9. $(2z + 1)(z - 3)$ **10.** $(3t - 1)(2t + 1)$

11. $(4r + 3)(2r - 1)$ **12.** $(2z - 1)(3z + 5)$

13. $(2x - a)(2x + a)$ **14.** $(3t - 4s)(3t + 4s)$

15. $3(x - 4)(x + 5)$ **16.** $-2(x + 3)(x - 5)$

17. $(x + 3)^2$ **18.** $(y - 4)^2$

19. $-3(x - 1)^2$ **20.** $5(x + 1)^2$

▲ *Simplify each product. See Example 3.*

21. $(y + 2)(y^2 - 2y + 3)$ **22.** $(t + 4)(t^2 - t - 1)$

23. $(x - 3)(x^2 + 5x - 6)$ **24.** $(x - 7)(x^2 - 3x + 1)$

25. $(x - 2)(x - 1)(x + 3)$

26. $(y + 2)(y - 2)(y + 4)$

27. $(z - 3)(z + 2)(z + 1)$ **28.** $(z - 5)(z + 6)(z - 1)$.

29. $(2x + 3)(3x^2 - 4x + 2)$

30. $(3x - 2)(4x^2 + x - 2)$

▲ *Simplify each expression. See Example 4.*

31. $2[4x + (x + 1)^2]$ **32.** $3[2x + (x + 2)^2]$

33. $-x + 2x[4 - (x - 3)^2]$

34. $-2x + x[3 - (x + 4)^2]$

35. $-2x[x + (2x - 1)^2 - 4]$

36. $-x[2x - (2x + 1)^2 + 3]$

37. $-4[2x^2 - 2(x + 1)(x - 2) - 4x]$

38. $-3[2x^2 - 3(x - 2)(x + 3) + 3x]$

39. $-2[(x - 1)^2 + (x + 2)^2]$

40. $-3[(x + 1)^2 - (x - 3)^2]$

Miscellaneous Exercises

▲ *Show that the left-hand member is equivalent to the right-hand member.*

41. $(x + a)(x^2 - ax + a^2) = x^3 + a^3$

42. $(x - a)(x^2 + ax + a^2) = x^3 - a^3$

43. Use a counterexample to show that $(x + y)^2$ is not equivalent to $x^2 + y^2$.

44. Use a counterexample to show that $(x - y)^2$ is not equivalent to $x^2 - y^2$.

45. Three cylindrical kitchen canisters are each 18 centimeters tall but are of different radii. The radius of the second canister is 2 centimeters greater than the radius of the first, and the radius of the third canister is 2 centimeters greater than the radius of the second.

   a. Write algebraic expressions for the radii of the three canisters.

   b. Write an expression for the volume of each canister.

   c. Write an expression for the total volume of the set of canisters. Express the volume as a polynomial.

46. A square metal cake pan is made from a sheet of metal measuring 20 inches by 20 inches as follows. First, four equal squares are cut from the corners. The sides are then bent up and welded together as shown. The cut-out squares are x inches on a side.

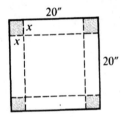
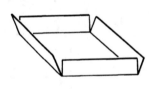

   a. Write expressions for the length, width, and height of the cake pan.

   b. Write an expression for the volume of the cake pan. Express the volume as a polynomial.

   c. Write an expression for the surface area of the cake pan. Express the surface area as a polynomial.

3.4 | FACTORING QUADRATIC POLYNOMIALS

A common type of factoring involves one of the following quadratic (second-degree) binomials or trinomials:

$$x^2 + (a + b)x + ab = (x + a)(x + b) \qquad (1)$$

$$x^2 + 2ax + a^2 = (x + a)^2 \qquad (2)$$

$$x^2 - a^2 = (x + a)(x - a) \qquad (3)$$

The factorization of the polynomials in (1) to (3) above can be easily verified by using the distributive property on each right-hand member.

Again, we shall require integral coefficients and positive integral exponents on the variables when factoring these polynomials.

As an example of the application of form (1) above, consider the trinomial

$$x^2 + 6x - 16$$

We desire, if possible, to find two binomial factors,

$$(x + a)(x + b)$$

whose product is the given trinomial. We see from form (1) that a and b are two integers such that $a + b = 6$ and $ab = -16$; that is, their sum must be the coefficient of the linear term $6x$, and their product must be -16. By inspection, or by trial and error, we determine that the two numbers are 8 and -2, so that

$$x^2 + 6x - 16 = (x + 8)(x - 2)$$

Checking, we note that $(x + 8)(x - 2) = x^2 + 6x - 16$.

EXAMPLE 1   Factor.

   a. $x^2 - 7x + 12$ **b.** $x^2 - x - 12$

Solutions   **a.** We want to find two numbers whose product is 12 and whose sum is -7. Since the product is positive and the sum is negative, the two numbers must both be negative. By inspection, or trial and error, the two numbers are -4 and -3. Hence,

$$x^2 - 7x + 12 = (x - 4)(x - 3)$$

   b. We want to find two numbers whose product is -12 and whose sum is -1. Since the product is negative, the two numbers must be of opposite sign, and their sum must be -1. By inspection, or trial and error, the two numbers are -4 and 3. Hence,

$$x^2 - x - 12 = (x - 4)(x + 3)$$

Although we have not specifically noted the check in the above examples, the check should be done mentally for each factorization.

Perfect-Square Trinomials

Form (2), the square of a binomial, is simply a special case of (1).

EXAMPLE 2

Factor.

a. $x^2 + 8x + 16$ b. $x^2 - 10x + 25$

Solutions

a. Two numbers whose product is 16 and whose sum is 8 are 4 and 4. Hence,
$$x^2 + 8x + 16 = (x + 4)(x + 4)$$
$$= (x + 4)^2$$

b. Two numbers whose product is 25 and whose sum is -10 are -5 and -5. Hence,
$$x^2 - 10x + 25 = (x - 5)(x - 5)$$
$$= (x - 5)^2$$

Expressions of form (2) are sometimes called **perfect-square trinomials** because they are the squares of binomials.

Difference of Two Squares

Form (3) is another special case of (1), in which the coefficient of the first-degree term in x is 0. For example,

$$x^2 - 25 = x^2 + 0x - 25 = (x - 5)(x + 5)$$

In particular, form (3) states:

▲   *The difference of the squares of two numbers is equal to the product of the sum and the difference of the two numbers.*

The factors $x - 5$ and $x + 5$ in the above example are called **conjugates** of each other. In general, any binomials of the form $a - b$ and $a + b$ are called **conjugate pairs**.

EXAMPLE 3

Factor.

a. $x^2 - 81$ b. $x^2 + 81$

Solutions

a. $x^2 - 81$ can be written as the difference of two squares, $(x)^2 - (9)^2$,   which can be factored as a conjugate pair.
$$x^2 - 81 = x^2 - 9^2 = (x - 9)(x + 9)$$

b. $x^2 + 81$,   equivalent to $x^2 + 0x + 81$,   is *not* of form (3). It is *not* factorable, because no two real numbers have a product of 81 and a sum of 0.

In the following factorization we are confronted with a quadratic trinomial in which the coefficient of x^2 is other than 1.

EXAMPLE 4 | To factor $8x^2 - 9 - 21x$,

1. Write in decreasing powers of x.
$$8x^2 - 21x - 9$$

2. Consider possible combinations of first-degree factors of the first term.
$$(8x \quad)(x \quad)$$
$$(4x \quad)(2x \quad)$$

3. Consider combinations of the factors ① of the last term.

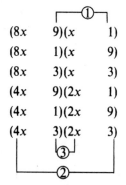

4. Select the combination(s) of products ② and ③ whose sum(s) could be the second term ($-21x$).
$$(8x \quad 3)(x \quad 3)$$

5. Insert the proper signs.
$$(8x + 3)(x - 3)$$

Although the process in the above example can normally be done mentally, it was written in detail for the purposes of illustration.

Signs on Factors Factoring trinomials of the form $Ax^2 + Bx + C$, where A is positive, can be facilitated by making use of the following considerations.

1. If both B and C are positive, both signs in the factored form are positive. For example, as a first step in factoring $6x^2 + 11x + 4$, we could write
$$(\quad + \quad)(\quad + \quad)$$

2. If B is negative and C is positive, both signs in the factored form are negative. Thus, as the first step in factoring $6x^2 - 11x + 4$, we could write
$$(\quad - \quad)(\quad - \quad)$$

3. If C is negative, the signs in the factored form are opposite. Thus, as a first step in factoring $6x^2 - 5x - 4$, we could write
$$(\quad + \quad)(\quad - \quad) \text{ or } (\quad - \quad)(\quad + \quad)$$

EXAMPLE 5

a. $6x^2 + 5x + 1$

$= (\quad + \quad)(\quad + \quad)$

$= (3x + 1)(2x + 1)$

b. $6x^2 - 5x + 1$

$= (\quad - \quad)(\quad - \quad)$

$= (3x - 1)(2x - 1)$

c. $6x^2 - x - 1$

$= (\quad + \quad)(\quad - \quad)$

$= (3x + 1)(2x - 1)$

d. $6x^2 + x - 2$

$= (\quad + \quad)(\quad - \quad)$

$= (3x + 2)(2x - 1)$

Difference of Two Squares

The following examples are special cases of form (3) on page 58.

EXAMPLE 6

a. $16y^2 - 1$

$= (4y)^2 - (1)^2$

$= (4y - 1)(4y + 1)$

b. $4x^2 - 9y^2$

$= (2x)^2 - (3y)^2$

$= (2x - 3y)(2x + 3y)$.

If a polynomial of more than one term contains a common monomial factor in each of its terms, this monomial should be factored from the polynomial before seeking other factors.

EXAMPLE 7

a. $32x^2 - 84x - 36$

$= 4(8x^2 - 21x - 9)$

$= 4(8x + 3)(x - 3)$

b. $4x^2 - 100$

$= 4(x^2 - 25)$

$= 4(x - 5)(x + 5)$

Suggestions for factoring are summarized as follows:

Factoring Polynomials

1. Write a polynomial in one variable in descending powers of the variable.
2. Factor out any factors that are common to each term in the polynomial.
3. Factor any binomial that is the difference of two squares as the product of conjugate pairs.
4. Factor any trinomials that can be factored.
5. Check the result of the factoring by multiplying the factors.

The examples and suggestions above are primarily concerned with factoring second-degree polynomials. However, the suggestions are also applicable to polynomials of higher degree.

EXAMPLE 8

a. $x^4 + 2x^2 + 1$

$= (x^2 + 1)(x^2 + 1)$

$= (x^2 + 1)^2$

b. $x^4 - 3x^2 - 4$

$= (x^2 - 4)(x^2 + 1)$

$= (x - 2)(x + 2)(x^2 + 1)$

EXERCISE SET 3.4

▲ *Factor completely. See Examples 1–6.*

1. $x^2 + 5x + 6$ **2.** $x^2 + 5x + 4$

3. $y^2 - 7y + 12$ **4.** $y^2 - 7y + 10$

5. $x^2 - x - 6$ **6.** $x^2 - 2x - 15$

7. $y^2 - 3y - 10$ **8.** $y^2 + 4y - 21$

9. $2x^2 + 3x - 2$ **10.** $3x^2 - 7x + 2$

11. $4x^2 + 7x - 2$ **12.** $6x^2 - 5x + 1$

13. $3x^2 - 4x + 1$ **14.** $4x^2 - 5x + 1$

15. $9x^2 - 21x - 8$ **16.** $10x^2 - 3x - 18$

17. $10x^2 - x - 3$ **18.** $8x^2 + 5x - 3$

19. $4x^2 + 12x + 9$ **20.** $4y^2 + 4y + 1$

21. $3x^2 - 7ax + 2a^2$ **22.** $9x^2 + 9ax - 10a^2$

23. $9x^2y^2 + 6xy + 1$ **24.** $4x^2y^2 + 12xy + 9$

25. $x^2 - 25$ **26.** $x^2 - 36$ **27.** $(xy)^2 - 1$

28. $(xy)^2 - 4$ **29.** $y^4 - 9$ **30.** $y^4 - 49$

31. $x^2 - 4y^2$ **32.** $9x^2 - y^2$

33. $4x^2 - 25y^2$ **34.** $16x^2 - 9y^2$

35. $16x^2y^2 - 1$ **36.** $64x^2y^2 - 1$

▲ *Factor completely. See Example 7.*

37. $3x^2 + 12x + 12$ **38.** $2x^2 + 6x - 20$

39. $2a^3 - 8a^2 - 10a$ **40.** $2a^3 + 15a^2 + 7a$

41. $4a^2 - 8ab + 4b^2$ **42.** $20a^2 + 60ab + 45b^2$

43. $4x^2y - 36y$ **44.** $x^2 - 4x^2y^2$

45. $12x - x^2 - x^3$ **46.** $x^2 - 2x^3 + x^4$

47. $x^4y^2 - x^2y^2$ **48.** $x^3y - xy^3$

▲ *Factor completely. See Example 8.*

49. $y^4 + 3y^2 + 2$ **50.** $a^4 + 5a^2 + 6$

51. $3x^4 + 7x^2 + 2$ **52.** $4x^4 - 11x^2 - 3$

53. $x^4 + 3x^2 - 4$ **54.** $x^4 - 6x^2 - 27$

55. $x^4 - 5x^2 + 4$ **56.** $y^4 - 13y^2 + 36$

57. $2a^4 - a^2 - 1$ **58.** $3x^4 - 11x^2 - 4$

59. $6a^4 - 13a^2 - 5$ **60.** $6a^4 + a^2 - 12$

Miscellaneous Exercises

▲ *Factor completely.*

61. $x^2 + xy - 2y^2$ **62.** $2x^2 - xy - y^2$

63. $2x^2 + 3xy + y^2$ **64.** $9x^2 - 3xy - 2y^2$

65. $6x^2 + 4xy - 2y^2$ **66.** $3x^2 + 3xy - 6y^2$

67. $x^4 - y^4$ **68.** $x^4 - 9y^4$

69. $x^4 - x^2y - 2y^2$ **70.** $x^4 + 2x^2y - 3y^2$

3.5 | **SOLUTION OF QUADRATIC EQUATIONS BY FACTORING**

Standard Form

A second-degree equation in one variable is called a **quadratic equation** in that variable. We shall designate as **standard form** for such equations

$$ax^2 + bx + c = 0$$

where a, b, and c are constants representing real numbers and $a > 0$.

     If $b = 0$ or $c = 0$, then the equations are of the form

$$ax^2 + c = 0 \quad \text{or} \quad ax^2 + bx = 0$$

and are called incomplete quadratic equations.

Writing Equivalent Equations

In Chapter 2 we solved first-degree equations by performing certain elementary operations that are equally applicable to equations of higher degree and, in particular, to quadratic equations. For example, adding $8x^2 - 6$ to each side of

$$2x = 6 - 8x^2$$

we obtain

$$2x + 8x^2 - 6 = 6 - 8x^2 + 8x^2 - 6$$

from which

$$8x^2 + 2x - 6 = 0$$

Then, dividing each side by 2, we have

$$4x^2 + x - 3 = 0$$

The three equations are equivalent.

Solution by Factoring   If the left side of a quadratic equation in standard form is factorable, we may solve the equation by making use of the following principle.

A product equals 0 if at least one of its factors equals 0.

Thus,

$$ab = 0 \quad \textit{if and only if} \quad a = 0 \quad \textit{or} \quad b = 0$$

EXAMPLE 1 $(x - 1)(2x + 3) = 0$ if and only if

$$x - 1 = 0 \quad (x = 1)$$

or

$$2x + 3 = 0 \quad \left(x = -\frac{3}{2}\right)$$

The word "or" in the above example is used in an inclusive sense to mean either one *or* the other *or* both.

The above principle enables us to solve quadratic equations if the left side of an equation in standard form is factorable.

EXAMPLE 2   Solve $x^2 + 2x = 15$.   (1)

Solution   First write the equation in standard form, and then factor the left side to obtain

$$x^2 + 2x - 15 = 0$$
$$(x + 5)(x - 3) = 0$$

(2)

which will be true if and only if

$$x + 5 = 0 \quad \text{or} \quad x - 3 = 0$$
$$x = -5 \qquad\qquad x = 3$$

Thus, either -5 or 3, when substituted for x in (2) or (1), will make the left side 0. The solution set is $\{-5, 3\}$.

E X A M P L E 3 | Solve $3x(x + 1) = 2x + 2$.

Solution | Write the equation in standard form and factor the left side to obtain

$$3x^2 + x - 2 = 0$$
$$(3x - 2)(x + 1) = 0$$

Set each factor equal to 0 and solve the equations.

$$3x - 2 = 0 \quad \text{or} \quad x + 1 = 0$$
$$x = \frac{2}{3} \qquad\qquad x = -1$$

The solution set is $\left\{\frac{2}{3}, -1\right\}$.

In general, the solution set of a quadratic equation can be expected to contain two elements. However, if the left side of a quadratic equation in standard form is the square of a binomial, we find that the solution set contains only one member. For example, to solve

$$x^2 - 2x + 1 = 0$$

we factor the left side to obtain

$$(x - 1)(x - 1) = 0$$

and the solution set is $\{1\}$, which contains only one element.

For reasons of convenience and consistency in more advanced work, the unique solution obtained in the above example is said to be of **multiplicity two**.

Writing Equations from Given Solutions

Notice that the solution set of the quadratic equation

$$(x - r_1)(x - r_2) = 0 \tag{3}$$

is $\{r_1, r_2\}$.* Therefore, if r_1 and r_2 are given as solutions of a quadratic equation, the equation can be written directly as (3). By completing the indicated multiplication the equation can be transformed to standard form.

E X A M P L E 4 | If **2** and **−3** are given as solutions of a quadratic equation, then

$$[x - (2)][x - (-3)] = 0$$
$$(x - 2)(x + 3) = 0$$
$$x^2 + x - 6 = 0$$

---

* The subscripts 1 and 2 used in r_1 and r_2 in this equation are used to identify constants. The symbols are read "r sub one" and "r sub two" or simply "r one" and "r two."

EXERCISE SET 3.5

▲ *Solve. Determine your answer by inspection or follow the procedure in Example 1.*

1. $(x + 2)(x - 5) = 0$
2. $(x + 3)(x - 4) = 0$
3. $(2x + 5)(x - 2) = 0$
4. $(x + 1)(3x - 1) = 0$
5. $x(2x + 1) = 0$
6. $x(3x - 7) = 0$
7. $4(x - 6)(2x + 3) = 0$
8. $5(2x - 7)(x + 1) = 0$
9. $3(x - 2)(2x + 1) = 0$
10. $7(x + 5)(3x - 1) = 0$
11. $4(2x - 5)(3x + 2) = 0$
12. $2(3x - 4)(2x + 5) = 0$

▲ *Solve. See Examples 2 and 3.*

13. $x^2 - 3x = 0$
14. $x^2 + 5x = 0$
15. $2x^2 = 6x$
16. $3x^2 = 3x$
17. $x^2 - 9 = 0$
18. $x^2 - 4 = 0$
19. $2x^2 - 18 = 0$
20. $3x^2 - 3 = 0$
21. $9x^2 = 4$
22. $25x^2 = 4$
23. $4x^2 - 9 = 0$
24. $9x^2 - 25 = 0$
25. $x^2 - 5x + 4 = 0$
26. $x^2 + 5x + 6 = 0$
27. $x^2 - 5x - 14 = 0$
28. $x^2 - x - 42 = 0$
29. $3x^2 - 6x = -3$
30. $12x^2 = 8x + 15$
31. $x(2x - 3) = -1$
32. $2x(x - 2) = x + 3$
33. $(x - 2)(x + 1) = 4$
34. $x(3x + 2) = (x + 2)^2$
35. $(x - 1)^2 = 2x^2 + 3x - 5$
36. $x(x + 1) = 4 - (x + 2)^2$
37. $t(t + 4) - 1 = 4$
38. $z(z + 5) + 18 = 4(1 - z)$
39. $2z(z + 3) = 3 + z$
40. $(n - 3)(n + 2) = 6$
41. $(t + 2)(t - 5) = 8$
42. $(x + 1)(2x - 3) = 3$
43. $(y - 1)^2 = 4(y - 2)$
44. $6y = (y + 1)^2 + 3$
45. $4x - [(x + 1)(x - 2) + 6] = 0$
46. $2x - [(x + 2)(x - 3) + 8] = 0$
47. $[(x + 1)^2 - 2x = 10$
48. $3[(x + 2)^2 - 4x] = 15$

▲ *Given the solutions of a quadratic equation, r_1 and r_2, write the equation in standard form with integral coefficients. See Example 4.*

49. -2 and 1
50. -4 and 3
51. 0 and -5
52. 0 and 5
53. -3 and -3
54. 4 and 4
55. a and b
56. $-a$ and $-b$

Miscellaneous Exercises

▲ *Solve each equation for x in terms of a and b.*

57. $x^2 - 4b^2 = 0$
58. $x^2 - (a + b)^2 = 0$
59. $x^2 - 3ax - 4a^2 = 0$
60. $x^2 - 4bx - 12b^2 = 0$
61. $x^2 - (a + b)x + ab = 0$
62. $x^2 + (2a - b)x - 2ab = 0$
63. $x^2 + \left(a + \dfrac{b}{2}\right)x + \dfrac{ab}{2} = 0$
64. $x^2 - \dfrac{1}{2}(a + b)x + \dfrac{ab}{4} = 0$
65. $b^2x^2 - 4a^2 = 0$
66. $ax^2 - 9b^2 = 0$

3.6   APPLICATIONS

In some cases the mathematical model we obtain for a physical situation is a quadratic equation and hence may have two solutions. It may be that one but not both of the solutions of the equation fits the physical situation. For example, if we were asked to find two consecutive *natural numbers* whose product is 72, we would write the equation

$$x(x + 1) = 72 \qquad \text{If } x \text{ is a natural number, then } x + 1 \text{ is the next consecutive natural number.}$$

as our model. Solving this equation, we have

$$x^2 + x - 72 = 0 \qquad \text{Factor trinomial.}$$
$$(x + 9)(x - 8) = 0 \qquad \text{Set each factor equal to 0.}$$

where the solution set is $\{8, -9\}$. Since -9 is not a natural number, we must reject it as a possible answer to the original question; however, the solution 8 leads to the consecutive natural numbers 8 and 9. As additional examples, observe that we would not accept -6 feet as the height of a man or $\frac{27}{4}$ for the number of people in a room.

A quadratic equation used as a model for a physical situation may have two, one, or no meaningful solutions—meaningful, that is, in a physical sense. Answers to word problems should always be checked in the original problem.

We will continue to follow the step-by-step procedure that we used in Chapter 2 to solve word problems, giving careful attention to the construction of the mathematical model.

EXAMPLE 1

The length of a rectangle is 4 centimeters greater than the width, and the area is 77 square centimeters. Find the dimensions of the rectangle.

Solution

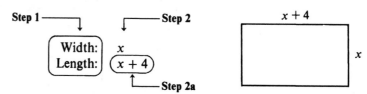

Step 3   Write a model for the conditions on the variable. Since the area (77 square centimeters) of a rectangle is the product of its width and length, the model is

$$x(x + 4) = 77$$

Step 4   Solve the equation. First write the equation in standard form.

$$x^2 + 4x - 77 = 0 \qquad \text{Factor trinomial.}$$

$$(x + 11)(x - 7) = 0 \qquad \text{Set each factor, } (x + 11) \text{ and } (x - 7), \text{ equal to 0 and solve.}$$

Step 5   The solution set is $\{-11, 7\}$. Since a dimension cannot be negative, the only acceptable value for x is 7. If $x = 7$, then $x + 4 = 11$, and the dimensions are 7 centimeters and 11 centimeters.

EXAMPLE 2

A ball thrown vertically upward reaches a height h in feet given by the equation $h = 64t - 16t^2$, where t is the time in seconds after the throw. How long will it take the ball to reach a height of 48 feet on its way up?

Solution

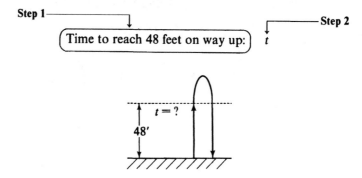

Step 3   In this case the model is given

$$h = 64t - 16t^2$$

Step 4 Substitute 48 for *h* and solve for *t*.

$$48 = 64t - 16t^2 \qquad \text{Write in standard form.}$$

$$16t^2 - 64t + 48 = 0 \qquad \text{Factor common factor 16.}$$

$$16(t^2 - 4t + 3) = 0 \qquad \text{Factor trinomial.}$$

$$16(t - 1)(t - 3) = 0 \qquad \text{Set each factor, } (t - 1) \text{ and } (t - 3), \text{ equal to 0.}$$

$$t = 1 \qquad \text{or} \qquad t = 3$$

Step 5 Use the figure to interpret the two solutions: It takes 1 second to reach 48 feet *on the way up*. (In 3 seconds the ball is also at 48 feet on its way down.)

EXAMPLE 3 A deck of uniform width was constructed around a 20- by 25-foot rectangular pool. Find the width of the deck if 196 square feet of brick was used.

Solution

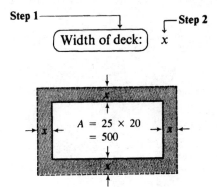

Step 3 Since the area of the deck is 196 square feet:

$$\text{enlarged area} - \text{area of pool} = 196$$

$$(25 + 2x)(20 + 2x) - 500 = 196 \qquad \text{Simplify left side.}$$

Step 4 Solve the equation.

$$500 + 90x + 4x^2 - 500 = 196 \qquad \text{Write the equation in standard form.}$$

$$4x^2 + 90x - 196 = 0 \qquad \text{Factor 2 from left side.}$$

$$2(2x^2 + 45x - 98) = 0 \qquad \text{Factor trinomial.}$$

$$2(2x + 49)(x - 2) = 0 \qquad \text{Set each factor } (2x + 49) \text{ and } (x - 2) \text{ equal to 0 and solve.}$$

$$x = -49/2 \qquad \text{or} \qquad x = 2$$

Step 5 The width cannot be $-\frac{49}{2}$. Hence, the width of the deck is 2 feet.

The above examples show that when solving quadratic equations that are models for stated conditions in word problems, solutions are sometimes obtained that do not apply. As we have noted, it is important always to check solutions to see whether they are meaningful for the stated conditions.

EXERCISE SET 3.6

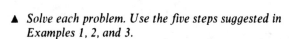

▲ *Solve each problem. Use the five steps suggested in Examples 1, 2, and 3.*

1. Find two positive numbers that differ by 3 and have a product of 40.

2. Find two negative numbers that differ by 7 and have a product of 60.

3. Find two consecutive negative integers such that the sum of their squares is 61.

4. Find two consecutive positive integers such that the sum of their squares is 85.

5. The sum of the squares of three consecutive positive integers is 149. Find the integers.

6. The sum of the squares of three consecutive negative integers is 434. Find the integers.

7. A rectangular lawn is 2 meters longer than it is wide. If its area is 63 square meters, what are the dimensions of the lawn?

8. The length of a rectangular steel plate is 2 centimeters greater than 2 times its width. If the area of the plate is 40 square centimeters, find its dimensions.

9. The area of a triangle is 27 square inches. Find the lengths of the base and the altitude if the base is 3 inches shorter than the altitude.

10. The area of a triangle is 70 square centimeters. Find the lengths of the base and the altitude if the base is 13 centimeters longer than the altitude.

11. The hypotenuse of a right triangle is 10 centimeters. A second side is 2 centimeters longer than the third side. What are the lengths of the two shorter sides?

12. One side of a right triangle is 7 inches smaller than a second side. If the length of the hypotenuse is 13 inches, how long are the two shorter sides?

13. Using the information in Example 2 on pages 66–67, determine how long after the ball was thrown it will take for the ball to reach a height of 28 feet on the way down.

14. Using the information in Example 2, determine how long after the ball was thrown it will return to the ground.

15. The position of a particle moving in a straight line is given by the formula

$$s = t^2 - 5t$$

where s is the distance from the starting point (in centimeters) and t is the time (in seconds) that the particle has been in motion. How long will it take for the particle to move 24 centimeters in a positive direction?

16. Using the motion of the particle in Exercise 15, where will the particle be in 2 seconds? 3 seconds? When will the particle be back at its starting point?

17. A photographer uses 48 square inches for a picture on a mat whose length is twice its width. If the margin around the picture is to be 2 inches uniformly, what are the dimensions of the mat?

18. A book designer wants to use 35 square inches of type on a page and to make the height of the page 2 inches longer than its width. If the margin is to be 1 inch uniformly, what are the dimensions of the page?

19. A rectangular garden measuring 25 by 50 meters has its area increased by 318 square meters by a border of uniform width along both shorter sides and one longer side. Find the width of the border.

20. A rectangular garden measuring 12 by 18 meters has its area increased by 216 square meters by a border of uniform width on all sides. Find the width of the border.

21. A tray is formed from a rectangular piece of metal whose length is 2 centimeters greater than its width by cutting a square with sides 2 centimeters in length from each corner and then bending up the sides. Find the dimensions of the tray if the volume is 160 cubic centimeters.

22. A tray is formed from a rectangular piece of metal whose length is twice its width by cutting a square with sides 1 centimeter in length from each corner and then bending up the sides. Find the dimensions of the tray if the volume is 144 cubic centimeters. (See the figure for Exercise 21.)

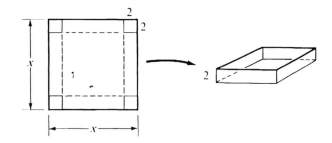

Exercise 21

3.7 | FACTORING OTHER POLYNOMIALS

Most applications we encounter that require factoring involve first- and second-degree binomials and trinomials like those that we factored previously in this chapter. However, a few other kinds of polynomials sometimes occur in advanced work in mathematics and thus justify a study of their factorization.

Factoring by Grouping

Sometimes a polynomial is factorable by grouping. For example, we can factor a from the first two terms of

$$ax + ay + bx + by$$

and b from the last two terms to obtain

$$ax + ay + bx + by = a(x + y) + b(x + y)$$

Now, since the factor $x + y$ is a common factor of both terms, we can write

$$ax + ay + bx + by = (x + y)(a + b)$$

EXAMPLE 1

To factor $3x^2y + 2y + 3xy^2 + 2x$, we first rewrite the expression in the form
$$3x^2y + 2x + 3xy^2 + 2y$$

We then factor the common monomial x from the first group of two terms and the common monomial y from the second group of two terms to obtain
$$3x^2y + 2x + 3xy^2 + 2y = x(3xy + 2) + y(3xy + 2)$$

If we now factor the common binomial $(3xy + 2)$ from each term, we have
$$3x^2y + 2x + 3xy^2 + 2y = (3xy + 2)(x + y)$$

The polynomials in the following examples are factored in a similar way.

EXAMPLE 2

a. $yb - ya + xb - xa$
$= y(b - a) + x(b - a)$
$= (b - a)(y + x)$

b. $x^2 + xb - ax - ab$
$= x(x + b) - a(x + b)$
$= (x + b)(x - a)$

In the above examples we accomplished the factorization of the expression by grouping the four terms as the sum or difference of two binomials. Sometimes it is necessary to view an expression of four terms as a trinomial and monomial in order to factor the expression.

EXAMPLE 3

a. $(x^2 - 2x) + (1 - y^2)$
$= (x - 1)^2 - y^2$
$= (x - 1 - y)(x - 1 + y)$

b. $x^2 - y^2 + 4yz - 4z^2$
$= x^2 - (y^2 - 4yz + 4z^2)$
$= x^2 - (y - 2z)^2$
$= [x - (y - 2z)][x + (y - 2z)]$
$= (x - y + 2z)(x + y - 2z)$

Sum and Difference of Cubes

Two other factorizations are of special interest. These are the sum of two cubes, $x^3 + y^3$, and the difference of two cubes, $x^3 - y^3$. Our ability to factor these binomials is a result of observing that

$$(x + y)(x^2 - xy + y^2) = x^3 - x^2y + xy^2 + yx^2 - xy^2 + y^3$$
$$= x^3 + y^3$$

and that

$$(x - y)(x^2 + xy + y^2) = x^3 + x^2y + xy^2 - yx^2 - xy^2 - y^3$$
$$= x^3 - y^3$$

Viewing the two equations from right to left, we have the following special factorizations:

$$x^3 + y^3 = (x + y)(x^2 - xy + y^2)$$
$$x^3 - y^3 = (x - y)(x^2 + xy + y^2)$$

To memorize these factorizations, it is helpful to note that the binomial factor in each factored form has the same sign as the original binomial.

EXAMPLE 4

a. $8a^3 + b^3$
$$= (2a)^3 + b^3$$
$$= (2a + b)[(2a)^2 - 2ab + b^2]$$
$$= (2a + b)(4a^2 - 2ab + b^2)$$

b. $x^3 - 27y^3$
$$= x^3 - (3y)^3$$
$$= (x - 3y)[x^2 + 3xy + (3y)^2]$$
$$= (x - 3y)(x^2 + 3xy + 9y^2)$$

EXERCISE SET 3.7

▲ *Factor. See Examples 1 and 2.*

1. $ax + a + bx + b$
2. $5a + ab + 5b + b^2$
3. $ax^2 + x + a^2x + a$
4. $a + ab + b + b^2$
5. $x^2 + ax + xy + ay$
6. $x^3 - x^2y + xy - y^2$
7. $3ab - cb - 3ad + cd$
8. $2ac - bc + 2ad - bd$
9. $3x + y - 6x^2 - 2xy$
10. $5xz - 5yz - x + y$
11. $a^3 + 2ab^2 - 2a^2b - 4b^3$
12. $6x^3 - 4x^2 + 3x - 2$
13. $x^2 - x + 2xy - 2y$
14. $2a^2 - 3a - 2ab - 3b$
15. $2a^2b + 6a^2 - b - 3$
16. $2ab^2 + 5a - 8b^2 - 20$
17. $x^3y^2 + x^3 - 3y^2 - 3$
18. $12 - 4y^3 - 3x^2 + x^2y^3$
19. $x^3 + 2x^2 + 4x + 8$
20. $x^3 + 3x^2 + 3x + 9$

21. $2x^3 - 3x^2 + 2x - 3$
22. $2x^3 + 7x^2 + 4x + 14$
23. $x^3 - x^2 + x - 1$
24. $x^3 - 2x^2 - 3x + 6$

▲ *Factor. See Example 3.*

25. $(x + 2)^2 - y^2$
26. $x^2 - (y - 3)^2$
27. $x^2 + 2x + 1 - y^2$
28. $x^2 - 6x + 9 - y^2$
29. $y^2 - x^2 + 2x - 1$
30. $y^2 - x^2 + 4x - 4$
31. $4x^2 + 4x + 1 - 4y^2$
32. $9x^2 - 6x + 1 - 9y^2$

▲ *Factor. See Example 4.*

33. $x^3 - 1$
34. $y^3 + 27$
35. $(2x)^3 + y^3$
36. $y^3 - (3x)^3$
37. $a^3 - 8b^3$
38. $27a^3 + b^3$
39. $(xy)^3 - 1$
40. $8 + x^3y^3$
41. $27a^3 + 64b^3$
42. $a^3 - 125b^3$
43. $64a^3b^3 - 1$
44. $8a^3b^3 + 1$

Miscellaneous Exercises

▲ *Factor.*

45. $x^3 + (x - y)^3$

46. $(x + y)^3 - z^3$

47. $(x + 1)^3 - 1$

48. $x^6 + (x - 2y)^3$

49. $(x + 1)^3 - (x - 1)^3$

50. $(2y - 1)^3 + (y - 1)^3$

51. Show that $ac - ad + bd - bc$ can be factored as $(a - b)(c - d)$ and as $(b - a)(d - c)$.

52. Show that $a^2 - b^2 - c^2 + 2bc$ can be factored as $(a - b + c)(a + b - c)$.

CHAPTER SUMMARY

[3.1] The following laws of exponents are useful in rewriting powers:

$$a^m \cdot a^n = a^{m+n}, \quad (a^m)^n = a^{mn}, \quad (ab)^m = a^m b^m$$

The distributive property in the form

$$a(b + c + d + \cdots) = ab + ac + ad + \cdots$$

is used to rewrite products as equivalent expressions without parentheses.

[3.2] A natural number greater than 1 that has no natural-number factors other than itself and 1 is a prime number. A natural number greater than 1 that is not a prime number is a composite number, and it has one and only one prime factorization.

The process of using the distributive property to rewrite a polynomial as a single term comprised of two or more factors is called factoring. If a polynomial of more than one term contains a common factor in each of its terms, this common factor can be factored from the polynomial.

[3.3] The **FOIL** method is an efficient way to multiply binomials.

$$(a + b)(c + d) = ac + ad + bc + bd$$

The following products are special cases of products of binomials:

$$\text{I.} \quad (x + a)^2 = x^2 + 2ax + a^2$$

$$\text{II.} \quad (x - a)^2 = x^2 - 2ax + a^2$$

$$\text{III.} \quad (x + a)(x - a) = x^2 - a^2$$

[3.4] Some trinomials of the form $ax^2 + bx + c$ can be factored by trial and error. The right sides of the three special relationships above can be factored directly as the three left sides, respectively.

[3.5] The **standard form** for a quadratic equation in one variable is

$$ax^2 + bx + c = 0$$

where a, b, and c are constants with $a \neq 0$.

To solve an equation by **factoring**, we use the fact that the product of two factors is 0 if and only if one or both of the factors equals 0. That is,

$$ab = 0 \qquad \text{if and only if} \qquad a = 0 \qquad \text{or} \qquad b = 0$$

[3.6]   Quadratic equations are sometimes useful as mathematical models in physical situations. In such cases it may be that not all the solutions of an equation are meaningful.

[3.7]   Some polynomials that consist of more than three terms can be factored by first grouping terms with like factors. Thus,

$$ax + ay + bx + by = a(x + y) + b(x + y)$$
$$= (a + b)(x + y)$$

Two special cases of factoring involve the sum and difference of cubes:

$$x^3 + y^3 = (x + y)(x^2 - xy + y^2)$$
$$x^3 - y^3 = (x - y)(x^2 + xy + y^2)$$

REVIEW EXERCISES

[3.1]

▲ *Simplify each expression.*

1. **a.** $(2x^2y)(-3xy^3)$ **b.** $(3xy)(2xz^2)(-y^2z)$
2. **a.** $(-2x^2y^3z)^3$ **b.** $(xy^2)^3 - (2x^3y)^2$
3. **a.** $(x^2y)(3xy^2)^2$ **b.** $(xy_i^2)^2(2x^2y)$
4. **a.** $(2xy)(3yz^2)(xy)^2$ **b.** $(yz)^2(3xy^2)(2xz)$
5. **a.** $3x^2(xy^2) + 2x(xy)^2 - x^2y(xy)^2$
    b. $x(x^2y^3) - 3x(xy)^2 + 4(xy)^3$
6. **a.** $(-xy)^2 + 2x(x^2y) + 4x^2y^2$
    b. $(2x)^2y^3 + 3xy^2(xy) - x^2y^2(y)$
7. **a.** $xy(x^2y - xy^2)$ **b.** $-2xy^2(xy - y^2)$
8. **a.** $x^2y(x^2 - xy + y^2)$
    b. $-xy^2(x^3 + xy^2 - y^3)$
9. **a.** $3[x - 2(x + 1) - 3]$
    b. $-x[1 - 2(x + 3) + x]$
10. **a.** $y[y - 2(y - 1) + 4]$
    b. $-y[4y - (2y + 1) - 3]$

[3.2]

▲ *Factor each polynomial.*

11. **a.** $12x^2 - 8x + 4$ **b.** $x^3 - 3x^2 - x$
12. **a.** $4y^3 - 8y^2$
    b. $4x^3y^2 - 2x^2y^2 + 6xy^2$

13. **a.** $3x - y = -(\underline{?})$ **b.** $2x - y + z = -(\underline{?})$
14. **a.** $-x^2 + 2x = -x(\underline{?})$
    b. $-6x^2y + 3xy - 3xy^2 = -3xy(\underline{?})$
15. **a.** $x(a + 2) - (a + 2)$ **b.** $2a(x - y) + b(x - y)$
16. **a.** $x + 2y - x(x + 2y)$ **b.** $y(x + y) + (x + y)$

[3.3]

▲ *Write each expression as a polynomial in simple form.*

17. **a.** $(y + 3)(y - 2)$ **b.** $(x + 4)(x - 1)$
18. **a.** $(2x - 5)(3x + 1)$ **b.** $(3x + 4)(4x - 1)$
19. **a.** $(2x - 1)^2$ **b.** $(3y + 2)^2$
20. **a.** $(y + 1)(y^2 - 2y + 1)$
    b. $(2x - 1)(x^2 + 3x - 2)$
21. **a.** $(x + 1)(x - 1)(x + 2)$
    b. $(y + 2)(y - 2)(y + 1)$
22. **a.** $2[x - (x + 1)^2]$ **b.** $-3[(y - 3)^2 + 2y]$

[3.4]

▲ *Factor each polynomial.*

23. **a.** $x^2 - 2x - 35$ **b.** $y^2 + 4y - 32$
24. **a.** $(xy)^2 - 36$ **b.** $a^2 - 49b^2$
25. **a.** $3y^2 + 11y - 4$ **b.** $x^3 + 3x^2 - 10x$
26. **a.** $9x^2 - 36$ **b.** $12x^2 - 3y^2$

27. a. $2x^2 + 3xy - 2y^2$ b. $6x^2 - xy - y^2$
28. a. $15a^2 + 28ab + 12b^2$ b. $12a^2 - 18ab + 6b^2$
29. a. $x^4 + 2x^2 - 3$ b. $y^4 - 3y^2 - 4$
30. a. $9x^4 - 1$ b. $16y^4 - 9$

[3.5]

▲ *Solve for x by factoring.*

31. a. $x^2 - 2x = 0$ b. $x^2 - 5x + 6 = 0$
32. a. $(x - 6)(x + 4) = -9$ b. $x(x + 1) = 6$
33. a. $4x - 4 = x^2$ b. $x^2 + 3 = 4x$

▲ *Given the solutions of a quadratic equation, write the equation in standard form.*

34. a. -2 and 5 b. 0 and -3

[3.6]

▲ *Solve.*

35. The base of a triangle is 1 inch longer than 2 times the length of its altitude, and its area is 18 square inches. Find the length of the base and the altitude.

36. The width of a rectangle is 4 centimeters less than its length, and the area is 60 square centimeters. Find the dimensions of the rectangle.

37. The sum of the squares of three consecutive positive integers is 194. Find the integers.

38. The distance d (in meters) that an object travels in t seconds when given an initial velocity of 15 meters per second is given by
$$d = 15t + 2t^2$$
Find the time necessary for an object to travel 63 meters.

[3.7]

▲ *Factor each polynomial.*

39. a. $2xy + 2x^2 + y + x$ b. $xy - 3x - y + 3$
40. a. $ax - 2bx + ay - 2by$
   b. $2ax - 4ay + bx - 2by$
41. a. $2a^3 - a^2 - 8a + 4$ b. $a^3 + 2a^2 - 4a - 8$
42. a. $(2y - 3)^2 - 4x^2$ b. $4y^2 - 4y + 1 - x^2$
43. a. $y^2 - 4x^2 - 4x - 1$ b. $x^2 - y^2 + 8y - 16$
44. a. $(2x)^3 - y^3$ b. $x^3 + (4y)^3$
45. a. $27y^3 + z^3$ b. $x^3 - 8a^3$
46. a. $8x^3y^3 - 125$ b. $1 + 64x^3y^3$

The numbers in brackets refer to the sections in which such problems are first considered.

▲ *Simplify each expression 1–6.*

1. $\dfrac{-4 + 3 \cdot 6 + 2}{4 - 2 \cdot 3}$ **[1.3]**

2. $\dfrac{4 - 2|-3| + 6}{|4 - 6|}$ **[1.3]**

3. $4 - 3 \cdot 2^2 + (-3 \cdot 2)^2$ **[2.1]**

4. $-2 \cdot 4^2 - (2 \cdot 4)^2 + 4$ **[2.1]**

5. $x^2 - x - (2x^2 - x + 1)$ **[2.2]**

6. $-2[x^2 - (x + 1)(x - 2)]$ **[3.3]**

7. Graph $-4 < x \leqslant 1$, x an integer. **[1.1]**

8. Express the fact that $y - 3$ is nonnegative using inequality symbols. **[1.1]**

9. Evaluate $3x^2 - y^2$ for $x = -2$ and $y = -2$. **[2.1]**

10. Evaluate $\frac{1}{2}gt^2 - 6t + 4$ for $g = 32$ and $t = 2$. **[2.1]**

11. For what value of x is $\dfrac{x}{x - 3}$ undefined? **[1.2]**

12. For what values of x and y is $\dfrac{y}{x - y}$ undefined? **[1.2]**

13. Given that $P(x) = x^3 - 2x^2 + 4$, **[2.1]**
    a. What is the degree of $P(x)$?
    b. What is the coefficient of the second-degree term?
    c. Find $P(-2)$.

14. Given that $P(x) = -x^2$ and $Q(x) = (-x)^2$, find $P(2) + Q(4)$. **[2.1]**

▲ *Solve each equation.*

15. $5(x - 2) - 4(x + 3) = 12$ **[2.3]**

16. $0.06y + 0.04(y + 6000) = 4000$ **[2.3]**

17. $x^2 + x = 12$ **[3.5]**

18. $2[(x - 2)^2 + 4x] = 16$ **[3.5]**

19. $4R^2 - 16r^2 = 0$ for R in terms of r **[3.5]**

20. $R^2 - (r_1 + r_2)^2 = 0$ for R in terms of r_1 and r_2 **[3.5]**

21. The volume of a pyramid with a square base is given by $\frac{1}{3}s^2h$, where s is the side of the base and h is the height. Find the volume of the Great Pyramid of Cheops in Egypt to the nearest tenth if its height is 250 yards and the side of its base is 160 yards. **[2.1]**

22. What is the radius of a circle to the nearest hundredth if the circumference exceeds the radius by 38.4 inches? **[2.4]**

23. What is the circumference of a circle to the nearest hundreth if the circumference exceeds the diameter by 18.6 inches? **[2.4]**

24. The price of housing in urban areas has been increasing at a rate of 4% per year. If a house costs $100,000 today, what was its cost one year ago to the nearest dollar? **[2.5]**

25. Rachel built a deck of uniform width around her 12- by 30-foot rectangular pool. If she used 400 square feet of cedar decking, how wide was the deck? **[3.6]**

4 RATIONAL EXPRESSIONS

Recall from Section 1.1 that integers and quotients of integers (divisor not equal to zero) are called rational numbers. In a similar way, polynomials and quotients of polynomials are called **rational expressions**. For example,

$$x^2 + 2x, \qquad 3y, \qquad \frac{y}{y+1}, \qquad \text{and} \qquad \frac{x^2 - 2x + 1}{2x}$$

are rational expressions. If the denominator is not zero, a rational expression represents a real number for each replacement of the variable(s). Of course, for any value of the variable(s) for which the denominator vanishes (is equal to zero), the fraction does not represent a real number and is said to be *undefined*.

4.1 | REDUCING FRACTIONS

Fundamental Principle of Fractions

There are infinitely many fractions that correspond to a given quotient. Thus, for example,

$$\frac{1}{2} = \frac{2}{4} = \frac{3}{6} = \frac{4}{8} \cdots \qquad \text{and} \qquad \frac{3}{5} = \frac{6}{10} = \frac{9}{15} = \frac{12}{20} \cdots$$

The following property enables us to write such **equivalent fractions**:

> *An equivalent fraction is obtained if the numerator and the denominator of a fraction are each multiplied or divided by the same nonzero number.*

This property is called **the fundamental principle of fractions** and is expressed in symbols as follows:

$$\frac{a}{b} = \frac{ac}{bc} \qquad (b, c \neq 0)$$

Signs on Fractions   There are three signs associated with a fraction: a sign for the numerator, a sign for the denominator, and a sign for the fraction itself. Although there are eight different possible combinations of a, b, and the two signs "$+$" and "$-$," these combinations represent only two real numbers, a/b and its additive inverse $-(a/b)$. Thus we have the following property of fractions:

$$\frac{a}{b} = \frac{-a}{-b} = -\frac{a}{-b} = -\frac{-a}{b} \qquad (b \neq 0) \tag{1}$$

$$\frac{-a}{b} = \frac{a}{-b} = -\frac{a}{b} = -\frac{-a}{-b} \qquad (b \neq 0) \tag{2}$$

EXAMPLE 1   **a.** $\dfrac{2}{3} = \dfrac{-2}{-3} = -\dfrac{2}{-3} = -\dfrac{-2}{3}$ **b.** $\dfrac{-2}{3} = \dfrac{2}{-3} = -\dfrac{2}{3} = -\dfrac{-2}{-3}$

The fraction $\dfrac{2}{3}$ in Example 1a is considered the simplest form of the four positive fractions. Either $\dfrac{-2}{3}$ or $-\dfrac{2}{3}$ are considered as simple forms for the negative fractions in Example 1b. However because the forms $\dfrac{a}{b}$ and $\dfrac{-a}{b}$, in which the sign of the fraction and the sign of the denominator are both positive, are generally the most convenient representations in much of our work, they will be referred to as **standard forms**. Thus,

$$\frac{-3}{5}, \qquad \frac{3}{5}, \qquad \text{and} \qquad \frac{7}{10}$$

are in standard form, whereas

$$\frac{3}{-5}, \qquad -\frac{3}{5}, \qquad \text{and} \qquad -\frac{7}{-10}$$

are not.

If the numerator or denominator of a fraction is an expression containing more than one term, there are alternative standard forms. For example, since

$$a - b = -(b - a)$$

we have

$$\frac{-b}{a-b} = \frac{-b}{-(b-a)} = \frac{b}{b-a}$$

and either

$$\frac{-b}{a-b} \qquad \text{or} \qquad \frac{b}{b-a}$$

may be taken as standard form.

Particular care should be taken when writing a fraction in standard form if the numerator contains more than one term. For example,

$$-\frac{a-b}{c} = \frac{-(a-b)}{c}$$

where the minus sign in the right member preceds *the entire numerator a − b.* This fraction can now be written as

$$\frac{-a+b}{c} \qquad \text{or} \qquad \frac{b-a}{c}$$

COMMON ERROR   *In particular, note that* $-\dfrac{a-b}{c} \neq \dfrac{-a-b}{c}.$

EXAMPLE 2   Write each fraction in standard form, and specify any values of the variables for which the fraction is undefined.

a. $-\dfrac{5}{-y}$ b. $-\dfrac{a}{a-2}$ c. $-\dfrac{x-1}{3}$

Solutions   a. $-\dfrac{5}{-y} = \dfrac{5}{y}$ $(y \neq 0)$ b. $-\dfrac{a}{a-2} = \dfrac{-a}{a-2}$

$\qquad\qquad\qquad\qquad\qquad\qquad\qquad\qquad$ or $\dfrac{a}{2-a}$ $(a \neq 2)$

c. $-\dfrac{x-1}{3} = \dfrac{-(x-1)}{3}$

$\qquad$ or $\dfrac{-x+1}{3}$

COMMON ERROR   *In Example 2c, note that* $-\dfrac{x-1}{3} \neq \dfrac{-x-1}{3}.$

EXAMPLE 3 Write each fraction on the left as an equivalent fraction in standard form with the denominator shown on the right.

a. $\dfrac{-1}{2-x}$; $\dfrac{}{x-2}$ b. $-\dfrac{a}{b-a}$; $\dfrac{}{a-b}$ c. $\dfrac{3}{3x-2y}$; $\dfrac{}{2y-3x}$

Solutions

a. $\dfrac{-1}{2-x}$

$= \dfrac{-1}{-(x-2)}$

$= \dfrac{1}{x-2}$

b. $-\dfrac{a}{b-a}$

$= -\dfrac{a}{-(a-b)}$

$= \dfrac{a}{a-b}$

c. $\dfrac{3}{3x-2y}$

$= \dfrac{3}{-(2y-3x)}$

$= \dfrac{-3}{2y-3x}$

Reducing Fractions A fraction is said to be in lowest terms if the numerator and denominator do not contain common factors. If the numerator and denominator of a fraction are polynomials, then the fraction is said to be in lowest terms if the numerator and denominator do not contain a common polynomial factor other than 1 or −1.

To express a given fraction in lowest terms (to **reduce** the fraction), we factor the numerator and denominator and then apply the fundamental principle of fractions.

EXAMPLE 4

a. $\dfrac{yz^2}{y^3z} = \dfrac{z \cdot yz}{y^2 \cdot yz}$

$= \dfrac{z}{y^2}$ $(y, z \neq 0)$

b. $\dfrac{8x^3y}{6x^2y^3} = \dfrac{4x \cdot 2x^2y}{3y^2 \cdot 2x^2y}$

$= \dfrac{4x}{3y^2}$ $(x, y \neq 0)$

Slash lines are sometimes used to abbreviate the procedure in the above examples. For example, instead of writing

$$\frac{y}{y^2} = \frac{1 \cdot y}{y \cdot y} = \frac{1}{y} \qquad (y \neq 0)$$

we can write

$$\frac{y}{y^2} = \frac{\overset{1}{\cancel{y}}}{\underset{y}{\cancel{y^2}}} = \frac{1}{y} \qquad (y \neq 0) \tag{3}$$

or simply

$$\frac{\cancel{y}}{\underset{y}{\cancel{y^2}}} = \frac{1}{y} \qquad (y \neq 0) \tag{4}$$

where we have omitted the 1 above y in the numerator.

COMMON ERROR *You may prefer to use the procedure in (3) above and show the 1 above y to avoid the error*

$$\frac{y}{y^2} = \frac{\cancel{y}}{\underset{y}{\cancel{y^2}}} = \frac{0}{y} = 0$$

The division of a polynomial by a monomial may be considered a special case of changing a fraction to lowest terms, provided that the monomial is a factor of each term of the polynomial.

EXAMPLE 5   **a.** $\dfrac{6y - 3}{3} = \dfrac{\cancel{3}(2y - 1)}{\cancel{3}}$ **b.** $\dfrac{9x^3 - 6x^2 + 3x}{3x} = \dfrac{\cancel{3x}(3x^2 - 2x + 1)}{\cancel{3x}}$

$\qquad\qquad\qquad = 2y - 1$ $\qquad\qquad\qquad\qquad = 3x^2 - 2x + 1 \qquad (x \neq 0)$

It is usually necessary to factor polynomials in the numerator and denominator to see the common factors.

EXAMPLE 6   **a.** $\dfrac{x^2 - 7x + 6}{x^2 - 36}$ **b.** $\dfrac{a - b}{b^2 - a^2}$

$\qquad\qquad = \dfrac{\cancel{(x - 6)}(x - 1)}{\cancel{(x - 6)}(x + 6)}$ $\qquad = \dfrac{-1\cancel{(b - a)}}{(b + a)\cancel{(b - a)}}$

$\qquad\qquad = \dfrac{x - 1}{x + 6} \qquad (x \neq 6, -6)$ $\qquad = \dfrac{-1}{b + a} \qquad (a \neq b, -b)$

Notice that in Example b it was necessary to write $a - b$ in the numerator as $-1(b - a)$ so that the common factors $b - a$ could be "divided out."

EXAMPLE 7   **a.** $\dfrac{y^2 - 5y + 4}{y - 1}$ **b.** $\dfrac{2x^2 + x - 15}{x + 3}$

$\qquad\qquad = \dfrac{(y - 4)\cancel{(y - 1)}}{\cancel{y - 1}}$ $\qquad = \dfrac{(2x - 5)\cancel{(x + 3)}}{\cancel{x + 3}}$

$\qquad\qquad = y - 4 \qquad (y \neq 1)$ $\qquad = 2x - 5 \qquad (x \neq -3)$

COMMON ERRORS   *Note that the fundamental principle of fractions enables us to divide out any nonzero factors that are common to both numerator and denominator of a fraction. The fundamental principle of fractions does not apply to common terms. For example,*

$$\frac{2xy}{3y} = \frac{2x}{3} \qquad (y \neq 0)$$

because y is a common factor in the numerator and denominator of the left member. However,

$$\frac{2x + y}{3 + y} \neq \frac{2x}{3}$$

because y *is a common term but is not a common factor of the numerator and the denominator. Furthermore,*

$$\frac{5x + 3}{5y} \neq \frac{x + 3}{y}$$

because 5 is not *a common factor of the* entire *numerator.*

E X A M P L E 8   **a.** $\dfrac{2x + 4}{4}$ **b.** $\dfrac{3x + 6}{3}$ **c.** $\dfrac{9x^2 + 3}{6x + 3}$

Solutions   **a.** $\dfrac{2x + 4}{4}$ **b.** $\dfrac{3x + 6}{3}$ **c.** $\dfrac{9x^2 + 3}{6x + 3}$

$= \dfrac{\cancel{2}(x + 2)}{\cancel{2}(2)}$ $= \dfrac{\cancel{3}(x + 2)}{\cancel{3}}$ $= \dfrac{\cancel{3}(3x^2 + 1)}{\cancel{3}(2x + 1)}$

$= \dfrac{x + 2}{2}$ $= x + 2$ $= \dfrac{3x^2 + 1}{2x + 1}$ $\left(x \neq -\dfrac{1}{2}\right)$

COMMON ERRORS   *Note that, in Example 8a,*

$$\frac{2x + 4}{4} \neq \frac{2x + \cancel{4}}{\cancel{4}}$$

in Example 8b,

$$\frac{3x + 6}{3} \neq \frac{\cancel{3}x + 6}{\cancel{3}}$$

and in Example 8c,

$$\frac{9x^2 + 3}{6x + 3} \neq \frac{9x^2 + \cancel{3}}{6x + \cancel{3}}$$

To avoid the necessity of always having to note restrictions on divisors (denominators), we shall assume in the remaining exercise sets in this chapter that no denominator is 0. However, we will continue to show restrictions in the examples in the text.

||| E X E R C I S E   S E T   4.1

▲ *Write in standard form and specify any values of the variables for which the fraction is undefined. See Examples 1 and 2.*

1. $\dfrac{1}{-4}$ **2.** $-\dfrac{1}{3}$ **3.** $-\dfrac{3}{-5}$

4. $-\dfrac{-3}{4}$ **5.** $\dfrac{-2}{-5}$ **6.** $\dfrac{-6}{-7}$

7. $-\dfrac{-3}{-7}$ **8.** $-\dfrac{-4}{-5}$ **9.** $-\dfrac{2x}{y}$

10. $\dfrac{x}{-3y}$ **11.** $-\dfrac{-3x}{4y}$ **12.** $-\dfrac{x}{-2y}$

13. $\dfrac{x + 1}{-x}$ **14.** $\dfrac{x + 3}{-x}$

15. $-\dfrac{x - y}{y + 2}$ **16.** $-\dfrac{y - x}{y - 1}$

▲ *Write each fraction on the left as an equal fraction in standard form with the denominator shown on the right. (Assume that no denominator equals 0.)*

17. $-\dfrac{4}{3 - y}; \dfrac{}{y - 3}$ **18.** $\dfrac{-3}{2 - x}; \dfrac{}{x - 2}$

19. $\dfrac{1}{x-y}; \dfrac{}{y-x}$

20. $\dfrac{-6}{x-y}; \dfrac{}{y-x}$

21. $\dfrac{x-2}{3-x}; \dfrac{}{x-3}$

22. $\dfrac{2x-5}{3-y}; \dfrac{}{y-3}$

23. $\dfrac{x+1}{x-y}; \dfrac{}{y-x}$

24. $\dfrac{x+3}{y-x}; \dfrac{}{x-y}$

25. $-\dfrac{x-2}{x-y}; \dfrac{}{y-x}$

26. $-\dfrac{x-4}{x-2y}; \dfrac{}{2y-x}$

27. $\dfrac{-a+1}{-3a-b}; \dfrac{}{3a+b}$

28. $\dfrac{-a-1}{2b-3a}; \dfrac{}{3a-2b}$

29. Show by a counterexample that $-\dfrac{x+3}{2}$ is not equivalent to $\dfrac{-x+3}{2}$.

30. Show by a counterexample that $-\dfrac{2x-y}{3}$ is not equivalent to $\dfrac{-2x-y}{3}$.

▲ *Use the fundamental principle of fractions to reduce each fraction to lowest terms in standard form. (Assume that no denominator is 0.) See Example 4 for Exercises 31–42.*

31. $\dfrac{6x^3y^2}{3xy^3}$

32. $\dfrac{12a^4b^2}{4a^2b^4}$

33. $\dfrac{14tr^4}{7t^2r^2}$

34. $\dfrac{22a^2bc^3}{11a^4c^2}$

35. $\dfrac{14cd}{-7c^2d^3}$

36. $\dfrac{100mn}{-5m^2n^3}$

37. $\dfrac{abc}{a^4bc^3}$

38. $\dfrac{xyz}{xy^2z^3}$

39. $\dfrac{m^2np}{-6m^2np^3}$

40. $\dfrac{abc}{-7abc^3}$

41. $\dfrac{-12r^2st}{-6rst^2}$

42. $\dfrac{-15xy^3z}{-3y^2z^4}$

▲ *See Examples 5–8 for Exercises 43–66.*

43. $\dfrac{4x+6}{6}$

44. $\dfrac{2y-8}{8}$

45. $\dfrac{9x-3}{9}$

46. $\dfrac{5y-10}{5}$

47. $\dfrac{a^3-3a^2+2a}{-a}$

48. $\dfrac{3x^3-6x^2+3x}{-3x}$

49. $\dfrac{y^2+5y-14}{y-2}$

50. $\dfrac{x^2+5x+6}{x+3}$

51. $\dfrac{5a-10}{3a-6}$

52. $\dfrac{6x+9}{10x+15}$

53. $\dfrac{(a-b)^2}{2a-2b}$

54. $\dfrac{x^2-16}{2x+8}$

55. $\dfrac{6t^2-6}{(t-1)^2}$

56. $\dfrac{4x^2-4}{(x+1)^2}$

57. $\dfrac{2y^2-8}{2y+4}$

58. $\dfrac{5y^2-20}{2y-4}$

59. $\dfrac{6-2y}{y^2-9}$

60. $\dfrac{4-2y}{y^2-4}$

61. $\dfrac{y^2-x^2}{(x-y)^2}$

62. $\dfrac{(2x-y)^2}{y^2-4x^2}$

63. $\dfrac{x^2-5x+4}{x^2-1}$

64. $\dfrac{y^2-2y-3}{y^2-9}$

65. $\dfrac{2y^2+y-6}{y^2+y-2}$

66. $\dfrac{6x^2-x-1}{2x^2+9x-5}$

Miscellaneous Exercises

▲ *Reduce fractions.*

67. $\dfrac{x^2+xy-2y^2}{x^2-y^2}$

68. $\dfrac{4x^2-9y^2}{2x^2+xy-6y^2}$

69. $\dfrac{x^2+ax+xy+ay}{2x+2a}$

70. $\dfrac{ax^2+x+a^2x+a}{3x+3a}$

71. $\dfrac{ax-2bx+ay-2by}{a^2-4b^2}$

72. $\dfrac{2ax-4ay+bx-2by}{x^2-4y^2}$

73. $\dfrac{8y^3-27}{4y^2-9}$

74. $\dfrac{8x^3-1}{4x^2-1}$

75. Show by a counterexample that $\dfrac{2x+y}{y}$ is not equivalent to $2x$.

76. Show by a counterexample that $\dfrac{4x-y}{4}$ is not equivalent to $x-y$.

4.2 DIVIDING POLYNOMIALS

In Section 4.1 we used the fundamental principle of fractions to reduce fractions. We can use other methods to rewrite fractions if the numerator and the denominator do not have common factors.

Monomial Denominators

Recall from arithmetic that we can write a single fraction as the sum of two fractions. For example,

$$\frac{5}{7} = \frac{2+3}{7} = \frac{2}{7} + \frac{3}{7}$$

Similarly, in algebra we can write the single fraction $\frac{a+b}{c}$ as $\frac{a}{c} + \frac{b}{c}$. In fact, we can write a single algebraic fraction with a monomial denominator and a numerator that contains two or more terms as the sum of several fractions. Once the quotient is written as separate fractions, each can be reduced as before.

EXAMPLE 1

a. $\dfrac{6y^2 + 4y + 1}{2}$

$= \dfrac{6y^2}{2} + \dfrac{4y}{2} + \dfrac{1}{2}$

$= 3y^2 + 2y + \dfrac{1}{2}$

b. $\dfrac{9x^3 - 6x^2 + 4}{3x}$

$= \dfrac{9x^3}{3x} - \dfrac{6x^2}{3x} + \dfrac{4}{3x}$

$= 3x^2 - 2x + \dfrac{4}{3x}$ $\qquad (x \neq 0)$

Long Division

If the divisor is not a monomial, we can use a method similar to the long division process used in arithmetic to rewrite the quotient as the sum of a polynomial and a fraction. The division process terminates when the degree of the remainder is less than the degree of the divisor.

The following example shows the similarity between the long division process for an arithmetic quotient and for an algebraic quotient.

EXAMPLE 2

Rewrite each quotient using long division.

a. $\dfrac{784}{32}$

b. $\dfrac{2x^2 + x - 7}{x + 3}$

Solutions

a. $32\overline{)784}$

Divide 3 into 7.

$\quad\;\; 2$
$32\overline{)784}$

Multiply 32 by 2.

$\quad\;\; 2$
$32\overline{)784}$
$\quad\;\; 64$

Subtract. (Change the sign and add.)

$\quad\;\; 2$
$32\overline{)784}$
$\;-64$
$\quad\;\; \overline{14}$

b. $x + 3\overline{)2x^2 + x - 7}$

Divide x into $2x^2$.

$\qquad\quad 2x$
$x + 3\overline{)2x^2 + x - 7}$

Multiply $x + 3$ by $2x$.

$\qquad\quad 2x$
$x + 3\overline{)2x^2 + x - 7}$
$\qquad\;\; 2x^2 + 6x$

Subtract. (Change the signs and add.)

$\qquad\quad 2x$
$x + 3\overline{)2x^2 + x - 7}$
$\qquad\; -2x^2 - 6x$
$\qquad\quad \overline{-5x}$

Bring down 4.

$$\begin{array}{r} 2 \\ 32\overline{)784} \\ -64\!\downarrow \\ \hline 144 \end{array}$$

Bring down −7.

$$\begin{array}{r} 2x \\ x+3\overline{)2x^2+x-7} \\ -2x^2-6x\downarrow \\ \hline -5x-7 \end{array}$$

Divide 3 into 14.

$$\begin{array}{r} 24 \\ 32\overline{)784} \\ -64 \\ \hline 144 \end{array}$$

Divide x into $-5x$.

$$\begin{array}{r} 2x-5 \\ x+3\overline{)2x^2+x-7} \\ -2x^2-6x \\ \hline -5x-7 \end{array}$$

Multiply 32 by 4.

$$\begin{array}{r} 24 \\ 32\overline{)784} \\ -64 \\ \hline 144 \\ 128 \end{array}$$

Multiply $x+3$ by −5.

$$\begin{array}{r} 2x-5 \\ x+3\overline{)2x^2+x-7} \\ -2x^2-6x \\ \hline -5x-7 \\ -5x-15 \end{array}$$

Subtract. (Change the sign and add.)

$$\begin{array}{r} 24 \\ 32\overline{)784} \\ -64 \\ \hline 144 \\ -128 \\ \hline 16 \end{array}$$

Subtract. (Change the signs and add.)

$$\begin{array}{r} 2x-5 \\ x+3\overline{)2x^2+x-7} \\ -2x^2-6x \\ \hline -5x-7 \\ +5x+15 \\ \hline 8 \end{array}$$

The remainder is 16.

$$\begin{array}{r} 24\dfrac{16}{32} \text{ or } 24\dfrac{1}{2} \\ 32\overline{)784} \\ -64 \\ \hline 144 \\ -128 \\ \hline 16 \end{array}$$

The remainder is 8.

$$\begin{array}{r} 2x-5+\dfrac{8}{x+3} \\ x+3\overline{)2x^2+x-7} \\ -2x^2-6x \\ \hline -5x-7 \\ +5x+15 \\ \hline 8 \end{array}$$

The answer is $24\dfrac{1}{2}$.

The answer is

$$2x-5+\frac{8}{x+3}$$

When using this process of long division, we must write the dividend in descending powers of the variable. Furthermore, it is sometimes helpful to insert a term with a zero coefficient so that like terms will be aligned for convenient computation.

EXAMPLE 3 Rewrite $\dfrac{3x - 1 + 4x^3}{2x - 1}$ using the long division process.

Solution We first write $3x - 1 + 4x^3$ in descending powers as $4x^3 + 3x - 1$. Then we insert $0x^2$ between $4x^3$ and $3x$ and divide.

$$
\begin{array}{r}
2x^2 + x + 2 \\
2x - 1 \overline{\smash{)}\, 4x^3 + 0x^2 + 3x - 1} \\
\text{Change signs} \rightarrow \underline{4x^3 - 2x^2} \\
\text{and add.} \\
2x^2 + 3x \\
\text{Change signs} \rightarrow \underline{2x^2 - x} \\
\text{and add.} \\
4x - 1 \\
\text{Change signs} \rightarrow \underline{4x - 2} \\
\text{and add.} \\
1
\end{array}
$$

Hence,

$$\frac{3x - 1 + 4x^3}{2x - 1} = 2x^2 + x + 2 + \frac{1}{2x - 1} \qquad \left(x \neq \frac{1}{2}\right)$$

We call an expression such as

$$2x^2 + x + 2 + \frac{1}{2x - 1}$$

a **mixed expression** just as we call symbols such as $3\frac{1}{2}$ equal to $3 + \frac{1}{2}$ mixed numbers.

We can also use long division to rewrite quotients when the degree of the divisor is greater than 1.

EXERCISE SET 4.2

▲ *Divide. See Example 1.*

1. $\dfrac{8a^2 + 4a + 1}{2}$

2. $\dfrac{15t^3 - 12t^2 + 5t}{3t^2}$

3. $\dfrac{7y^4 - 14y^2 + 3}{7y^2}$

4. $\dfrac{21n^4 + 14n^2 - 7}{7n^2}$

5. $\dfrac{18r^2s^2 - 15rs + 6}{3rs}$

6. $\dfrac{12x^3 - 8x^2 + 3x}{4x}$

7. $\dfrac{8a^2x^2 - 4ax^2 + ax}{2ax}$

8. $\dfrac{9a^2b^2 + 3ab^2 + 4a^2b}{ab^2}$

9. $\dfrac{25m^6 - 15m^3 + 7}{-5m^3}$

10. $\dfrac{36t^5 + 24t^3 - 12t}{-12t^2}$

11. $\dfrac{40m^4 - 25m^2 + 7m}{5m^2}$

12. $\dfrac{15s^{10} - 21s^5 + 6}{3s^2}$

▲ *Divide. See Examples 2 and 3.*

13. $\dfrac{4y^2 + 12y + 7}{2y + 1}$

14. $\dfrac{2n^2 + 13n - 6}{2n - 1}$

15. $\dfrac{4t^2 - 4t - 5}{2t - 1}$

16. $\dfrac{2x^2 - 3x - 15}{2x + 5}$

17. $\dfrac{x^3 + 2x^2 + x + 1}{x - 2}$

18. $\dfrac{2x^3 - 3x^2 - 2x + 4}{x + 1}$

19. $\dfrac{2a - 3a^2 + a^4 - 1}{a + 3}$

20. $\dfrac{3 + 2b^2 + 2b^4}{b - 4}$

21. $\dfrac{4z^2 + 5z + 8z^4 + 3}{2z + 1}$

22. $\dfrac{7 - 3t^3 - 23t^2 + 10t^4}{2t + 3}$

23. $\dfrac{x^4 - 1}{x - 2}$

24. $\dfrac{y^5 + 1}{y - 1}$

Miscellaneous Exercises

▲ *Divide.*

25. $\dfrac{x^3 - 3x^2 + 2x + 5}{x^2 - 2x + 7}$

26. $\dfrac{2y^3 + 5y^2 - 3y + 2}{y^2 - y - 3}$

27. $\dfrac{4a^4 + 3a^3 - 2a + 1}{a^2 + 3a - 1}$

28. $\dfrac{2b^4 - 3b^2 + b + 2}{b^2 + b - 3}$

29. $\dfrac{t^4 - 3t^3 + 2t^2 - 2t + 1}{t^3 - 2t^2 + t + 2}$

30. $\dfrac{r^4 + r^3 - 2r^2 + r + 5}{r^3 + 2r + 3}$

31. Determine k so that the polynomial $x^3 - 3x + k$ has $x - 2$ as a factor.

32. Determine k so that the polynomial $x^3 + 2x^2 + k$ has $x + 3$ as a factor.

4.3 | BUILDING FRACTIONS

Just as we reduced fractions in Section 4.1 by applying the fundamental principle in the form

$$\frac{ac}{bc} = \frac{a}{b} \qquad (b, c \neq 0)$$

we can also change fractions to equivalent fractions in higher terms by applying the fundamental principle in the form

$$\frac{a}{b} = \frac{ac}{bc} \qquad (b, c \neq 0)$$

For example, $\frac{1}{2}$ can be changed to an equivalent fraction with a denominator of 8 by *multiplying* the numerator and the denominator by **4**. Thus,

$$\frac{1}{2} = \frac{1 \cdot 4}{2 \cdot 4} = \frac{4}{8}$$

This process is called **building** a fraction, and the number 4 is called a **building factor**. The fraction $\frac{4}{8}$ is said to be in **higher terms** than $\frac{1}{2}$.

In general, when building a/b to an equivalent fraction with bc as a denominator (i.e., $a/b = ?/bc$), we can usually determine the building factor c by inspection and then multiply the numerator and the denominator of the original fraction by this building factor. If we cannot obtain the building factor by inspection, we can divide the desired denominator (bc) by the given denominator (b).

EXAMPLE 1   Build each fraction to an equivalent fraction with the given denominator.

a. $\dfrac{5x}{3y} = \dfrac{?}{12y^2}$

b. $\dfrac{2}{y - 1} = \dfrac{?}{y^2 - 1}$

Solutions   **a.** By inspection we note that the building factor is **4y**. Alternatively,

$$12y^2 \div 3y = 4y$$

Hence,

$$\frac{5x(4y)}{3y(4y)} = \frac{20xy}{12y^2}$$

b. We first factor $y^2 - 1$ as $(y - 1)(y + 1)$. Then by inspection we note that the building factor is $y + 1$. Alternatively,

$$(y^2 - 1) \div (y - 1) = y + 1$$

Hence,

$$\frac{2(y + 1)}{(y - 1)(y + 1)} = \frac{2y + 2}{y^2 - 1}$$

Least Common Denominator

Sometimes it is necessary to change two or more fractions with unlike denominators into fractions with a common denominator. In particular, the common denominator that is the most useful is the **least common multiple (LCM)** of the denominators, called the **least common denominator (LCD)**. The LCM of two or more natural numbers is the smallest natural number that is exactly divisible by each of the given numbers. Thus, 24 is the LCM of 6 and 8, because 24 is the smallest natural number each will divide into without a remainder.

In the preceding example it was easy to find the LCM of 6 and 8 (24) by inspection. Sometimes it is necessary to factor each number first to find the LCM.

Finding the LCM of a Set of Natural Numbers

1. Express each number in completely factored form.

2. Write as factors of a product each *different* prime factor occurring in any of the numbers, including each factor the greatest number of times it occurs in any one of the given numbers.

EXAMPLE 2 Find the LCM of 12, 9, and 15.

Solution

	12	9	15
The numbers			
Appear in prime factor form as	$2 \cdot 2 \cdot 3$	$3 \cdot 3$	$3 \cdot 5$
The LCM contains the factors		$2 \cdot 2 \cdot 3 \cdot 3 \cdot 5$	
The LCM is		180	

The factors 2 and 3 are each used twice because 2 appears twice as a factor of 12 and 3 appears twice as a factor of 9.

We define the LCM of a set of polynomials as the polynomial of lowest degree yielding a polynomial quotient upon division by each of the given polynomials. We can find the LCM of a set of polynomials with integral coefficients in a manner comparable to that used with a set of natural numbers.

EXAMPLE 3

Find the LCM of $x^2 - 9$ and $x^2 - x - 6$.

Solution

We first factor each polynomial.

$$x^2 - 9 \qquad x^2 - x - 6$$
$$(x - 3)(x + 3) \qquad (x - 3)(x + 2)$$

Hence, the LCM is $(x - 3)(x + 3)(x + 2)$.

We can now write two or more fractions with unlike denominators as equivalent fractions with a common denominator—in particular, with the least common denominator (LCD).

EXAMPLE 4

Write the fractions $\dfrac{1}{12}, \dfrac{2}{9}$, and $\dfrac{4}{15}$ as equivalent fractions with the LCD of the fractions.

Solution

From Example 2, the LCM of 12, 9, and 15 is 180. Hence, the LCD is 180, and we seek numerators such that

$$\frac{1}{12} = \frac{?}{180}, \qquad \frac{2}{9} = \frac{?}{180}, \qquad \text{and} \qquad \frac{4}{15} = \frac{?}{180}$$

Since $180 \div 12 = 15$, $180 \div 9 = 20$, and $180 \div 15 = 12$, we have

$$\frac{1\,(15)}{12\,(15)} = \frac{15}{180}, \qquad \frac{2\,(20)}{9\,(20)} = \frac{40}{180}, \qquad \text{and} \qquad \frac{4\,(12)}{15\,(12)} = \frac{48}{180}$$

A similar procedure is used if the fractions involve variables.

EXAMPLE 5

Build the fractions $\dfrac{3}{x^2 - 9}$ and $\dfrac{4x}{x^2 - x - 6}$ to equivalent fractions with the LCD of the fractions.

Solution

From Example 3 above, the LCM of $x^2 - 9$ and $x^2 - x - 6$ is the product $(x - 3)(x + 3)(x + 2)$. Hence, the LCD is $(x - 3)(x + 3)(x + 2)$, and we seek numerators such that

$$\frac{3}{x^2 - 9} = \frac{3}{(x - 3)(x + 3)} = \frac{?}{(x - 3)(x + 3)(x + 2)}$$

and

$$\frac{4x}{x^2 - x - 6} = \frac{4x}{(x - 3)(x + 2)} = \frac{?}{(x - 3)(x + 3)(x + 2)}$$

By inspection we can see the building factors are

$$(x + 2) \qquad \text{and} \qquad (x + 3)$$

respectively, and we have

$$\frac{3(x + 2)}{(x^2 - 9)(x + 2)} = \frac{3x + 6}{(x - 3)(x + 3)(x + 2)}$$

and

$$\frac{4x(x + 3)}{(x^2 - x - 6)(x + 3)} = \frac{4x^2 + 12x}{(x - 3)(x + 3)(x + 2)}$$

E X E R C I S E   S E T   4 . 3

▲ *Build each fraction to an equivalent fraction with the given denominator. See Example 1.*

1. $\dfrac{2}{3} = \dfrac{?}{9}$

2. $\dfrac{3}{4} = \dfrac{?}{8}$

3. $\dfrac{-15}{7} = \dfrac{?}{14}$

4. $\dfrac{-12}{5} = \dfrac{?}{20}$

5. $4 = \dfrac{?}{5}$

6. $6 = \dfrac{?}{7}$

7. $\dfrac{2}{6x} = \dfrac{?}{18x}$

8. $\dfrac{5}{3y} = \dfrac{?}{21y}$

9. $\dfrac{-a^2}{b^2} = \dfrac{?}{b^3}$

10. $\dfrac{-a}{b} = \dfrac{?}{ab^2}$

11. $y = \dfrac{?}{xy}$

12. $x = \dfrac{?}{xy^3}$

13. $\dfrac{3}{a-b} = \dfrac{?}{a^2-b^2}$

14. $\dfrac{5}{2a+b} = \dfrac{?}{4a^2-b^2}$

15. $\dfrac{3x}{y+2} = \dfrac{?}{y^2-y-6}$

16. $\dfrac{5x}{y+3} = \dfrac{?}{y^2+y-6}$

17. $\dfrac{-2}{x+1} = \dfrac{?}{x^2+3x+2}$

18. $\dfrac{-3}{a+2} = \dfrac{?}{a^2+3a+2}$

▲ *Find the LCM. See Examples 2 and 3.*

19. 4, 6, 10

20. 3, 4, 5

21. 6, 8, 15

22. 4, 15, 18

23. 14, 21, 36

24. 4, 11, 22

25. $2ab, 6b^2$

26. $12xy, 24x^3y^2$

27. $6xy, 8x^2, 3xy^2$

28. $7x, 8y, 6z$

29. $(a-b), a(a-b)^2$

30. $6(x+y)^2, 4xy^2$

31. $a^2-b^2, a-b$

32. $x+2, x^2-4$

33. $a^2+5a+4, (a+1)^2$

34. $x^2-3x+2, (x-1)^2$

35. $x^2+3x-4, (x-1)^2$

36. $x^2-x-2, (x-2)^2$

37. $x^2-x, (x-1)^3$

38. $y^2+2y, (y+2)^2$

39. $4a^2-4, (a-1)^2, 2$

40. $3x^2-3, (x-1)^2, 4$

41. $x^3, x^2-x, (x-1)^2$

42. $y, y^3-y, (y-1)^3$

▲ *Build each fraction equivalently with the LCD of the given fractions. See Examples 4 and 5.*

43. $\dfrac{2}{3x}$ and $\dfrac{1}{6xy}$

44. $\dfrac{1}{4y}$ and $\dfrac{3}{8xy}$

45. $\dfrac{3}{4y^2}$ and $\dfrac{2}{3y}$

46. $\dfrac{1}{5x}$ and $\dfrac{3}{2x^2}$

47. $\dfrac{1}{2x+2}$ and $\dfrac{1}{2}$

48. $\dfrac{3}{4x-4}$ and $\dfrac{1}{4}$

49. $\dfrac{3}{y-3}$ and $\dfrac{2}{y+2}$

50. $\dfrac{1}{y+4}$ and $\dfrac{3}{y-1}$

51. $\dfrac{5}{3y-6}$ and $\dfrac{1}{6y+3}$

52. $\dfrac{3}{2y+4}$ and $\dfrac{5}{4y-6}$

53. $\dfrac{2}{a^2-1}$ and $\dfrac{3}{a-1}$

54. $\dfrac{4}{(a-1)^2}$ and $\dfrac{2}{a-1}$

55. $\dfrac{1}{a^2-5a+4}$ and $\dfrac{2}{a^2-2a+1}$

56. $\dfrac{3}{a^2-1}$ and $\dfrac{1}{a^2+a-2}$

57. $\dfrac{3y}{y^2+3y+2}$ and $\dfrac{y}{y^2+4y+4}$

58. $\dfrac{y}{y^2+5y+4}$ and $\dfrac{y}{y^2-16}$

59. $\dfrac{2x}{4x^2-y^2}$ and $\dfrac{3x}{(2x-y)^2}$

60. $\dfrac{x}{(3x+y)^2}$ and $\dfrac{2x}{9x^2-y^2}$

Miscellaneous Exercises

▲ *Build each fraction equivalently with the LCD of the given fractions.*

61. $\dfrac{5y}{x^2+2xy+y^2}$ and $\dfrac{3}{2x+2y}$

62. $\dfrac{2x}{x^2-6xy+9y^2}$ and $\dfrac{4}{3x-9y}$

63. $\dfrac{1}{x^3-1}$ and $\dfrac{3}{x-1}$

64. $\dfrac{3}{x^3+8}$ and $\dfrac{1}{x+2}$

65. $\dfrac{4x}{x^3+y^3}$ and $\dfrac{y}{x+y}$

66. $\dfrac{y}{x^3-y^3}$ and $\dfrac{2x}{x-y}$

67. $\dfrac{3x}{(x-y)^2}$ and $\dfrac{2x}{y-x}$

68. $\dfrac{2y}{y-2x}$ and $\dfrac{5y}{(2x-y)^2}$

69. $\dfrac{1}{x-2y}$ and $\dfrac{3}{4y-2x}$

70. $\dfrac{4}{6x-3y}$ and $\dfrac{2}{y-2x}$

| 4.4 | **SUMS AND DIFFERENCES**

Fractions with Common Denominators

As in arithmetic, the sum or difference of two fractions with common denominators can be written as a single fraction as follows:

$$\frac{a}{c} + \frac{b}{c} = \frac{a+b}{c}$$

$$\frac{a}{c} - \frac{b}{c} = \frac{a-b}{c} \qquad (c \neq 0)$$

EXAMPLE 1

a. $\dfrac{2x}{9} + \dfrac{5x}{9}$

$$= \frac{2x + 5x}{9}$$

$$= \frac{7x}{9}$$

b. $\dfrac{a+1}{b} - \dfrac{a-1}{b}$

$$= \frac{a + 1 - (a - 1)}{b}$$

$$= \frac{a + 1 - a + 1}{b} = \frac{2}{b}$$

COMMON ERROR   *Note that in Example 1b,* $-(a - 1) \neq -a - 1$.

Fractions with Unlike Denominators

If the fractions in a sum or difference have unlike denominators, we can build the fractions to equivalent fractions that have common denominators and then rewrite the sum as above.

EXAMPLE 2

$$\frac{2y}{9} + \frac{5y}{6} - \frac{y}{4}$$

The LCD is $3 \cdot 3 \cdot 2 \cdot 2 = 36$. We build each fraction to a fraction with this LCD.

$$\frac{(4)2y}{(4)9} = \frac{8y}{36}; \qquad \frac{(6)5y}{(6)6} = \frac{30y}{36}; \qquad \frac{(9)y}{(9)4} = \frac{9y}{36}$$

Then we obtain

$$\frac{8y}{36} + \frac{30y}{36} - \frac{9y}{36} = \frac{8y + 30y - 9y}{36} = \frac{29y}{36}$$

EXAMPLE 3

$$\frac{1}{3}x - \frac{3}{8}x + \frac{1}{2}x$$

The LCD is $3 \cdot 2 \cdot 2 \cdot 2 = 24$. We build each fraction to a fraction with this LCD.

$$\frac{(8)}{(8)} \cdot \frac{1}{3}x = \frac{8}{24}x; \qquad \frac{(3)}{(3)} \cdot \frac{3}{8}x = \frac{9}{24}x; \qquad \frac{(12)}{(12)} \cdot \frac{1}{2}x = \frac{12}{24}x$$

Then we obtain

$$\frac{8}{24}x - \frac{9}{24}x + \frac{12}{24}x = \frac{8 - 9 + 12}{24}x = \frac{11}{24}x$$

EXAMPLE 4 $\dfrac{3x}{x + 2} - \dfrac{2x}{x - 3}$

The LCD is $(x + 2)(x - 3)$. We build each fraction to a fraction with this LCD.

$$\frac{3x}{x + 2} = \frac{3x(x - 3)}{(x + 2)(x - 3)}; \qquad \frac{2x}{x - 3} = \frac{2x(x + 2)}{(x - 3)(x + 2)}$$

Then we obtain

$$\frac{3x}{x + 2} - \frac{2x}{x - 3} = \frac{3x^2 - 9x - (2x^2 + 4x)}{(x + 2)(x - 3)}$$

$$= \frac{3x^2 - 9x - 2x^2 - 4x}{(x + 2)(x - 3)}$$

$$= \frac{x^2 - 13x}{(x + 2)(x - 3)}$$

Remember that polynomial denominators should be written in factored form to find their LCD.

EXAMPLE 5 $\dfrac{2}{x^2 - 9} - \dfrac{1}{x^2 - x - 6}$

The LCD is $(x - 3)(x + 3)(x + 2)$. We build each fraction to a fraction with this LCD.

$$\frac{2}{(x - 3)(x + 3)} = \frac{2(x + 2)}{(x - 3)(x + 3)(x + 2)}$$

$$\frac{1}{(x - 3)(x + 2)} = \frac{1(x + 3)}{(x - 3)(x + 2)(x + 3)}$$

Then we obtain

$$\frac{2(x + 2)}{(x - 3)(x + 3)(x + 2)} - \frac{(x + 3)}{(x - 3)(x + 2)(x + 3)} = \frac{2x + 4 - (x + 3)}{(x - 3)(x + 3)(x + 2)}$$

$$= \frac{x + 1}{(x - 3)(x + 3)(x + 2)}$$

It is usually advantageous to leave the LCD in factored form rather than carry out the multiplication. Sometimes it is also convenient to leave denominators of fractions in factored form, as we did in the above examples.

EXAMPLE 6 $\dfrac{2}{x^2 - 4} - \dfrac{3}{x^2 - 5x + 6} + \dfrac{1}{x - 3}$

The LCD is $(x + 2)(x - 2)(x - 3)$. We build each fraction to a fraction with this LCD.

$$\frac{2}{(x+2)(x-2)} = \frac{2(x-3)}{(x+2)(x-2)(x-3)}$$

$$\frac{3}{(x-2)(x-3)} = \frac{3(x+2)}{(x-2)(x-3)(x+2)}$$

$$\frac{1}{x-3} = \frac{1(x-2)(x+2)}{(x-3)(x-2)(x+2)}$$

Then we obtain

$$\frac{2(x-3)}{(x+2)(x-2)(x-3)} - \frac{3(x+2)}{(x+2)(x-2)(x-3)} + \frac{1(x-2)(x+2)}{(x-3)(x-2)(x+2)}$$

$$= \frac{2x-6-3x-6+x^2-4}{(x-3)(x-2)(x+2)} = \frac{x^2-x-16}{(x-3)(x-2)(x+2)}$$

EXERCISE SET 4.4

▲ *Write each sum or difference as a single fraction in lowest terms. See Example 1.*

1. $\dfrac{x}{2} - \dfrac{3}{2}$

2. $\dfrac{y}{7} - \dfrac{5}{7}$

3. $\dfrac{1}{6}a + \dfrac{1}{6}b - \dfrac{1}{6}c$

4. $\dfrac{1}{3}x - \dfrac{2}{3}y + \dfrac{1}{3}z$

5. $\dfrac{x-1}{2y} + \dfrac{x}{2y}$

6. $\dfrac{y+1}{b} + \dfrac{y-1}{b}$

7. $\dfrac{3}{x+2y} - \dfrac{x+3}{x+2y} - \dfrac{x-1}{x+2y}$

8. $\dfrac{2}{a-3b} - \dfrac{b-2}{a-3b} + \dfrac{b}{a-3b}$

9. $\dfrac{a+1}{a^2-2a+1} + \dfrac{5-3a}{a^2-2a+1}$

10. $\dfrac{x+4}{x^2-x+2} + \dfrac{2x-3}{x^2-x+2}$

▲ *See Examples 2 and 3.*

11. $\dfrac{x}{2} + \dfrac{2x}{3}$

12. $\dfrac{3y}{4} + \dfrac{y}{3}$

13. $\dfrac{y}{3} - \dfrac{2y}{5}$

14. $\dfrac{3x}{5} - \dfrac{x}{2}$

15. $\dfrac{2x}{3} - \dfrac{3x}{4} + \dfrac{x}{2}$

16. $\dfrac{y}{2} + \dfrac{2y}{3} - \dfrac{3y}{4}$

17. $\dfrac{1}{2}x + \dfrac{2}{3}x$

18. $\dfrac{3}{4}y + \dfrac{2}{3}y$

19. $\dfrac{5}{6}y - \dfrac{3}{4}y$

20. $\dfrac{3}{4}x - \dfrac{1}{6}x$

21. $\dfrac{2}{3}y - \dfrac{1}{6}y + \dfrac{1}{4}y$

22. $\dfrac{3}{4}y + \dfrac{1}{3}y - \dfrac{5}{6}y$

▲ *See Example 4.*

23. $\dfrac{x+1}{x} + \dfrac{2y-1}{y}$

24. $\dfrac{y-2}{y} + \dfrac{2x-3}{x}$

25. $\dfrac{1}{2y} - \dfrac{2}{3x}$

26. $\dfrac{2}{3x} - \dfrac{1}{2y}$

27. $\dfrac{5}{x+1} - \dfrac{3}{y-1}$

28. $\dfrac{2}{y+2} - \dfrac{3}{x-1}$

29. $\dfrac{x}{3x+2} + \dfrac{x}{x-1}$

30. $\dfrac{2y}{y-1} + \dfrac{y}{2y+1}$

31. $\dfrac{y}{2y-1} - \dfrac{2y}{y+1}$

32. $\dfrac{2x}{3x+1} - \dfrac{x}{x-2}$

33. $\dfrac{x+1}{x+2} + \dfrac{x+2}{x+3}$

34. $\dfrac{y-2}{y+1} + \dfrac{y+3}{y-2}$

35. $\dfrac{y-1}{y+1} - \dfrac{y-2}{2y-3}$

36. $\dfrac{x-2}{2x+1} - \dfrac{x+1}{x-1}$

▲ *See Example 5.*

37. $\dfrac{3}{2x+4} + \dfrac{4}{3x+6}$

38. $\dfrac{5}{4y-8} + \dfrac{3}{5y-10}$

39. $\dfrac{7}{5x-10} - \dfrac{5}{3x-6}$

40. $\dfrac{2}{3y+6} - \dfrac{3}{2y+4}$

41. $\dfrac{2}{x^2-x-2} + \dfrac{2}{x^2+2x+1}$

42. $\dfrac{1}{y^2-1} + \dfrac{1}{y^2+2y+1}$

43. $\dfrac{y}{y^2-16} - \dfrac{y+1}{y^2-5y+4}$

44. $\dfrac{x}{x^2-5x+6} - \dfrac{x-1}{x^2-9}$

45. $\dfrac{x}{x^2 - 1} - \dfrac{2x + 1}{x^2 - 2x + 1}$

46. $\dfrac{y}{y^2 + 3y - 10} - \dfrac{2y - 1}{y^2 - 4}$

47. $\dfrac{y - 1}{y^2 - 3y} - \dfrac{y + 1}{y^2 + 2y}$

48. $\dfrac{x + 1}{x^2 + 2x} - \dfrac{x - 1}{x^2 - 3x}$

49. $\dfrac{2x + 1}{x^2 - 4} - \dfrac{3x - 2}{x^2 - 4x + 4}$

50. $\dfrac{3y - 1}{y^2 - 4y + 3} - \dfrac{y + 2}{(y - 3)^2}$

▲ *See Example 6.*

51. $\dfrac{1}{z^2 - 7z + 12} + \dfrac{2}{z^2 - 5z + 6} - \dfrac{3}{z^2 - 6z + 8}$

52. $\dfrac{4}{a^2 - 4b^2} + \dfrac{2}{a^2 + 3ab + 2b^2} + \dfrac{4}{a^2 - ab - 2b^2}$

53. $x + \dfrac{1}{x - 1} - \dfrac{1}{(x - 1)^2}$ $\left[\textit{Hint: Write x as } \dfrac{x}{1}. \right]$

54. $y - \dfrac{2}{y^2 - 1} + \dfrac{3}{y + 1}$ $\left[\textit{Hint: Write y as } \dfrac{y}{1}. \right]$

55. $y - \dfrac{y^2}{y - 1} + \dfrac{y^2}{y + 1}$

56. $x + \dfrac{2x^2}{x + 2} - \dfrac{3x^2}{x - 1}$

57. $1 - \dfrac{x - 2}{(x + 1)^2} + \dfrac{2x - 1}{x^2 - 1}$

58. $1 + \dfrac{y + 1}{y^2 - 4} - \dfrac{y - 1}{(y + 2)^2}$

Miscellaneous Exercises

a. *Write each expression as a single fraction.*
b. *Use long division to rewrite the result obtained for part a in the form*

$$P(x) + \frac{r}{x - a}$$

59. $x - 1 + \dfrac{3}{x + 2}$ **60.** $x + 3 + \dfrac{1}{x - 1}$

61. $x + 2 - \dfrac{2}{x + 3}$ **62.** $x - 3 - \dfrac{3}{x - 2}$

▲ *Show that each pair of expressions is equivalent, given that $c^2 + s^2 = 1$. Assume that the variables represent numbers for which each expression is defined. [Hint: Simplify the first expression.]*

63. $\dfrac{c}{s} + \dfrac{s}{c}; \quad \dfrac{1}{sc}$ **64.** $\dfrac{1}{c^2} + \dfrac{1}{s^2}; \quad \dfrac{1}{c^2 s^2}$

65. $c + \dfrac{s^2}{c}; \quad \dfrac{1}{c}$ **66.** $\left(\dfrac{c}{s}\right)^2 + 1; \quad \dfrac{1}{s^2}$

67. $\dfrac{(c - 1)(c + 1)}{s^2} + 1; \quad 0$

68. $s + \dfrac{c(c - s)}{s}; \quad \dfrac{1 - cs}{s}$

69. $\dfrac{s - c}{s + c} + \dfrac{2sc}{s^2 - c^2}; \quad \dfrac{1}{s^2 - c^2}$

70. $\dfrac{c^3 + c^2 s}{c^2 - s^2} - s; \quad \dfrac{1 - cs}{c - s}$

4.5 | **PRODUCTS AND QUOTIENTS**

Products of Fractions

In earlier mathematics courses we learned that, for example,

$$\frac{2}{3} \cdot \frac{4}{5} = \frac{2 \cdot 4}{3 \cdot 5} = \frac{8}{15}$$

In general, fractions are multiplied as follows.

$$\frac{a}{b} \cdot \frac{c}{d} = \frac{ac}{bd} \qquad (b, d \neq 0) \tag{1}$$

In other words, the product of two fractions equals the product of their numerators divided by the product of their denominators. For example,

$$\frac{6x^2}{y} \cdot \frac{xy}{2} = \frac{6x^2 \cdot xy}{y \cdot 2} = \frac{6x^3 y}{2y}$$

$$= \frac{3x^3 \,(2y)}{1 \,(2y)} = 3x^3 \qquad (y \neq 0)$$

We can arrive at the same result for this example by using slash lines to divide out common factors before we multiply the fractions:

$$\frac{6x^2}{y} \cdot \frac{xy}{2} = \frac{\overset{3}{\cancel{6x^2}}}{\cancel{y}} \cdot \frac{\overset{1}{\cancel{xy}}}{\cancel{2}} = 3x^3 \qquad (y \neq 0)$$

In the preceding example we have shown the factors 1. Although you may find it helpful to continue to do so, we will omit showing such factors in the following examples, except for factors -1.

If any of the fractions in a product have negative factors, it is advisable to proceed as if all the signs were positive and then attach the appropriate sign to the simplified product. If an even number of negative factors is involved, the result has a positive sign; if an odd number of negative factors is involved, the result has a negative sign.

EXAMPLE 1

a. $\dfrac{-x}{y^2} \cdot \dfrac{-2y^3}{x^2} = \dfrac{\overset{-1}{\cancel{-x}}}{\cancel{y^2}} \cdot \dfrac{\overset{y}{-2y^3}}{\underset{x}{\cancel{x^2}}} = \dfrac{2y}{x} \qquad (x, y \neq 0)$

b. $\dfrac{-4x^2}{3y} \cdot \dfrac{y}{2x} \cdot \dfrac{3}{5} = \dfrac{\overset{-2x}{\cancel{-4x^2}}}{\cancel{3y}} \cdot \dfrac{\cancel{y}}{\cancel{2x}} \cdot \dfrac{\cancel{3}}{5} = \dfrac{-2x}{5} \qquad (x, y \neq 0)$

c. $\dfrac{-4}{9} x^2 \cdot \dfrac{3}{4} x = \dfrac{\overset{-1}{\cancel{-4}}}{\underset{3}{\cancel{9}}} x^2 \cdot \dfrac{\cancel{3}}{\cancel{4}} x = \dfrac{-x^3}{3}$

Polynomials in a fraction should be factored and common factors in numerators and denominators divided out before Property (1) is applied.

EXAMPLE 2

a. $\dfrac{x^2 - 5x + 4}{3x} \cdot \dfrac{x}{x^2 - 1} = \dfrac{(x-4)\cancel{(x-1)}}{3\cancel{x}} \cdot \dfrac{\cancel{x}}{(x+1)\cancel{(x-1)}}$

$$= \dfrac{x-4}{3(x+1)} \qquad (x \neq -1, 0, 1)$$

b. $\dfrac{4y^2 - 1}{y^2 - 4} \cdot \dfrac{y^2 + 2y}{4y + 2} = \dfrac{(2y-1)\cancel{(2y+1)}}{(y-2)\cancel{(y+2)}} \cdot \dfrac{y\cancel{(y+2)}}{2\cancel{(2y+1)}}$

$$= \dfrac{y(2y-1)}{2(y-2)} \qquad (y \neq -2, 2)$$

We can use the distributive property along with Property (1) to rewrite products that involve fractions.

EXAMPLE 3

a. $\dfrac{2}{3}x\left(\dfrac{1}{2}x - 9\right) = \dfrac{2}{3}x\left(\dfrac{1}{2}x\right) - \dfrac{2}{3}x\overset{3}{(9)}$

$\qquad = \dfrac{1}{3}x^2 - 6x$

b. $\left(x - \dfrac{1}{2}\right)^2 = \left(x - \dfrac{1}{2}\right)\left(x - \dfrac{1}{2}\right)$

$\qquad = x^2 - \dfrac{1}{2}x - \dfrac{1}{2}x + \dfrac{1}{4}$

$\qquad = x^2 - x + \dfrac{1}{4}$

Quotients of Fractions

Recall that in arithmetic we could rewrite the quotient of two fractions as a product. For example, $\dfrac{2}{3} \div \dfrac{5}{7}$ can be written as $\dfrac{2}{3}\cdot\dfrac{7}{5}$. We can rewrite the quotient of two algebraic fractions in the same way:

$$\frac{a}{b} \div \frac{c}{d} = \frac{a}{b}\cdot\frac{d}{c} \qquad (b, c, d \neq 0) \tag{2}$$

Thus, to find the quotient of two fractions, we can multiply the first fraction by the reciprocal of the second fraction.

EXAMPLE 4

a. $\dfrac{2x^3}{3y} \div \dfrac{4x}{5y^2}$

$\quad = \dfrac{\overset{x^2}{2x^3}}{3y}\cdot\dfrac{5y^2}{4x}$

$\quad = \dfrac{5x^2y}{6} \qquad (x, y \neq 0)$

b. $\dfrac{x^2 - 1}{x + 3} \div \dfrac{x^2 - x - 2}{x^2 + 5x + 6}$

$\quad = \dfrac{(x - 1)(x + 1)}{x + 3}\cdot\dfrac{(x + 3)(x + 2)}{(x + 1)(x - 2)}$

$\quad = \dfrac{(x - 1)(x + 2)}{(x - 2)}$

$\quad = \dfrac{x^2 + x - 2}{x - 2} \qquad (x \neq -3, -1, 2)$

As special cases of Property (2), observe that

$$a \div \frac{c}{d} = \frac{a}{1}\cdot\frac{d}{c} \qquad \frac{a}{b} \div c = \frac{a}{b}\cdot\frac{1}{c} \qquad 1 \div \frac{a}{b} = 1\cdot\frac{b}{a}$$

$$= \frac{ad}{c} \qquad\qquad = \frac{a}{bc} \qquad\qquad = \frac{b}{a}$$

EXAMPLE 5

a. $2x \div \dfrac{x}{y}$ **b.** $\dfrac{x}{y} \div 2x$ **c.** $1 \div \dfrac{x}{y}$

$= 2x \cdot \dfrac{y}{x}$ $= \dfrac{x}{y} \cdot \dfrac{1}{2x}$ $= 1 \cdot \dfrac{y}{x}$

$= 2y$ $= \dfrac{1}{2y}$ $= \dfrac{y}{x}$

$(x, y \neq 0)$ $(x, y \neq 0)$ $(x, y \neq 0)$

EXERCISE SET 4.5

▲ *Write each product as a single fraction in lowest terms. See Example 1.*

1. $\dfrac{16}{38} \cdot \dfrac{19}{12}$ **2.** $\dfrac{4}{15} \cdot \dfrac{3}{16}$ **3.** $\dfrac{21}{4} \cdot \dfrac{2}{15}$

4. $\dfrac{7}{8} \cdot \dfrac{48}{64}$ **5.** $\dfrac{24}{3} \cdot \dfrac{20}{36} \cdot \dfrac{3}{4}$ **6.** $\dfrac{3}{10} \cdot \dfrac{16}{27} \cdot \dfrac{30}{36}$

7. $\dfrac{7x}{12} \cdot \dfrac{3}{14x^2}$ **8.** $\dfrac{4a^2}{3} \cdot \dfrac{6b}{2a}$

9. $\dfrac{15n^2}{3p} \cdot \dfrac{5p^2}{n^3}$ **10.** $\dfrac{21t^2}{5s} \cdot \dfrac{15s^3}{7st}$

11. $\dfrac{-4}{3n} \cdot \dfrac{6n^2}{16}$ **12.** $\dfrac{14a^3b}{3b} \cdot \dfrac{-6}{7a^2}$

13. $\dfrac{1}{3}x^2 \cdot \dfrac{6}{7}x^3$ **14.** $\dfrac{2}{3}y \cdot \dfrac{9}{10}y^2$

15. $\dfrac{3}{4}x^2y \cdot \dfrac{2}{3}xy^2$ **16.** $\dfrac{1}{4}x^3y \cdot \dfrac{2}{5}xy$

17. $-\dfrac{1}{2}xyz^2 \cdot \dfrac{2}{3}x^2y$ **18.** $-\dfrac{3}{5}x^2y \cdot \dfrac{5}{6}xy^2z$

19. $\dfrac{-12a^2b}{5c} \cdot \dfrac{10b^2c}{24a^3b}$ **20.** $\dfrac{a^2}{xy} \cdot \dfrac{3x^3y}{4a}$

21. $\dfrac{-2ab}{7c} \cdot \dfrac{3c^2}{4a^3} \cdot \dfrac{-6a}{15b^2}$ **22.** $\dfrac{10x}{12y} \cdot \dfrac{3x^2z}{5x^3z} \cdot \dfrac{6y^2x}{3yz}$

23. $5a^2b^2 \cdot \dfrac{1}{a^3b^3}$ **24.** $15x^2y \cdot \dfrac{3}{45xy^2}$

▲ *See Example 2.*

25. $\dfrac{5x + 25}{2x} \cdot \dfrac{4x}{2x + 10}$ **26.** $\dfrac{3y}{4xy - 6y^2} \cdot \dfrac{2x - 3y}{12x}$

27. $\dfrac{4a^2 - 1}{a^2 - 16} \cdot \dfrac{a^2 - 4a}{2a + 1}$ **28.** $\dfrac{9x^2 - 25}{2x - 2} \cdot \dfrac{x^2 - 1}{6x - 10}$

29. $\dfrac{x^2 - x - 20}{x^2 + 7x + 12} \cdot \dfrac{(x + 3)^2}{(x - 5)^2}$

30. $\dfrac{4x^2 + 8x + 3}{2x^2 - 5x + 3} \cdot \dfrac{6x^2 - 9x}{1 - 4x^2}$

31. $\dfrac{x^2 - 6x + 5}{x^2 + 2x - 3} \cdot \dfrac{x^2 - 4x - 21}{x^2 - 10x + 25}$

32. $\dfrac{x^2 - x - 2}{x^2 + 4x + 3} \cdot \dfrac{x^2 - 4x - 5}{x^2 - 3x - 10}$

▲ *Write each product as a polynomial. See Example 3.*

33. $\dfrac{1}{2}x\left(\dfrac{2}{5}x - 6\right)$ **34.** $\dfrac{3}{4}y\left(\dfrac{1}{6}y + 8\right)$

35. $\left(x + \dfrac{1}{3}\right)\left(x + \dfrac{1}{3}\right)$ **36.** $\left(y - \dfrac{1}{3}\right)\left(y - \dfrac{1}{3}\right)$

37. $\left(y - \dfrac{1}{4}\right)^2$ **38.** $\left(y + \dfrac{1}{4}\right)^2$

▲ *Write each quotient as a single fraction in lowest terms. See Example 4.*

39. $\dfrac{3}{4} \div \dfrac{9}{16}$ **40.** $\dfrac{2}{3} \div \dfrac{9}{15}$

41. $\dfrac{xy}{a^2b} \div \dfrac{x^3y^2}{ab}$ **42.** $\dfrac{9ab^3}{x} \div \dfrac{3}{2x^3}$

43. $\dfrac{28x^2y^3}{a^2} \div \dfrac{21x^2y^2}{5a}$ **44.** $\dfrac{24a^3b}{x^2} \div \dfrac{3a^2b}{7x}$

45. $\dfrac{4x - 8}{3y} \div \dfrac{6x - 12}{y}$

46. $\dfrac{6y - 27}{5x} \div \dfrac{4y - 18}{x}$

47. $\dfrac{a^2 - a - 6}{a^2 + 2a - 15} \div \dfrac{a^2 - 4}{a^2 + 6a + 5}$

48. $\dfrac{a^2 + 2a - 15}{a^2 + 3a - 10} \div \dfrac{a^2 - 9}{a^2 - 9a + 14}$

▲ *See Example 5.*

49. $1 \div \dfrac{x^2 - 1}{x + 2}$

50. $1 \div \dfrac{x^2 + 3x + 1}{x - 2}$

51. $(x^2 - 5x + 4) \div \dfrac{x^2 - 1}{x^2}$

52. $(x^2 - 9) \div \dfrac{x^2 - 6x + 9}{3x}$

53. $\dfrac{x^2 + 3x}{2y} \div 3x$

54. $\dfrac{2y^2 + y}{3x} \div 2y$

Miscellaneous Exercises

▲ *Write as a single fraction in lowest terms.*

55. $\dfrac{x^3 + y^3}{x} \div \dfrac{x + y}{3x}$

56. $\dfrac{8x^3 - y^3}{x + y} \div \dfrac{2x - y}{x^2 - y^2}$

57. $\dfrac{xy - 3x + y - 3}{x - 2} \div \dfrac{x + 1}{x^2 - 4}$

58. $\dfrac{2xy + 4x + 3y + 6}{2x + 3} \div \dfrac{y + 2}{y - 1}$

59. $\dfrac{x^3 - 1}{x} \cdot \dfrac{x^2 - 1}{x^2 + x + 1} \div \dfrac{(x - 1)^3}{x}$

60. $\dfrac{x}{x^3 - 8} \div \dfrac{1}{x^2 + 2x + 4} \cdot \dfrac{(x - 2)^2}{2x}$

▲ *Find each missing expression.* [*Hint: Construct a simple model first.*]

61. $\dfrac{x - 1}{x + 2}(?) = \dfrac{4x^2 - 4}{(x + 2)^2}$

62. $(?)\dfrac{(x^2 - 9)}{x + 1} = \dfrac{3x - 9}{x^2 + 5x + 4}$

63. $(?) \div \dfrac{x^3 - y^3}{2y^3} = \dfrac{y^2}{x - y}$

64. $(?) \div \dfrac{x^3 + y^3}{4x} = \dfrac{x}{2(x + y)}$

65. $\dfrac{(a - 1)^2}{a} \div (?) = \dfrac{2a - 2}{3a}$

66. $\dfrac{4a}{(a + 1)^2} \div (?) = \dfrac{a}{3a + 3}$

4.6   COMPLEX FRACTIONS

A fraction that contains one or more fractions in either its numerator or denominator or both is called a complex fraction. For example,

$$\dfrac{\dfrac{2}{3}}{\dfrac{1}{6}} \quad \text{and} \quad \dfrac{x + \dfrac{3}{4}}{x - \dfrac{1}{2}}$$

are complex fractions. Like simple fractions, complex fractions represent quotients. For example,

$$\dfrac{\dfrac{2}{3}}{\dfrac{5}{6}} = \dfrac{2}{3} \div \dfrac{5}{6} \quad \textbf{(1)} \quad \text{and} \quad \dfrac{x + \dfrac{3}{4}}{x - \dfrac{1}{2}} = \left(x + \dfrac{3}{4}\right) \div \left(x - \dfrac{1}{2}\right) \quad \textbf{(2)}$$

In cases like fraction (1), in which the denominator of the complex fraction does not contain sums or differences, we can simply multiply the numerator by the reciprocal of the denominator.

EXAMPLE 1 **a.** $\dfrac{\frac{2}{3}}{\frac{5}{6}} = \dfrac{2}{3} \div \dfrac{5}{6}$ **b.** $\dfrac{\frac{x}{8}}{\frac{y}{4}} = \dfrac{x}{8} \div \dfrac{y}{4}$

$$= \frac{2}{\cancel{3}} \cdot \frac{\cancel{6}}{5} = \frac{4}{5}$$

$$= \frac{x}{\cancel{8}} \cdot \frac{\cancel{4}}{y} = \frac{x}{2y}$$

In a complex fraction like fraction (2), in which the numerator or denominator contains sums or differences, we can use the fundamental principle of fractions to simplify the fractions. In fact, we can also use the fundamental principle of fractions to simplify complex fractions of form (1). In both cases, we multiply the numerator and denominator of the complex fraction by the LCD of all the simple fractions involved in both numerator and denominator.

EXAMPLE 2 Simplify $\dfrac{\frac{2}{3}}{\frac{5}{6}}$ by using the fundamental principle of fractions.

Solution Multiplying the numerator $\frac{2}{3}$ and the denominator $\frac{5}{6}$ by 6, the LCD of the two small fractions in the larger one, we obtain

$$\frac{\frac{2}{3}}{\frac{5}{6}} = \frac{\frac{2}{\cancel{3}}(\cancel{6})}{\frac{5}{\cancel{6}}(\cancel{6})} = \frac{4}{5}$$

a simple fraction equivalent to the original fraction.

EXAMPLE 3 Simplify $\dfrac{x + \frac{3}{4}}{x - \frac{1}{2}}$ [the fraction in (2) on page 96]

Solution Multiplying the numerator and denominator by 4, the LCD of the fractions $\frac{3}{4}$ and $\frac{1}{2}$, we obtain

$$\frac{4\left(x + \frac{3}{4}\right)}{4\left(x - \frac{1}{2}\right)} = \frac{4(x) + 4\left(\frac{3}{4}\right)}{4(x) - 4\left(\frac{1}{2}\right)} = \frac{4x + 3}{4x - 2} \quad \left(x \neq \frac{1}{2}\right)$$

Sometimes it is difficult to use the fundamental principle directly to simplify a complex fraction. In such cases we can simplify the fraction in small steps.

EXAMPLE 4

Simplify

$$\frac{a}{a + \dfrac{3}{3 + \dfrac{1}{2}}}$$

Solution

We can first simplify part of the complex fraction:

$$\frac{3}{3 + \dfrac{1}{2}} = \frac{(3) \cdot 2}{\left(3 + \dfrac{1}{2}\right) \cdot 2} = \frac{6}{6 + 1} = \frac{6}{7}$$

Then substituting $\frac{6}{7}$ and applying the fundamental principle of fractions again, we have

$$\frac{a}{a + \dfrac{6}{7}} = \frac{(a) \cdot 7}{\left(a + \dfrac{6}{7}\right) \cdot 7} = \frac{7a}{7a + 6}$$

‖ E X E R C I S E   S E T   4.6

▲ *Write each complex fraction as a single fraction in lowest terms. See Examples 1 and 2.*

1. $\dfrac{\dfrac{3}{7}}{\dfrac{2}{7}}$

2. $\dfrac{\dfrac{4}{5}}{\dfrac{7}{5}}$

3. $\dfrac{\dfrac{2}{9}}{\dfrac{7}{3}}$

4. $\dfrac{\dfrac{5}{2}}{\dfrac{21}{4}}$

5. $\dfrac{\dfrac{b}{c}}{\dfrac{b^2}{a}}$

6. $\dfrac{\dfrac{5x}{6y}}{\dfrac{4x}{5y}}$

7. $\dfrac{\dfrac{2x}{5y}}{\dfrac{3x}{10y^2}}$

8. $\dfrac{\dfrac{3ab}{4}}{\dfrac{3b}{8a^2}}$

9. $\dfrac{\dfrac{3}{4}}{4 - \dfrac{1}{4}}$

10. $\dfrac{\dfrac{1}{3}}{4 + \dfrac{2}{3}}$

11. $\dfrac{1 - \dfrac{2}{3}}{3 + \dfrac{1}{3}}$

12. $\dfrac{\dfrac{1}{2} + \dfrac{3}{4}}{\dfrac{1}{2} - \dfrac{3}{4}}$

13. $\dfrac{\dfrac{2}{3}}{\dfrac{1}{3} + \dfrac{3}{4}}$

14. $\dfrac{\dfrac{1}{4}}{\dfrac{2}{3} + \dfrac{1}{2}}$

15. $\dfrac{\dfrac{1}{5} + \dfrac{1}{6}}{\dfrac{1}{2} + \dfrac{2}{3}}$

16. $\dfrac{\dfrac{3}{4} + \dfrac{1}{3}}{\dfrac{1}{2} + \dfrac{5}{6}}$

17. $\dfrac{\dfrac{2}{a} + \dfrac{3}{2a}}{5 + \dfrac{1}{a}}$

18. $\dfrac{1 + \dfrac{2}{a}}{1 - \dfrac{4}{a^2}}$

19. $\dfrac{x + \dfrac{x}{y}}{1 + \dfrac{1}{y}}$

20. $\dfrac{1 + \dfrac{1}{x}}{1 - \dfrac{1}{x}}$

21. $\dfrac{1}{1 - \dfrac{1}{x}}$

22. $\dfrac{4}{\dfrac{2}{x} + 2}$

23. $\dfrac{y - 2}{y - \dfrac{4}{y}}$

24. $\dfrac{y + 3}{\dfrac{9}{y} - y}$

25. $\dfrac{\dfrac{1}{y + 1}}{1 - \dfrac{1}{y^2}}$

26. $\dfrac{\dfrac{1}{y - 1}}{\dfrac{1}{y^2} + 1}$

27. $\dfrac{x - \dfrac{x}{y}}{y + \dfrac{y}{x}}$

28. $\dfrac{y + \dfrac{x}{y}}{x - \dfrac{y}{x}}$

▲ *Write each complex fraction as a single fraction in lowest terms. See Example 4.*

29. $\dfrac{1 + \dfrac{1}{1 - \dfrac{a}{b}}}{1 - \dfrac{3}{1 - \dfrac{a}{b}}}$

30. $\dfrac{1 - \dfrac{1}{\dfrac{a}{b} + 2}}{1 + \dfrac{3}{\dfrac{a}{2b} + 1}}$

31. $\dfrac{a + 2 - \dfrac{12}{a + 3}}{a - 5 + \dfrac{16}{a + 3}}$

32. $\dfrac{a + 4 - \dfrac{7}{a - 2}}{a - 1 + \dfrac{2}{a - 2}}$

33. $\dfrac{\dfrac{1}{ab} + \dfrac{2}{bc} + \dfrac{3}{ac}}{\dfrac{2a + 3b + c}{abc}}$

34. $\dfrac{\dfrac{a}{bc} - \dfrac{b}{ac} + \dfrac{c}{ab}}{\dfrac{1}{a^2b^2} - \dfrac{1}{a^2c^2} + \dfrac{1}{b^2c^2}}$

Miscellaneous Exercises

▲ *Write each quotient as a complex fraction and then as a single fraction in lowest terms.*

35. $\left(\dfrac{1}{y^2} - \dfrac{1}{4}\right) \div \left(\dfrac{1}{y} + \dfrac{1}{2}\right)$

36. $\left(\dfrac{4}{y} - \dfrac{1}{3}\right) \div \left(\dfrac{16}{y^2} - \dfrac{1}{9}\right)$

37. $\left(\dfrac{9}{y^2} - 1\right) \div \left(\dfrac{3}{y} + 1\right)$

38. $\left(1 + \dfrac{1}{y^3}\right) \div \left(1 + \dfrac{1}{y}\right)$

▲ *Show that each pair of expressions is equivalent, given that $c^2 + s^2 = 1$. Assume that the variables represent numbers for which each expression is defined. [Hint: Simplify the first expression.]*

39. $\dfrac{\dfrac{(c + s)^2}{c - s} - \dfrac{1}{c - s}}{2cs}; \quad \dfrac{1}{c - s}$

40. $\dfrac{\dfrac{s}{s} - \dfrac{2sc}{s + c}}{\dfrac{s}{s + c}}; \quad \dfrac{1}{s + c}$

41. $\dfrac{\dfrac{1}{s - c}}{\dfrac{s}{s^2 - c^2}} + \dfrac{s - c}{s}; \quad 2$

42. $\dfrac{\dfrac{1}{s^2} + \dfrac{1}{c^2}}{\dfrac{1}{s \cdot c}} - \dfrac{c}{s}; \quad \dfrac{s}{c}$

4.7 **SOLUTION OF EQUATIONS**

The properties used in previous chapters to solve equations can also be used to solve equations that contain fractions.

Very often, it is helpful to begin by finding an equivalent equation without fractions. We can do this by multiplying each side of the equation by the LCD of the fractions involved.

EXAMPLE 1   Solve $\dfrac{x}{3} + 2 = \dfrac{x}{2}$.

Solution   We first multiply each number by **6**, the LCM of the denominators 3 and 2, to generate an equivalent equation free of fractions and obtain

$$6\left(\dfrac{x}{3} + 2\right) = 6\left(\dfrac{x}{2}\right)$$
$$2x + 12 = 3x$$

Now adding $-2x$ to each member, we obtain

$$2x + 12 + (-2x) = 3x + (-2x)$$
$$12 = x$$

Hence, the solution set is $\{12\}$.

Multiplying by Zero

Care must be exercised in an application of the multiplication property, for we have specifically excluded *multiplication by* 0. For example, the equation $x = 3$, whose solution set is $\{3\}$, is not equivalent to $0 \cdot x = 0 \cdot 3$, which is true for *all* real numbers.

EXAMPLE 2

Solve $\dfrac{x}{x-3} = \dfrac{3}{x-3} + 2.$ $\qquad\qquad$ **(1)**

Solution

We first multiply each member by $(x - 3)$ to attempt to produce an equivalent equation that is free of fractions. We have

$$(x-3)\frac{x}{x-3} = (x-3)\frac{3}{x-3} + (x-3)2$$

$$x = 3 + 2x - 6 \qquad\qquad \textbf{(2)}$$

from which

$$x = 3$$

and 3 *appears* to be a solution of (1). But, upon substituting 3 for x in (1), we have

$$\frac{3}{0} = \frac{3}{0} + 2$$

where neither member is defined. In obtaining Equation (2), each member of Equation (1) was multiplied by $(x - 3)$. But if x is 3, then $(x - 3)$ is 0, and Equation (2) is not equivalent to Equation (1). Equation (1) has no solution. Its solution set is $\varnothing$.

Multiplying both sides of an equation by an algebraic expression may introduce "extraneous solutions" such as $x = 3$ above. Therefore, when solving an equation by multiplying both sides by an algebraic expression, always check to eliminate extraneous solutions. Multiplying both sides of an equation by a constant does not introduce an extraneous solution. In this case the resulting equation is equivalent to the original equation and a check is not necessary.

We shall dispense with checking solutions in the examples that follow *except in cases in which we multiply or divide by an expression containing a variable.*

Proportions

A **proportion** is the equality of two fractions. The proportion $\dfrac{a}{b} = \dfrac{c}{d}$ can be read "*a* is to *b* as *c* is to *d*." The numbers *a*, *b*, *c*, and *d* are called the first, second, third, and fourth **terms** of the proportion, respectively. The first and fourth terms are called the **extremes** of the proportion, and the second and third terms are called the **means** of the proportion:

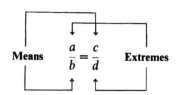

Means $\qquad \dfrac{a}{b} = \dfrac{c}{d} \qquad$ Extremes

If each member of the proportion is multiplied by *bd*, we have

$$(\cancel{b}d)\frac{a}{\cancel{b}} = (b\cancel{d})\frac{c}{\cancel{d}}$$

$$ad = bc$$

Thus,

$$\textbf{If} \quad \frac{a}{b} = \frac{c}{d}, \quad \textbf{then} \quad ad = bc \tag{3}$$

In any proportion the product of the extremes is equal to the product of the means.

This property provides a "shortcut" way to solve an equation that is a proportion. When using this property, we say that we have "cross-multiplied" to obtain *ad = bc* in (3).

EXAMPLE 3   Solve $\dfrac{x+6}{3} = \dfrac{x+1}{2}$.

Solution   Using Property (3), we set the product of the extremes equal to the product of the means to obtain

$$2(x + 6) = 3(x + 1)$$

from which

$$2x + 12 = 3x + 3$$
$$9 = x$$

Hence, the solution set is {9}. *Note:* We would of course obtain the same result if we had multiplied each member of the original equation by the LCD, 6.

COMMON ERROR   *Property (3) can be used only in solving a proportion. It is not applicable for other kinds of fractional equations. For example, equations such as*

$$\frac{x}{3} + 2 = \frac{x}{2} \quad and \quad \frac{x+2}{3} = \frac{x}{2} - 5 \quad \underset{\text{fraction}}{\overset{\text{Not a single}}{}}$$

are not proportions and Property (3) cannot be used. These equations can be solved by using the general method of first multiplying each member by the least common denominator as shown in Example 1.

All the equations that we solved in the preceding examples were first-degree equations. The fractional equation in the next example is quadratic. After we obtain an equivalent equation without fractions, we use the procedure we followed in Section 3.5 to complete the solution.

EXAMPLE 4 | Solve $x^2 - \dfrac{17}{3}x = 2$.

Solution | Write in standard form.

$$x^2 - \frac{17}{3}x - 2 = 0$$

Multiply each side by **3** and simplify.

$$3(x^2) - 3\left(\frac{17}{3}x\right) - 3(2) = 3(0)$$
$$3x^2 - 17x - 6 = 0$$

Factor the left-hand side.

$$(3x + 1)(x - 6) = 0$$

Set each factor equal to 0 and solve the equations.

$$3x + 1 = 0 \quad \text{or} \quad x - 6 = 0$$
$$x = -\frac{1}{3} \qquad\qquad x = 6$$

The solution set is $\{-\frac{1}{3}, 6\}$.

Solving for Specified Variables

The suggestions given in Section 2.3 for solving an equation for a specified variable in terms of other variables also apply to equations that contain fractions. In such an equation it usually is helpful to write the equation as an equivalent equation without fractions first.

EXAMPLE 5 | Temperature is commonly measured in Fahrenheit (F) or Celsius (C) units. These units are related by the formula $F = \dfrac{9}{5}C + 32$. Solve for C.

Solution | Multiply each side by **5**.

$$5(F) = 5\left(\frac{9}{5}C + 32\right)$$
$$5F = 9C + 160$$

Add -160 to each side:

$$5F - 160 = 9C + 160 - 160$$
$$5F - 160 = 9C$$

Multiply each side by $\frac{1}{9}$ (or divide by **9**):

$$\frac{5F - 160}{9} = \frac{9C}{9}$$
$$C = \frac{5F - 160}{9}$$

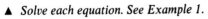

EXERCISE SET 4.7

▲ *Solve each equation. See Example 1.*

1. $7 + \dfrac{5x}{3} = x - 2$

2. $x + 4 = \dfrac{2}{5}x - 3$

3. $1 + \dfrac{x}{9} = \dfrac{4}{3}$

4. $4 + \dfrac{x}{5} = \dfrac{5}{3}$

5. $\dfrac{1}{5}x - \dfrac{1}{2}x = 9$

6. $\dfrac{1}{4}x = 2 - \dfrac{1}{3}x$

7. $\dfrac{2x - 1}{5} - \dfrac{x + 1}{2} = 0$

8. $\dfrac{2x}{3} - \dfrac{2x + 5}{6} = \dfrac{1}{2}$

▲ *Solve each equation. See Example 2.*

9. $\dfrac{x}{x - 2} = \dfrac{2}{x - 2} + 7$

10. $\dfrac{x}{x - 3} + \dfrac{9}{x + 3} = 1$

11. $\dfrac{2}{y + 1} + \dfrac{1}{3y + 3} = \dfrac{1}{6}$

12. $\dfrac{5}{x - 3} = \dfrac{x + 2}{x - 3} + 3$

13. $\dfrac{4}{2x - 3} + \dfrac{4x}{4x^2 - 9} = \dfrac{1}{2x + 3}$

14. $\dfrac{y}{y + 2} - \dfrac{3}{y - 2} = \dfrac{y^2 + 8}{y^2 - 4}$

▲ *Solve each proportion. See Examples 1 and 3.*

15. $\dfrac{2}{3} = \dfrac{x}{x + 2}$

16. $\dfrac{7}{5} = \dfrac{x}{x - 2}$

17. $\dfrac{y + 3}{y + 5} = \dfrac{1}{3}$

18. $\dfrac{y}{6 - y} = \dfrac{1}{2}$

19. $\dfrac{3}{4} = \dfrac{y + 2}{12 - y}$

20. $\dfrac{-3}{4} = \dfrac{y - 7}{y + 14}$

21. $\dfrac{50}{r} = \dfrac{75}{r + 20}$

22. $\dfrac{30}{r} = \dfrac{20}{r - 10}$

▲ *Solve each equation. See Example 4.*

23. $\dfrac{2x^2}{3} + \dfrac{x}{3} - 2 = 0$

24. $2x - \dfrac{5}{3} = \dfrac{x^2}{3}$

25. $\dfrac{x^2}{6} + \dfrac{x}{3} = \dfrac{1}{2}$

26. $\dfrac{x}{4} - \dfrac{3}{4} = \dfrac{1}{x}$

27. $3 = \dfrac{10}{x^2} - \dfrac{7}{x}$

28. $\dfrac{4}{3x} + \dfrac{3}{3x + 1} + 2 = 0$

▲ *Solve each formula for the specified variable. See Example 5.*

29. $S = \dfrac{a}{1 - r}$, for r

30. $A = \dfrac{h}{2}(b + c)$, for c

31. $\dfrac{1}{r} = \dfrac{1}{s} + \dfrac{2}{t}$, for t

32. $S = \dfrac{n}{2}(a + s_n)$, for s_n

33. $V = C\left(1 - \dfrac{t}{15}\right)$, for t

34. $\dfrac{1}{R_n} = \dfrac{1}{R_1} + \dfrac{1}{R_2} + \dfrac{1}{R_3}$, for R_3

35. $B = \dfrac{2}{5}w\left(1 + \dfrac{2n}{100}\right)$, for n

36. $C = \dfrac{5F - 160}{9}$ and $K = C + 273$, for F in terms of K

Miscellaneous Exercises

▲ *Solve.*

37. The normal weight w, in pounds, of a male between 60 and 70 inches tall is related to his height h, in inches, by

$$w = \dfrac{11}{2}h - 220$$

What should be the height of a boy who weighs 143 pounds?

38. Celsius (C) and Fahrenheit (F) temperatures are related by

$$F = \dfrac{9}{5}C + 32$$

What is the Celsius temperature when the Fahrenheit temperature is $-40°$?

39. The pressure p, in pounds per square inch, is related to the depth d, in feet below the surface of an ocean, by

$$p = \dfrac{5}{11}d + 15$$

At what depth is the pressure 75 pounds per square inch?

40. The horsepower (H) generated by water flowing over a dam of height s, in feet, is given by

$$H = \dfrac{62.4N \cdot s}{33,000}$$

where N is the number of cubic feet of water flowing over the dam per minute. Find the number of cubic feet of water that flowed over a 165-foot dam if 468 hp were generated.

41. The net resistance R_n of an electrical circuit is given by

$$\dfrac{1}{R_n} = \dfrac{1}{R_1} + \dfrac{1}{R_2}$$

where R_1 and R_2* are individual resistors in parallel. If one of the individual resistors is 40 ohms, what must the other be if the net resistance is 30 ohms?

42. The net resistance R_n of an electrical circuit containing resistors R_1, R_2, and R_3* in parallel is given by

$$\frac{1}{R_n} = \frac{1}{R_1} + \frac{1}{R_2} + \frac{1}{R_3}$$

If two of the individual resistors are 20 ohms and 40 ohms, what must the third resistor be if the net resistance is 10 ohms?

43. A manufacturer plans to depreciate a large lathe that cost $12,000. The value V in t years is given by the formula

$$V = C\left(1 - \frac{t}{15}\right)$$

where C is the original cost. In how many years will the value be $5,000? In how many years will the lathe be completely depreciated?

44. The force F necessary to raise a weight w using a special pulley system is given by

$$F = \frac{w}{2}\left(\frac{D_1 - D_2}{D_1}\right)$$

Find the weight that can be lifted by using a force of 45 pounds, where $D_1 = 25$ and $D_2 = 22$.

45. Three units are normally used as a measure of temperature, namely, Celsius (C), Fahrenheit (F), and Kelvin (K). These units are related by the formulas

$$C = \frac{5F - 160}{9} \quad \text{and} \quad K = C + 273$$

What Fahrenheit temperature corresponds to a temperature of 290° Kelvin?

46. Use the formulas in Problem 45 to find the Kelvin temperature that corresponds to a temperature of 98.6° Fahrenheit.

47. The number of diagonals, D, of a polygon of n sides is given by

$$D = \frac{n}{2}(n - 3)$$

How many sides does a polygon with 90 diagonals have?

48. The formula

$$s = \frac{n}{2}(n + 1)$$

gives the sum of the first n natural numbers $1, 2, 3, \ldots$. How many consecutive natural numbers starting with 1 will give a sum of 406?

4.8 | APPLICATIONS

Suggestions were made in Section 2.4 on how to solve word problems involving polynomials. In this section we consider problems in which the equations that we obtain involve fractions.

Proportions   Proportions are widely used as mathematical models in the solution of word problems involving the ratio of two quantities.

E X A M P L E 1   Rick's car uses 8 gallons of gas to travel 140 miles. Under the same driving conditions, how many gallons will be required for a trip of 450 miles?

Solution

Step 1 ⟶   ⌐Step 2
Gallons of gas needed for 450 miles: x

Set up a ratio between gallons of gas and miles, using the given values, and set up a second ratio using the unknown quantity. Make sure that you use the same quantity (gallons in this case) in the numerator of each ratio. The two ratios can then be equated.

---

*The subscripts 1, 2, and 3 used in R_1, R_2, and R_3 in the equations are read "R sub one," "R sub two," and "R sub three."

Step 3

$$\frac{8 \text{ gallons}}{140 \text{ miles}} = \frac{x \text{ gallons}}{450 \text{ miles}}$$

Step 4 Solve the proportion by cross multiplying.

$$8(450) = 140x$$

$$x = \frac{8(450)}{140} \approx 25.7$$

Step 5 Hence, approximately 25.7 gallons of gas are needed to travel 450 miles.

Similar Triangles

One application of proportion that occurs frequently involves a special property of triangles.

   If two triangles have the *same shape* but are not necessarily the same size, that is, if their corresponding angles are equal, then the triangles are called **similar triangles**. Thus, in Figure 4.1, if $\angle A = \angle A'$, $\angle B = \angle B'$, and $\angle C = \angle C'$, the triangles are similar.

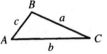

Figure 4.1

   Because the sum of the angles in any triangle is 180°, it follows that if any two corresponding angles are equal, then the third angles are equal and the triangles are similar.

   In geometry, it is shown that lengths of corresponding sides of similar triangles are proportional. From Figure 4.1, because the triangles are similar, we know that

$$\frac{a}{a'} = \frac{b}{b'} = \frac{c}{c'}$$

EXAMPLE 2

For the triangles in Figure 4.1, find the length of b' to the nearest tenth, given that $a' = 12$ cm, $a = 4.5$ cm, and $b = 6.2$ cm.

Solution

Since the triangles are similar, the sides are proportional and

$$\frac{4.5}{12} = \frac{6.2}{b'}$$

Hence, by cross multiplying, we get

$$4.5(b') = 12(6.2)$$

from which

$$b' = \frac{12(6.2)}{4.5} \approx 16.533\ldots$$

Hence, to the nearest tenth, side $b' = 16.5$ centimeters.

EXAMPLE 3 A 6-foot man standing 18 feet from a streetlight pole casts an 8-foot shadow. Find the height of the light pole.

Solution

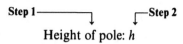

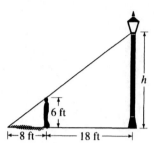

Height of pole: h

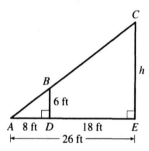

In this case a sketch of the geometric conditions is particularly helpful. Note that $\angle A$ is common to triangles ABD and ACE. Note also that each triangle has a 90° angle. Since two angles of triangle ABD equal two angles of triangle ACE, the triangles are similar and their sides are proportional.

Step 3 Set up a proportion involving the variable h.

$$\frac{h}{6} = \frac{26}{8}$$

Step 4 Solve the proportion. First cross multiply.

$$8h = 6 \cdot 26$$

$$h = \frac{6 \cdot 26}{8} = 19.5$$

Step 5 Hence, the height of the light pole is 19.5 feet.

Uniform-Motion Problems

Recall that the distance traveled at a uniform rate is equal to the product of the rate and the time traveled. This relationship may be expressed by any one of the three equations

$$d = rt, \qquad r = \frac{d}{t}, \qquad t = \frac{d}{r}$$

Using a table and a figure to solve these problems is frequently helpful.

EXAMPLE 4   An express train travels 150 miles in the same time that a freight train travels 100 miles. If the express goes 20 miles per hour faster than the freight, find the rate of each.

Solution

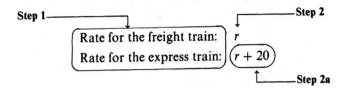

Step 1 ─────────┐   ┌─────── Step 2

Rate for the freight train: r

Rate for the express train: $r + 20$

└───── Step 2a

Step 3   Construct a mathematical model. A table and/or a figure can be helpful.

	d	r	$t = d/r$
Freight	100	r	$\dfrac{100}{r}$
Express	150	$r + 20$	$\dfrac{150}{r + 20}$

Freight $d = 100$ rate: r

Express $d = 150$ rate: $r + 20$

The fact that the times are the same provides the significant equality in the problem.

$$[t \text{ freight}] = [t \text{ express}]$$

$$\frac{100}{r} = \frac{150}{r + 20}$$

Step 4   Solve the equation. Because the equation is a proportion, set the product of the extremes equal to the product of the means.

$$100(r + 20) = 150(r)$$
$$100r + 2000 = 150r$$
$$-50r = -2000$$
$$r = 40$$
$$r + 20 = 60$$

Step 5   Thus, the freight train's rate is 40 miles per hour, and the express train's rate is 60 miles per hour.

E X E R C I S E   S E T   4.8

▲ *Solve each problem. See Example 1.*

1.   A mason can lay 450 bricks in 3 hours. At the same rate, how many bricks can he lay in a 40-hour week?

2.   An automobile uses 6 gallons of gasoline to travel 102 miles. How many gallons are required to make a trip of 459 miles?

3.   If 2.5 pounds of tin are required to make 12 pounds of a certain alloy, how many pounds of tin are needed to make 90 pounds of the alloy?

4.   A man walks approximately 6.4 miles in 2 hours. At the same rate, how far can he walk in 5 hours?

5.   It takes 3 hours to address 144 envelopes. At the same rate, how many envelopes can be addressed in 5 hours?

6.   If $\frac{3}{4}$ of a centimeter on a map represents 10 kilometers, how many kilometers does 9 centimeters represent?

▲ *In Exercises 7–10, the lengths of certain sides of*
triangles are given. In each case, find the missing
lengths. See Examples 2 and 3.

7. Given: Triangle *ABC* is similar to triangle *DEF*.

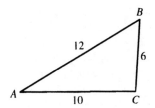

8. Given: Triangle *PQR* is similar to triangle *P'Q'R'*.

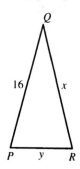 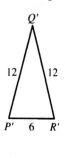

9. Given: ∠*ACB* = ∠*AED*.

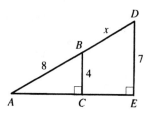

10. Given: ∠*BCA* = ∠*DEA*.

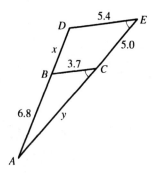

11. A 6′ 6″ tall man standing next to his elm tree casts a
shadow of 14.2 feet, and the tree casts a shadow of
39.4 feet. How tall is the tree?

12. A surveyor set up two markers on either side of a
small lake and made the measurements shown in the
figure so that similar triangles would be formed. Find
the distance across the lake to the nearest tenth of a
mile.

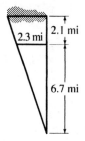

▲ *Solve. See Example 4.*

13. An airplane travels 1260 miles in the same time that
an automobile travels 420 miles. If the rate of the
airplane is 120 miles per hour greater than the rate of
the automobile, find the rate of each.

14. Two planes leave an airport at the same time and
travel in opposite directions. If one plane averages
440 miles per hour over the ground and the other
averages 560 miles per hour, in how long will they be
2500 miles apart?

15. A ship traveling at 20 knots is 5 nautical miles out
from a harbor when another ship leaves the harbor
at 30 knots sailing on the same course. How long
does it take the second ship to catch up to the first?

16. A boat sails due west from a harbor at 36 knots. An
hour later, another boat leaves the harbor on the
same course at 45 knots. How far out at sea will the
second boat overtake the first?

17. A woman drives 120 miles in the same time that a
man drives 80 miles. If the speed of the woman is
20 miles per hour greater than the speed of the man,
find the speed of each.

18. Two men drive from town A to town B, a distance of
400 miles. If one man drives twice as fast as the other
and arrives at town B 5 hours ahead of the other,
how fast was each driving?

19. A riverboat that travels at 18 miles per hour in still
water can go 30 miles up a river in 1 hour less time
than it can go 63 miles down the river. What is the
speed of the current in the river?

20. If a boat travels 20 miles per hour in still water and
takes 3 hours longer to go 90 miles up a river than it
does to go 75 miles down the river, what is the speed
of the current in the river?

Miscellaneous Exercises

21. A recipe for applesauce bread calls for $1\frac{1}{2}$ cups of flour and $\frac{1}{3}$ cup of honey. How much honey should be used if the flour is increased to $2\frac{1}{2}$ cups?

22. The instructions for planting an azalea call for $\frac{3}{4}$ pound of peat moss mixed with $1\frac{1}{3}$ pounds of nitrohumus. How many pounds of nitrohumus will you need to make azalea mix with a 7-pound bag of peat moss?

23. A secretary earns $6200 in 20 weeks. At the same rate of earnings, how much would she earn in one year (52 weeks)?

24. A typist can type 200 words in 5 minutes. Typing at the same rate, how long would it take this typist to type 10 pages of a manuscript that averages 240 words per page?

25. A commuter takes a train 10 miles to his job in a city. The train returns him home at a rate 10 miles per hour greater than the rate of the train that takes him to work. If he spends a total of 50 minutes a day commuting, what is the rate of each train?

26. On a 50-mile trip, a woman traveled 10 miles in heavy traffic and then 40 miles in less congested traffic. If her average rate in heavy traffic was 20 miles per hour less than her average rate in light traffic, what was each rate if the trip took 1 hour and 30 minutes?

CHAPTER SUMMARY

[4.1] A **fraction** is an expression that denotes a quotient. If the numerator and denominator are polynomials, then the fraction is a **rational expression**. The **fundamental principle of fractions** states:

▲ *If the numerator and the denominator of a fraction are multiplied or divided by the same nonzero number, the result is a fraction **equivalent** to the given fraction.*

$$\frac{a}{b} = \frac{ac}{bc} \quad (b, c \neq 0)$$

For a given fraction the replacement of any two of the three elements of the fraction—the fraction itself, the numerator, the denominator—by their opposites results in an equivalent fraction.

$$\frac{a}{b} = \frac{-a}{-b} = -\frac{a}{-b} = -\frac{-a}{b} \quad (b \neq 0)$$

$$\frac{-a}{b} = \frac{a}{-b} = -\frac{a}{b} = -\frac{-a}{-b} \quad (b \neq 0)$$

Standard forms for fractions are $\frac{a}{b}$ and $\frac{-a}{b}$.

A fraction is in **lowest terms** if the numerator and the denominator do not contain factors in common. We can reduce a fraction to lowest terms by using the fundamental principle of fractions to divide the numerator and the denominator by their common nonzero factors.

[4.2] Some quotients of polynomials can be rewritten as equivalent **mixed expressions**. A method similar to the long division process used in arithmetic can be used for this purpose.

[4.3] The **least common denominator (LCD)** of a set of fractions with natural-number denominators is the smallest natural number that is exactly divisible by each of the denominators.

[4.4] The operations of addition and subtraction of fractions are governed by the following properties:

$$\frac{a}{c} + \frac{b}{c} = \frac{a+b}{c} \quad \text{and} \quad \frac{a}{c} - \frac{b}{c} = \frac{a-b}{c} \quad (c \neq 0)$$

If the fractions in a sum or difference have unlike denominators, we can build each fraction to higher terms by using the fundamental principle of fractions in order to obtain fractions with a common denominator.

[4.5] The operations of multiplication and division of fractions are governed by the following properties:

$$\frac{a}{b} \cdot \frac{c}{d} = \frac{ac}{bd} \quad (b, d \neq 0) \quad \text{and} \quad \frac{a}{b} \div \frac{c}{d} = \frac{a}{b} \cdot \frac{d}{c} \quad (b, c, d \neq 0)$$

[4.6] A **complex fraction** is a fraction containing other fractions in its numerator or denominator or both. It is often convenient to use the fundamental principle to simplify such fractions.

[4.7–4.8] Equations that contain fractions can be solved by using the properties introduced in previous chapters.

A **proportion** is a special type of equation of the form $\frac{a}{b} = \frac{c}{d}$. In such equations the product of the extremes a and d equals the product of the means b and c. Thus, $ad = bc$.

▌▌▌ R E V I E W   E X E R C I S E S

▲ *Assume that no denominator is 0.*

[4.1]

1. **a.** Write six fractions equal to $\dfrac{1}{a-b}$ by changing the sign or signs of the numerator, the denominator, or the fraction itself.

    b. What are the conditions on a and b for the fraction in part a to represent a positive number? A negative number?

2. Express $-\dfrac{1}{1-a}$ in standard form in two ways.

▲ *Reduce each fraction to lowest terms.*

3. **a.** $\dfrac{4x^2 y^3}{10xy^4}$ **b.** $\dfrac{2x^2 - 8}{2x + 4}$

4. **a.** $\dfrac{4x^2 - 1}{1 - 2x}$ **b.** $\dfrac{x^2 - y^2}{2y^2 - 2x^2}$

[4.2]

▲ *Divide.*

5. **a.** $\dfrac{12x^2 - 6x + 3}{2x}$ **b.** $\dfrac{6y^3 + 3y^2 - y}{3y^2}$

6. **a.** $\dfrac{2y^2 - 3y + 1}{2y + 3}$ **b.** $\dfrac{6x^4 - 3x^3 + 2x + 2}{x - 1}$

7.   a. $\dfrac{x^3 - x + 1}{x - 1}$ b. $\dfrac{2x^4 - x^2 - 2}{x + 1}$

8.   a. $\dfrac{x^4 - 1}{x - 1}$ b. $\dfrac{x^5 - 1}{x - 1}$

[4.2]

▲ *Express each given fraction as an equivalent fraction with the given denominator.*

9.   a. $\dfrac{-3}{4} = \dfrac{?}{24}$ b. $\dfrac{x}{2y} = \dfrac{?}{2xy^2}$

10.   a. $\dfrac{2}{x + 3y} = \dfrac{?}{x^2 - 9y^2}$ b. $\dfrac{y}{3 - y} = \dfrac{?}{y^2 - 4y + 3}$

▲ *Write each expression in Exercises 11–30 as a single fraction in lowest terms.*

[4.4]

11.   a. $\dfrac{3x + y}{3} + \dfrac{x - y}{3}$ b. $\dfrac{x - 2y}{4x} - \dfrac{2x - y}{4x}$

12.   a. $\dfrac{2}{5x} - \dfrac{3}{4y} + \dfrac{7}{20xy}$ b. $\dfrac{y}{2y - 6} + \dfrac{2}{3y - 9}$

13.   a. $\dfrac{5}{x - 2} - \dfrac{3}{x + 3}$ b. $\dfrac{1}{x + 2y} + \dfrac{3}{x^2 - 4y^2}$

14.   a. $\dfrac{2}{x^2 - 1} + \dfrac{3}{x^2 - 2x + 1}$ b. $\dfrac{y}{y^2 - 16} - \dfrac{y + 1}{y^2 - 5y + 4}$

[4.5]

15.   a. $\dfrac{2x}{y^2} \cdot \dfrac{3y^3}{8x} \cdot \dfrac{4x^2}{9y}$ b. $\dfrac{4x}{2xy + 8y^2} \cdot \dfrac{x + 4y}{x}$

16.   a. $\dfrac{x^2 + 2x - 3}{x^2 + 6x + 9} \cdot \dfrac{2x + 6}{2x - 2}$

     b. $\dfrac{y^3 - y}{2y + 1} \cdot \dfrac{4y + 2}{y^2 + 2y + 1}$

17.   a. $\dfrac{10x^2y^3}{9} \div \dfrac{2xy^2}{3}$ b. $\dfrac{2y - 6}{y + 2x} \div \dfrac{4y - 12}{2y + 4x}$

18.   a. $\dfrac{y^2 + 4y + 3}{y^2 - y - 2} \div \dfrac{y^2 - 4y - 5}{y^2 - 3y - 10}$

     b. $\dfrac{x^2}{y - x} \div \dfrac{x^3 - x^2}{x - y}$

[4.4–4.5]

19. $\dfrac{2x - y}{3} - \dfrac{x}{4}$ 20. $\dfrac{4x + 2}{y} \div \dfrac{2x + 1}{2y}$

21. $\dfrac{x^2 - 2x}{x + 3} \cdot \dfrac{x^2 - 9}{x - 2}$

22. $\dfrac{3}{x^2 - 9} - \dfrac{4}{x^2 + 6x + 9}$

23. $\dfrac{1}{x - 3y} + \dfrac{x}{x^2 - 9y^2}$

24. $\dfrac{x^2 - 5x + 4}{x + 2} \div \dfrac{x^2 - 16}{x^2 + 4x + 4}$

25. $\dfrac{x}{x^2 - 1} - \dfrac{x - 2}{x + 1}$ 26. $\dfrac{y}{y^2 + 2y + 1} \cdot \dfrac{y^2 - 1}{y - 1}$

[4.6]

27.   a. $\dfrac{\frac{3x}{2y}}{\frac{9x}{10y}}$ b. $\dfrac{\frac{2}{3}}{4 - \frac{1}{3}}$

28.   a. $\dfrac{2 + \frac{3}{x}}{1 - \frac{2}{3x}}$ b. $\dfrac{y - \frac{1}{y}}{y + \frac{1}{y}}$

29.   a. $\dfrac{2}{x - \frac{1}{x}}$ b. $\dfrac{\frac{y}{2} + \frac{y}{3}}{\frac{y}{3} - \frac{y}{4}}$

30.   a. $\dfrac{y - \frac{1}{y}}{1 - \frac{1}{y + 1}}$ b. $\dfrac{x + \frac{1}{x}}{1 - \frac{1}{x - 1}}$

[4.7]

▲ *Solve.*

31.   a. $2 - \dfrac{x}{3} = \dfrac{11}{6}$ b. $\dfrac{1}{4}x + \dfrac{2}{3}x = 11$

32.   a. $\dfrac{3}{y - 1} + \dfrac{2}{3y - 3} = \dfrac{11}{9}$

     b. $\dfrac{1}{y + 1} - \dfrac{3}{y + 1} = \dfrac{14}{3}$

33.   a. $\dfrac{2}{5} = \dfrac{x}{x - 2}$ b. $\dfrac{x + 2}{x - 3} = \dfrac{3}{4}$

34.   a. $\dfrac{1}{x} + 2x = \dfrac{33}{4}$ b. $\dfrac{1}{x} + \dfrac{2}{x - 2} = \dfrac{2}{3}$

[4.8]

35.   An enlargement is made of a 4- by 5-inch photograph. What is the dimension of the larger side if the smaller side of the enlargement is 11 inches?

36.   A car and a light plane start together and travel in the same direction. The plane travels three times as fast as the car. How fast is each traveling if they are 100 miles apart at the end of one hour?

37. A passenger train and a freight train leave a station at the same time and travel in opposite directions. The passenger train averages 60 miles per hour, and the freight train averages 20 miles per hour. How long after leaving the station will they be 200 miles apart?

38. A boy got 17 hits on his first 60 times at bat. How many hits does he need in the next 20 times at bat to have an average of 0.300?

39. Two student pilots leave the airport at the same time. Both fly at an air speed of 180 miles per hour, but one flies with the wind and the other flies against the wind. Both pilots check in with their instructor at the same time, and the first pilot has traveled 500 miles while the second pilot has gone 400 miles. Find the speed of the wind.

40. Pam's outboard motorboat travels at 20 miles per hour in still water. Pam drove 8 miles upstream to the gas station in two-thirds of the time it took her to travel 18 miles downstream to Marie's house. What is the speed of the current in the river?

41. A chartered sight-seeing flight over the Grand Canyon is scheduled to return to its departure point in 3 hours. If the plane flies at 100 miles per hour in still air and there is a head wind of 20 miles per hour on the outward journey, how far can the plane go before it must turn around?

42. The Explorer's Club plans a canoe trip up the Lazy River. Club members plan to paddle for 6 hours each day, and they take enough food for 4 days. If they paddle at 8 miles per hour in still water and the current in the Lazy River is 2 miles per hour, how far can they go upriver before they must turn around?

43. A conical tank is 12 feet deep, and the diameter of the top is 8 feet. If the tank is filled with water to a depth of 7 feet, what is the area of the surface of the water?

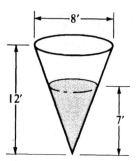

44. To measure the distance EC across the lake shown in the figure, stand at A and sight point C across the lake, then mark point B. Then sight to point E and mark point D so that DB is parallel to CE. If $AD = 25$ yards, $AE = 60$ yards, and $BD = 30$ yards, how wide is the lake?

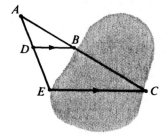

CUMULATIVE EXERCISES

The numbers in brackets refer to the sections in which such problems are first considered.

▲ *Simplify each expression in Exercises 1–6.*

1. $-6 - |-3| - |6 - 3|$ **[1.3]**

2. $\dfrac{-3^2 - 3(-2)^3}{3 - (-2)^2}$ **[2.1]**

3. $2x - [3 - (x - 2) + x]$ **[2.2]**

4. $(-2b)^3 - a^2(ab^2)^2$ **[3.1]**

5. $3[4 - (x - 1)^2 + x]$ **[3.3]**

6. $\dfrac{6x^2 + x - 2}{2x - 1}$ **[4.1]**

7. If $P(x) = 2x^2 - 2x + 3$, find $P(-2) + P(3)$. **[2.1]**

8. Evaluate $ar^{n-1} - br^{n+1}$ for $r = 2$, $a = 2$, $b = -3$, and $n = 3$. **[2.1]**

9. Graph $-4 \leqslant x < 3$, x a real number. **[1.1]**

10. Divide $\dfrac{x^3 - x + 1}{x + 2}$ **[4.2]**

11. Write $\dfrac{2x - 1}{x^2 - 4x + 3} - \dfrac{x + 4}{x^2 - x - 6}$ as a single fraction. **[4.4]**

12. Simplify $\dfrac{a - 3 - \dfrac{2}{a - 1}}{a + 2 - \dfrac{3}{a - 1}}$. **[4.6]**

▲ *Solve each equation in Exercises 13–18.*

13. $0.30(x - 2) = 1.80$ **[2.3]**

14. $0.08x + 0.12(x - 3000) = 1240$ **[2.3]**

15. $2x^2 - 7x = -3$ **[3.5]**

16. $6x - [(x - 2)(x + 5) - 8] = 0$ **[3.5]**

17. $\dfrac{6}{x} + \dfrac{1}{x - 1} = \dfrac{4}{x}$ **[4.7]**

18. $\dfrac{x + 1}{x - 1} = \dfrac{2}{x^2 - 1} + \dfrac{1}{x + 1}$ **[4.7]**

19. Solve $A = P + Prt$ for t. **[2.3]**

20. Solve $S = 2\pi r(r + h)$ for h. **[2.3]**

21. Thirty-two percent of the freshman class are from out of state. If 493 freshmen are in-state students, how large is the freshman class? **[2.4]**

22. How many liters of 80% acid must be added to 40 liters of 30% acid to obtain a mixture that is 60% acid? **[2.4]**

23. The length of a rectangular garden is twice its width. The garden is bordered by a 3-foot-wide path. The area of the garden including the path is 972 square feet more than the area of the garden alone. Find the dimensions of the garden. **[2.4]**

24. The hypotenuse of a right triangle is 3 inches shorter than twice the length of the shortest leg. The longer leg is 12 inches long. Find the lengths of the other two sides. **[3.6]**

25. A car travels 10 miles per hour less than a train. On a 300-mile trip, the train takes 1 hour less than the car. Fine the speed of the train. **[4.8]**

5

EXPONENTS, ROOTS, AND RADICALS

In Chapter 4 we worked with rational numbers. These numbers can always be expressed as quotients of integers. In this chapter we consider numbers that cannot be expressed as such quotients. First, however, we will extend our study of the laws of exponents, which were introduced in Chapter 3.

5.1 POSITIVE INTEGRAL EXPONENTS

In Section 2.1 the expression a^n, where n is a natural number, was defined as follows:

$$a^n = a \cdot a \cdot a \cdot \cdots \cdot a \qquad \text{(n factors)}$$

The following three laws were developed from this definition in Section 3.1:

Laws of Exponents for Products

$$\text{I.} \quad a^m \cdot a^n = a^{m+n}$$
$$\text{II.} \quad (a^m)^n = a^{mn}$$
$$\text{III.} \quad (ab)^m = a^m b^m$$

EXAMPLE 1

a. $x^5 \cdot x^2 = x^{5+2}$
$\qquad\quad = x^7$

b. $(x^5)^2 = x^{5 \cdot 2}$
$\qquad\quad = x^{10}$

c. $(x^2 y^3)^2 = (x^2)^2 (y^3)^2$
$\qquad\qquad\quad = x^4 y^6$

Laws of Exponents for Quotients   Consider the following simplifications of two quotients that use the fundamental principle of fractions:

$$\frac{x^5}{x^2} = \frac{xxxxx}{xx} = x^3 \qquad \text{and} \qquad \frac{x^2}{x^5} = \frac{xx}{xxxxx} = \frac{1}{x^3}$$

We can obtain the same results by subtracting exponents appropriately. Thus,

$$\frac{x^5}{x^2} = x^{5-2} = x^3 \qquad \text{and} \qquad \frac{x^2}{x^5} = \frac{1}{x^{5-2}} = \frac{1}{x^3}$$

In general, note that if $m > n$,

$$\frac{a^m}{a^n} = \frac{\overbrace{(a \cdot a \cdot a \cdots a)}^{(m-n) \text{ factors}} \overbrace{(a \cdot a \cdot a \cdots a)}^{n \text{ factors}}}{\underbrace{(a \cdot a \cdot a \cdots a)}_{n \text{ factors}}}$$

$$= a^{m-n}$$

Furthermore, if $m < n$,

$$\frac{a^m}{a^n} = \frac{\overbrace{(a \cdot a \cdots a)}^{m \text{ factors}}}{\underbrace{(a \cdot a \cdots a)}_{m \text{ factors}} \underbrace{(a \cdot a \cdots a)}_{(n-m) \text{ factors}}}$$

$$= \frac{1}{a^{n-m}}$$

The following laws proceed from these arguments:

IV. $\dfrac{a^m}{a^n} = a^{m-n} \qquad (m > n, \quad a \neq 0)$

IVa. $\dfrac{a^m}{a^n} = \dfrac{1}{a^{n-m}} \qquad (m < n, \quad a \neq 0)$

EXAMPLE 2

a. $\dfrac{x^4 y^6}{x^2 y} = x^{4-2} y^{6-1}$

$\qquad = x^2 y^5 \qquad (x, y \neq 0)$

b. $\dfrac{x^2 y}{x^3 y^2} = \dfrac{1}{x^{3-2} y^{2-1}}$

$\qquad = \dfrac{1}{xy} \qquad (x, y \neq 0)$

Note that the fourth law of exponents is consistent with the process of reducing fractions by using the fundamental principle of fractions. The same results would be obtained in the preceding examples by using the fundamental principle of fractions.

Now, since

$$\left(\frac{a}{b}\right)^n = \overbrace{\frac{a}{b} \cdot \frac{a}{b} \cdot \frac{a}{b} \cdots \cdots \left(\frac{a}{b}\right)}^{n \text{ factors}} = \overbrace{\frac{a \cdot a \cdot a \cdots \cdots a}{\underbrace{b \cdot b \cdot b \cdots \cdots b}_{n \text{ factors}}}}^{n \text{ factors}}$$

$$= \frac{a^n}{b^n}$$

we have another useful law for powers:

> **V.** $\left(\dfrac{a}{b}\right)^n = \dfrac{a^n}{b^n}$ $(b \neq 0)$

EXAMPLE 3   **a.** $\left(\dfrac{x}{y}\right)^3 = \dfrac{x^3}{y^3}$ $(y \neq 0)$ **b.** $\left(\dfrac{2x^2}{y}\right)^4 = \dfrac{(2x^2)^4}{y^4}$ $(y \neq 0)$

Ordinarily, two or more of the laws of exponents are required to simplify expressions containing exponents. In Example 3b we can further simplify the result: From Law III,

$$\frac{(2x^2)^4}{y^4} = \frac{2^4(x^2)^4}{y^4}   (y \neq 0)$$

and from Law II,

$$\frac{2^4(x^2)^4}{y^4} = \frac{16x^8}{y^4}   (y \neq 0)$$

EXAMPLE 4   **a.** $\left(\dfrac{2x^3}{y}\right)^2 = \dfrac{2^2 \cdot x^6}{y^2}$ **b.** $\left(\dfrac{2+x}{3y^2}\right)^3 = \dfrac{(2+x)^3}{(3y^2)^3}$

$\qquad\qquad\qquad = \dfrac{4x^6}{y^2}$ $(y \neq 0)$ $\qquad\qquad\quad = \dfrac{(2+x)^3}{27y^6}$ $(y \neq 0)$

COMMON ERROR   *Note that in Example 4b,*

$$(2+x)^3 \neq 2^3 + x^3; \qquad (2+x)^3 = (2+x)(2+x)(2+x)$$

In the exercise sets in this chapter we shall assume that no denominator equals 0 unless otherwise stated.

EXERCISE SET 5.1

▲ *Using one or more of the laws of exponents, write each expression as a product or quotient in which each variable occurs only once and all exponents are positive. See Example 1.*

1. $x^2 \cdot x^3$ **2.** $y \cdot y^4$ **3.** $a^3 \cdot a^5$

4. $b^5 \cdot b^4$ **5.** $(a^2)^3$ **6.** $(b^3)^4$

7. $(x^2)^3$ **8.** $(y^4)^2$ **9.** $(xy^2)^3$

10. $(x^2y^3)^2$ **11.** $(abc^2)^4$ **12.** $(a^2b^3c)^2$

13. $(2x)(-2x)^3$ **14.** $(-3x^2)^2(-5x)$

15. $(ab^2)^3(-2a^2)^2$ **16.** $(a^2b^2)^3(-ab^2)^3$

▲ *See Examples 1–4.*

17. $\dfrac{x^5}{x^3}$ **18.** $\dfrac{y^2}{y^6}$ **19.** $\dfrac{x^2y^4}{xy^2}$

20. $\dfrac{x^4y^3}{x^2y}$ **21.** $\left(\dfrac{x}{y^2}\right)^3$ **22.** $\left(\dfrac{y^2}{z^3}\right)^2$

23. $\left(\dfrac{2x}{y^2}\right)^3$ **24.** $\left(\dfrac{3y^2}{x}\right)^2$ **25.** $\left(\dfrac{-2x}{3y^2}\right)^3$

26. $\left(\dfrac{-x^2}{2y}\right)^4$ **27.** $\dfrac{(4x)^3}{(2x^2)^2}$ **28.** $\dfrac{(5x)^2}{(3x^2)^3}$

29. $\dfrac{(xy^2)^3}{(x^2y)^2}$ **30.** $\dfrac{(-xy^2)^2}{(x^2y)^3}$

31. $\dfrac{(xy)^2(x^2y)^3}{(x^2y^2)^2}$ **32.** $\dfrac{(-x)^2(-x^2)^4}{(x^2)^3}$

33. $\left(\dfrac{2x}{y^2}\right)^3\left(\dfrac{y^2}{3x}\right)^2$ **34.** $\left(\dfrac{x^2z}{2}\right)^2\left(-\dfrac{2}{x^2z}\right)^3$

35. $\left(\dfrac{-3}{y^2}\right)^2(2y^3)^2$ **36.** $\left(\dfrac{y}{x}\right)^2\left(-\dfrac{3}{4xy}\right)^3$

37. $\left[\left(\dfrac{r^2s^3t}{xy}\right)^3\left(\dfrac{x^2y}{r^3st^2}\right)^2\right]^2$

38. $\left[\left(\dfrac{a^3bc}{x^2y}\right)^4\left(\dfrac{x^2yz}{ab^2c^3}\right)^2\right]^2$

39. $\left(\dfrac{x^2}{a^2b}\right)^2\left(-\dfrac{ab}{x^3}\right)^3\left(\dfrac{x}{ab}\right)^2$

40. $\left(\dfrac{m^3n^2p}{r^2s}\right)^2\left(\dfrac{rs}{mn^2p^2}\right)^3\left(-\dfrac{mnp}{rs}\right)^2$

41. $\left(\dfrac{y+z}{x^2}\right)^3\left(\dfrac{x}{y+z}\right)^2$ **42.** $\left(\dfrac{y^2+z}{y}\right)^2\left(\dfrac{y^2}{x^2+z}\right)^3$

Miscellaneous Exercises

43. Use a counterexample to show that $(x^2 + y^2)^3$ is not equivalent to $x^6 + y^6$.

44. Rewrite $(x^2 + y^2)^3$ as an equivalent expression without using parentheses.

▲ *Write each expression as a product or quotient in which each variable occurs only once.*

45. $x^n \cdot x^n$ **46.** $\dfrac{x^{2n}x^n}{x^{n+1}}$

47. $\dfrac{(x^{n+1}x^{2n-1})^2}{x^{3n}}$ **48.** $\left(\dfrac{y^2 \cdot y^3}{y}\right)^{2n}$

49. $\left(\dfrac{x^{3n}x^{2n}}{x^{4n}}\right)^2$ **50.** $\dfrac{(y^{n+1})^n}{y^n}$

5.2 ZERO AND NEGATIVE INTEGRAL EXPONENTS

Zero Exponent   Note that if the fourth law of exponents holds for the case in which $m = n$, we have

$$\frac{a^n}{a^n} = a^{n-n} = a^0 \qquad (a \neq 0) \tag{1}$$

By definition of a quotient,

$$\frac{a^n}{a^n} = 1 \qquad (a \neq 0) \tag{2}$$

Since $a^n/a^n = a^0$ by Equation (1) above and $a^n/a^n = 1$ by Equation (2) above, a^0 must be defined as 1:

$$a^0 = 1 \qquad (a \neq 0)$$

EXAMPLE 1 | **a.** $3^0 = 1$ **b.** $-4^0 = -(4^0) = -1$ **c.** $(-2)^0 = 1$

Negative Integer We would like the laws of exponents to hold also for negative exponents. In particular
Exponents for $a \neq 0$,

$$a^n \cdot a^{-n} = a^{n-n} = a^0 = 1$$

However,

$$a^n \cdot \frac{1}{a^n} = 1 \qquad (a \neq 0)$$

So for consistency we provide the following definition:

$$a^{-n} = \frac{1}{a^n} \qquad (a \neq 0) \qquad\qquad (3)$$

Note carefully that a^{-n} is the reciprocal of a^n.

EXAMPLE 2 | **a.** $3^{-2} = \dfrac{1}{3^2}$ **b.** $\dfrac{1}{2^{-3}} = 2^3$ **c.** $4^{-2} + 4^2 = \dfrac{1}{16} + 16$

$$= \frac{1}{9} \qquad\qquad\quad = 8 \qquad\qquad\qquad = \frac{1}{16} + \frac{256}{16}$$

$$= \frac{257}{16}$$

We can use Property (3) to rewrite algebraic expressions so that all exponents are positive. Furthermore, we can now use the laws of exponents given in Section 5.1 to simplify expressions that have negative exponents.

EXAMPLE 3 | **a.** $x^{-3} \cdot x^5$ **b.** $(x^2 y^{-3})^{-1}$ **c.** $(3x^2 \cdot x^{-3})^2$

$$= x^{-3+5} \qquad\qquad = x^{-2} y^3 \qquad\qquad = (3x^{-1})^2$$

$$= x^2 \qquad\qquad\quad = \frac{y^3}{x^2} \qquad\qquad\quad = 9x^{-2}$$

$$= \frac{9}{x^2}$$

COMMON ERROR *Note that in Example 3c,* $9x^{-2} = \dfrac{9}{x^2}$ *and not* $\dfrac{1}{9x^2}$. *The exponent applies only to the base* x.

We can establish an additional property that will help us simplify quotients with negative exponents. From Law V on page 116,

$$\left(\frac{a}{b}\right)^{-n} = \frac{a^{-n}}{b^{-n}}$$

and then from (3) on page 118,

$$\frac{a^{-n}}{b^{-n}} = \frac{b^n}{a^n} = \left(\frac{b}{a}\right)^n$$

Hence, we have the following property:

VI. $\left(\dfrac{a}{b}\right)^{-n} = \left(\dfrac{b}{a}\right)^{n}$ $(a, b \neq 0)$

The laws of exponents that we have now established can be applied in different orders.

EXAMPLE 4 Write $\left(\dfrac{x^3}{x^2}\right)^{-3}$ as a quotient in which the variable occurs only once with a positive exponent.

Solutions **a.** We can first apply Law IV to write

$$\left(\frac{x^3}{x^2}\right)^{-3} = (x)^{-3} = \frac{1}{x^3}$$

b. Or we can first apply Law V and then Law II to write

$$\left(\frac{x^3}{x^2}\right)^{-3} = \frac{(x^3)^{-3}}{(x^2)^{-3}} = \frac{x^{-9}}{x^{-6}}$$

from which, by Law IV, we have

$$\frac{x^{-9}}{x^{-6}} = \frac{1}{x^{-6-(-9)}} = \frac{1}{x^3}$$

c. Or we can first use Law VI to obtain

$$\left(\frac{x^3}{x^2}\right)^{-3} = \left(\frac{x^2}{x^3}\right)^{3} = \left(\frac{1}{x}\right)^{3} = \frac{1}{x^3}$$

The laws of exponents that we have established apply only to products and quotients. Special care must be taken in simplifying powers that contain sums and differences. In such cases it is best to rewrite all powers with positive exponents before using the other laws of exponents.

EXAMPLE 5 Write each of the following expressions as a single fraction involving positive exponents only:

a. $x^{-1} + y^{-2}$ **b.** $(x^{-1} + x^{-2})^{-1}$ **c.** $\dfrac{x^{-1} + y}{x^{-1}}$

Solutions

a. $x^{-1} + y^{-2}$

$$= \frac{1}{x} + \frac{1}{y^2}$$

$$= \frac{(y^2)}{(y^2)}\frac{1}{x} + \frac{1(x)}{y^2(x)}$$

$$= \frac{y^2 + x}{xy^2}$$

b. $(x^{-1} + x^{-2})^{-1}$

$$= \frac{1}{\dfrac{1}{x} + \dfrac{1}{x^2}}$$

$$= \frac{1(x^2)}{\left(\dfrac{1}{x} + \dfrac{1}{x^2}\right)(x^2)}$$

$$= \frac{x^2}{x + 1}$$

c. $\dfrac{x^{-1} + y}{x^{-1}}$

$$= \frac{\dfrac{1}{x} + y}{\dfrac{1}{x}}$$

$$= \frac{\left(\dfrac{1}{x} + y\right)x}{\left(\dfrac{1}{x}\right)x}$$

$$= 1 + xy$$

COMMON ERROR   *Note in Example 5b that* $(x^{-1} + x^{-2})^{-1} \neq (x^{-1})^{-1} + (x^{-2})^{-1}.$

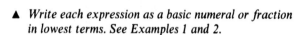

EXERCISE SET 5.2

▲ *Write each expression as a basic numeral or fraction in lowest terms. See Examples 1 and 2.*

1. 2^{-1} **2.** 3^{-2} **3.** $\dfrac{1}{3^{-1}}$ **4.** $\dfrac{3}{4^{-2}}$

5. $(-2)^{-3}$ **6.** $\dfrac{1}{(-3)^{-2}}$ **7.** $\dfrac{5^{-1}}{3^0}$

8. $\dfrac{2^0}{3^{-2}}$ **9.** $\left(\dfrac{3}{5}\right)^{-1}$ **10.** $\left(\dfrac{1}{3}\right)^{-2}$

11. $\dfrac{5^{-1}}{3^{-2}}$ **12.** $\dfrac{3^{-3}}{6^{-2}}$ **13.** $3^{-2} + 3^2$

14. $5^{-1} + 25^0$ **15.** $4^{-1} - 4^{-2}$ **16.** $8^{-2} - 2^0$

▲ *Write each expression as a product or quotient of powers in which each variable occurs only once and all exponents are positive. See Examples 3 and 4.*

17. $x^2 y^{-3}$ **18.** $\dfrac{x^3}{y^{-2}}$ **19.** $(x^2 \cdot y)^{-3}$

20. $(xy^3)^{-2}$ **21.** $\left(\dfrac{x}{y^3}\right)^2$ **22.** $\left(\dfrac{2x}{y^2}\right)^3$

23. $\dfrac{(xy^2)^3}{(x^2 y)^2}$ **24.** $\left(\dfrac{3x}{y^2}\right)^2\left(\dfrac{2y^3}{x}\right)^2$

25. $x^{-3} \cdot x^7$ **26.** $\dfrac{x^3}{x^{-2}}$ **27.** $(x^{-2} y^0)^3$

28. $(x^{-2} y^3)^0$ **29.** $\dfrac{x^{-1}}{y^{-1}}$ **30.** $\dfrac{x^{-3}}{y^{-2}}$

31. $\dfrac{8^{-1} x^0 y^{-3}}{(2xy)^{-5}}$ **32.** $\left(\dfrac{x^{-1} y^3}{2x^0 y^{-5}}\right)^{-2}$

33. $\left(\dfrac{x^0 y^2}{z^2}\right)^{-1}$ **34.** $\left(\dfrac{x^{-1} y z^0}{x y^{-1} z}\right)^{-1}$

35. $\left(\dfrac{x^2 y}{z^3}\right)\left(\dfrac{x}{z^2}\right)^{-1}$ **36.** $\left(\dfrac{2y^{-1}}{x^2}\right)^{-1} \cdot \dfrac{y^2}{x}$

37. $\left(\dfrac{x^{-2} y^2}{z^{-1}}\right)^{-1} \cdot \left(\dfrac{xy^0}{z}\right)^{-2}$ **38.** $\left(\dfrac{2y^2 x}{3z}\right)^2 \cdot \left(\dfrac{2x^2}{9z}\right)^{-2}$

▲ *Write each expression as a single fraction involving positive exponents only. See Example 5.*

39. $x^{-2} + y^{-2}$ **40.** $x^{-1} - y^{-3}$ **41.** $\dfrac{x}{y^{-1}} + \dfrac{x^{-1}}{y}$

42. $\dfrac{x^{-1}}{y^{-1}} + \dfrac{y}{x}$ **43.** $(x - y)^{-2}$

44. $(x + y)^{-3}$ **45.** $x^{-1} y - xy^{-1}$

46. $xy^{-1} + x^{-1}y$

47. $\dfrac{x^{-1} - y}{x^{-1}}$

48. $\dfrac{x + y^{-1}}{y^{-1}}$

49. $\dfrac{x^{-1} + y^{-1}}{(xy)^{-1}}$

50. $\dfrac{x^{-2} - y^{-2}}{(xy)^{-1}}$

▲ *Write each expression as a product free of fractions in which each variable occurs only once.*

53. $a^{3-n}a^{2n+1}$

54. $x^{-n}x^{n+1}$

55. $\left(\dfrac{a^{2n}}{a^{n+1}}\right)^{-2}$

56. $\dfrac{x^n y^{n+1}}{x^{2n-1} y^n}$

57. $\dfrac{b^n c^{2n-1}}{b^{n+1} c^{2n}}$

58. $\left(\dfrac{x^{n-1} y^n}{x^{-2} y^{-n}}\right)^2$

59. $\left(\dfrac{x^n}{x^{n-1}}\right)^{-1}$

60. $\left(\dfrac{a^{2n} b^{n-1}}{a^{n-1} b}\right)^2$

Miscellaneous Exercises

51. Use a counterexample to show that $(x + y)^{-2}$ is not equivalent to $\dfrac{1}{x^2 + y^2}$.

52. Use a counterexample to show that $(x + y)^{-2}$ is not equivalent to $\dfrac{1}{x^2} + \dfrac{1}{y^2}$.

5.3 SCIENTIFIC NOTATION

In scientific applications of mathematics that involve very large or very small quantities, it is often convenient to use an exponential form of notation. For example, the mass of the Earth is approximately

$$5{,}980{,}000{,}000{,}000{,}000{,}000{,}000{,}000{,}000 = 5.98 \times 10^{27} \text{ grams}$$

and the mass of a hydrogen atom is approximately

$$0.00000000000000000000000167 = 1.67 \times 10^{-24} \text{ gram}$$

In each case we have represented the number as the product of a number between 1 and 10, including 1, and a power of 10; that is, we have factored a power of 10 from each number.

We first consider several simple cases to see how large and small numbers can be factored.

In the following factored forms of 38,400, one of the factors is a power of 10:

$$38{,}400 = 3840 \times 10$$
$$= 384 \times 10^2$$
$$= 38.4 \times 10^3$$
$$= 3.84 \times 10^4$$

Although any one of such factored forms may be more useful than the original form of the number, a special name is given to the last form. A number expressed as the product of a number between 1 and 10 (including 1) and a power of 10 is said to be in **scientific form** or **scientific notation**. For example,

$$4.18 \times 10^4, \qquad 9.6 \times 10^2, \qquad \text{and} \qquad 4 \times 10^5$$

are in scientific form.

Now, let us consider some factored forms of 0.0057:

$$0.0057 = \frac{0.057}{10} = 0.057 \times \frac{1}{10} = 0.057 \times 10^{-1}$$

$$= \frac{0.57}{100} = 0.57 \times \frac{1}{10^2} = 0.57 \times 10^{-2}$$

$$= \frac{5.7}{1000} = 5.7 \times \frac{1}{10^3} = 5.7 \times 10^{-3}$$

In this case, 5.7×10^{-3} is the scientific form for 0.0057 because 5.7 is between 1 and 10. These examples suggest the following procedure:

Writing a Number in Scientific Form

1. Move the decimal point so that there is one nonzero digit to the left of the decimal point.

2. Multiply the result by a power of ten with an exponent equal to the number of places the decimal point was moved. The exponent is positive if the decimal point has been moved to the left, and it is negative if the decimal point has been moved to the right.

EXAMPLE 1

a. $478,000 = 4.78000 \times 10^5$
   $\underbrace{\qquad}_{\textbf{5 places}}$
   $= 4.78 \times 10^5$

b. $0.00032 = 00003.2 \times 10^{-4}$
   $\underbrace{\qquad}_{\textbf{4 places}}$
   $= 3.2 \times 10^{-4}$

Note that we expressed a large or small number N in scientific notation by writing it in the form

$$N = n \times 10^c$$

where $1 \leqslant n < 10$ and c is an integer.

A number written in scientific notation can be written in **standard form** by reversing the above procedure:

Going from Scientific Notation to Decimal Notation

Move the decimal point the number of places indicated by the exponent on 10—to the right if the exponent is positive and to the left if it is negative.

EXAMPLE 2

a. $3.75 \times 10^4 = 37500.$
   $\underbrace{\qquad}_{\textbf{4 places}}$
   $= 37,500$

b. $2.03 \times 10^{-3} = .00203$
   $\underbrace{\qquad}_{\textbf{3 places}}$
   $= 0.00203$

c. $\dfrac{1}{4 \times 10^3} = \dfrac{1}{4} \times \dfrac{1}{10^3}$
   $= 0.25 \times 10^{-3}$
   $= 0.00025$

d. $\dfrac{1}{5 \times 10^{-1}} = \dfrac{1}{5} \times \dfrac{1}{10^{-1}}$
   $= 0.2 \times 10^1$
   $= 2$

Sometimes it is more convenient to express a number as a product of a power of 10 and a number that is not between 1 and 10. For example, under certain circumstances, any of the following forms may be a useful representation for 6280:

$$628 \times 10, \qquad 62.8 \times 10^2, \qquad 6.28 \times 10^3, \qquad 0.628 \times 10^4$$

A factored form in which the factors do not contain decimals is generally easiest to use to simplify calculations by hand.

EXAMPLE 3
a. $\dfrac{10^2 \times 10^{-5} \times 10^4}{10^{-3} \times 10}$

$= \dfrac{10^{2+(-5)+4}}{10^{-3+1}}$

$= \dfrac{10}{10^{-2}} = 10^3$

b. $\dfrac{0.0024 \times 0.0007}{0.000021}$

$= \dfrac{24 \times 10^{-4} \times 7 \times 10^{-4}}{21 \times 10^{-6}}$

$= 8 \times 10^{-2} = 0.08$

Using a Scientific Calculator*
c

Because most four-function calculators have only an 8-digit display, they cannot be used with very large or very small numbers. For example, the products

$$34{,}000 \times 76{,}000 = 2{,}584{,}000{,}000$$

and

$$0.00017 \times 0.0052 = 0.000000884$$

could not be obtained by using a four-function calculator. However, these computations can be made by using a scientific calculator. The results will appear in the display screen in scientific notation as

$\boxed{2.584 \quad 09}$ and $\boxed{8.84 \quad -07}$

respectively, where only the exponent on the power of 10 is displayed; the base 10 is understood. The results can now be written as

$$2.584 \times 10^9 \qquad \text{and} \qquad 8.84 \times 10^{-7}$$

To enter a number in scientific notation, look for a key labeled $\boxed{\text{EXP}}$ or $\boxed{\text{EE}}$ on your calculator. To enter the number 7.8×10^{13}, press

$$7.8 \;\boxed{\text{EXP}}\; 13$$

The calculator will display

$\boxed{7.8 \quad 13}$

To enter a negative power of 10, for example 2.4×10^{-5}, press

$$2.4 \;\boxed{\text{EXP}}\; 5 \;\boxed{+/-}$$

---

*The ability to use a scientific calculator is not a prerequisite for work in the following chapters. The symbol **c** is used for optional material in the text and exercises that requires the use of a scientific calculator.

and the calculator will display

$$\boxed{2.4 \quad -05}$$

EXAMPLE 4 | Use a calculator to compute

$$\frac{(3.6 \times 10^{18}) \cdot (4.8 \times 10^{-9})}{6.4 \times 10^{23}}$$

Solution | Use the following keying sequence:

3.6 $\boxed{\text{EXP}}$ 18 $\boxed{\times}$ 4.8 $\boxed{\text{EXP}}$ 9 $\boxed{+/\_}$ $\boxed{\div}$ 6.4 $\boxed{\text{EXP}}$ 23 $\boxed{=}$

The calculator will display the result

$$\boxed{2.7 \quad -14},$$

so the answer is 2.7×10^{-14}.

Note that your calculator will show the result of a computation in standard form if the display can accommodate the number of digits in the result.

EXAMPLE 5 | Compute $(6.9 \times 10^{13}) \cdot (4.3 \times 10^{-10})$.

Solution | Use the following keying sequence:

6.9 $\boxed{\text{EXP}}$ 13 $\boxed{\times}$ 4.3 $\boxed{\text{EXP}}$ 10 $\boxed{+/\_}$ $\boxed{=}$

The display will show $\boxed{29670}$. The result can be written as 2.967×10^4.

EXERCISE SET 5.3

▲ *Express each number using scientific notation. See Example 1.*

1.	285	**2.**	3476	**3.**	21
4.	68,742	**5.**	8,372,000	**6.**	481,000
7.	0.024	**8.**	0.0063	**9.**	0.421
10.	0.000523	**11.**	0.000004	**12.**	0.0006

▲ *Express each number using standard form. See Example 2.*

13. 2.4×10^2 **14.** 4.8×10^3 **15.** 6.87×10^5

16. 8.31×10^4 **17.** 5.0×10^{-3} **18.** 8.0×10^{-1}

19. 2.02×10^{-2} **20.** 4.31×10^{-3} **21.** 12.27×10^3

22. 14.38×10^4 **23.** 23.5×10^{-4} **24.** 621.0×10^{-2}

25. $\dfrac{1}{2 \times 10^3}$ **26.** $\dfrac{1}{4 \times 10^4}$ **27.** $\dfrac{1}{8 \times 10^{-2}}$

28. $\dfrac{1}{5 \times 10^{-3}}$ **29.** $\dfrac{3}{5 \times 10^4}$ **30.** $\dfrac{5}{8 \times 10^2}$

▲ *Compute by hand. See Example 3.*

31. $\dfrac{10^3 \times 10^{-6}}{10^2}$ **32.** $\dfrac{10^3 \times 10^{-7} \times 10^2}{10^{-2} \times 10^4}$

33. $\dfrac{10^2 \times 10^5 \times 10^{-3}}{10^2 \times 10^2}$ **34.** $\dfrac{(4 \times 10^3)(6 \times 10^{-2})}{3 \times 10^{-7}}$

35. $\dfrac{(2 \times 10^2)^2 (3 \times 10^{-3})}{2 \times 10^4}$ **36.** $\dfrac{(3 \times 10)^3 (2 \times 10^{-1})}{2 \times 10^{-2}}$

37. $\dfrac{(2 \times 10^{-3})(6 \times 10^2)^2}{(2 \times 10^{-2})^2}$ **38.** $\dfrac{(8 \times 10^4)^2 (3 \times 10)^3}{(6 \times 10^{-2})^2}$

▲ *Compute by hand. See Example 3.*

39. $\dfrac{0.6 \times 0.00084 \times 0.093}{0.00021 \times 0.00031}$ **40.** $\dfrac{0.065 \times 2.2 \times 50}{1.30 \times 0.011 \times 0.05}$

41. $\dfrac{28 \times 0.0006 \times 450}{1.5 \times 700 \times 0.018}$

42. $\dfrac{0.0054 \times 0.05 \times 300}{0.0015 \times 0.27 \times 80}$

43. $\dfrac{420 \times 0.0016 \times 800}{0.0028 \times 1200 \times 20}$

44. $\dfrac{0.0027 \times 0.004 \times 650}{260 \times 0.0001 \times 0.009}$

51. $(6.3 \times 10^{-4}) \cdot (5.71 \times 10^{-4})$

52. $(3.14 \times 10^{-5}) \cdot (2.7 \times 10^{-6})$

53. $\dfrac{(5.4 \times 10^{-7}) \cdot (6.1 \times 10^{8})}{8 \times 10^{2}}$

54. $\dfrac{(6.2 \times 10^{5}) \cdot (8.1 \times 10^{-7})}{3.1 \times 10^{-1}}$

55. $\dfrac{(4.25 \times 10^{5}) \cdot (6.3 \times 10^{-2})}{4.7 \times 10^{-6}}$

56. $\dfrac{(1.07 \times 10^{-7}) \cdot (3.2 \times 10^{2})}{5.1 \times 10^{5}}$

▲ *Compute using a scientific calculator. See Examples 4 and 5.*

45. $652{,}000 \times 15{,}000$

46. $49{,}000 \times 7100$

47. 0.000076×0.0095

48. 0.0047×0.00028

49. $(2.3 \times 10^{5}) \cdot (4.7 \times 10^{4})$

50. $(5.24 \times 10^{3}) \cdot (1.7 \times 10^{8})$

Miscellaneous Exercises

57. The speed of light is approximately 300,000,000 meters per second.

   a. Write this number in scientific notation.

   b. Express the speed of light in inches per second (1 inch equals 2.54 centimeters, and 1 meter equals 100 centimeters).

58. One light-year is the number of miles traveled by light in 1 year (365 days), and the speed of light is approximately 186,000 miles per second. Express in scientific notation the number of miles in 1 light-year.

59. Light travels at a speed of 300,000,000 meters per second. Write this number in scientific form.

60. Visible blue light has a wavelength of 0.000 000 45 meter. Write this number in scientific form.

61. The average body cell of an animal has a diameter of 0.000 015 meter. Write this number in scientific form.

62. The diameter of the Earth is approximately 6,450,000 meters. Write this number in scientific form.

5.4 RATIONAL EXPONENTS

If the laws of exponents developed in Section 5.1 are to hold for rational exponents, *meanings consistent with these laws must be assigned to powers with rational exponents.* Let us first consider exponents that are reciprocals of natural numbers, that is, exponents of the form $1/n$, where n is a natural number.

$a^{1/n}$, n a Natural Number

We shall first define powers of the form $a^{1/n}$ to be consistent with Law II of exponents (page 114). We shall make this definition in two parts: for n an even natural number and for n an odd natural number.

> If n is an even natural number and $a > 0$, then $a^{1/n}$ is the positive number such that
>
> $$(a^{1/n})^n = a^{n/n} = a$$

The number $a^{1/n}$ is called the **positive nth root of a.**

EXAMPLE 1

a. $16^{1/2} = 4$ because $4^2 = 16$.

b. $-16^{1/2} = -(16)^{1/2} = -4$ because $-4^2 = -(4^2) = -16$.

c. $(-16)^{1/2}$ is not defined in the set of real numbers because there is no real number a for which $a^2 = -16$.

The restriction that $a > 0$ in the definition for $a^{1/n}$ is not necessary if n is an odd natural number.

> If n is an odd natural number, then $a^{1/n}$ is the number such that
>
> $$(a^{1/n})^n = a$$

EXAMPLE 2

a. $(8)^{1/3} = 2$ because $2^3 = 8$.

b. $(-8)^{1/3} = -2$ because $(-2)^3 = -8$.

c. $(-64)^{1/3} = -4$ because $(-4)^3 = -64$.

> If n is an even or odd natural number,
>
> $$0^{1/n} = 0$$

EXAMPLE 3   **a.** $0^{1/2} = 0$ **b.** $0^{1/3} = 0$

$a^{m/n}$, n a Natural Number

Powers with positive bases and positive rational exponents can be defined in two ways:

> $$a^{m/n} = (a^{1/n})^m = (a^m)^{1/n}   (a^{1/n} \text{ a real number})$$

Thus, we can look at $a^{m/n}$ either as the mth power of the nth root of a or as the nth root of the mth power of a.

EXAMPLE 4

a. $8^{2/3} = (8^{1/3})^2$ **b.** $8^{2/3} = (8^2)^{1/3}$

$= (2)^2 = 4$ $= (64)^{1/3} = 4$

Hereafter, we shall use whichever form is most convenient for the purpose at hand. In Example 4a above, the form $(8^{1/3})^2$ is preferred because it is easier to extract the root first than it is to recognize the root after the number is squared.

To extend meaning to powers with negative rational exponents, we define $a^{-m/n}$ as follows:

> *For m and n positive integers,*
>
> $$a^{-m/n} = \frac{1}{a^{m/n}} \qquad (a^{1/n} \text{ a real number, } a \neq 0)$$

EXAMPLE 5

a. $27^{-2/3} = \dfrac{1}{27^{2/3}} = \dfrac{1}{(27^{1/3})^2}$

$\quad = \dfrac{1}{3^2} = \dfrac{1}{9}$

b. $(-8)^{-5/3} = \dfrac{1}{(-8)^{5/3}} = \dfrac{1}{[(-8)^{1/3}]^5}$

$\quad = \dfrac{1}{(-2)^5} = -\dfrac{1}{32}$

With the definitions that we have made, it can be shown that powers with rational exponents—positive, negative, or 0—obey the laws of exponents set forth in previous sections.

EXAMPLE 6

a. $y^{3/4}y^{-1/2}$

$\quad = y^{3/4+(-1/2)}$

$\quad = y^{1/4}$

b. $\dfrac{x^{5/6}}{x^{2/3}} = \dfrac{x^{5/6}}{x^{4/6}}$

$\quad = x^{5/6-4/6}$

$\quad = x^{1/6}$

c. $\dfrac{(x^{1/2}y^2)^2}{(x^{2/3}y)^3} = \dfrac{xy^4}{x^2y^3}$

$\quad = \dfrac{y^{4-3}}{x^{2-1}}$

$\quad = \dfrac{y}{x}$

EXAMPLE 7

a. $y^{1/3}(y + y^{2/3})$

$\quad = y^{1/3+1} + y^{1/3+2/3}$

$\quad = y^{4/3} + y$

b. $x^{-3/4}(x^{1/4} + x^{3/4})$

$\quad = x^{-3/4+1/4} + x^{-3/4+3/4}$

$\quad = x^{-2/4} + x^0$

$\quad = x^{-1/2} + 1$

Recall from Section 1.1 that any number that can be expressed as the quotient of two integers is called a rational number and any real number that cannot be so expressed is called an irrational number. Some powers with rational-number exponents are rational numbers, and some are irrational numbers. Any expression such as $a^{1/n}$ represents a rational number if and only if a is the nth power of a rational number. For example,

$4^{1/2}, (-27/8)^{1/3},$ and $(81)^{1/4}$ are rational numbers equal to 2, $-3/2$, and 3, respectively;

and

$2^{1/2}, 5^{1/3},$ and $7^{1/4}$ are irrational numbers, such that $(2^{1/2})^2 = 2$, $(5^{1/3})^3 = 5$, and $(7^{1/4})^4 = 7$.

In Section 5.5 we shall consider how to obtain rational approximations for some irrational numbers.

||| **E X E R C I S E   S E T   5.4**

▲ *Assume that all variable bases in this exercise are positive unless otherwise specified.*

▲ *Write each expression using a basic numeral or fraction in lowest terms. See Examples 1 and 2.*

1. $9^{1/2}$ 2. $25^{1/2}$ 3. $32^{1/5}$

4. $27^{1/3}$ 5. $(-8)^{1/3}$ 6. $(-27)^{1/3}$

7. $64^{1/2}$ 8. $81^{1/2}$

▲ *See Examples 4 and 5.*

9. $81^{3/4}$ 10. $125^{2/3}$ 11. $(-8)^{4/3}$

12. $(-64)^{2/3}$ 13. $16^{-1/2}$ 14. $8^{-1/3}$

15. $16^{-3/4}$ 16. $27^{-2/3}$ 17. $27^{2/3}$

18. $32^{3/5}$ 19. $(-27)^{4/3}$ 20. $8^{-2/3}$

▲ *Write each expression as a product or quotient of powers in which each variable occurs only once and all exponents are positive. See Example 6.*

21. $x^{1/3}x^{1/3}$ 22. $y^{1/2}y^{3/2}$ 23. $\dfrac{x^{2/3}}{x^{1/3}}$

24. $\dfrac{x^{3/4}}{x^{1/4}}$ 25. $(a^{1/2})^3$ 26. $(b^6)^{2/3}$

27. $x^{-3/4}x^{1/4}$ 28. $y^{-2/3}y^{5/3}$ 29. $(a^{2/3}b)^{1/2}$

30. $(a^{1/2}b^{1/3})^6$ 31. $\left(\dfrac{a^6}{b^3}\right)^{2/3}$ 32. $\left(\dfrac{a^{1/2}}{a^2}\right)^2$

33. $(r^{-2/3}t)^{-3}$ 34. $(x^{1/4}y^{1/2})^8$ 35. $\left(\dfrac{z^3}{t^6}\right)^{-1/3}$

36. $\left(\dfrac{a^{-1/2}}{b^{1/3}}\right)^6$ 37. $\left(\dfrac{x^{-2}y^{-1/3}z}{x^{-5/3}y^{-2/3}z^{2/3}}\right)^3$

38. $\left(\dfrac{x^{1/4}y^{3/4}z^{-1}}{x^{-3/4}y^{1/4}z^0}\right)^2$

▲ *Write each product so that each base of a power occurs at most once in each term. See Example 7.*

39. $x^{1/2}(x + x^{1/2})$ 40. $x^{1/5}(x^{2/5} + x^{4/5})$

41. $x^{1/3}(x^{2/3} - x^{1/3})$ 42. $x^{3/8}(x^{1/4} - x^{1/2})$

43. $x^{-3/4}(x^{-1/4} + x^{3/4})$ 44. $y^{-1/4}(y^{3/4} + y^{5/4})$

45. $t^{3/5}(t^{2/5} + t^{-3/5})$ 46. $a^{-2/7}(a^{9/7} + a^{2/7})$

47. $b^{3/4}(b^{1/4} + b^{-1/2})$ 48. $x^{5/6}(x^{-5/6} + x^{1/6})$

49. $x^{1/2}(x^{3/2} + 2x^{1/2} - x^{-1/2})$

50. $x^{2/3}(x^{4/3} - x^{1/3} + x^{-1/3})$

51. $(2x^{1/2} - 1)(x^{1/2} + 1)$ 52. $(2x^{1/2} + 1)(x^{1/2} - 1)$

53. $(x^{1/2} - 2)^2$ 54. $(x^{1/2} + 3)^2$

55. $(x^{1/2} - 2x)(x^{1/2} + x)$ 56. $(x^{1/2} - x)(x^{1/2} + 2x)$

Miscellaneous Exercises

57. Use a counterexample to show that $(a + b)^{1/2}$ is not equivalent to $a^{1/2} + b^{1/2}$.

58. Use a counterexample to show that $(a + b)^{-1/2}$ is not equivalent to $a^{-1/2} + b^{-1/2}$.

▲ *Simplify. Assume that $m, n > 0$.*

59. $x^n \cdot x^{n/2}$ 60. $(a^2)^{n/2} \cdot (b^{2n})^{2/n}$

61. $\dfrac{x^{2n}}{x^{n/2}}$ 62. $\left(\dfrac{a^n}{b}\right)^{1/2}\left(\dfrac{b}{a^{2n}}\right)^{3/2}$

63. $\dfrac{x^{3n}y^{2m+1}}{(x^n y^m)^{1/2}}$ 64. $\left(\dfrac{m^a n^{2a}}{n^{4a}}\right)^{1/a}$

65. $\left(\dfrac{x^{2n} \cdot y^{3n}}{x^n}\right)^{1/3}$ 66. $\left(\dfrac{x^{n+1} \cdot y^{n+2}}{xy^2}\right)^{1/n}$

| **5.5** | **RADICALS** |

Radical Notation   In Section 5.4 we agreed to refer to $a^{1/n}$ (when it exists) as the nth root of a. An alternative symbol is often used for $a^{1/n}$.

> *For all natural numbers $n \geqslant 2$,*
> $$a^{1/n} = \sqrt[n]{a}$$

In such a representation, the symbol $\sqrt{}$ is called a **radical**, a is called the **radicand**, n is called the **index**, and the expression is said to be a **radical of order n**. If no index is written, the index is understood to be 2.

EXAMPLE 1
a. $5^{1/2} = \sqrt{5}$
b. $x^{1/5} = \sqrt[5]{x}$
c. $2x^{1/3} = 2\sqrt[3]{x}$
d. $\sqrt{7} = 7^{1/2}$
e. $\sqrt[4]{2y} = (2y)^{1/4}$
f. $\sqrt[3]{2x} - 2\sqrt{y}$
$= (2x)^{1/3} - 2y^{1/2}$

We shall define $\sqrt[n]{a}$ to conform to our definition of $a^{1/n}$. It is convenient to do so in two parts: for n an even natural number and for n an odd natural number.

> *For n an even natural number and $a \geqslant 0$, $\sqrt[n]{a}$ is the nonnegative number such that*
> $$(\sqrt[n]{a})^n = a$$
> *In particular, for $n = 2$,*
> $$(\sqrt{a})^2 = \sqrt{a}\sqrt{a} = a$$

EXAMPLE 2
a. $\sqrt[4]{81} = 3$ because $3^4 = 81$
b. $\sqrt{16} = 4$ because $4^2 = 16$
c. $(\sqrt{5})^2 = \sqrt{5}\sqrt{5} = 5$
d. $\sqrt{-16} \neq -4$ because $(-4)^2 \neq -16$

Although each positive number a has two square roots, *the symbol $\sqrt{a}$ represents the positive value only.* Thus, the symbol $\sqrt{16}$ represents only the positive square root, 4, as in Example 2b above. The negative square root is denoted by $-\sqrt{16}$.

The restriction that $a > 0$ is not necessary if n is an odd natural number.

> *For n an odd natural number, $\sqrt[n]{a}$ is the number such that*
> $$(\sqrt[n]{a})^n = a$$

EXAMPLE 3
a. $\sqrt[3]{8} = 2$ because $2^3 = 8$
b. $\sqrt[3]{-8} = -2$ because $(-2)^3 = -8$
c. $(\sqrt[3]{4})^3 = \sqrt[3]{4}\sqrt[3]{4}\sqrt[3]{4}$
$= 4$
d. $(\sqrt[3]{-2})^3 = \sqrt[3]{-2}\sqrt[3]{-2}\sqrt[3]{-2}$
$= -2$

Since, from Section 5.4, for $a \geqslant 0$,
$$a^{m/n} = (a^m)^{1/n} = (a^{1/n})^m$$

we may write a power with a rational exponent in radical form:

> $$a^{m/n} = \sqrt[n]{a^m} = (\sqrt[n]{a})^m \qquad (a \geqslant 0)$$

▲ *Note that the denominator of the exponent is the index of the radical, and the numerator of the exponent is either the exponent of the radicand or the exponent of the root.*

E X A M P L E 4

a. $x^{2/3} = \sqrt[3]{x^2}$
$= (\sqrt[3]{x})^2$

b. $8^{2/3} = \sqrt[3]{8^2} = \sqrt[3]{64} = 4$ or
$8^{2/3} = (\sqrt[3]{8})^2 = 2^2 = 4$

Since we have restricted the index of a radical to be a natural number, we must always express a fractional exponent in standard form (m/n or $-m/n$) before writing the power in radical form.

E X A M P L E 5

a. $x^{-(3/4)} = x^{(-3/4)}$
$= \sqrt[4]{x^{-3}}$

b. $8^{-(2/3)} = 8^{-2/3} = \sqrt[3]{8^{-2}}$
$= \sqrt[3]{\dfrac{1}{64}} = \dfrac{1}{4}$

Sometimes you may find it helpful to simplify radical expressions by first writing such expressions in exponential form.

E X A M P L E 6

a. $\sqrt[3]{-8}$
$= -8^{1/3}$
$= -2$

b. $\sqrt[3]{x^6 y^3}$
$= (x^6 y^3)^{1/3}$
$= x^2 y$

c. $-\sqrt[4]{81x^4}$
$= -(81x^4)^{1/4}$
$= -3x$

We can also use fractional exponents to simplify a radical expression.

E X A M P L E 7

a. $\sqrt[4]{5^2} = 5^{2/4}$
$= 5^{1/2}$
$= \sqrt{5}$

b. $\sqrt[6]{9} = (3^2)^{1/6}$
$= 3^{1/3}$
$= \sqrt[3]{3}$

c. $\sqrt[8]{x^2} = x^{2/8}$
$= x^{1/4}$
$= \sqrt[4]{x}$

$\sqrt[n]{a^n}$, *n* an Even Number

Because we have defined a radical with an even index to be a nonnegative number, we have the following special relationship for all values of a:

$$\sqrt[n]{a^n} = |a| \qquad (n \text{ even})$$

In particular,

$$\sqrt{a^2} = |a|$$

In considering odd indices, no ambiguous interpretation is possible.

For all a,

$$\sqrt[n]{a^n} = a \qquad (n \text{ odd})$$

EXAMPLE 8 | a. $\sqrt{2^2} = |2| = 2$ b. $\sqrt{(-2)^2} = |-2| = 2$

c. $\sqrt[3]{4^3} = 4$ d. $\sqrt[3]{(-4)^3} = -4$

If a radical has an even index and the variables in the radicand represent negative as well as positive real numbers, we must use absolute-value notation when the expression is written without radical notation.

EXAMPLE 9 | a. $\sqrt{16x^2} = 4|x|$ b. $\sqrt{x^2 - 2xy + y^2} = \sqrt{(x - y)^2}$

$$= |x - y|$$

Radical Notation for Rational Numbers   Because, as observed in Section 5.4, $a^{1/n}$ represents a rational number if and only if a is the nth power of a rational number, the same is true of $\sqrt[n]{a}$. Thus,

$$\sqrt{4}, \qquad -\sqrt[3]{27}, \qquad \sqrt[4]{\frac{81}{16}}, \qquad \text{and} \qquad \sqrt[5]{-32}$$

are rational numbers equal to

$$2, \qquad -3, \qquad \frac{3}{2}, \qquad \text{and} \qquad -2$$

respectively.

Approximations for Irrational Numbers   In contrast, numbers such as $\sqrt{31}$, $\sqrt[3]{37}$, and $\sqrt[4]{73}$ are irrational numbers such that

$$(\sqrt{31})^2 = 31, \qquad (\sqrt[3]{37})^3 = 37, \qquad \text{and} \qquad (\sqrt[4]{73})^4 = 73$$

Although $\sqrt{31}$, $\sqrt[3]{37}$, and $\sqrt[4]{73}$ do not have terminating or repeating decimal representations, we can obtain approximations for these numbers and other irrational numbers using a scientific calculator. We consider the use of calculators for this purpose in Section 5.6.

Sometimes, it is useful to estimate the value of an irrational number without the aid of a calculator. For example, to estimate $\sqrt{31}$, we note that

$$\sqrt{25} < \sqrt{31} < \sqrt{36}$$

($\sqrt{25}$ and $\sqrt{36}$ were chosen because they have square roots that are integers), so

$$5 < \sqrt{31} < 6$$

EXAMPLE 10 | a. $3 < \sqrt[3]{37} < 4$, because $\sqrt[3]{27} < \sqrt[3]{37} < \sqrt[3]{64}$.

b. $2 < \sqrt[4]{73} < 3$, because $\sqrt[4]{16} < \sqrt[4]{73} < \sqrt[4]{81}$.

Table for Square Roots   If a calculator is not available, the table in Appendix D can be used to obtain approximations of irrational numbers that are square roots of numbers between 1 and 100. For example, using the table, we find

$$\sqrt{2} \approx 1.414$$

EXERCISE SET 5.5

▲ In Problems 1–72, assume that each variable and each radicand represents a positive number.

▲ Write each expression in exponential form. See Example 1.

1. $\sqrt{7}$ **2.** $\sqrt{5}$ **3.** $\sqrt[3]{2x}$

4. $\sqrt[3]{4y}$ **5.** $\sqrt[3]{x} - 3\sqrt{y}$ **6.** $\sqrt{x} - 2\sqrt[3]{y}$

7. $\sqrt[3]{x}\sqrt{y}$ **8.** $\sqrt{x}\sqrt[3]{xy}$

▲ Write each expression in radical form. See Example 1.

9. $3^{1/2}$ **10.** $7^{1/2}$ **11.** $4x^{1/3}$

12. $3x^{1/4}$ **13.** $(x-2)^{1/4}$ **14.** $(y+2)^{1/3}$

15. $3(xy)^{1/3}$ **16.** $2(x+y)^{1/5}$

▲ Find the root or power indicated. See Examples 2 and 3.

17. $\sqrt{9}$ **18.** $\sqrt{36}$ **19.** $(\sqrt[4]{2})^4$

20. $(\sqrt{7})^2$ **21.** $\sqrt[3]{27}$ **22.** $\sqrt[3]{-27}$

23. $(\sqrt[3]{5})^3$ **24.** $(\sqrt[3]{-5})^3$

▲ Write each expression in radical notation. See Examples 4 and 5.

25. $x^{2/3}$ **26.** $y^{3/4}$ **27.** $3x^{3/5}$

28. $5y^{2/3}$ **29.** $(x+2y)^{3/2}$ **30.** $(x-2y)^{2/3}$

31. $y^{-1/2}$ **32.** $x^{-1/3}$ **33.** $x^{-2/3}$

34. $y^{-2/7}$ **35.** $3y^{-2/3}$ **36.** $4x^{-3/2}$

▲ Write each expression with positive fractional exponents. See Example 6.

37. $\sqrt[3]{x^2}$ **38.** $\sqrt{y^3}$ **39.** $\sqrt[3]{(xy)^2}$

40. $\sqrt[3]{xy^2}$ **41.** $\sqrt{xy^3}$ **42.** $\sqrt{(xy)^3}$

43. $\dfrac{1}{\sqrt{x}}$ **44.** $\dfrac{2}{\sqrt[3]{y}}$

▲ Find the indicated root. See Examples 2, 3, and 6.

45. $\sqrt[3]{27}$ **46.** $\sqrt[3]{125}$ **47.** $\sqrt[3]{-64}$

48. $\sqrt[5]{-32}$ **49.** $\sqrt[3]{x^3}$ **50.** $\sqrt[5]{y^5}$

51. $\sqrt{x^4}$ **52.** $\sqrt{a^6}$ **53.** $\sqrt[3]{8y^6}$

54. $\sqrt[3]{27y^9}$ **55.** $-\sqrt{x^4y^6}$

56. $-\sqrt{a^8b^{10}}$ **57.** $\sqrt{\dfrac{4}{9}x^2y^8}$

58. $\sqrt{\dfrac{9}{16}a^2b^4}$ **59.** $\sqrt[3]{\dfrac{-8}{125}x^3}$

60. $\sqrt[3]{\dfrac{8}{27}a^3b^6}$ **61.** $\sqrt[4]{16x^4y^8}$

62. $\sqrt[5]{-32x^5y^{10}}$ **63.** $-\sqrt[3]{-8a^6b^9}$

64. $\sqrt[4]{81a^8b^{12}}$

▲ Reduce the order of each radical. See Example 7.

65. $\sqrt[4]{3^2}$ **66.** $\sqrt[6]{2^2}$ **67.** $\sqrt[6]{3^3}$

68. $\sqrt[8]{5^2}$ **69.** $\sqrt[6]{81}$ **70.** $\sqrt[10]{32}$

71. $\sqrt[6]{x^3}$ **72.** $\sqrt[9]{y^3}$

▲ Approximate each irrational number between two integers without the aid of a calculator. See Example 10.

73. $\sqrt{173}$ **74.** $\sqrt{370}$ **75.** $\sqrt[3]{408}$

76. $\sqrt[3]{206}$ **77.** $\sqrt[3]{-87.3}$ **78.** $\sqrt[3]{-49.1}$

79. $\sqrt[4]{130}$ **80.** $\sqrt[4]{321}$

Miscellaneous Exercises

▲ Graph each set of real numbers on a separate line graph. (Use a calculator or the Table of Squares, Square Roots, and Prime Factors in Appendix D to obtain rational-number approximations for irrational numbers.)

81. $-\sqrt{7}, -\sqrt{1}, \sqrt{5}, \sqrt{9}$

82. $-\dfrac{2}{3}, 0, \sqrt{3}, -\sqrt{11}$

83. $-\sqrt{20}, -\sqrt{6}, \sqrt{1}, 6$

84. $\sqrt{41}, \sqrt{7}, -\sqrt{7}, \dfrac{3}{4}$

85. Use a counterexample to show that $\sqrt{a^2}$ is not equivalent to a.

86. Use a counterexample to show that $\sqrt{(a-1)^2}$ is not equivalent to $a-1$.

▲ In the foregoing problems, variables and radicands were restricted to represent positive numbers. In Problems 87–92, consider variables and radicands to represent elements of the set of real numbers, and use absolute-value notation as needed.

87. $\sqrt{4x^2}$ **88.** $\sqrt{9x^2y^4}$

89. $\sqrt{x^2+2x+1}$ **90.** $\sqrt{4x^2-4x+1}$

91. $\dfrac{2}{\sqrt{x^2+2xy+y^2}}$ **92.** $\sqrt{x^4+2x^2y^2+y^4}$

5.6 | USING CALCULATORS

In this section we will use scientific calculators to obtain decimal approximations for irrational numbers that occur as powers with fractional exponents and in radical notation.

Rational Numbers

Recall from Sections 1.1 and 5.4 that any number that can be expressed as the quotient of two integers is a rational number. (Of course, the denominator cannot be zero.) A rational number has a decimal representation that either terminates or has a repeating fixed block of digits.

EXAMPLE 1

By using a calculator, we find that

$$\frac{5}{8} = 0.625 \qquad \frac{5}{6} = 0.8333\ldots \qquad \text{and} \qquad \frac{3}{11} = 0.272727\ldots$$

Irrational Numbers

Also recall that any real number that cannot be expressed as the quotient of two integers is an irrational number. The decimal form of an irrational number never terminates, and it does not follow a repeating pattern; consequently, it is impossible to write an exact decimal equivalent for an irrational number. However, we can obtain decimal *approximations* that are correct to any desired degree of accuracy by rounding off. For example, the decimal representation for π, an irrational number that appears in many geometric formulas, is given by a calculator with a 10-digit display as 3.141592654. This is not the *exact* value of π, but for most calculations it is quite sufficient.

A simple four-function calculator can be used to obtain approximations for irrational numbers that are square roots. Scientific calculators can be used to approximate irrational numbers of the form $\sqrt[n]{a}$ or $a^{1/n}$ for $n \geqslant 2$. Some calculators have a radical key $\sqrt[x]{y}$, and others have power keys $y^{1/x}$ and/or y^x.

EXAMPLE 2

To approximate $\sqrt[3]{56}$, press

$$56 \boxed{\sqrt[x]{y}} \; 3 \boxed{=} \; 3.825862366$$

or, since $\sqrt[3]{56} = 56^{1/3}$,

$$56 \boxed{y^{1/x}} \; 3 \boxed{=} \; 3.825862366$$

or

$$56 \boxed{y^x} \; 3 \boxed{\frac{1}{x}} \boxed{=} \; 3.825862366$$

Round off results as needed.

In the next example we obtain an approxmation for an irrational number of the form of $a^{m/n}$ or $\sqrt[n]{a^m}$.

EXAMPLE 3 | Approximate $7^{5/3}$ to the nearest thousandth.

Solution | $7^{5/3} = (7^{1/3})^5$, so we press

$$7 \boxed{y^x} 3 \boxed{\tfrac{1}{x}} \boxed{y^x} 5 \boxed{=} 25.61513997$$

Or alternatively, $7^{5/3} = (\sqrt[3]{7})^5$, so we press

$$7 \boxed{\sqrt[x]{y}} 3 \boxed{y^x} 5 \boxed{=} 25.61513997$$

Thus, $7^{5/3} \approx 25.615$.

The approximation of powers with decimal exponents is straightforward.

EXAMPLE 4 | Approximate $1.6^{0.7}$ to the nearest tenth.

Solution | We press

$$1.6 \boxed{y^x} 0.7 \boxed{=} 1.389581386$$

so $1.6^{0.7} \approx 1.4$.

EXERCISE SET 5.6

▲ *Find a decimal representation for each rational number. Does the decimal terminate or repeat a pattern? See Example 1.*

1. $\dfrac{3}{8}$ 2. $-\dfrac{7}{8}$ 3. $-\dfrac{2}{9}$ 4. $\dfrac{4}{9}$

5. $\dfrac{7}{5}$ 6. $-\dfrac{9}{5}$ 7. $-\dfrac{7}{6}$ 8. $-\dfrac{11}{6}$

▲ *Approximate each irrational number to the nearest hundredth. See Example 2.*

9. $\sqrt[3]{29}$ 10. $-\sqrt[3]{37}$ 11. $-\sqrt[4]{41}$

12. $\sqrt[4]{73}$ 13. $\sqrt[5]{21.6}$ 14. $-\sqrt[5]{62.4}$

15. $-\sqrt[5]{1280}$ 16. $\sqrt[5]{3420}$

▲ *Approximate each irrational number to the nearest thousandth. See Example 3.*

17. $21^{3/5}$ 18. $121^{2/5}$ 19. $144^{3/7}$

20. $66^{5/7}$ 21. $(\sqrt{68})^3$ 22. $(\sqrt{44})^3$

23. $(\sqrt[3]{20})^2$ 24. $(\sqrt[3]{32})^4$

▲ *Approximate each irrational number to the nearest tenth. See Example 4.*

25. $28^{1.5}$ 26. $-62^{1.6}$ 27. $-128^{0.7}$

28. $208^{0.3}$ 29. $28.4^{2.1}$ 30. $-41.4^{1.2}$

31. $0.87^{3.3}$ 32. $0.96^{4.1}$

Miscellaneous Exercises

▲ *Approximate each computation to the nearest tenth.*

33. $\sqrt[3]{(3.42)(42.12)}$ 34. $\sqrt[3]{(40.3)(0.91)}$

35. $\sqrt[5]{\dfrac{124.2}{3.7}}$ 36. $\sqrt[5]{\dfrac{184.3}{21.2}}$

37. $\left[\dfrac{(2.3)(41.3)}{7.2}\right]^{1/4}$ 38. $\left[\dfrac{(121)(69.2)}{23.4}\right]^{1/4}$

39. The time in seconds for a pendulum of length L feet to complete one full swing is given by $2\pi\sqrt{L/g}$, where $g = 32$. How long does it take a pendulum of length 4 feet to complete one swing?

40. When a car brakes suddenly, its speed in miles per hour can be estimated from the length of its skid marks, d, by using the formula $\sqrt{30kd}$. The constant k is determined by the friction of the road surface against the tires and has the value 0.8 for a dry concrete road. If a car leaves skid marks 160 feet long, how fast was it traveling when it braked?

41. The radius of a sphere of volume V is given by $\sqrt[3]{3V/4\pi}$. Find the radius a spherical hot air balloon that holds 17,157 cubic feet of air.

42. A windmill will generate P watts of power when the wind velocity, in miles per hour, is $\sqrt[3]{P/0.015}$. Find the wind velocity necessary to generate 500 watts of power.

5.7 | CHANGING FORMS OF RADICALS

From the definition of a radical and the laws of exponents, we can derive two important relationships.

Laws of Radicals

> For $a, b > 0$ and n a natural number,
>
> $$\sqrt[n]{ab} = \sqrt[n]{a}\,\sqrt[n]{b} \qquad (1)$$

This property follows from the fact that

$$\sqrt[n]{ab} = (ab)^{1/n} = a^{1/n}b^{1/n} = \sqrt[n]{a}\,\sqrt[n]{b}$$

Relationship (1) can be used to write a radical in a simplified form in which the radicand contains no factor that has an exponent greater than or equal to the index of the radical.

EXAMPLE 1

First factor the largest square that occurs as a factor in the radicand.

a. $\sqrt{18} = \sqrt{3^2 \cdot 2}$

$\quad\quad = \sqrt{3^2}\,\sqrt{2}$

$\quad\quad = 3\sqrt{2}$

In b and c, first factor the largest cube that occurs as a factor in the radicand.

b. $\sqrt[3]{x^{10}} = \sqrt[3]{x^9 \cdot x}$

$\quad\quad\quad = \sqrt[3]{x^9}\,\sqrt[3]{x}$

$\quad\quad\quad = x^3\,\sqrt[3]{x}$

c. $\sqrt[3]{16x^7y^5} = \sqrt[3]{8x^6y^3 \cdot 2xy^2}$

$\quad\quad\quad\quad = \sqrt[3]{8x^6y^3}\,\sqrt[3]{2xy^2}$

$\quad\quad\quad\quad = 2x^2y\,\sqrt[3]{2xy^2}$

The second important relationship involves quotients.

> For $a, b > 0$ and n a natural number,
>
> $$\sqrt[n]{\frac{a}{b}} = \frac{\sqrt[n]{a}}{\sqrt[n]{b}} \qquad (2)$$

This property follows from the fact that

$$\sqrt[n]{\frac{a}{b}} = \left(\frac{a}{b}\right)^{1/n} = \frac{a^{1/n}}{b^{1/n}} = \frac{\sqrt[n]{a}}{\sqrt[n]{b}}$$

We can sometimes use Relationship (2) to rewrite a radical so that the radicand contains no fraction.

EXAMPLE 2

a. $\sqrt{\dfrac{3}{4}} = \dfrac{\sqrt{3}}{\sqrt{4}} = \dfrac{\sqrt{3}}{2}$ b. $\sqrt[3]{\dfrac{5}{8}} = \dfrac{\sqrt[3]{5}}{\sqrt[3]{8}} = \dfrac{\sqrt[3]{5}}{2}$

If a radical in the denominator of a fraction cannot be simplified, we can use the fundamental principle of fractions to obtain a denominator free of radicals. In particular, a fraction of the form $\dfrac{a}{\sqrt{b}}$ can be simplified by multiplying by $\dfrac{\sqrt{b}}{\sqrt{b}}$.

EXAMPLE 3

a. $\sqrt{\dfrac{1}{3}} = \dfrac{\sqrt{1}}{\sqrt{3}}$

$= \dfrac{1\sqrt{3}}{\sqrt{3}\sqrt{3}} = \dfrac{\sqrt{3}}{3}$

b. $\sqrt{\dfrac{2}{5x}} = \dfrac{\sqrt{2}}{\sqrt{5x}}$

$= \dfrac{\sqrt{2}\sqrt{5x}}{\sqrt{5x}\sqrt{5x}} = \dfrac{\sqrt{10x}}{5x}$

The foregoing process is called *rationalizing the denominator* of a fraction.

EXAMPLE 4

Rationalize the denominator: $\dfrac{1}{\sqrt[3]{2x}}$.

Solution

Because we need a third power, $(2x)^3$, beneath the radical sign in the denominator to write it without a radical sign, we must multiply $\sqrt[3]{2x}$ by two additional factors of $\sqrt[3]{2x}$. Thus, using the fundamental principle of fractions, we obtain

$$\dfrac{1}{\sqrt[3]{2x}} = \dfrac{1\sqrt[3]{2x}\sqrt[3]{2x}}{\sqrt[3]{2x}\sqrt[3]{2x}\sqrt[3]{2x}}$$

$$= \dfrac{\sqrt[3]{(2x)^2}}{\sqrt[3]{(2x)^3}} = \dfrac{\sqrt[3]{4x^2}}{2x}$$

Sometimes fractions that contain radicals can be simplified by first applying the preceding Properties (1) and (2) and then reducing.

EXAMPLE 5

a. $\dfrac{\sqrt{a}\sqrt{ab^3}}{\sqrt{b}} = \sqrt{\dfrac{a^2b^3}{b}}$

$= \sqrt{a^2b^2}$

$= ab$

b. $\dfrac{\sqrt[3]{16y^4}}{\sqrt[3]{y}} = \sqrt[3]{\dfrac{16y^4}{y}}$

$= \sqrt[3]{2^4y^3}$

$= 2y\sqrt[3]{2}$

Writing Equivalent Radical Expressions

Application of Properties (1) and/or (2) on page 135 can be used to rewrite radical expressions in various ways and, in particular, to write them in what is called **simplest form**.

> **Simplest Form of Radical Expression**
>
> 1. The radicand contains no polynomial factor raised to a power equal to or greater than the index of the radical.
> 2. The radicand contains no fractions.
> 3. No radical expressions are contained in denominators of fractions.

The answers in the preceding Examples 1 through 5 are in simplest form. Although we generally change the form of radicals to one of the forms described here, there are times when such forms are not preferred. For example, in certain situations, $\sqrt{\dfrac{1}{2}}$ or $\dfrac{1}{\sqrt{2}}$ may be more useful than the equivalent form $\dfrac{\sqrt{2}}{2}$. In such cases we may want to rationalize the numerator of a fraction.

EXAMPLE 6 Rationalize each numerator:

a. $\dfrac{\sqrt{2}}{2}$

b. $\dfrac{\sqrt{2x}}{x}$

Solutions

a. $\dfrac{\sqrt{2}}{2} = \dfrac{\sqrt{2} \cdot \sqrt{2}}{2 \cdot \sqrt{2}}$
$= \dfrac{2}{2\sqrt{2}} = \dfrac{1}{\sqrt{2}}$

b. $\dfrac{\sqrt{2x}}{x} = \dfrac{\sqrt{2x} \cdot \sqrt{2x}}{x \cdot \sqrt{2x}}$
$= \dfrac{2x}{x\sqrt{2x}} = \dfrac{2}{\sqrt{2x}}$

EXERCISE SET 5.7

▲ *Assume that all variables in radicands in this exercise set denote positive real numbers.*

▲ *Change to simplest form. See Example 1.*

1. $\sqrt{18}$
2. $\sqrt{50}$
3. $\sqrt{20}$
4. $\sqrt{72}$
5. $\sqrt{75}$
6. $\sqrt{48}$
7. $\sqrt{x^4}$
8. $\sqrt{y^6}$
9. $\sqrt{x^3}$
10. $\sqrt{y^{11}}$
11. $\sqrt{9x^3}$
12. $\sqrt{4y^5}$
13. $\sqrt{8x^6}$
14. $\sqrt{18y^8}$
15. $\sqrt[4]{x^5}$
16. $\sqrt[3]{y^4}$
17. $\sqrt[5]{x^7y^9z^{11}}$
18. $\sqrt[5]{a^{12}b^{15}}$
19. $\sqrt[6]{a^7b^{12}c^{15}}$
20. $\sqrt[6]{m^8n^7}$
21. $\sqrt[7]{3^7a^8b^9c^{10}}$
22. $\sqrt[7]{4^8x^9y^{10}z^{14}}$
23. $\sqrt{18}\sqrt{2}$
24. $\sqrt{3}\sqrt{27}$
25. $\sqrt{xy}\sqrt{x^5y}$
26. $\sqrt{a}\sqrt{ab^2}$
27. $\sqrt[3]{2}\sqrt[3]{4}$
28. $\sqrt[4]{3}\sqrt[4]{27}$

29. $\sqrt{3 \times 10^2}$
30. $\sqrt{5 \times 10^3}$
31. $\sqrt{60,000}$
32. $\sqrt{800,000}$

▲ *Rationalize each denominator. See Examples 2 and 3.*

33. $\sqrt{\dfrac{1}{5}}$
34. $\sqrt{\dfrac{2}{3}}$
35. $\dfrac{-1}{\sqrt{2}}$
36. $\dfrac{-\sqrt{3}}{\sqrt{7}}$
37. $\sqrt{\dfrac{x}{2}}$
38. $-\sqrt{\dfrac{y}{3}}$
39. $-\sqrt{\dfrac{y}{x}}$
40. $\sqrt{\dfrac{2a}{b}}$
41. $\dfrac{x}{\sqrt{x}}$
42. $\dfrac{-x}{\sqrt{2y}}$
43. $\sqrt{\dfrac{y}{2x}}$
44. $\sqrt{\dfrac{y}{6x}}$

▲ *Rationalize each denominator. See Example 4.*

45. $\dfrac{1}{\sqrt[3]{x^2}}$
46. $\dfrac{1}{\sqrt[4]{y^3}}$
47. $\sqrt[3]{\dfrac{2}{3y}}$

48. $\sqrt[4]{\dfrac{2}{3x}}$ **49.** $\sqrt[3]{\dfrac{x}{4y^2}}$ **50.** $\sqrt[4]{\dfrac{x}{8y^3}}$

51. $\sqrt[5]{\dfrac{3}{2x^3}}$ **52.** $\sqrt[5]{\dfrac{2}{9y^2}}$

▲ *Change to simplest form. See Example 5.*

53. $\dfrac{\sqrt{a^5 b^3}}{\sqrt{ab}}$ **54.** $\dfrac{\sqrt{x}\sqrt{xy^3}}{\sqrt{y}}$ **55.** $\dfrac{\sqrt{98x^2 y^3}}{\sqrt{xy}}$

56. $\dfrac{\sqrt{45x^3}\sqrt{y^3}}{\sqrt{5y}}$ **57.** $\dfrac{\sqrt[3]{8b^4}}{\sqrt[3]{a^6}}$ **58.** $\dfrac{\sqrt[3]{16r^4}}{\sqrt[3]{4t^3}}$

59. $\dfrac{\sqrt[5]{a}\sqrt[5]{b^2}}{\sqrt[5]{ab}}$ **60.** $\dfrac{\sqrt[5]{x^2}\sqrt[5]{y^2}}{\sqrt[5]{xy^2}}$

▲ *Rationalize each numerator. See Example 6.*

61. $\dfrac{\sqrt{3}}{3}$ **62.** $\dfrac{\sqrt{2}}{3}$ **63.** $\dfrac{\sqrt{x}}{\sqrt{y}}$

64. $\dfrac{\sqrt{xy}}{x}$

Miscellaneous Exercises

65. Use a counterexample to show that $(\sqrt{a} + \sqrt{b})^2$ is not equivalent to $a + b$.

66. Use a counterexample to show that $\sqrt{a + b}$ is not equivalent to $\sqrt{a} + \sqrt{b}$.

▲ *Simplify. Assume that all variables and radicands represent positive numbers.*

67. $\sqrt{8(x-1)^3}$ **68.** $\sqrt{12(x+2)^3}$

69. $\sqrt{x^3(y-2)^5}$ **70.** $\sqrt{y^5(x+1)^3}$

71. $\sqrt{\dfrac{(y-3)^3}{xy^3}}$ **72.** $\sqrt{\dfrac{(x+2)^5}{x^3 y}}$

73. $\sqrt[3]{4x^5 - x^3}$ **74.** $\sqrt[3]{2y^4 - y^3}$

75. $\sqrt[3]{\dfrac{(x-1)^4}{xy^2}}$ **76.** $\sqrt[3]{\dfrac{(y+1)^4}{x^2 y}}$

77. $\dfrac{\sqrt{9(x-1)^2}}{\sqrt{3x}\sqrt{x^3 - x^2}}$ **78.** $\dfrac{\sqrt{4(y+2)^2}}{\sqrt{4y}\sqrt{y^3 + 2y^2}}$

5.8   EXPRESSIONS CONTAINING RADICALS

Sums and Differences

The distributive property,

$$a(b + c) = ab + ac \qquad (1)$$

is assumed to hold for all real numbers. By the symmetric property of equality and the commutative property of multiplication, (1) can be written as

$$ba + ca = (b + c)a$$

Since at this time all radical expressions have been defined so that they represent real numbers, the distributive property holds for radical expressions. Hence, we may write sums or differences containing radicals of the same index and radicand as a single term.

EXAMPLE 1

a. $3\sqrt{3} + 4\sqrt{3} = (3 + 4)\sqrt{3}$
$$= 7\sqrt{3}$$

b. $7\sqrt{x} - 2\sqrt{x} = (7 - 2)\sqrt{x}$
$$= 5\sqrt{x}$$

Sometimes it is necessary to simplify radical expressions in a sum or a difference before they can be written as a single term.

EXAMPLE 2

a. $3\sqrt{20} + \sqrt{45}$
$$= 3 \cdot 2\sqrt{5} + 3\sqrt{5}$$
$$= 6\sqrt{5} + 3\sqrt{5}$$
$$= 9\sqrt{5}$$

b. $\sqrt{32x} + \sqrt{2x} - \sqrt{18x}$
$$= 4\sqrt{2x} + \sqrt{2x} - 3\sqrt{2x}$$
$$= 2\sqrt{2x}$$

Products and Factors

The distributive property permits us to multiply expressions involving sums or differences of radicals.

EXAMPLE 3

a. $x(\sqrt{2} + \sqrt{3}) = x\sqrt{2} + x\sqrt{3}$

b. $\sqrt{3}(\sqrt{2x} + \sqrt{6}) = \sqrt{6x} + \sqrt{18}$
$$= \sqrt{6x} + \sqrt{9}\sqrt{2}$$
$$= \sqrt{6x} + 3\sqrt{2}$$

c. For $x \geqslant 0$,
$$\sqrt{x}(\sqrt{2x} - \sqrt{x})$$
$$= \sqrt{2x^2} - x$$
$$= x\sqrt{2} - x$$

d. For $x \geqslant 0$, $y \geqslant 0$,
$$(\sqrt{x} - \sqrt{y})(\sqrt{x} + \sqrt{y})$$
$$= \sqrt{x^2} - \sqrt{y^2}$$
$$= x - y$$

Using the distributive property in the form

$$ab + ac = a(b + c)$$

We can factor expressions containing radicals.

EXAMPLE 4

a. $3 + \sqrt{18}$
$$= 3 + 3\sqrt{2}$$
$$= 3(1 + \sqrt{2})$$

b. $\dfrac{\sqrt{a} + \sqrt{ab}}{\sqrt{a}} = \dfrac{\sqrt{a} + \sqrt{a}\sqrt{b}}{\sqrt{a}}$
$$= \dfrac{\sqrt{a}(1 + \sqrt{b})}{\sqrt{a}}$$
$$= 1 + \sqrt{b}$$

Quotients

Recall from Section 5.7 that a monomial denominator of a fraction of the form $a/\sqrt{b}$ can be rationalized by multiplying the numerator and the denominator by $\sqrt{b}$. For example,

$$\frac{2}{\sqrt{3}} = \frac{2\sqrt{3}}{\sqrt{3}\sqrt{3}} = \frac{2\sqrt{3}}{3} \quad \text{and} \quad \frac{a}{\sqrt{b}} = \frac{a\sqrt{b}}{\sqrt{b}\sqrt{b}} = \frac{a\sqrt{b}}{b}$$

The distributive property provides us with a means of rationalizing binomial denominators which contain radicals. To accomplish this, we first recall that

$$(a - b)(a + b) = a^2 - b^2$$

where the product contains no first-degree term. Each of the two factors $a - b$ and $a + b$ is said to be the **conjugate** of the other.

Now consider a fraction of the form

$$\frac{a}{b + \sqrt{c}} \quad (b + \sqrt{c} \neq 0)$$

If we multiply the numerator and the denominator of this fraction by the conjugate of the denominator, the denominator of the resulting fraction will contain no term linear in $\sqrt{c}$; hence, it will be free of radicals. That is,

$$\frac{a(b - \sqrt{c})}{(b + \sqrt{c})(b - \sqrt{c})} = \frac{ab - a\sqrt{c}}{b^2 - c} \qquad (b^2 - c \neq 0)$$

where the denominator has been rationalized.

This process also applies to fractions of the form

$$\frac{a}{\sqrt{b} + \sqrt{c}}$$

since

$$\frac{a(b - \sqrt{c})}{(\sqrt{b} + \sqrt{c})(b - \sqrt{c})} = \frac{a\sqrt{b} - a\sqrt{c}}{b - c} \qquad (b - c \neq 0)$$

EXAMPLE 5   Rationalize each denominator.

a. $\dfrac{2}{\sqrt{3} - 1}$

b. $\dfrac{x}{2 + \sqrt{x}}$

Solutions

a. $\dfrac{2}{\sqrt{3} - 1} = \dfrac{2(\sqrt{3} + 1)}{(\sqrt{3} - 1)(\sqrt{3} + 1)}$

$= \dfrac{2(\sqrt{3} + 1)}{3 - 1}$

$= \sqrt{3} + 1$

b. $\dfrac{x}{2 + \sqrt{x}} = \dfrac{x(2 - \sqrt{x})}{(2 + \sqrt{x})(2 - \sqrt{x})}$

$= \dfrac{x(2 - \sqrt{x})}{4 - x}$

$= \dfrac{2x - x\sqrt{x}}{4 - x}$

As noted in Section 5.7, we can rationalize the numerator of a fraction as well as the denominator.

EXAMPLE 6   Rationalize each numerator:

a. $\dfrac{\sqrt{2} - 1}{2}$

b. $\dfrac{\sqrt{x} + 1}{x}$

Solutions

a. $\dfrac{\sqrt{2} - 1}{2} = \dfrac{(\sqrt{2} - 1)(\sqrt{2} + 1)}{2(\sqrt{2} + 1)}$

$= \dfrac{2 - 1}{2(\sqrt{2} + 1)}$

$= \dfrac{1}{2\sqrt{2} + 2}$

b. $\dfrac{\sqrt{x} + 1}{x} = \dfrac{(\sqrt{x} + 1)(\sqrt{x} - 1)}{x(\sqrt{x} - 1)}$

$= \dfrac{x - 1}{x(\sqrt{x} - 1)}$

$= \dfrac{x - 1}{x\sqrt{x} - x}$

EXERCISE SET 5.8

▲ *Assume that all radicands and variables in this exercise set are positive real numbers.*

▲ *Write each expression as a single term. See Examples 1 and 2.*

1. $3\sqrt{7} + 2\sqrt{7}$

2. $5\sqrt{2} - 3\sqrt{2}$

3. $4\sqrt{3} - \sqrt{27}$

4. $\sqrt{75} + 2\sqrt{3}$

5. $\sqrt{50x} + \sqrt{32x}$

6. $\sqrt{8y} - \sqrt{18y}$

7. $3\sqrt{4xy^2} - 4\sqrt{9xy^2}$

8. $2\sqrt{8y^2z} + 3\sqrt{32y^2z}$

9. $3\sqrt{8a} + 2\sqrt{50a} - \sqrt{2a}$

10. $\sqrt{3b} - 2\sqrt{12b} + 3\sqrt{48b}$

11. $3\sqrt[3]{16} - \sqrt[3]{2}$

12. $\sqrt[3]{54} + 2\sqrt[3]{128}$

▲ *Write each expression without parentheses and all radicals in simple form.*

13. $2(3 - \sqrt{5})$

14. $5(2 - \sqrt{7})$

15. $\sqrt{2}(\sqrt{6} + \sqrt{10})$

16. $\sqrt{3}(\sqrt{12} - \sqrt{15})$

17. $(3 + \sqrt{5})(2 - \sqrt{5})$

18. $(1 - \sqrt{2})(2 + \sqrt{2})$

19. $(\sqrt{x} - 3)(\sqrt{x} + 3)$

20. $(2 + \sqrt{x})(2 - \sqrt{x})$

21. $(\sqrt{2} - \sqrt{3})(\sqrt{2} + 2\sqrt{3})$

22. $(\sqrt{3} - \sqrt{5})(2\sqrt{3} + \sqrt{5})$

23. $(\sqrt{5} - \sqrt{2})^2$

24. $(\sqrt{2} - 2\sqrt{3})^2$

▲ *Change each expression to the form indicated. See Example 4.*

25. $2 + 2\sqrt{3} = 2(? + ?)$

26. $5 + 10\sqrt{2} = 5(? + ?)$

27. $2\sqrt{27} + 6 = 6(? + ?)$

28. $5\sqrt{5} - \sqrt{25} = 5(? - ?)$

29. $4 + \sqrt{16y} = 4(? + ?)$

30. $3 + \sqrt{18x} = 3(? + ?)$

31. $\sqrt{2} - \sqrt{6} = \sqrt{2}(? - ?)$

32. $\sqrt{12} - 2\sqrt{6} = 2\sqrt{3}(? - ?)$

▲ *Reduce each fraction to lowest terms after factoring the numerator. See Example 4.*

33. $\dfrac{2 + 2\sqrt{3}}{2}$

34. $\dfrac{6 + 2\sqrt{5}}{2}$

35. $\dfrac{6 + 2\sqrt{18}}{6}$

36. $\dfrac{8 - 2\sqrt{12}}{4}$

37. $\dfrac{x - \sqrt{x^3}}{x}$

38. $\dfrac{xy - x\sqrt{xy^2}}{xy}$

39. $\dfrac{x\sqrt{y} - \sqrt{y^3}}{\sqrt{y}}$

40. $\dfrac{\sqrt{x} - y\sqrt{x^3}}{\sqrt{x}}$

▲ *Rationalize each denominator. See Example 5.*

41. $\dfrac{4}{1 + \sqrt{3}}$

42. $\dfrac{1}{2 - \sqrt{2}}$

43. $\dfrac{2}{\sqrt{7} - 2}$

44. $\dfrac{2}{4 - \sqrt{5}}$

45. $\dfrac{x}{\sqrt{x} - 3}$

46. $\dfrac{y}{\sqrt{3} - y}$

47. $\dfrac{\sqrt{6} - 3}{2 - \sqrt{6}}$

48. $\dfrac{\sqrt{x} + \sqrt{y}}{\sqrt{x} - \sqrt{y}}$

▲ *Rationalize each numerator. See Example 6.*

49. $\dfrac{1 - \sqrt{2}}{2}$

50. $\dfrac{\sqrt{3} + \sqrt{2}}{\sqrt{3}}$

51. $\dfrac{\sqrt{x} - 1}{3}$

52. $\dfrac{4 - \sqrt{2y}}{2}$

53. $\dfrac{\sqrt{x} - \sqrt{y}}{x}$

54. $\dfrac{2\sqrt{x} + \sqrt{y}}{\sqrt{xy}}$

Miscellaneous Exercises

▲ *Write each expression as a single fraction in which the denominator is rationalized.*

55. $\sqrt{x + 1} - \dfrac{x}{\sqrt{x + 1}}$

56. $\sqrt{x^2 - 2} - \dfrac{x^2 + 1}{\sqrt{x^2 - 2}}$

57. $\dfrac{x}{\sqrt{x^2 + 1}} - \dfrac{\sqrt{x^2 + 1}}{x}$

58. $\dfrac{x}{\sqrt{x^2 - 1}} + \dfrac{\sqrt{x^2 - 1}}{x}$

▲ *Rationalize each numerator.*

59. $\dfrac{\sqrt{x - 1} - 1}{\sqrt{x - 1}}$

60. $\dfrac{1 - \sqrt{x + 1}}{\sqrt{x + 1}}$

61. $\dfrac{\sqrt{x + 1} - \sqrt{x}}{\sqrt{x + 1} + \sqrt{x}}$

62. $\dfrac{\sqrt{x - 1} + \sqrt{x}}{\sqrt{x - 1} - \sqrt{x}}$

| 5.9 | **COMPLEX NUMBERS** |

In Section 3.5 we considered only quadratic equations with solutions in the set of real numbers. Some quadratic equations do not have real solutions. For example, if $b > 0$, then $x^2 = -b$ has no real-number solution, because there is no real number whose square is negative. For this reason the expression $\sqrt{-b}$, for $b > 0$, is undefined in the set of real numbers. In this section we consider a larger set of numbers that contains the square roots of negative real numbers as well as all the real numbers. We shall see that this new set of numbers, called the set C of **complex numbers**, provides solutions for all quadratic equations in one variable with real coefficients.

Imaginary Numbers Let us first define a set of numbers among whose members are square roots of negative real numbers. We define $\sqrt{-b}$, where b is a positive real number, to be a number whose square is equal to $-b$:

> *For* $b > 0$,
>
> $$(\sqrt{-b})^2 = -b$$
>
> *In particular,*
>
> $$(\sqrt{-1})^2 = -1$$

It is customary to use the symbol i for $\sqrt{-1}$. With this convention,

$$i^2 = -1$$

Next, assuming that for $b > 0$,

$$(i\sqrt{b})(i\sqrt{b}) = i^2 b = -1 \cdot b = -b$$

we have the alternative definition of $\sqrt{-b}$:

> $$\sqrt{-b} = \sqrt{-1}\sqrt{b} = i\sqrt{b}$$

Hence, a square root of any negative real number can be represented as the product of a real number and the number $\sqrt{-1}$ or i.

EXAMPLE 1 a. $\sqrt{-4} = \sqrt{-1}\sqrt{4}$ b. $-\sqrt{-3} = -\sqrt{-1}\sqrt{3}$
$\qquad = i\sqrt{4} = 2i$ $\qquad\qquad = -i\sqrt{3}$

The numbers represented by the symbols $\sqrt{-b}$ and $-\sqrt{-b}$, where b is a real number greater than zero, are called **pure imaginary numbers**.

Now, consider all the possible expressions of the form $a + bi$, where a and b are real numbers, and $i = \sqrt{-1}$, which are the sums of all real numbers and all pure imaginary numbers. Such an expression names a complex number, that is, a number in the set C. If $b = 0$, then $a + bi = a$, and it is evident that the set of real numbers is contained in the set C of complex numbers. If $b \neq 0$, then $a + bi$ is called an **imaginary number** (see Figure 5.1), where a is the real part of the number and b is the imaginary part. For example, the numbers -7, $3 + 2i$, and $4i$ are all complex numbers. However, -7 is also a real number, and $3 + 2i$ and $4i$ are also imaginary numbers. Furthermore, $4i$ is a pure imaginary number.

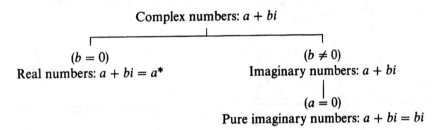

Complex numbers: $a + bi$

$(b = 0)$
Real numbers: $a + bi = a$*

$(b \neq 0)$
Imaginary numbers: $a + bi$

$(a = 0)$
Pure imaginary numbers: $a + bi = bi$

Figure 5.1

EXAMPLE 2 Write each expression in the form $a + bi$ or $a + ib$.

a. $3\sqrt{-18}$

b. $2 - 3\sqrt{-16}$

Solutions

a. $3\sqrt{-18} = 3\sqrt{-1 \cdot 9 \cdot 2}$
$= 3\sqrt{-1}\sqrt{9}\sqrt{2}$
$= 3i(3)\sqrt{2}$
$= 9i\sqrt{2}$

b. $2 - 3\sqrt{-16} = 2 - 3\sqrt{-1 \cdot 16}$
$= 2 - 3\sqrt{-1}\sqrt{16}$
$= 2 - 3i(4)$
$= 2 - 12i$

Sums and Differences To add or subtract complex numbers, we simply add or subtract their real parts and their imaginary parts.

EXAMPLE 3

a. $(2 + 3i) + (5 - 4i)$
$= (2 + 5) + (3 - 4)i$
$= 7 - i$

b. $(2 + 3i) - (5 - 4i)$
$= (2 - 5) + [3 - (-4)]i$
$= -3 + 7i$

Note that the way we add and subtract complex numbers is similar to the way we add and subtract like terms when we add polynomials.

Products To multiply complex numbers, we treat them as though they were binomials and replace i^2 with -1.

EXAMPLE 4

a. $(2 - i)(1 + 3i)$
$= 2 + 6i - i - 3i^2$
$= 2 + 6i - i - 3(-1)$
$= 2 + 6i - i + 3$
$= 5 + 5i$

b. $(3 - i)^2 = (3 - i)(3 - i)$
$= 9 - 3i - 3i + i^2$
$= 9 - 6i + (-1)$
$= 8 - 6i$

Quotients Recall from Section 5.8 that, for $b > 0$, the *conjugate* of $a + \sqrt{b}$ is $a - \sqrt{b}$. Similarly, the conjugate of $a + \sqrt{-b}$ is $a - \sqrt{-b}$.

---

*See Figure 1.1, page 2, for sets of numbers that are contained in the set of real numbers.

EXAMPLE 5
   a. The conjugate of $2 + 3i$ is $2 - 3i$.

   b. The conjugate of $-3 - i$ is $-3 + i$.

   c. The conjugate of $2i$ is $-2i$.

   d. The conjugate of $-4 + i$ is $-4 - i$.

The quotient

$$\frac{a + bi}{c + di}$$

can be written as a complex number by multiplying the numerator and the denominator by $c - di$, the conjugate of the denominator. That is,

$$\frac{a + bi}{c + di} = \frac{(a + bi)(c - di)}{(c + di)(c - di)}$$

EXAMPLE 6
   a.
$$\frac{4 - i}{-2i} = \frac{(4 - i)i}{-2i \cdot i}$$
$$= \frac{4i - i^2}{-2i^2}$$
$$= \frac{4i - (-1)}{-2(-1)}$$
$$= \frac{4i + 1}{2} = \frac{1}{2} + 2i$$

   b.
$$\frac{4 + i}{2 + 3i} = \frac{(4 + i)(2 - 3i)}{(2 + 3i)(2 - 3i)}$$
$$= \frac{8 - 10i - 3i^2}{4 - 9i^2}$$
$$= \frac{8 - 10i + 3}{4 + 9}$$
$$= \frac{11}{13} - \frac{10}{13}i$$

Radical Notation
The symbol $\sqrt{-b}$ $(b > 0)$ should be used with care, since certain relationships involving the square root symbol that are valid for real numbers are not valid when the symbol does not represent a real number. For instance,

$$\sqrt{-2}\sqrt{-3} = (i\sqrt{2})(i\sqrt{3}) = i^2\sqrt{6} = -\sqrt{6}$$

but

$$\sqrt{-2}\sqrt{-3} \neq \sqrt{(-2)(-3)} = \sqrt{6}$$

To avoid difficulty with this point,

▲ *Rewrite all expressions of the form* $\sqrt{-b}$ $(b > 0)$ *in the form* $i\sqrt{b}$ *before performing any computations.*

EXAMPLE 7
   a.
$$\sqrt{-2}(3 - \sqrt{-5})$$
$$= i\sqrt{2}(3 - i\sqrt{5})$$
$$= 3i\sqrt{2} - i^2\sqrt{10}$$
$$= 3i\sqrt{2} - (-1)\sqrt{10}$$
$$= \sqrt{10} + 3i\sqrt{2}$$

   b.
$$(2 + \sqrt{-3})(2 - \sqrt{-3})$$
$$= (2 + i\sqrt{3})(2 - i\sqrt{3})$$
$$= 4 - 3i^2$$
$$= 4 - 3(-1)$$
$$= 7$$

c. $\dfrac{2}{\sqrt{-3}}$

$= \dfrac{2 \cdot i\sqrt{3}}{i\sqrt{3} \cdot i\sqrt{3}}$

$= \dfrac{2i\sqrt{3}}{(-1)(3)}$

$= \dfrac{-2\sqrt{3}}{3} i$

d. $\dfrac{1}{3 - \sqrt{-1}} = \dfrac{1}{3 - i}$

$= \dfrac{1 \cdot (3 + i)}{(3 - i)(3 + i)}$

$= \dfrac{3 + i}{9 - i^2}$

$= \dfrac{3 + i}{9 - (-1)} = \dfrac{3}{10} + \dfrac{1}{10} i$

E X E R C I S E   S E T   5.9

▲ *Write each expression in the form* $a + bi$ *or* $a + ib$. *See Examples 1 and 2.*

1. $\sqrt{-4}$
2. $\sqrt{-9}$
3. $\sqrt{-32}$
4. $\sqrt{-50}$
5. $3\sqrt{-8}$
6. $4\sqrt{-18}$
7. $3\sqrt{-24}$
8. $2\sqrt{-40}$
9. $5\sqrt{-64}$
10. $7\sqrt{-81}$
11. $-2\sqrt{-12}$
12. $-3\sqrt{-75}$
13. $4 + 2\sqrt{-1}$
14. $5 - 3\sqrt{-1}$
15. $3\sqrt{-50} + 2$
16. $5\sqrt{-12} - 1$
17. $\sqrt{4} + \sqrt{-4}$
18. $\sqrt{20} - \sqrt{-20}$

▲ *Write each expression in the form* $a + bi$ *or* $a + ib$. *See Example 3.*

19. $(2 + 4i) + (3 + i)$
20. $(2 - i) + (3 - 2i)$
21. $(4 - i) - (6 - 2i)$
22. $(2 + i) - (4 - 2i)$
23. $3 - (4 + 2i)$
24. $(2 - 6i) - 3$

▲ *See Example 4.*

25. $(2 - i)(3 + 2i)$
26. $(1 - 3i)(4 - 5i)$
27. $(3 + 2i)(5 + i)$
28. $(-3 - i)(2 - 3i)$
29. $(6 - 3i)(4 - i)$
30. $(7 + 3i)(-2 - 3i)$
31. $(2 - i)^2$
32. $(2 + 3i)^2$
33. $(2 - i)(2 + i)$
34. $(1 - 2i)(1 + 2i)$

▲ *See Examples 5 and 6.*

35. $\dfrac{1}{3i}$
36. $\dfrac{-2}{5i}$
37. $\dfrac{3 - i}{5i}$
38. $\dfrac{4 + 2i}{3i}$
39. $\dfrac{2}{1 - i}$
40. $\dfrac{-3}{2 + i}$

41. $\dfrac{2 + i}{1 + 3i}$
42. $\dfrac{3 - i}{1 + i}$
43. $\dfrac{2 - 3i}{3 - 2i}$
44. $\dfrac{6 + i}{2 - 5i}$
45. $\dfrac{3 + 2i}{5 - 3i}$
46. $\dfrac{-4 - 3i}{2 + 7i}$

▲ *See Example 7.*

47. $\sqrt{-4}(1 - \sqrt{-4})$
48. $\sqrt{-9}(3 + \sqrt{-16})$
49. $(2 + \sqrt{-9})(3 - \sqrt{-9})$
50. $(4 - \sqrt{-2})(3 + \sqrt{-2})$
51. $\dfrac{3}{\sqrt{-4}}$
52. $\dfrac{-1}{\sqrt{-25}}$
53. $\dfrac{2 - \sqrt{-1}}{2 + \sqrt{-1}}$
54. $\dfrac{1 + \sqrt{-2}}{3 - \sqrt{-2}}$

Miscellaneous Exercises

55. For what values of x will $\sqrt{x - 5}$ be real? Imaginary?
56. For what values of x will $\sqrt{x + 3}$ be real? Imaginary?
57. Simplify. [*Hint:* $i^2 = -1$ and $i^4 = 1$.]
    a. i^6
    b. i^{12}
    c. i^{15}
    d. i^{102}
58. Express with a positive exponent and simplify.
    a. i^{-1}
    b. i^{-2}
    c. i^{-3}
    d. i^{-6}
59. Evaluate $x^2 + 2x + 3$ for $x = 1 + i$.
60. Evaluate $2y^2 - y + 2$ for $y = 2 - i$.

CHAPTER SUMMARY

[5.1–5.2] For n a natural number,

$$a^n = a \cdot a \cdot a \cdot \cdots \cdot a \qquad \text{(n factors)}$$

for n an integer,

$$a^{-n} = \frac{1}{a^n} \qquad (a \neq 0)$$

also,

$$a^0 = 1 \qquad (a \neq 0)$$

The laws of exponents are determined by the definitions adopted for powers:

I. $a^m \cdot a^n = a^{m+n}$ 　　　　IV. $\dfrac{a^m}{a^n} = a^{m-n} \qquad (a \neq 0)$

II. $(a^m)^n = a^{mn}$ 　　　　V. $\left(\dfrac{a}{b}\right)^n = \dfrac{a^n}{b^n} \qquad (b \neq 0)$

III. $(ab)^n = a^n b^n$ 　　　　VI. $\left(\dfrac{a}{b}\right)^{-n} = \left(\dfrac{b}{a}\right)^n \qquad (a, b \neq 0)$

[5.3] A number is expressed in **scientific notation** when it is expressed as a product of a number between 1 and 10 and a power of 10.

[5.4] For each natural number n the number $a^{1/n}$, when it exists, is called an **nth root of a**.

    If n is an even natural number and $a \geqslant 0$, then $a^{1/n}$ is the nonnegative number such that

$$(a^{1/n})^n = a$$

If n is an odd natural number, then $a^{1/n}$ is the number such that

$$(a^{1/n})^n = a$$

For $a^{1/n}$ a real number,

$$a^{m/n} = (a^{1/n})^m = (a^m)^{1/n}$$

[5.5] An nth root of a is also designated by the **radical expression** $\sqrt[n]{a}$, where n is the **index** and a is the **radicand**. For all natural numbers $n \geqslant 2$,

$$\sqrt[n]{a} = a^{1/n}$$

For n an even natural number:
    If $a > 0$, $\sqrt[n]{a}$ is the positive number such that $(\sqrt[n]{a})^n = a$.
    In particular, for $n = 2$, $(\sqrt{a})^2 = \sqrt{a}\sqrt{a} = a$.
    For $a < 0$, $\sqrt[n]{a^n} = |a|$.
For n an odd natural number, $(\sqrt[n]{a})^n = a$.
For $\sqrt[n]{a}$ a real number, $a^{m/n} = \sqrt[n]{a^m} = (\sqrt[n]{a})^m$.

[5.6] Scientific calculators can be used to obtain decimal approximations for irrational numbers.

[5.7] Two laws of radicals follow from corresponding laws for exponents:

$$\sqrt[n]{ab} = \sqrt[n]{a}\sqrt[n]{b} \quad \text{and} \quad \sqrt[n]{\frac{a}{b}} = \frac{\sqrt[n]{a}}{\sqrt[n]{b}}$$

A radical expression is in simplest form if:

1. The radicand contains no polynomial factor raised to a power equal to or greater than the index of the radical.
2. The radicand contains no fractions.
3. No radical expressions are contained in denominators of fractions.

[5.8] Expressions containing radicals can be rewritten by using properties of real numbers. In particular, the fundamental principle of fractions can be used to rationalize the denominator (or the numerator) of a fraction containing radicals.

[5.9] A number of the form $a + bi$, where a, b are real numbers and $i = \sqrt{-1}$, is called a **complex number**. It is a real number if $b = 0$, it is an **imaginary number** if $b \neq 0$, and it is a **pure imaginary number** if $a = 0$ and $b \neq 0$.

The sum and the product of two complex numbers are defined so that they conform to the sum and the product of two binomials, respectively.

REVIEW EXERCISES

▲ Assume that all variables denote positive numbers and that no denominator equals 0.

[5.1–5.2]

▲ Simplify.

1. a. $\dfrac{x^4 y^3}{xy}$ b. $(3x^2 y)^3$

2. a. $\dfrac{x^{-2} \cdot y^{-1}}{x}$ b. $\left(\dfrac{x^2 y^{-2}}{x^{-2} y}\right)^{-2}$

3. a. $3^{-2} + 2^{-1}$ b. $xy^{-1} + x^{-1}y$

4. a. $\dfrac{(2x+1)^{-1}}{(2x)^{-1} + 1^{-1}}$ b. $\dfrac{x^{-2} - y^{-2}}{(x-y)^{-2}}$

[5.3]

▲ Write each number in scientific notation.

5. a. 0.000000000023   b. 307,000,000,000

▲ Express each number using standard form.

6. a. 3.49×10^{-5} b. $\dfrac{3}{4 \times 10^2}$

▲ Compute.

7. a. $\dfrac{(2 \times 10^{-3})(3 \times 10^4)}{6 \times 10^{-1}}$ b. $\dfrac{(4 \times 10^3)(6 \times 10^{-4})}{3 \times 10^{-2}}$

▲ Compute to the nearest tenth.

8. a. $\dfrac{24.8 \times 0.032 \times 0.01}{0.0024 \times 0.064}$ b. $\dfrac{420 \times 6200 \times 0.02}{14{,}000 \times 150 \times 0.004}$

[5.4]

▲ Simplify.

9. a. $(-27)^{2/3}$ b. $4^{-1/2}$

10. a. $x^{3/2} \cdot x^{1/2}$ b. $\left(\dfrac{x^{2/3} y^{1/2}}{x^{1/3}}\right)^6$

▲ *Multiply.*

11. **a.** $x^{2/3}(x^{1/3} - x)$ **b.** $y^{-1/4}(y^{5/4} - y^{1/4})$

▲ *Factor as indicated.*

12. **a.** $x^{4/5} = x^{1/5}(\underline{?})$ **b.** $y^{-3/4} = y^{-1/2}(\underline{?})$

[5.5]

▲ *Express in radical notation.*

13. **a.** $(1 - x^2)^{2/3}$ **b.** $(1 - x^2)^{-2/3}$

▲ *Express in exponential notation.*

14. **a.** $\sqrt[3]{x^2 y}$ **b.** $\dfrac{1}{\sqrt[3]{(a + b)^2}}$

▲ *Find each root indicated.*

15. **a.** $\sqrt{4y^2}$ **b.** $\sqrt[3]{-8x^3 y^6}$

16. **a.** $\sqrt{\dfrac{1}{4} x^4 y^6}$ **b.** $\sqrt[4]{\dfrac{1}{16} y^4}$

[5.6]

🖩 ▲ *Approximate each irrational number to the nearest thousandth.*

17. **a.** $\sqrt[3]{27.4}$ **b.** $\sqrt[4]{124.6}$

18. **a.** $64.5^{1/5}$ **b.** $37.9^{1/3}$

19. **a.** $(\sqrt[3]{29.2})^2$ **b.** $127^{6/7}$

20. **a.** $24.6^{1.3}$ **b.** $125^{0.8}$

▲ *Simplify.*

21. **a.** $\sqrt{180}$ **b.** $\sqrt[4]{32x^4 y^5}$

22. **a.** $\dfrac{1}{\sqrt{2}}$ **b.** $\dfrac{1}{\sqrt{3}}$

23. **a.** $\dfrac{x}{\sqrt{xy}}$ **b.** $\dfrac{\sqrt{xy}\sqrt{6x^3 y}}{\sqrt{2xy}}$

24. **a.** $\sqrt[3]{\dfrac{1}{2}}$ **b.** $\sqrt[4]{\dfrac{2}{3x}}$

25. **a.** $\sqrt[3]{\dfrac{x^7 y^5}{x^2 y}}$ **b.** $\dfrac{\sqrt[3]{x^5 y^4}}{\sqrt[3]{x^2 y}}$

26. **a.** $\dfrac{\sqrt[3]{12x^4}\sqrt[3]{4y^4}}{\sqrt[3]{6x}}$ **b.** $\dfrac{\sqrt[5]{x^3}\sqrt[5]{(xy)^3}}{\sqrt[5]{xy}}$

▲ *Rationalize each numerator.*

27. **a.** $\dfrac{\sqrt{3x}}{2}$ **b.** $\dfrac{\sqrt{2x}}{y}$

28. **a.** $\dfrac{3\sqrt{2xy}}{\sqrt{y}}$ **b.** $\dfrac{2\sqrt{3xy}}{\sqrt{3y}}$

[5.8]

▲ *Simplify.*

29. **a.** $4\sqrt{12} + 2\sqrt{75}$

     b. $3\sqrt{2x} - \sqrt{32x} + 4\sqrt{50x}$

30. **a.** $9\sqrt{2xy^2} - 3y\sqrt{8x}$ **b.** $\sqrt{75x^3} - x\sqrt{3x}$

▲ *Write each expression without parentheses, and then write all radicals in simple form.*

31. **a.** $\sqrt{3}(\sqrt{6} - 2)$ **b.** $\sqrt{5}(\sqrt{10} - \sqrt{5})$

32. **a.** $(2 - \sqrt{3})(3 - 2\sqrt{3})$ **b.** $(\sqrt{x} + 2)(\sqrt{x} - 2)$

▲ *Simplify each expression.*

33. **a.** $\dfrac{3 + 2\sqrt{18}}{3}$ **b.** $\dfrac{4 - 2\sqrt{8}}{4}$

34. **a.** $\dfrac{x + \sqrt{x^3 y}}{x}$ **b.** $\dfrac{xy - \sqrt{x^3 y^2}}{xy}$

35. **a.** $\dfrac{3}{2\sqrt{x}} - \dfrac{1}{\sqrt{x}}$ **b.** $\dfrac{4}{\sqrt{y}} - \dfrac{2}{3\sqrt{y}}$

▲ *Rationalize each denominator.*

36. **a.** $\dfrac{4}{2 - \sqrt{3}}$ **b.** $\dfrac{2}{\sqrt{5} + 2}$

37. **a.** $\dfrac{y}{\sqrt{y} - 3}$ **b.** $\dfrac{x - y}{\sqrt{x} + \sqrt{y}}$

▲ *Rationalize each numerator.*

38. **a.** $\dfrac{4 + \sqrt{3}}{2}$ **b.** $\dfrac{\sqrt{x} + 4}{x}$

[5.9]

▲ *Write each expression in the form $a + bi$ or $a + ib$.*

39. **a.** $4 + 2\sqrt{-9}$ **b.** $5 - 3\sqrt{-12}$

40. **a.** $(2 - 3i) + (4 + 2i)$ **b.** $(6 + 2i) - (1 - i)$

41. **a.** $(5 + i)(2 + 3i)$ **b.** $i(3 - 4i)$

42. **a.** $\dfrac{4}{3i}$ **b.** $\dfrac{1 - 3i}{2 - i}$

43. **a.** $\sqrt{-4}(\sqrt{-4} + 3)$ **b.** $(4 + \sqrt{-3})(2 - \sqrt{-3})$

44. **a.** $\dfrac{-2}{\sqrt{-9}}$ **b.** $\dfrac{\sqrt{-2} + 1}{\sqrt{-2} - 1}$

The numbers in brackets refer to the sections in which such problems are first considered.

▲ *Simplify each expression.*

1. $2[(x - 2)(x + 3) - 4]$ **[3.3]**

2. $\dfrac{2x^2 - 10x + 8}{2x - 2}$ **[4.1]**

3. $\dfrac{|-3 - 2| + |-4|}{-2|-3|}$ **[1.3]**

4. $\left(\dfrac{x^{-3}y}{xy^{-2}}\right)^{-2}$ **[5.2]**

5. $\dfrac{(3 \times 10^{-3})(8 \times 10^2)}{4 \times 10^{-1}}$ **[5.3]**

6. $\dfrac{4}{x^2 - 3x + 2} - \dfrac{2}{(x - 1)^2}$ **[4.4]**

7. $\dfrac{-3^2 - 2(-3)^2}{3}$ **[2.1]**

8. $\dfrac{\sqrt{x^2y}\sqrt{18xy^3}}{\sqrt{2xy}}$ **[5.7]**

9. Evaluate $2a + (n - 1)d$ for $a = 3, n = 12,$ and $d = -2$.   **[1.3]**

10. If $P(x) = x^2 + 3x - 1$ and $Q(x) = 2x^2 + 1$, find $P(x) - Q(x)$.   **[2.2]**

11. Rationalize the denominator of $\dfrac{\sqrt{y}}{\sqrt{y} - \sqrt{2}}$.   **[5.7]**

12. Write $\dfrac{1}{\sqrt{-3} + 1}$ in the form $a + bi$.   **[5.8]**

13. Divide: $\dfrac{x^3 - 2x^2 + 1}{x - 2}$.   **[4.2]**

14. Graph $x < 5$ for
    a. x an integer   **b.** x a real number.   **[1.1]**

▲ *Solve each equation.*

15. $4[2x - (x + 2) + 1] = 3$ **[2.3]**

16. $x^2 + 2x + 1 = 4$ **[3.5]**

17. $\dfrac{2}{3}x - \dfrac{1}{4}x = 2$ **[4.7]**

18. $\dfrac{3}{x - 1} + \dfrac{6}{x + 2} = \dfrac{27}{10}$ **[4.7]**

19. $(x - 3)^2 - 4x = 0$ **[3.5]**

20. $0.03(x - 10,000) + 0.04x = 140$ **[2.3]**

▲ *Solve.*

21. Ernest has three accounts: checking, savings, and Christmas club. He divides his paycheck of $1484 between them. He puts $200 more into his savings account than into the Christmas club and twice as much into checking as into savings. How much does he deposit into each account?   **[2.4]**

22. If $16,000 is invested at 3%, how much must be invested at 6% to earn a return of 5% on the total investment?   **[2.4]**

23. The height h in feet of a ball thrown off a building is given by the equation $h = 500 - 28t - 16t^2$, where t is the time in seconds after the throw. How long will it take the ball to reach a height of 380 feet?   **[3.6]**

24. A student store sold $96 worth of notebooks in one month. The store could sell 20 fewer notebooks to get the same income if the price of each notebook was raised $0.40. How much did each notebook sell for originally?   **[4.8]**

25. A theater now has an income of $1200 for each performance that is sold out. The management could obtain the same income by adding 60 seats and lowering the ticket price $1.00. How many seats does the theater have now?   **[4.8]**

6 NONLINEAR EQUATIONS

In Section 3.5 we solved quadratic equations of the form

$$ax^2 + bx + c = 0$$

where in each case the left-hand member could be factored and the solutions were rational numbers. For example, the equation

$$2x^2 + 5x - 12 = 0$$

can be written as

$$(2x - 3)(x + 4) = 0$$

from which we can obtain the solution set $\{\frac{3}{2}, -4\}$. In this chapter we will solve quadratic equations by other methods. Furthermore, these methods will enable us to obtain solutions that may be irrational numbers or imaginary numbers.

6.1 SOLVING QUADRATIC EQUATIONS BY EXTRACTION OF ROOTS; COMPLETING THE SQUARE

Quadratic equations of the form

$$x^2 = b$$

may be solved by a method often termed the **extraction of roots**. If the equation has a solution, then from the definition of a square root, x must be a square root of b.

Since each nonzero real number b has two square roots (either real or imaginary), we have two solutions. These are given by

$$x = \sqrt{b} \qquad \text{and} \qquad x = -\sqrt{b}$$

and the solution set is $\{\sqrt{b}, -\sqrt{b}\}$, where the elements are real if $b > 0$ and imaginary if $b < 0$. If $b = 0$, we have one number, 0, satisfying the equation.

EXAMPLE 1 Solve.

    a. $2x^2 - 6 = 0$ **b.** $5x^2 = 0$ **c.** $4x^2 + 3 = 0$

Solutions

a.
$$2x^2 - 6 = 0$$
$$2x^2 = 6$$
$$x^2 = 3$$
$$x = \sqrt{3} \quad \text{or} \quad x = -\sqrt{3}$$
The solution set is $\{\sqrt{3}, -\sqrt{3}\}$.

b.
$$5x^2 = 0$$
$$x^2 = 0$$
$$x = 0$$
The solution set is $\{0\}$.

c.
$$4x^2 + 3 = 0$$
$$x^2 = -\frac{3}{4}; \qquad x = \sqrt{-\frac{3}{4}} \quad \text{or} \quad x = -\sqrt{-\frac{3}{4}}$$
The solution set is $\left\{\frac{1}{2}i\sqrt{3}, -\frac{1}{2}i\sqrt{3}\right\}$.

Equations of the form

$$(x - p)^2 = q \qquad (q \geq 0)$$

may also be solved by the method of extraction of roots.

EXAMPLE 2 Solve $(x - 2)^2 = 16$.

Solution The equation
$$(x - 2)^2 = 16$$
implies that $(x - 2)$ is a number whose square is 16. Hence,
$$x - 2 = 4 \quad \text{or} \quad x - 2 = -4$$
$$x = 6 \quad \text{or} \quad x = -2$$
The solution set is $\{6, -2\}$.

EXAMPLE 3 Solve $(x + 4)^2 = -9$.

Solution The equation
$$(x + 4)^2 = -9$$
implies that $(x + 4)$ is a number whose square is -9. Hence,
$$x + 4 = \sqrt{-9} \quad \text{or} \quad x + 4 = -\sqrt{-9}$$
$$x = -4 + 3i \quad \text{or} \quad x = -4 - 3i$$
The solution set is $\{-4 + 3i, -4 - 3i\}$.

Solution by Completing the Square

The method of extraction of roots can be used to find the solution set of any quadratic equation. Let us first consider a specific example,

$$x^2 - 4x - 12 = 0$$

which can be written

$$x^2 - 4x = 12$$

If the square of one-half of the coefficient of the first-degree term,

$$\left[\frac{1}{2}(-4)\right]^2 = 4$$

is added to each member, we obtain

$$x^2 - 4x + 4 = 12 + 4$$

in which the left-hand member is the square of $(x - 2)$. Therefore, the equation can be written

$$(x - 2)^2 = 16$$

and the solution set is obtained as in Example 2.

Now consider the general quadratic equation in standard form,

$$ax^2 + bx + c = 0$$

for the special case where $a = 1$; that is,

$$x^2 + bx + c = 0 \tag{1}$$

We begin by adding $-c$ to each member of (1), which yields

$$x^2 + bx = -c \tag{2}$$

If we then add the square of one-half of the coefficient of x, $\left(\dfrac{b}{2}\right)^2$, to each member of (2), the result is

$$x^2 + bx + \left(\frac{b}{2}\right)^2 = -c + \left(\frac{b}{2}\right)^2 \tag{3}$$

where the left-hand member is equivalent to $\left(x + \dfrac{b}{2}\right)^2$, and we have

$$\left(x + \frac{b}{2}\right)^2 = -c + \frac{b^2}{4} \tag{4}$$

Since we have performed only elementary transformations, Equation (4) is equivalent to Equation (1), and we can solve Equation (4) by the method used in the preceding examples.

The technique used to obtain Equations (3) and (4) is called **completing the square**. Note that we completed the square in Equation (2) by dividing the coefficient b of the linear term by 2 and squaring the result. The expression obtained,

$$x^2 + bx + \left(\frac{b}{2}\right)^2$$

was then written in the equivalent form $(x + \frac{b}{2})^2$. When the left-hand member of an equation is in this form and the right-hand member does not contain the variable x, the equation can be solved by the method of extraction of roots. The following example shows the procedure that is used.

EXAMPLE 4   Solve $x^2 - 3x - 1 = 0$.

Solution   First rewrite the equation with the constant term as the right-hand member,

$$x^2 - 3x \quad = 1$$

Add $\left(-\frac{3}{2}\right)^2$, the square of one-half of the coefficient of the first-degree term, to each member.

$$x^2 - 3x + \left(-\frac{3}{2}\right)^2 = 1 + \left(-\frac{3}{2}\right)^2$$

Rewrite the left-hand member as the square of a binomial, and simplify the right-hand member.

$$\left(x - \frac{3}{2}\right)^2 = \frac{13}{4}$$

$$\frac{9}{4}$$

Set $\left(x - \frac{3}{2}\right)$ equal to each square root of $\frac{13}{4}$.

$$x - \frac{3}{2} = \sqrt{\frac{13}{4}} \qquad \text{or} \qquad x - \frac{3}{2} = -\sqrt{\frac{13}{4}}$$

$$x = \frac{3}{2} + \frac{\sqrt{13}}{2} \qquad\qquad x = \frac{3}{2} - \frac{\sqrt{13}}{2}$$

The solution set is $\left\{\dfrac{3 + \sqrt{13}}{2}, \dfrac{3 - \sqrt{13}}{2}\right\}$.

The two square roots of an expression can be written in a concise way. For example, $\sqrt{13/4}$ and $-\sqrt{13/4}$ in Example 4 can be written as $\pm\sqrt{13/4}$. The answer could then be written as $\left\{\dfrac{3 \pm \sqrt{13}}{2}\right\}$.

We began with the special case

$$x^2 + bx + c = 0 \tag{5}$$

rather than the general form

$$ax^2 + bx + c = 0 \tag{6}$$

because the term necessary to complete the square is obvious when $a = 1$. However, a quadratic equation in standard form can always be written in the form (5) by multiplying each member of Equation (6) by $\dfrac{1}{a}$ $(a \neq 0)$ and obtaining

$$x^2 + \frac{b}{a}x + \frac{c}{a} = 0$$

We can solve any equation of the form $ax^2 + bx + c = 0$ by completing the square using the following step-by-step procedure:

Step 1   If necessary, divide each side of the equation by a, the coefficient of x^2.

Step 2   Use the addition property of equality to obtain the constant term on the right side.

Step 3   Multiply b, the coefficient of x, by $\frac{1}{2}$ and square the result.

Step 4   Add the result of Step 3 to both sides of the equation from Step 2.

Step 5   Write the left side of the equation in the form $(x - k)^2$ or $(x + k)^2$, where k is the positive square root of the number added to both sides. Simplify the right side of the equation.

Step 6   Use extraction of roots to complete the solution.

EXAMPLE 5   Solve $2x^2 + x - 1 = 0$.

Solution   *Step 1*   Divide each side by 2, the coefficient of x^2.

$$x^2 + \frac{1}{2}x - \frac{1}{2} = 0$$

Step 2   Add the constant term $\dfrac{1}{2}$ to each side.

$$x^2 + \frac{1}{2}x \quad = \frac{1}{2}$$

Step 3   Multiply $\dfrac{1}{2}$, the coefficient of x, by $\dfrac{1}{2}$ and square the result to obtain

$$\left[\frac{1}{2}\left(\frac{1}{2}\right)\right]^2 = \frac{1}{16}$$

Step 4   Add 1/16 to each side of the equation.

$$x^2 + \frac{1}{2}x + \frac{1}{16} = \frac{1}{2} + \frac{1}{16}$$

Step 5   Rewrite the left side as the square of a binomial and simplify the right side.

$$\left(x + \frac{1}{4}\right)^2 = \frac{1(8)}{2(8)} + \frac{1}{16} = \frac{9}{16}$$

Step 6 Set $\left(x + \dfrac{1}{4}\right)$ equal to each square root of 9/16.

$$x + \frac{1}{4} = \frac{3}{4} \quad \text{or} \quad x + \frac{1}{4} = -\frac{3}{4}$$

$$x = \frac{1}{2} \qquad\qquad x = -1$$

The solution set is $\left\{\dfrac{1}{2}, -1\right\}$.

The methods used to solve equations in this section can also be used to solve equations that involve more than one variable.

E X A M P L E 6 Solve $(ax + b)^2 - c = 0$ in terms of a, b, and c.

Solution

$$(ax + b)^2 - c = 0 \qquad \text{Add } c \text{ to each side.}$$
$$(ax + b)^2 = c \qquad \text{Set } ax + b \text{ equal to each square root of } c.$$
$$ax + b = \pm\sqrt{c} \qquad \text{Add } -b \text{ to each side.}$$
$$ax = -b \pm \sqrt{c} \qquad \text{Divide each side by } a.$$
$$x = \frac{-b \pm \sqrt{c}}{a}$$

Pythagorean Theorem Quadratic equations arise in a variety of applications. You may recall the simple quadratic equation

$$c^2 = a^2 + b^2$$

an important geometric formula that relates the sides of a right triangle. (See Appendix E.) This relationship is known as the **Pythagorean Theorem** in honor of the Greek mathematician Pythagoras.

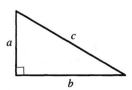

E X A M P L E 7 How high on a building wall will a 28-foot ladder reach if its foot is 12 feet from the wall against which the ladder is placed?

Solution

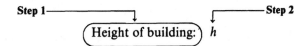

Step 1 ——————————— Step 2

Height of building: h

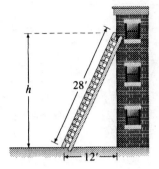

Step 3 Use the formula $c^2 = a^2 + b^2$.
$$(28)^2 = h^2 + (12)^2$$

Step 4 Solve the equation.

$$(28)^2 - (12)^2 = h^2$$
$$\sqrt{(28)^2 - (12)^2} = h$$
$$25.29 \approx h$$

Step 5 The ladder reaches a height of approximately 25.3 feet.

Although the formula developed in the next section is a more efficient way to solve quadratic equations than the methods used in this section, completing the square is an important procedure used in graphing techniques in advanced courses.

EXERCISE SET 6.1

▲ *Solve by the extraction of roots. See Example 1.*

1. $x^2 = 100$
2. $x^2 = 16$
3. $9x^2 = 25$
4. $4x^2 = 9$
5. $2x^2 = 14$
6. $3x^2 = 15$
7. $4x^2 + 24 = 0$
8. $3x^2 + 9 = 0$
9. $\dfrac{2x^2}{3} = 4$
10. $\dfrac{3x^2}{5} = 3$
11. $\dfrac{4x^2}{3} = -27$
12. $\dfrac{9x^2}{2} = -50$

▲ *Solve. See Examples 2 and 3.*

13. $(x - 2)^2 = 9$
14. $(x + 3)^2 = 4$
15. $(2x - 1)^2 = 16$
16. $(3x + 1)^2 = 25$
17. $(x + 2)^2 = -3$
18. $(x - 5)^2 = -7$
19. $\left(x - \dfrac{1}{2}\right)^2 = \dfrac{3}{4}$
20. $\left(x - \dfrac{2}{3}\right)^2 = \dfrac{5}{9}$
21. $\left(x + \dfrac{1}{3}\right)^2 = \dfrac{1}{81}$
22. $\left(x + \dfrac{1}{2}\right)^2 = \dfrac{1}{16}$
23. $(2x - 5)^2 = 9$
24. $(3x + 4)^2 = 16$
25. $(3x + 5)^2 = 9$
26. $(2x + 3)^2 = 36$

27. $(7x - 1)^2 = -15$
28. $(5x + 3)^2 = -7$
29. $(8x - 7)^2 = -8$
30. $(5x - 12)^2 = -24$

▲ *Rewrite each equation as $(x \pm a)^2 = c$ by completing the square. Solve. See Examples 4 and 5.*

31. $x^2 + 4x - 12 = 0$
32. $x^2 - x - 6 = 0$
33. $x^2 - 2x + 1 = 0$
34. $x^2 + 4x + 4 = 0$
35. $x^2 + 9x + 20 = 0$
36. $x^2 - x - 20 = 0$
37. $x^2 - 2x - 1 = 0$
38. $x^2 + 3x - 1 = 0$
39. $x^2 = 3 - 3x$
40. $x^2 = 5 - 5x$
41. $2x^2 + 4x - 3 = 0$
42. $3x^2 + x - 4 = 0$
43. $2x^2 - 5 = 3x$
44. $4x^2 - 3 = 2x$
45. $x^2 - x + 3 = 0$
46. $x^2 - 5x + 8 = 0$
47. $2x^2 + 4x = -3$
48. $3x^2 + x = -4$

▲ *Solve for x in terms of a, b, and c. See Example 6.*

49. $x^2 - a = 0$
50. $x^2 - 2a = 0$
51. $\dfrac{ax^2}{b} = c$
52. $\dfrac{bx^2}{c} - a = 0$

53. $(x - a)^2 = 16$ **54.** $(x + a)^2 = 36$

55. $(ax + b)^2 = 9$ **56.** $(ax - b)^2 = 25$

▲ *Solve. Express answers to the nearest tenth. See Example 7.*

57. How long must a wire be to stretch from the top of a 36-meter pole to a point on the ground 26 meters from the foot of the pole?

58. A 20-meter pine tree casts a shadow of 20 meters. How far is it from the tip of the shadow to the top of the tree?

59. A thin strip of sheet aluminum is to be bent into the shape shown in the figure. Find the length of the strip before it is bent.

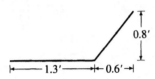

60. A roof truss has the dimensions shown in the figure. Find the length of a rafter.

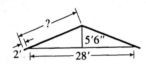

61. One leg of a right triangle is 14 centimeters shorter than the other leg, and the length of the hypotenuse is 22 centimeters less than twice that of the longer leg. Find the lengths of the sides of the triangle.

62. One leg of a right triangle is 7 centimeters longer than the other leg, and the length of the hypotenuse is 3 centimeters greater than twice that of the shorter leg. Find the length of the sides of the triangle.

Miscellaneous Exercises

63. Solve $a^2 + b^2 = c^2$ for b in terms of a and c.

64. Solve $S = h - r^2$ for r in terms of S and h.

65. Solve $A = P(1 + r)^2$ for r in terms of A and P.

66. Solve $s = \frac{1}{2}gt^2 + c$ for t in terms of s, g, and c.

67. Solve $x^2 + 9y^2 = 9$ for y in terms of x.

68. Solve $9x^2 + 4y^2 = 36$ for y in terms of x.

69. Solve $4x^2 - 9y^2 = 36$ for y in terms of x.

70. Solve $9x^2 - 25y^2 = 0$ for y in terms of x.

71. Solve $ax^2 + bx + c = 0$ for x in terms of a, b, and c by using the method of completing the square.

6.2 | THE QUADRATIC FORMULA

We now develop a formula that can be used to solve all quadratic equations, including those having imaginary solutions.

When a quadratic equation is written in its standard form,

$$ax^2 + bx + c = 0 \qquad (a > 0) \tag{1}$$

we can solve it by completing the square as follows:

$$x^2 + \frac{b}{a}x + \frac{c}{a} = 0 \qquad \text{Add } -\frac{c}{a} \text{ and } \left(\frac{1}{2} \cdot \frac{b}{a}\right)^2 \text{ to each side.}$$

$$x^2 + \frac{b}{a}x + \left(\frac{b}{2a}\right)^2 = -\frac{c}{a} + \left(\frac{b}{2a}\right)^2 \qquad \text{Write the left side as the square of a binomial.}$$

$$\left(x + \frac{b}{2a}\right)^2 = \frac{b^2}{4a^2} - \frac{c}{a} \qquad \text{Write the right side as a single fraction.}$$

$$\left(x + \frac{b}{2a}\right)^2 = \frac{b^2 - 4ac}{4a^2}$$ **Take the square roots of each side.**

$$x + \frac{b}{2a} = \pm\sqrt{\frac{b^2 - 4ac}{4a^2}}$$ **Add** $-\dfrac{b}{2a}$ **to each side.**

$$x = -\frac{b}{2a} \pm \frac{\sqrt{b^2 - 4ac}}{2a}$$

When the right-hand member is written as a single fraction, the resulting equation is called the **quadratic formula.**

$$x = \frac{-b \pm \sqrt{b^2 - 4ac}}{2a}$$

This is a formula for the solutions of a quadratic equation expressed in terms of the coefficients. The $\pm$ symbol is used to condense the two equations

$$x = \frac{-b + \sqrt{b^2 - 4ac}}{2a} \quad \text{or} \quad x = \frac{-b - \sqrt{b^2 - 4ac}}{2a}$$

into a single equation. We need only substitute the coefficients a, b, and c of a given quadratic equation in the formula to find the solution set for the equation.

Although the quadratic formula can be used to solve any quadratic equation in standard form, it is particularly useful when the left-hand member of a quadratic equation cannot be factored easily.

EXAMPLE 1   Solve $2x^2 - x - 2 = 0$.

Solution   Substitute 2 for a, -1 for b, and -2 for c in the quadratic formula.

$$x = \frac{-(-1) \pm \sqrt{(-1)^2 - 4(2)(-2)}}{2(2)}$$

$$= \frac{1 \pm \sqrt{1 + 16}}{4}$$

The solution set is $\left\{\dfrac{1 + \sqrt{17}}{4}, \dfrac{1 - \sqrt{17}}{4}\right\}$.

Notice in Example 1 that we could have expressed the solutions as $\dfrac{1}{4} + \dfrac{\sqrt{17}}{4}$ and $\dfrac{1}{4} - \dfrac{\sqrt{17}}{4}$.   In fact, it is clear from the form

$$x = \frac{-b}{2a} \pm \frac{\sqrt{b^2 - 4ac}}{2a}$$

that, if the solutions of a quadratic equation are irrational or imaginary, they are conjugates:

$$\frac{-b}{2a} + \frac{\sqrt{b^2 - 4ac}}{2a} \quad \text{and} \quad \frac{-b}{2a} - \frac{\sqrt{b^2 - 4ac}}{2a}$$

A quadratic equation must be written in standard form before the values of a, b, and c can be determined.

EXAMPLE 2

Solve $\dfrac{x^2}{4} + x = \dfrac{5}{4}$.

Solution

Write in standard form.

$$4\left(\frac{x^2}{4} + x\right) = \left(\frac{5}{4}\right)(4)$$

$$x^2 + 4x = 5$$

$$x^2 + 4x - 5 = 0$$

Substitute 1 for a, 4 for b, and -5 for c in the quadratic formula.*

$$x = \frac{-(4) \pm \sqrt{(4)^2 - 4(1)(-5)}}{2(1)}$$

$$= \frac{-4 \pm \sqrt{16 + 20}}{2} = \frac{-4 \pm 6}{2}$$

The solution set is $\{-5, 1\}$.

EXAMPLE 3

Solve $x = \dfrac{-2}{2x - 1}$.

Solution

First multiply each side of the equation by $2x - 1$ to eliminate fractions.

$$(2x - 1)x = \frac{-2}{2x - 1}(2x - 1) \qquad \text{Simplify each side.}$$

$$2x^2 - x = -2 \qquad \text{Add } +2 \text{ to each side.}$$

$$2x^2 - x + 2 = 0$$

Now that the equation is in standard form, substitute 2 for a, -1 for b, and 2 for c in the quadratic formula to obtain

$$x = \frac{-(-1) \pm \sqrt{(-1)^2 - 4(2)(2)}}{2(2)}$$

$$= \frac{1 \pm \sqrt{-15}}{4} = \frac{1 \pm i\sqrt{15}}{4}$$

The solution set is $\left\{\dfrac{1 - i\sqrt{15}}{4}, \dfrac{1 + i\sqrt{15}}{4}\right\}$.

---

*Note that the equation could be solved by the factoring method, as could many of the following exercises. However, the intent in this section is to practice using the quadratic formula.

Discriminant

In the quadratic formula the number represented by $b - 4ac$ is called the **discriminant** of the equation. If a, b, and c are real numbers, the discriminant can be used to predict the nature of the solution(s).

1. If $b^2 - 4ac = 0$, there is one real solution (of multiplicity two).
2. If $b^2 - 4ac > 0$, there are two unequal real solutions.
3. If $b^2 - 4ac < 0$, there are two unequal imaginary solutions.

EXAMPLE 4

Find the discriminant for each equation and determine whether the solution(s) are real or imaginary.

a. $x^2 - x - 3 = 0$ b. $2x^2 + x + 1 = 0$

Solution

a. Substitute 1 for a, -1 for b, and -3 for c in the discriminant.
$$b^2 - 4ac = (-1)^2 - 4(1)(-3)$$
$$= 1 + 12 = 13$$

Because $13 > 0$, the solutions are real and unequal.

b. Substitute 2 for a, 1 for b, and 1 for c in the discriminant.
$$b^2 - 4ac = 1^2 - 4(2)(1)$$
$$= 1 - 8 = -7$$

Because $-7 < 0$, the solutions are imaginary.

We can use the quadratic formula to solve a quadratic equation in more than one variable for a specified variable in terms of the other variables.

EXAMPLE 5

Solve $x^2 - xy + y = 2$ for x in terms of y.

Solution

Write the equation in standard form.
$$x^2 - yx + (y - 2) = 0$$

Substitute 1 for a, $-y$ for b, and $y - 2$ for c in the quadratic formula.
$$x = \frac{-(-y) \pm \sqrt{(-y)^2 - 4(1)(y - 2)}}{2(1)}$$
$$= \frac{y \pm \sqrt{y^2 - 4y + 8}}{2}$$

Applied problems may lead to quadratic equations that cannot be solved by factoring. In such cases, extraction of roots or the quadratic formula can be used.

The following example is similar to Example 2 in Section 3.6, but it cannot be solved by factoring.

EXAMPLE 6

A ball thrown vertically upward from the top of an 64-foot building reaches a height h in feet above the ground, given by the equation
$$h = -16t^2 + 64t + 64$$

where t is the time in seconds after the ball is thrown. Approximately how long will it take the ball to reach the ground?

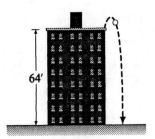

64′

Solution

Step 1 ⌐   ⌐ Step 2

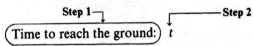

(Time to reach the ground:) t

Step 3   Since the goal is to find t when $h = 0$,   write the model as

$$0 = -16t^2 + 64t + 64$$

which can be simplified and written in standard form as

$$t^2 - 4t - 4 = 0$$

Step 4   Since the left side of the equation is not factorable, use the quadratic formula.

$$t = \frac{4 \pm \sqrt{(-4)^2 - 4(1)(-4)}}{2(1)}$$

$$= \frac{4 \pm \sqrt{32}}{2} = \frac{4 \pm 4\sqrt{2}}{2} = 2 \pm 2\sqrt{2}$$

To the nearest tenth, $t = 4.8$ or $t = -0.8$.

Step 5   Only the positive value for t is relevant, so the ball will reach the ground in approximately 4.8 seconds.

EXERCISE   SET   6.2

▲ *In Exercises 1–24, solve for x, y, or z using the quadratic formula. See Examples 1, 2, and 3.*

1. $x^2 - 5x + 4 = 0$

2. $x^2 - 4x + 4 = 0$

3. $y^2 + 3y = 4$

4. $y^2 - 5y = 6$

5. $z^2 = 3z - 1$

6. $2z^2 = 7z - 6$

7. $0 = x^2 - \frac{5}{3}x + \frac{1}{3}$

8. $0 = x^2 - \frac{1}{2}x + \frac{1}{2}$

9. $5z + 6 = 6z^2$

10. $13z + 5 = 6z^2$

11. $x^2 - 5x = 0$

12. $y^2 + 3y = 0$

13. $4y^2 + 8 = 0$

14. $2z^2 + 1 = 0$

15. $2y^2 = y - 1$

16. $x^2 + 2x = -5$

17. $y = \frac{1}{y - 3}$

18. $2z = \frac{3}{z - 2}$

19. $3y = \frac{1 + y}{y - 1}$

20. $2x = \frac{x + 1}{x - 1}$

21. $2y^2 = y - 2 - y^2$

22. $3z^2 + 2z + 2 = z$

23. $2x = \frac{-1}{2x - 1}$

24. $y = \frac{-1}{y - 1}$

▲ *In Exercises 25–30, find only the discriminant and determine whether the solution(s) are*

   a. *One real*   **b.** *Real and unequal*

   c. *Imaginary and unequal*

   See Example 4.

25. $x^2 - 7x + 12 = 0$

26. $y^2 - 2y - 3 = 0$

27. $5x^2 + 2x + 1 = 0$ **28.** $2y^2 + 3y + 7 = 0$
29. $9x^2 - 6x + 1 = 0$ **30.** $4y^2 - 12y + 9 = 0$

▲ *Solve for x in terms of the other variables or constants. See Example 5.*

31. $x^2 - kx - 2k^2 = 0$ $k \geq 0$
32. $2x^2 - kx + 3 = 0$ **33.** $ax^2 - x + c = 0$
34. $x^2 + 2x + k + 3 = 0$ **35.** $x^2 + 2x - y = 0$
36. $2x^2 - 3x + 2y = 0$ **37.** $3x^2 + xy + y^2 = 2$
38. $x^2 - 3xy + y^2 = 3$

Miscellaneous Exercises

39. In Exercise 37, solve for y in terms of x.
40. In Exercise 38, solve for y in terms of x.

▲ *Solve each problem. Round off answers to the nearest tenth of a unit.*

41. A car traveling at s miles per hour on a dry road surface will require approximately d feet to stop, where d is given by $d = \dfrac{s^2}{24} + \dfrac{s}{2}$. If a car must be able to stop in 50 feet, what is the maximum speed at which it can travel safely?

42. A car traveling at s miles per hour on a wet road surface will require approximately d feet to stop, where d is given by $d = \dfrac{s^2}{12} + \dfrac{s}{2}$. If a car failed to stop in 100 feet, what speed did it exceed?

43. A skydiver jumps out of an airplane at 11,000 feet. Her altitude in feet t seconds after jumping is given by $h = -16t^2 - 16t + 11,000$.
  a. If she must open her parachute at 1000 feet, how long can she free-fall?
  b. If the skydiver drops a marker just before she opens her parachute, how long will it take the marker to hit the ground?

44. A high diver jumps from the 10-meter springboard. His height in meters above the water t seconds after leaving the board is given by $h = -9.8t^2 + 8t + 10$.
  a. How long is it before the diver passes the board on the way down?
  b. How long is it before the diver hits the water?

6.3   EQUATIONS INVOLVING RADICALS

To solve equations containing radicals, we shall make use of the following property:

> *If each member of an equation is raised to the same natural-number power, the solutions of the original equation are contained in the solution set of the resulting equation.*

This property can be expressed in symbols as follows:

> *For n a natural number the solution set of*
> $$[P(x)]^n = [Q(x)]^n \tag{1}$$
> *contains all the solutions of*
> $$P(x) = Q(x) \tag{2}$$

Extraneous Solutions   Note that an application of this property does not always result in an equivalent equation. Equation (1) actually may have additional solutions that are not solutions of Equation (2). With respect to Equation (2), these are called **extraneous solutions**. For example, the solution set of the equation

$$x^2 = 9$$

obtained from

$$x = 3$$

by squaring each member, is $\{3, -3\}$. This set contains -3 as an extraneous solution of the equation $x = 3$, since -3 does not satisfy the equation $x = 3$.

Because the result of applying the foregoing property is not always an equivalent equation, each solution obtained through its use *must* be checked in the original equation to verify its validity. The check is part of the solution process.

EXAMPLE 1   Solve $\sqrt{x - 3} = 2$.

Solution   First square each member to remove the radical, and then solve for x.

$$(\sqrt{x - 3})^2 = 2^2$$
$$x - 3 = 4$$
$$x = 7$$

Check: Does $\sqrt{7 - 3} = 2$?   Yes. The solution set is $\{7\}$.

EXAMPLE 2   Solve $\sqrt{x + 2} + 4 = x$.

Solution   Obtain $\sqrt{x + 2}$ as the only term in one member.

$$\sqrt{x + 2} = x - 4 \qquad \text{\textbf{Square each side.}}$$
$$(\sqrt{x + 2})^2 = (x - 4)^2$$
$$x + 2 = x^2 - 8x + 16 \qquad \text{\textbf{Write equation in standard form.}}$$
$$x^2 - 9x + 14 = 0 \qquad \text{\textbf{Solve equation by first factoring left side.}}$$
$$(x - 7)(x - 2) = 0$$
$$x = 7 \qquad x = 2$$

Check: Does $\sqrt{7 + 2} + 4 = 7$?   Yes.   Does $\sqrt{2 + 2} + 4 = 2$?   No.   Therefore, 2 is not a solution. The solution set is $\{7\}$.

Sometimes it is necessary to square each member of an equation more than once to obtain an equation free of radicals.

EXAMPLE 3   Solve $\sqrt{x - 7} + \sqrt{x} = 7$.

Solution   First add $-\sqrt{x}$ to each member to obtain
$$\sqrt{x - 7} = 7 - \sqrt{x}$$

which contains only one term with a radical in the left-hand member. Now square each member to remove *one* radical.

$$(\sqrt{x - 7})^2 = (7 - \sqrt{x})^2$$
$$x - 7 = 49 - 14\sqrt{x} + x \qquad \text{\textbf{Add} } -x - 49 \text{ \textbf{to each side to obtain} } -14\sqrt{x}$$
$$-56 = -14\sqrt{x} \qquad \qquad \text{\textbf{as the only term on the right side.}}$$
$$4 = \sqrt{x}$$

Now square each member again to obtain
$$(4)^2 = (\sqrt{x})^2$$
$$16 = x$$

Check: Does $\sqrt{16 - 7} + \sqrt{16} = 7$? Yes. The solution set is $\{16\}$.

Using the property introduced on page 162, we can solve formulas that involve radicals for specified variables in terms of the other variables in the formulas.

EXAMPLE 4 Solve $t = \sqrt{\dfrac{1 + s^2}{g}}$ for s.

Solution Squaring each member yields

$$t^2 = \frac{1 + s^2}{g} \qquad \text{Multiply each side by } g.$$

$$gt^2 = 1 + s^2 \qquad \text{Add } -1 \text{ to each side to obtain } s^2 \text{ as the only term on one side.}$$

$$gt^2 - 1 = s^2$$

Hence,

$$s = \pm\sqrt{gt^2 - 1}$$

EXERCISE SET 6.3

▲ *Solve and check. If there is no solution, so state. Assume that all variables represent real numbers. See Examples 1 and 2.*

1. $\sqrt{x - 5} = 3$
2. $\sqrt{x - 4} = 1$
3. $\sqrt{y + 6} = 2$
4. $\sqrt{y - 3} = 5$
5. $3z + 4 = \sqrt{3z + 10}$
6. $2z - 3 = \sqrt{7z - 3}$
7. $2x + 1 = \sqrt{10x + 5}$
8. $4x + 5 = \sqrt{3x + 4}$
9. $\sqrt{y + 4} = y - 8$
10. $4\sqrt{x - 4} = x$
11. $\sqrt{2y - 1} = \sqrt{3y - 6}$
12. $\sqrt{4y + 1} = \sqrt{6y - 3}$
13. $\sqrt{x - 3}\sqrt{x} = 2$
14. $\sqrt{x}\sqrt{x - 5} = 6$
15. $\sqrt[3]{x} = -3$
16. $\sqrt[3]{x} = -4$
17. $\sqrt[4]{x - 1} = 2$
18. $\sqrt[4]{x - 1} = 3$

▲ *See Example 3.*

19. $\sqrt{y + 4} = \sqrt{y + 20} - 2$
20. $4\sqrt{y} + \sqrt{1 + 16y} = 5$
21. $\sqrt{x} + \sqrt{2} = \sqrt{x + 2}$
22. $\sqrt{4x + 17} = 4 - \sqrt{x + 1}$
23. $(5 + x)^{1/2} + x^{1/2} = 5$
24. $(y + 7)^{1/2} + (y + 4)^{1/2} = 3$
25. $(y^2 - 3y + 5)^{1/2} - (y + 2)^{1/2} = 0$
26. $(z - 3)^{1/2} + (z + 5)^{1/2} = 4$

▲ *Solve. Leave the results in the form of an equation. Assume that no variable takes a value for which any denominator is 0. See Example 4.*

27. $r = \sqrt{\dfrac{A}{\pi}}$ for A
28. $t = \sqrt{\dfrac{2v}{g}}$ for g
29. $R\sqrt{RS} = 1$ for S
30. $P = \sqrt{\dfrac{l}{g}}$ for g
31. $r = \sqrt{t^2 - s^2}$ for t
32. $q - 1 = 2\sqrt{\dfrac{r^2 - 1}{3}}$ for r
33. $A = B + C\sqrt{D + E^2}$ for E
34. $A = B - C\sqrt{D - E^2}$ for E
35. In Exercise 27, specify the restrictions on each variable so that the solutions are real numbers.
36. In Exercise 28, specify the restrictions on each variable so that the solutions are real numbers.

Miscellaneous Exercises

37. The base of an isosceles triangle is 6 centimeters. Find the altitude if the perimeter is 20 centimeters.

38. The longer leg of a right triangle is 1 centimeter shorter than the hypotenuse. Find the hypotenuse if the perimeter is 30 centimeters.

39. Using the information given in the figure, find the length of the segment BC if $AC + CD$ equals 11 feet.

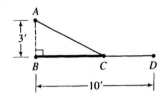

40. Using the information given in the figure, find the length of the segment AB if $AB + BD$ equals 14 centimeters.

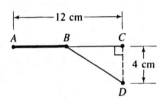

41. A cable television service wants to run a cable from its station at A to an island at C. It costs $150 per mile to run the cable underground and $500 per mile to run the cable underwater. If it costs $15,200 to run the cable to the island, how far is point P from the station?

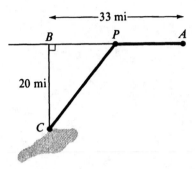

42. Two radio antennae are 75 feet apart. They are supported by a guy wire attached to the first antenna at a height of 20 feet, anchored to the ground between the antennae, and attached to the second antenna at a height of 25 feet. If the wire is 90 feet long, how far from the base of the first antenna should it be anchored to the ground?

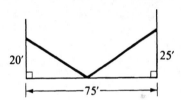

6.4   EQUATIONS THAT ARE QUADRATIC IN FORM

Some equations that are not quadratic equations are nevertheless quadratic in form—that is, they are of the form

$$au^2 + bu + c = 0 \tag{1}$$

where u represents some expression in terms of another variable. For example,

$$x^4 - 10x^2 + 9 = 0 \quad \text{or} \quad (x^2)^2 - 10(x^2) + 9 = 0 \tag{2}$$

is quadratic in x^2,

$$y - 2\sqrt{y} - 8 = 0 \quad \text{or} \quad (\sqrt{y})^2 - 2(\sqrt{y}) - 8 = 0 \tag{3}$$

is quadratic in $\sqrt{y}$, and

$$y^{2/3} - 5y^{1/3} + 4 = 0 \quad \text{or} \quad (y^{1/3})^2 - 5(y^{1/3}) + 4 = 0 \qquad \textbf{(4)}$$

is quadratic in $y^{1/3}$.

We can solve an equation of the form (1) by using a substitution procedure shown in the following examples:

EXAMPLE 1

Solve $x^4 - 10x^2 + 9 = 0$.

Solution

If we let $x^2 = u$, the equation reduces to
$$u^2 - 10u + 9 = 0$$

Solving this equation, we obtain
$$(u - 9)(u - 1) = 0$$
$$u = 9 \quad \text{or} \quad u = 1$$

Since $u = x^2$, we have
$$x^2 = 9 \quad \text{or} \quad x^2 = 1$$

from which we obtain the solution set $\{3, -3, 1, -1\}$.

The method illustrated in Example 1 is commonly called *substitution of variables*. Note that the equation in Example 1 could be solved by factoring the left-hand member to obtain

$$(x^2 - 9)(x^2 - 1) = 0$$

from which

$$x^2 - 9 = 0 \quad \text{or} \quad x^2 - 1 = 0$$
$$x = \pm 3 \qquad\qquad x = \pm 1$$

and the solution set is $\{3, -3, 1, -1\}$.

Because the substitution of variables method is a useful tool (there are many cases in which the factoring method shown here is not possible), we will use it in all the exercises in this section.

EXAMPLE 2

Solve $y - 2\sqrt{y} - 8 = 0$.

Solution

Let $\sqrt{y} = u$; therefore $y = u^2$. Substitute for y and $\sqrt{y}$.
$$u^2 - 2u - 8 = 0$$

Solve for u.

$$(u - 4)(u + 2) = 0$$
$$u = 4 \quad \text{or} \quad u = -2$$

Replace u with $\sqrt{y}$, and solve for y. Since $\sqrt{y}$ cannot be negative, only 4 need be considered.

$$\sqrt{y} = 4$$
$$y = 16$$

Check: Does $16 - 2\sqrt{16} - 8 = 0$? Yes.

Hence, $\{16\}$ is the solution set.

EXAMPLE 3 | Solve $y^{2/3} - 5y^{1/3} + 4 = 0$.

Solution | Let $y^{1/3} = u$;   therefore, $y^{2/3} = u^2$.   Substitute for $y^{2/3}$ and $y^{1/3}$.

$$u^2 - 5u + 4 = 0$$

Solve for u.

$$(u - 4)(u - 1) = 0$$
$$u = 4 \quad \text{or} \quad u = 1$$

Replace u with $y^{1/3}$, and solve for y.

$$y^{1/3} = 4 \quad \text{or} \quad y^{1/3} = 1$$
$$y = 64 \quad \text{or} \quad y = 1$$

Check: Does $64^{2/3} - 5(64)^{1/3} + 4 = 0$?

$$16 - 20 + 4 = 0? \quad \text{Yes.}$$

Does $(1)^{2/3} - 5(1)^{1/3} + 4 = 0$?

$$1 - 5 + 4 = 0? \quad \text{Yes.}$$

Hence, $\{1, 64\}$ is the solution set.

EXERCISE SET 6.4

▲ *Solve. See Example 1.*

1. $x^4 - 5x^2 + 4 = 0$
2. $x^4 - 13x^2 + 36 = 0$
3. $y^4 - 4y^2 + 3 = 0$
4. $y^4 - 6y^2 + 5 = 0$
5. $2x^4 + 17x^2 - 9 = 0$
6. $x^4 - 2x^2 - 24 = 0$
7. $z^4 + 4z^2 + 3 = 0$
8. $z^4 + 7z^2 + 10 = 0$

▲ *Solve. See Example 2.*

9. $x - 2\sqrt{x} - 15 = 0$
10. $x + 3\sqrt{x} - 10 = 0$
11. $y + 3\sqrt{y} + 2 = 0$
12. $y - 2\sqrt{y} + 1 = 0$
13. $y^2 + 7 - \sqrt{y^2 + 7} - 12 = 0$
14. $y^2 - 5 - 5\sqrt{y^2 - 5} + 6 = 0$
15. $x^2 - 1 - \sqrt{x^2 - 1} - 6 = 0$
16. $x^2 - 4 + 4\sqrt{x^2 - 4} + 3 = 0$

▲ *Solve. See Example 3.*

17. $y^{2/3} - 2y^{1/3} - 8 = 0$
18. $z^{2/3} - 2z^{1/3} = 35$

19. $x^{2/3} - 3x^{1/3} = 4$
20. $2y^{2/3} + 5y^{1/3} = 3$
21. $x - 9x^{1/2} + 18 = 0$
22. $z + z^{1/2} = 72$
23. $2x - 9x^{1/2} = -4$
24. $8x^{1/2} + 7x^{1/4} = 1$
25. $y^{-2} - y^{-1} - 12 = 0$
26. $z^{-2} + 9z^{-1} - 10 = 0$
27. $(x - 1)^{1/2} - 2(x - 1)^{1/4} - 15 = 0$
28. $(x - 2)^{1/2} - 11(x - 2)^{1/4} + 18 = 0$

Miscellaneous Exercises

▲ *Solve Exercises 29–32 in two ways:*
   a. *By the method of Section 6.3.*
   b. *By the method of this section.*

29. $y - 7\sqrt{y} + 12 = 0$
30. $x + \sqrt{x} - 6 = 0$
31. $x + 18 = 11\sqrt{x}$
32. $y + 2\sqrt{y} = 15$
33. $\sqrt{y - 2} = 8 - y$
34. $x - 8 = \sqrt{x + 4}$

CHAPTER SUMMARY

[6.1] To solve an equation by the **extraction of roots** method, we use the fact that

$$\text{if } x^2 = b, \quad \text{then} \quad x = \sqrt{b} \quad \text{or} \quad x = -\sqrt{b}$$

To solve an equation of the form $x^2 + bx = c$ by completing the square, we first add $\left(\dfrac{b}{2}\right)^2$ to both members.

The formula $a^2 + b^2 = c^2$ that relates the two legs a and b of a right triangle to the hypotenuse c is called the **Pythagorean Theorem**.

[6.2] The solutions of $ax^2 + bx + c = 0$ $(a \neq 0)$ are given by

$$x = \frac{-b + \sqrt{b^2 - 4ac}}{2a} \quad \text{and} \quad x = \frac{-b - \sqrt{b^2 - 4ac}}{2a}$$

The number represented by $b^2 - 4ac$ is the **discriminant** of the quadratic equation $ax^2 + bx + c = 0$.

[6.3] To solve equations containing radicals, we use the fact that if each member of an equation is raised to the same power, the solutions of the original equation are contained in the solution set of the resulting equation. That is:

▲ *For n a natural number, the solution set of* $[P(x)]^n = [Q(x)]^n$ *contains all the solutions of* $P(x) = Q(x)$.

[6.4] An equation of the form

$$au^2 + bu + c = 0$$

where u represents some expression in another variable, is said to be quadratic in form. Such equations may be solved by a method commonly called *substitution of variables*.

REVIEW EXERCISES

[6.1]

▲ *Solve for x by the extraction of roots.*

1. **a.** $2x^2 = 50$ **b.** $3x^2 + 7 = 0$
2. **a.** $(x + 3)^2 = 25$ **b.** $(x - 4)^2 = 15$
3. **a.** $\left(x - \dfrac{1}{3}\right)^2 = \dfrac{2}{9}$ **b.** $\left(x + \dfrac{2}{3}\right)^2 = \dfrac{5}{9}$
4. **a.** $(2x - 3)^2 = -5$ **b.** $(3x + 2)^2 = -7$

▲ *Solve by completing the square.*

5. **a.** $x^2 - 4x - 6 = 0$ **b.** $2x^2 + 3x - 3 = 0$
6. **a.** $x^2 + 3x = 3$ **b.** $3x^2 = 2x + 4$
7. **a.** $x^2 - x + 2 = 0$ **b.** $x^2 + 2x + 3 = 0$
8. **a.** $2x^2 = 2x - 3$ **b.** $3x^2 = 3x - 1$

[6.2]

▲ *Solve each equation using the quadratic formula.*

9. **a.** $\dfrac{1}{2}x^2 + 1 = \dfrac{3}{2}x$ **b.** $x^2 - 3x + 7 = 0$

10. **a.** $x^2 - 3x + 1 = 0$ **b.** $2x^2 + x - 3 = 0$
11. **a.** $x^2 - x + 2 = 0$ **b.** $x^2 - 2x + 4 = 0$
12. **a.** $2x^2 + 3x + 2 = 0$ **b.** $2x^2 - x + 3 = 0$
13. A travel agent offers a group rate of $2400 per person for a week in London if 15 people sign up for the tour. The price per person is reduced by another $100 each time an additional person signs up. How many people must sign up for the tour in order for the agent to collect $38,000?
14. The credit union divides $12,600 equally among its members each year as a dividend. This year there are six fewer members than last year, and each person receives $5 more. How many members are there this year?

[6.3]

▲ *Solve.*

15. $x - 3\sqrt{x} + 2 = 0$
16. $\sqrt{x + 1} + \sqrt{x + 8} = 7$

17. $p = \sqrt{\dfrac{1 - 2t^2}{s}}$ for t

18. $R = \dfrac{1 + \sqrt{p^2 + 1}}{2}$ for p

[6.4]

▲ *Solve.*

19. $x^4 - 3x^2 - 4 = 0$

20. $x - x^{1/2} = 12$

21. $y - 2\sqrt{y} - 8 = 0$

22. $y + 2 + 4\sqrt{y + 2} - 12 = 0$

23. $(x + 7)^{1/2} + x^{1/2} = 7$

24. $(y - 3)^{1/2} + (y + 4)^{1/2} = 7$

CUMULATIVE EXERCISES

▲ *The numbers in brackets refer to the sections in which such problems are first considered.*

▲ *Simplify each expression.*

1. $(2x^2)^2(xy^2) - 3xy^2(xy)^2$ **[3.1]**

2. $(-64)^{2/3}$ **[5.4]**

3. $\dfrac{6\sqrt{xy} - \sqrt{12x^3}}{2\sqrt{x}}$ **[5.7]**

4. $5x - 2x[x - 3(2 - 4x)(1 + x)]$ **[3.3]**

5. Factor $4x^2y^2 - x^2y^4$.   **[3.4]**

6. Multiply $-2x^{1/3}(x^{2/3} - 1)$.   **[5.4]**

7. Multiply $(3x - 4)(x^2 - 2x + 3)$.   **[3.3]**

8. Factor $8x^3 - 27y^3$.   **[3.7]**

9. Write $\dfrac{2 - i}{4 - 3i}$ in the form $a + bi$.   **[5.8]**

10. Express $1 + \dfrac{1}{x} - \dfrac{x + 1}{x^2 - x}$ as a single fraction in lowest terms. **[4.4]**

11. Subtract the sum of $2t^2 - 7t + 3$ and $-5t^2 - 5t - 2$ from $2t^2 - 3t - 1$.   **[2.2]**

12. Express $\dfrac{3}{-2x + 4}$ as an equivalent fraction with denominator $2x^3 - 8x$. **[4.3]**

13. Find the indicated root: $\sqrt[3]{-27x^3y^{12}}$.   **[5.5]**

14. Rationalize the denominator: $\sqrt[3]{\dfrac{3}{4x^2}}$.   **[5.6]**

▲ *Solve.*

15. $(x - 4)(x + 3) = -1 - (x + 1)(x - 3)$ **[3.5]**

16. $4 - \dfrac{3}{x - 2} = \dfrac{15}{x}$ **[4.6]**

17. $x^2 + 3 = 2x$ **[6.2]**

18. $(3x - 5)^2 = -18$ **[6.1]**

19. $C = \dfrac{s}{1 - d}$ for d **[4.7]**

20. $A = \sqrt{\dfrac{4 + Q}{2}}$ for Q **[6.3]**

▲ *Solve.*

21. Determine the area of a trapezoid with bases 10 and 12 centimeters and height 14 centimeters. (See Appendix E for geometric formulas.) **[1.3]**

22. Tulip bulbs cost $0.69 apiece, and daffodil bulbs cost $0.89 apiece. How many of each should be included in a package of 50 bulbs that sells for $40.50? **[2.4]**

23. One leg of a right triangle is 3 feet shorter than the hypotenuse. If the other leg is 9 feet long, find the length of the hypotenuse. **[3.6]**

24. If a car travels 504 miles on 18 gallons of gas, how much gas will be needed for a 602-mile trip? **[4.8]**

25. A balloonist travels 120 miles against a head wind of 8 miles per hour and returns with a tail wind of 8 mph. The round trip takes 8 hours. What is the speed of the balloon in still air? **[4.8]**

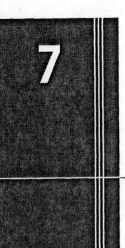

7 EQUATIONS IN TWO VARIABLES

The language of mathematics is particularly useful in representing relationships between two or more variable quantities. We can represent relationships in several ways: (a) by using equations, (b) by using tables, or (c) by using graphs.

In Section 7.1 we consider solutions of equations in two variables. In the following sections we will use tables and graphs to describe relationships between two quantities, with particular attention to graphs and properties of first-degree equations in two variables.

7.1 SOLUTION OF AN EQUATION IN TWO VARIABLES

Ordered Pairs An equation in two variables, such as $y = 2x + 3$, is said to be *satisfied* if the variables are replaced with a pair of numbers—one for x and one for y—that make the resulting statement true. The pair of numbers, usually written in the form (x, y), is a **solution** of the equation or inequality.

The pair (x, y) is called an **ordered pair** because it is understood that the numbers are considered in a particular order, x first and y second. These numbers are called the **first** and **second components** of the ordered pair, respectively. Although any letters may be used as variables, in this book we shall almost always use x and y.

To find ordered pairs that are solutions of a given equation, we can assign any real-number value to one of the variables and then determine the related value, if any, of the other. For example, for

$$y - x = 1$$

we can obtain solutions (ordered pairs) by assigning to x any real number as a value and then determining the corresponding value of y. For example, substituting 2, 3, and 4 for x, we have

$$y - (2) = 1 \quad \text{from which} \quad y = 3$$
$$y - (3) = 1 \quad \text{from which} \quad y = 4$$
$$y - (4) = 1 \quad \text{from which} \quad y = 5$$

Thus, $(2, 3)$, $(3, 4)$, and $(4, 5)$ are three solutions of $y - x = 1$. There are, of course, infinitely many solutions to this equation.

EXAMPLE 1 Find each missing component so that each ordered pair is a solution of the equation $y - 2x = 4$.

a. $(0, \underline{?})$ b. $(\underline{?}, 0)$ c. $(3, \underline{?})$

Solutions

a. $y - 2x = 4$
$\quad y - 2(0) = 4$
$\qquad y = 4$
$\qquad (0, 4)$

b. $y - 2x = 4$
$\quad (0) - 2x = 4$
$\qquad x = -2$
$\qquad (-2, 0)$

c. $y - 2x = 4$
$\quad y - 2(3) = 4$
$\qquad y = 10$
$\qquad (3, 10)$

EXAMPLE 2 List the ordered pairs that satisfy the equation $y = 3x + 1$ and have the x-components 1, 2, and 3.

Solution

For $x = 1$,
$\quad y = 3(1) + 1$
$\qquad = 4$

For $x = 2$,
$\quad y = 3(2) + 1$
$\qquad = 7$

For $x = 3$,
$\quad y = 3(3) + 1$
$\qquad = 10$

Thus, the desired solutions are $(1, 4)$, $(2, 7)$, and $(3, 10)$.

Equivalent Equations To find ordered pairs that satisfy a given equation, first expressing one variable in terms of the other is sometimes helpful. The properties in Section 2.3 that are used to generate equivalent equations in one variable apply also in transforming equations in two or more variables. For example, we can transform the equation

$$y - 3x = 4 \tag{1}$$

to the equivalent equation

$$y = 3x + 4 \tag{2}$$

Both equations have the same solution set. In Equation (1) the variables x and y are said to be **implicitly** related; in Equation (2), y is said to be expressed **explicitly** in terms of x.

EXAMPLE 3 Transform each equation into an equation in which y is expressed explicitly in terms of x, and then find values of y for the given values of x.

a. $3y - xy = 4; \quad 2, 5$ **b.** $x^2 + 4y^2 = 5; \quad 0, 1$

Solutions

a. $3y - xy = 4$

$\quad y(3 - x) = 4$

$$y = \frac{4}{3 - x}$$

When $x = 2$, $y = \dfrac{4}{3 - (2)}$

$\qquad\qquad\qquad = 4$

When $x = 5$, $y = \dfrac{4}{3 - (5)}$

$\qquad\qquad\qquad = -2$

b. $x^2 + 4y^2 = 5$

$\qquad\quad 4y^2 = 5 - x^2$

$\qquad\quad y^2 = \dfrac{1}{4}(5 - x^2)$

$\qquad\quad y = \pm\dfrac{1}{2}\sqrt{5 - x^2}$

When $x = 0$, $y = \pm\dfrac{1}{2}\sqrt{5}$

When $x = 1$, $y = \pm 1$

EXERCISE SET 7.1

▲ *Find each missing component so that each ordered pair is a solution of the equation. See Example 1.*

1. $y = x + 7$

a. $(0, \underline{?})$ **b.** $(2, \underline{?})$ **c.** $(-2, \underline{?})$

2. $y = 6 - 2x$

a. $(0, \underline{?})$ **b.** $(\underline{?}, 0)$ **c.** $(-1, \underline{?})$

3. $3x - 4y = 6$

a. $(0, \underline{?})$ **b.** $(\underline{?}, 0)$ **c.** $(-5, \underline{?})$

4. $x + 2y = 5$

a. $(0, \underline{?})$ **b.** $(5, \underline{?})$ **c.** $(-3, \underline{?})$

▲ *List the ordered pairs that satisfy each equation and have the given x-components. See Example 2.*

5. $y = x - 4; \quad -3, 0, 3$

6. $y = 2x + 6; \quad -2, 0, 2$

7. $y = \dfrac{3}{x + 2}; \quad 1, 2, 3$ **8.** $y = \dfrac{4x}{x^2 - 1}; \quad 0, 2, 4$

9. $y = \sqrt{x^2 - 1}; \quad 1, 2, 3$

10. $y = \dfrac{1}{2}\sqrt{4 - x^2}; \quad 0, 1, 2$

▲ *Transform each equation into one in which y is expressed explicitly in terms of x, and then find values for y for the given values of x. See Example 3.*

11. $2x + y = 6; \quad 2, 4$

12. $4x - y = 2; \quad -2, -4$

13. $xy - x = 2; \quad -2, 2$ **14.** $3x - xy = 6; \quad 1, 3$

15. $xy - y = 4; \quad 4, 8$

16. $x^2y - xy = -5; \quad 2, 4$

17. $x^2y - 4y = xy + 2; \quad -1, 1$

18. $x^2y - xy + 3 = 5y; \quad -2, 2$

19. $4 = \dfrac{x}{y^2 - 2}; \quad -1, 3$ **20.** $3 = \dfrac{x}{y^2 + 1}; \quad -2, 1$

21. $3x^2 - 4y^2 = 4; \quad 2, 3$ **22.** $5x^2 - 4y^2 = 2; \quad 2, 4$

Miscellaneous Exercises

▲ *Find the solution of each equation for the specified component.*

23. $y = |x| - 3$ for $x = -4$

24. $y = |x| + 5$ for $x = -2$

25. $y = |x - 1| + |x|$ for $x = -1$

26. $y = |2x + 1| - |x|$ for $x = -3$

27. $y = 2^x$ for $x = 3$

28. $y = 2^x$ for $x = -3$

29. $y = 2^{-x}$ for $x = 3$

30. $y = 2^{-x}$ for $x = -3$

31. Find k if $(1, 2)$ is a solution of $x + ky = 8$.

32. Find k if $(-6, 1)$ is a solution of $kx - 2y = 6$.

7.2 | GRAPHS; LINEAR EQUATIONS

Graphing is one of the most useful tools in the process of modeling. For example, the data in Table 7.1 show the atmospheric pressure at different altitudes above sea level on a certain day. Meteorologists regularly collect such data by attaching to a weather balloon a device called a radiosonde, which is equipped with a barometer and a radio transmitter. Altitudes are given in feet, and atmospheric pressures are given in inches of mercury.

Table 7.1

Altitude	Pressure
0	29.7
5000	24.8
10,000	20.5
20,000	14.6
30,000	10.6
40,000	8.5
50,000	7.3

We observe a generally decreasing trend in pressure as the altitude increases, but it is difficult to say anything more precise about the relationship between pressure and altitude. A clearer picture emerges if we plot the data on a graph. To do this, we use two perpendicular number lines called **axes**; we use the horizontal axis for the values of the first variable, altitude, and the vertical axis for the values of the second variable, pressure.

The entries in Table 7.1 are ordered pairs in which the first component is the altitude and the second component is the atmospheric pressure measured at that altitude. For example, the first two entries can be represented by $(0, 29.7)$ and $(5000, 24.8)$. We can then plot the points whose **coordinates** are given by the ordered pairs, as shown in Figure 7.1a.

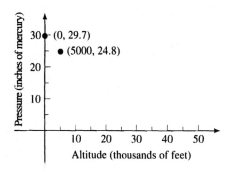

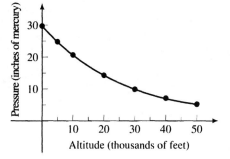

Figure 7.1   **a.**   **b.**

If we plot all the ordered pairs from the table, we can connect them with a smooth curve as shown in Figure 7.1b. In doing this we are really estimating the pressures that correspond to altitudes between those given, for example, altitudes of 15,000 feet or 37,000 feet. However, for many physical situations, variables are related so that one changes smoothly with respect to the other. We will assume that this is the case in most of the modeling we do.

EXAMPLE 1 | From the graph in Figure 7.1b, estimate

a. the atmospheric pressure measured at an altitude of 15,000 feet

b. the altitude at which the pressure is 12 inches of mercury.

Solutions | **a.** Note that the point on the graph with a first coordinate of 15,000 has a second coordinate of approximately 17.4 (see figure). Hence, we estimate the pressure at 15,000 feet to be 17.4 inches of mercury.

b. Note that the point on the graph with a second coordinate of 12 has a first coordinate of approximately 25,000, so an atmospheric pressure of 12 inches of mercury occurs at about 25,000 feet.

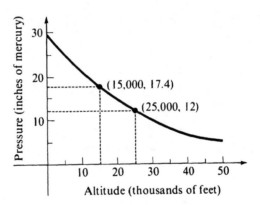

By using the graph of the data in Figure 7.1b we can obtain information about the relationship between altitude and pressure that would be difficult or impossible to obtain from the data alone.

EXAMPLE 2 | **a.** For what altitudes is the pressure less than 18 inches of mercury?

b. How much does the pressure decrease as the altitude increases from 15,000 to 25,000 feet?

c. For which 10,000-foot increase in altitude does the pressure change most rapidly?

Solutions | **a.** From the graph in Figure 7.1b, we see that the pressure has dropped to 18 inches of mercury at about 14,000 feet and that it continues to decrease as the altitude increases. Therefore, the pressure is less than 18 inches of mercury for altitudes greater than 14,000 feet.

b. At 15,000 feet the pressure is approximately 17.4 inches of mercury, and at 25,000 feet it is 12 inches. This represents a decrease in pressure of $17.4 - 12$, or 5.4, inches of mercury.

c. By studying the graph, we see that the pressure decreases most rapidly for low altitudes, so we conclude that the greatest drop in pressure occurs between 0 and 10,000 feet.

Cartesian Coordinate System

In Example 2 we used a graph to illustrate a collection of data given in a table. Graphs can also help us to analyze models given in the form of equations.

Since an equation in two variables often has infinitely many solutions, we cannot list them all. However, we can display the solutions on a graph. We first establish coordinate axes labeled with the variables they represent. Most commonly, the horizontal axis is called the **x-axis**, the vertical axis is called the **y-axis**, and their point of intersection is called the **origin**. The axes divide the plane into four regions called **quadrants**, which are referred to by Roman numerals, as illustrated in Figure 7.2.

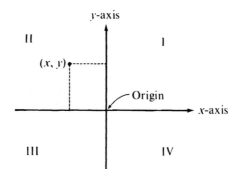

Figure 7.2

The system illustrated in Figure 7.2 is called the **Cartesian (or rectangular) coordinate system** (after the French mathematician René Descartes). Each point in the plane corresponds to an ordered pair of real numbers and every ordered pair of real numbers corresponds to a unique point in the plane. The first component of an ordered pair is the **x-coordinate** of the point and the second component is the **y-coordinate**.

The **graph** of an equation is the graph of all the solutions of the equation. Thus, a particular point is included in the graph of an equation if the coordinates of the point satisfy the equation. If the coordinates of a point do not satisfy the equation, then the point is not part of the graph. We can think of the graph of an equation as a picture of the solutions of the equation.

Most of the graphs we will study can be obtained by plotting a few solutions of the equation and then connecting these points by a smooth curve. For example, to graph

$$y = 3x - 2 \tag{1}$$

we first find a number of solutions of the equation by choosing values for x and solving for the corresponding y-values.

$$\text{For} \quad x = -2, \quad y = 3(-2) - 2 = -8$$
$$\text{For} \quad x = -1, \quad y = 3(-1) - 2 = -5$$
$$\text{For} \quad x = 0, \quad y = 3(0) - 2 = -2$$
$$\text{For} \quad x = 1, \quad y = 3(1) - 2 = 1$$
$$\text{For} \quad x = 2, \quad y = 3(2) - 2 = 4$$

We then tabulate these values and plot the ordered pairs.

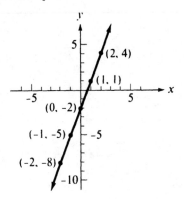

x	y	Solutions
-2	-8	$(-2, -8)$
-1	-5	$(-1, -5)$
0	-2	$(0, -2)$
1	1	$(1, 1)$
2	4	$(2, 4)$

Figure 7.3

By connecting the plotted points, we obtain the graph in Figure 7.3. The graph does not display *all* the solutions of Equation (1). Since there is a solution corresponding to every real number x, the graph extends infinitely in either direction, as indicated by the arrows.

Linear Equations

Any first-degree equation in two variables—that is, any equation that can be written equivalently in the form

$$ax + by + c = 0 \quad (a \text{ and } b \text{ not both } 0)$$

where a, b, and c are real numbers—has a graph that is a straight line. For this reason, such equations are often called **linear equations**. Since any two distinct points determine a straight line, it is evident that two solutions of such an equation determine its graph.

Intercept Method of Graphing

In practice, the two solutions that are easiest to find are those with second and first components, respectively, equal to 0—that is, the solutions $(x_1, 0)$ and $(0, y_1)$. Since these two points are the points where the graph intersects the x- and y-axes, they are easy to locate. The numbers x_1 and y_1 are called the **x-** and **y-intercepts**, respectively, of the graph. To find the x-intercept, substitute 0 for y in the equation and solve for x; to find the y-intercept, substitute 0 for x and solve for y.

EXAMPLE 3 Graph $3x + 4y = 12$.

Solution If $y = 0$, then

$$3x + 4(0) = 12$$
$$3x = 12$$
$$x = 4$$

The x-intercept is 4 with coordinates $(4, 0)$.

If $x = 0$, then

$$3(0) + 4y = 12$$
$$4y = 12$$
$$y = 3$$

The y-intercept is 3 with coordinates $(0, 3)$. Thus, the graph of the equation appears as shown.

EXAMPLE 4 Graph $3x - 4y = 24$.

Solution If $x = 0$, then

$$3(0) - 4y = 24$$
$$y = -6$$

If $y = 0$, then

$$3x - 4(0) = 24$$
$$x = 8$$

Hence, -6 is the y-intercept and 8 is the x-intercept. Graph these intercepts and draw a line through the points.

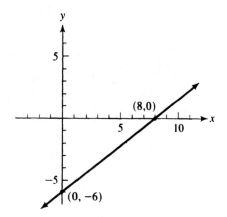

If the graph intersects the axes at or near the origin, either the intercepts do not represent two separate points or the points are too close together to be of much use in drawing the graph. It is then necessary to plot *at least* one other point at a distance far enough removed from the origin to establish the line with accuracy.

EXAMPLE 5

Graph $y = 3x$.

Solution

If $x = 0$, then $y = 0$, and both intercepts of the graph are at the point $(0, 0)$. Assigning any other replacement for x, say, 2, we obtain a second solution $(2, 6)$. We first graph the ordered pairs $(0, 0)$ and $(2, 6)$ and then complete the graph, as shown.

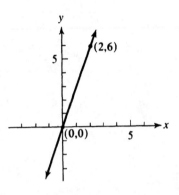

Special Cases of Linear Equations

There are two special cases of linear equations worth noting. First, an equation such as

$$y = 4$$

can be considered an equation in two variables,

$$0x + y = 4$$

For each x this equation assigns $y = 4$; that is, any ordered pair of the form $(x, 4)$ is a solution of the equation. For example,

$$(-1, 4), \quad (2, 4), \quad \text{and} \quad (4, 4)$$

are all solutions of the equation. If we draw a straight line through the graphs of these points, we obtain the graph shown in Figure 7.4 on page 180.

The other special case of a linear equation is of the type

$$x = 3$$

which may be looked upon as an equation in two variables,

$$x + 0y = 3$$

Here, only one value is permissible for x, namely, 3, while any value may be assigned to y; that is, any ordered pair of the form $(3, y)$ is a solution of this equation. If we choose two solutions, say, $(3, 1)$ and $(3, 3)$, and draw a straight line through the graphs of these points, we have the graph of the equation shown in Figure 7.5.

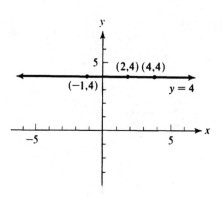

Figure 7.4

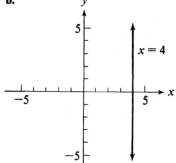

Figure 7.5

> *If k represents a constant (real number), then, in general, the graph of $y = k$ is a horizontal line and the graph of $x = k$ is a vertical line.*

EXAMPLE 6 **a.** Graph $y = 2$. **b.** Graph $x = 4$.

Solutions **a.**

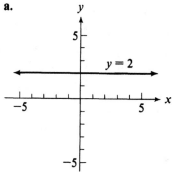

b.

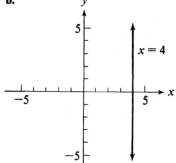

E X E R C I S E S E T 7.2

▲ *For Exercises 1–6, see Examples 1 and 2.*

1. The figure shows a graph of the temperature recorded during a winter day in Billings, Montana.

  a. What were the high and low temperatures recorded during the day?

  b. During what time intervals is the temperature above 5°F? Below −5°F?

  c. Estimate the temperatures at 7 A.M. and 2 A.M. At what time(s) is the temperature approximately 0°F? Approximately −12°F?

  d. How much did the temperature increase between 3 A.M. and 6 A.M.? Between 9 A.M. and noon? How

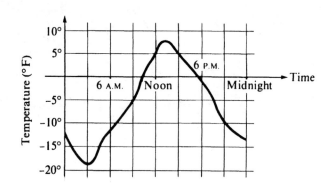

much did the temperature decrease between 6 P.M. and 9 A.M.?

e. During which 3-hour interval did the temperature increase most rapidly? Decrease most rapidly?

2. The figure shows a graph of the altitude of a commercial jetliner during its flight from Denver to Los Angeles.

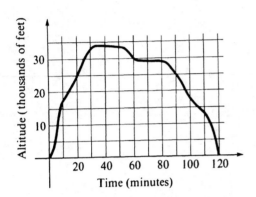

a. What was the highest altitude the jet achieved? At what time(s) was this altitude recorded?

b. During what time intervals was the altitude greater than 10,000 feet? Below 20,000 feet?

c. Estimate the altitude 15 minutes into the flight and 35 minutes into the flight. At what time(s) was the altitude approximately 16,000 feet? 32,000 feet?

d. How many feet did the jet climb during the first 10 minutes of flight? Between 20 minutes and 30 minutes? How many feet did the jet descend between 100 minutes and 120 minutes?

e. During which 10-minute interval did the jet ascend most rapidly? Descend most rapidly?

3. The graph shows the gas mileage achieved by an experimental model automobile at different speeds.

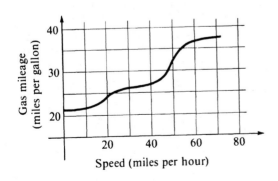

a. Estimate the gas mileage achieved at 43 miles per hour.

b. Estimate the speed at which a gas mileage of 34 miles per gallon is achieved.

c. At what speed is the best gas mileage achieved? Do you think that the gas mileage will continue to improve as the speed increases? Why or why not?

d. The data illustrated by the graph were collected under ideal test conditions. What factors might affect the gas mileage if the car were driven under more realistic conditions?

4. The graph shows the average height of young women aged 0 to 18 years.

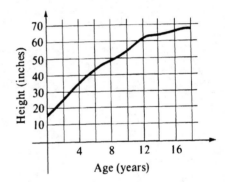

a. Estimate the average height of 5-year-old girls.

b. Estimate the age at which the average young woman is 50 inches tall.

c. At what age does the average woman achieve her adult height? Do you think that the height will continue to increase as age increases? Why or why not?

d. The data recorded in the graph reflect the average heights for young women at given ages. What factors might affect the data for specific individuals?

5. The graph shows the speed of a car during an hour-long journey.

a. When did the car stop at a traffic signal?

b. During what time interval did the car drive in stop-and-go city traffic?

c. During what time interval did the car travel on the freeway?

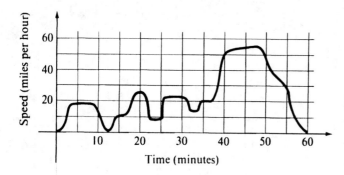

Speed (miles per hour) vs. Time (minutes)

6. The graph shows the fish population of a popular fishing pond.

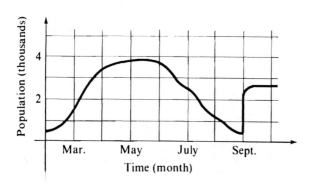

Population (thousands) vs. Time (month)

   a. During what months do the young fish hatch?
   b. During what months is fishing allowed?
   c. When does the park service restock the pond?

▲ *Graph each equation. See Examples 3 and 4.*

7. $y = x - 5$ **8.** $y = x + 3$
9. $y = 3x + 6$ **10.** $y = 4x - 8$
11. $x + 2y = 8$ **12.** $2x - y = 6$
13. $3x - 4y = 12$ **14.** $2x + 6y = 6$
15. $6x = y + 5$ **16.** $4x = y - 6$
17. $2x = 3y - 4$ **18.** $3x = 4y + 6$

▲ *Graph each equation. See Example 5.*

19. $2x - y = 0$ **20.** $x + 3y = 0$
21. $y = -3x$ **22.** $x = 2y$
23. $4x - y = 0$ **24.** $4x + y = 0$
25. $x + y = 0$ **26.** $x - y = 0$

▲ *Graph each equation. See Example 6.*

27. $y = -3$ **28.** $x = -2$ **29.** $2x = 8$
30. $3y = 15$ **31.** $x = 0$ **32.** $y = 0$

Miscellaneous Exercises

▲ *Which graph best illustrates the following?*

33. The stopping distances for cars traveling at various speeds

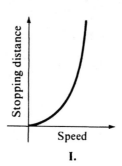
              I.   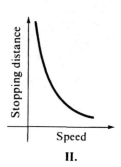 **II.**

34. Your pulse rate during an aerobics class

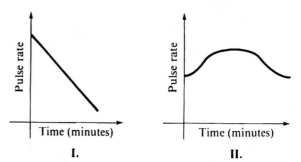
              I.   **II.**

35. Your income in terms of the number of hours you worked

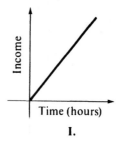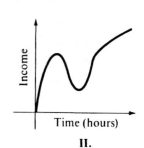
              I.   **II.**

36.   Your temperature during an illness

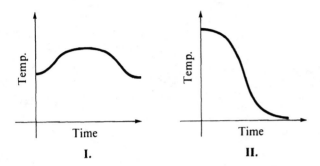

I.   II.

7.3 | DISTANCE AND SLOPE FORMULAS

Distance Formula   Any two distinct points in a plane are the endpoints of the line segment joining them. We shall discuss two fundamental properties of a line segment—its length and its slope with respect to the x-axis.

We first observe that either any two distinct points P_1 and P_2 lie on the same vertical line or one is to the right of the other. If we construct a line parallel to the y-axis through P_2 and a line parallel to the x-axis through P_1, the lines will meet at a point P_3, as shown in Figure 7.6.

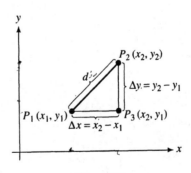

Figure 7.6

The x-coordinate of P_3 is the same as the x-coordinate of P_2, whereas the y-coordinate of P_3 is the same as that of P_1; hence, the coordinates of P_3 are (x_2, y_1). From Figure 7.6 we observe that the distance between P_2 and P_3 is $(y_2 - y_1)$, commonly designated by Δy, and the distance between P_1 and P_3 is $(x_2 - x_1)$, commonly designated by Δx.

The Pythagorean Theorem may now be used to find the length of the line segment joining P_1 and P_2. Referring to Figure 7.6, we note that

$$d^2 = (x_2 - x_1)^2 + (y_2 - y_1)^2$$

Since distances are always positive, if we consider only the positive square root of the right-hand member, we have the **distance formula**.

$$d = \sqrt{(x_2 - x_1)^2 + (y_2 - y_2)^2} \qquad\qquad (1)$$

EXAMPLE 1   Find the distance between $(2, -1)$ and $(4, 3)$

Solution   Substituting $(2, -1)$ for $P_1(x_1, y_1)$ and $(4, 3)$ for $P_2(x_2, y_2)$ in the distance formula, we obtain

$$\begin{aligned}
d &= \sqrt{(x_2 - x_1)^2 + (y_2 - y_1)^2} \\
&= \sqrt{[4 - 2]^2 + [3 - (-1)]^2} \\
&= \sqrt{4 + 16} \\
&= \sqrt{20} = 2\sqrt{5}
\end{aligned}$$

Notice that in Example 1 we would obtain the same answer if we used $(4, 3)$ for P_1 and $(2, -1)$ for P_2.

$$\begin{aligned}
d &= \sqrt{[2 - 4]^2 + [(-1) - 3]^2} \\
&= \sqrt{4 + 16} = 2\sqrt{5}
\end{aligned}$$

The distance formula still applies if P_1 and P_2 lie on the same horizontal or vertical line. If the points P_1 and P_2 lie on the same horizontal line (that is, if $y_2 = y_1$), then

$$d = \sqrt{(x_2 - x_1)^2 + 0^2} = |x_2 - x_1|$$

If they lie on the same vertical line (that is, if $x_2 = x_1$), then

$$d = \sqrt{0^2 + (y_2 - y_1)^2} = |y_2 - y_1|$$

EXAMPLE 2
a.   The points $(6, 2)$ and $(-3, 2)$ lie on the same horizontal line, namely, $y = 2$. The distance between the points is

$$|x_2 - x_1| = |6 - (-3)| = 9$$

b.   The points $(4, -5)$ and $(4, -2)$ lie on the same vertical line, namely, $x = 4$. The distance between the points is

$$|y_2 - y_1| = |(-5) - (-2)| = 3$$

Slope Formula   A second useful property of a line segment is its orientation in the plane. This property can be measured by comparing the change in y values with the change in x values as shown in Figure 7.7.

Figure 7.7   a.   b.

The ratio of the change in y values to the change in x values is the **slope** of the segment and is designated by the letter m. Thus, since the change in y-values is $(y_2 - y_1)$ and the change in x-values is $(x_2 - x_1)$, the slope of the segment joining P_1 and P_2 is given by the following formula:

$$\text{slope:} \quad m = \frac{\Delta y}{\Delta x} = \frac{y_2 - y_1}{x_2 - x_1} \quad (x_2 \neq x_1) \tag{2}$$

In Figure 7.7a the rise $(y_2 - y_1)$ is also positive, so the slope is positive. In Figure 7.7b the rise $(y_2 - y_1)$ is negative, so the slope is negative. When P_2 is to the right of P_1, as in Figure 7.7, the run $(x_2 - x_1)$ is positive. A positive slope indicates that a line is rising to the right; a negative slope indicates that a line is falling to the right. Notice that

$$\frac{y_2 - y_1}{x_2 - x_1} = \frac{-(y_1 - y_2)}{-(x_1 - x_2)} = \frac{y_1 - y_2}{x_1 - x_2}$$

so the points may be considered in either order. You can also verify that any two points on the line can be used to compute its slope.

EXAMPLE 3   Find the slope of the line segment joining the points $(2, -1)$ and $(4, 3)$.

Solution   Let $(2, -1)$ be (x_1, y_1) and $(4, 3)$ be (x_2, y_2). Then

$$m = \frac{y_2 - y_1}{x_2 - x_1} = \frac{3 - (-1)}{4 - 2}$$

$$= \frac{4}{2} = 2$$

Several lines with different slopes are shown in Figure 7.8 on page 186. In Figure 7.8a, where $m > 0$, the line "rises" from left to right. In Figure 7.8b, where $m < 0$, the line "falls" from left to right.

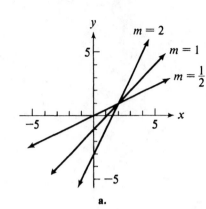
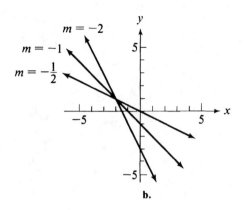

Figure 7.8   a.   b.

If a segment is horizontal, parallel to the x-axis, as shown in Figure 7.9a, then $y_2 - y_1 = 0$, and the segment will have a slope of 0. If a segment is vertical, parallel to the y-axis, as in Figure 7.9b, $x_2 - x_1 = 0$, and the segment's slope is not defined.

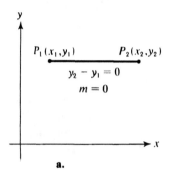
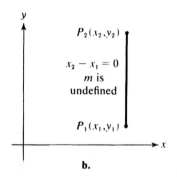

Figure 7.9   a.   b.

Parallel and Perpendicular Lines

The following two properties of line segments are important in mathematics and applications of mathematics:

> *Two line segments with slopes m_1 and m_2 are*
> $$\text{parallel if } \quad m_1 = m_2$$
> $$\text{perpendicular if } \quad m_1 m_2 = -1$$

Note that two lines are perpendicular if the slope of one is the negative reciprocal of the slope of the other $\left(m_1 = -\dfrac{1}{m_2} \right)$.

EXAMPLE 4   a.   In Figure a, line segment AB with slope

$$m_1 = \frac{5 - 3}{5 - 2} = \frac{2}{3}$$

is parallel to line segment CD with slope

$$m_2 = \frac{1 - (-1)}{4 - 1} = \frac{2}{3}$$

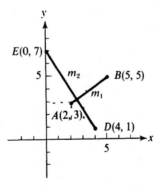

a.

b. In Figure b, line segment DE with slope

$$m_2 = \frac{1-7}{4-0} = \frac{-6}{4} = \frac{-3}{2}$$

is perpendicular to line segment AB with slope

$$m_1 = \frac{5-3}{5-2} = \frac{2}{3}$$

because

$$m_1 m_2 = \frac{2}{3}\left(\frac{-3}{2}\right) = -1$$

b.

EXERCISE SET 7.3

▲ *Find the distance between each of the given pairs of points, and find the slope of the line segment joining them. Sketch each line segment in the coordinate plane. See Examples 1–3.*

1. $(1, 1), (4, 5)$
2. $(-1, 1), (5, 9)$
3. $(-3, 2), (2, 14)$
4. $(-4, -3), (1, 9)$
5. $(2, 1), (4, 0)$
6. $(-3, 2), (0, 0)$
7. $(5, -4), (-1, 1)$
8. $(2, -3), (-2, -1)$
9. $(3, 5), (-2, 5)$
10. $(2, 0), (-2, 0)$
11. $(0, 5), (0, -5)$
12. $(-2, -5), (-2, 3)$

▲ *Use the distance formula to find the perimeter of the triangle whose vertices are given. Sketch each triangle in the coordinate plane.*

13. $(0, 6), (9, -6), (-3, 0)$ **14.** $(10, 1), (3, 1), (5, 9)$
15. $(5, 6), (11, -2), (-10, -2)$
16. $(-1, 5), (8, -7), (4, 1)$

▲ *For Exercises 17–20, see Example 4.*

17. Show that the two line segments whose endpoints are $(5, 4), (3, 0)$ and $(-1, 8), (-4, 2)$ are parallel.
18. Show that the two line segments whose endpoints are $(-4, 2), (2, -2)$ and $(3, 0), (-3, 4)$ are parallel.
19. Show that the two line segments whose endpoints are $(0, -7), (8, -5)$ and $(5, 7), (8, -5)$ are perpendicular.
20. Show that the two line segments whose endpoints are $(8, 0), (6, 6)$ and $(-3, 3), (6, 6)$ are perpendicular.

▲ *Specify the slope of each line.*

21.　**a.** l_1　　**b.** l_2

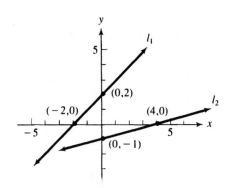

22.　**a.** l_1　　**b.** l_2

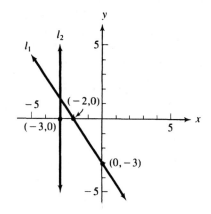

23.　**a.** l_1　　**b.** l_2

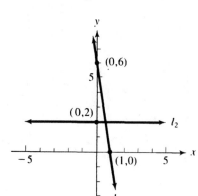

24.　**a.** l_1　　**b.** l_2

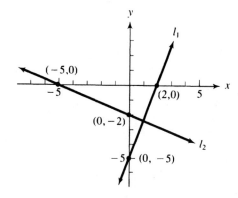

Miscellaneous Exercises

25. Show that the triangle described in Exercise 13 is a right triangle. [*Hint:* Use the converse of the Pythagorean theorem—that is, if $c^2 = a^2 + b^2$, the triangle is a right triangle. Alternatively, show that two sides are perpendicular.]
26. Show that the triangle with vertices at $(0, 0), (6, 0)$, and $(3, 3)$ is a right isosceles triangle—that is, a right triangle with two sides that have the same length.
27. Show that the points $(2, 4), (3, 8), (5, 1)$, and $(4, -3)$ are the vertices of a parallelogram. [*Hint:* A four-sided figure is a parallelogram if the opposite sides are parallel.]
28. Show that the points $(-5, 4), (7, -11), (12, 25)$, and $(0, 40)$ are the vertices of a parallelogram.
29. Given the points $P_1(4, -1)$, $P_2(2, 7)$, and $P_3(-3, 4)$, find the value of k in the ordered pair $P_4(5, k)$ that makes $P_1 P_2$ parallel to $P_3 P_4$.
30. Using the points in Exercise 29, find the k that makes $P_1 P_2$ perpendicular to $P_3 P_4$.

7.4 | FORMS OF LINEAR EQUATIONS

Let us designate

$$ax + by + c = 0 \quad \text{or} \quad ax + by = c \tag{1}$$

as **standard form** for a linear equation. We shall now consider two useful alternative forms.

Point-Slope Form Consider a line on the plane with given slope m and passing through a given point (x_1, y_1), as shown in Figure 7.10. If we choose *any other point on the line* and assign to it the coordinates (x, y), the slope of the line is given by

$$\frac{y - y_1}{x - x_1} = m \quad (x \neq x_1) \tag{2}$$

from which

$$y - y_1 = m(x - x_1) \quad (x \neq x_1) \tag{3}$$

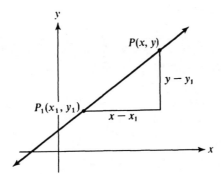

Figure 7.10

Hence, if we know one point (x_1, y_1) on a line and the slope m of the line, we can find the equation of the line by using the following formula.

$$y - y_1 = m(x - x_1) \tag{4}$$

Recall from page 186 that the slope of a vertical line is not defined. The equation of the line is simply $x = x_1$, where x_1 is its constant x-value.

Equation (4) is called the **point-slope form** for a linear equation.

EXAMPLE 1 **a.** Find an equation of the line that goes through the point $(1, -4)$ with slope $-\frac{3}{4}$.

b. Find an equation of the vertical line that goes through the point $(1, -4)$.

Solutions **a.** Substituting -4 for y_1, 1 for x_1, and $-\frac{3}{4}$ for m in the point-slope form for a linear equation, we obtain

$$y - (-4) = -\frac{3}{4}(x - 1)$$

To change the equation to standard form, we multiply each side by 4 to obtain

$4y + 16 = -3(x - 1)$ **Apply distributive property.**

$4y + 16 = -3x + 3$ **Add $3x$ and -3 to each side.**

$3x + 4y + 13 = 0$

b.   The x-value of a vertical line is constant. Hence the equation is $x = 1$.

We can now find an equation of the line whose graph includes two given points. We first use the slope formula developed in Section 7.3 and then use the point-slope formula with either of the two given points.

EXAMPLE 2   Find an equation of the line whose graph includes the points $(2, 2)$ and $(-4, 1)$.

Solution   First find the slope, selecting either point as (x_1, y_1) and the other point as (x_2, y_2).

$$m = \frac{y_2 - y_1}{x_2 - x_1} = \frac{1 - 2}{-4 - 2}$$

$$= \frac{-1}{-6} = \frac{1}{6}$$

Then use the point-slope formula with either ordered pair. Using $(2, 2)$ for (x_1, y_1) in the formula $y - y_1 = m(x - x_1)$ yields

$$y - 2 = \frac{1}{6}(x - 2) \qquad \qquad \textbf{(5)}$$

Multiply each side by 6 to obtain

$6(y - 2) = x - 2$ **Apply distributive law.**

$6y - 12 = x - 2$ **Add $-6y$ and $+2$ to each side.**

$-10 = x - 6y$

or

$$x - 6y = -10$$

Two-Point Formula   Note that we can substitute $\dfrac{y_2 - y_1}{x_2 - x_1}$ for m in the point-slope formula to obtain Equation (6).

$$y - y_1 = \frac{y_2 - y_1}{x_2 - x_1}(x - x_1) \qquad \qquad \textbf{(6)}$$

This equation is called the **two-point formula**. Given two points, we can make substitutions directly in this formula to obtain an equation of the line containing the two points. For example, substituting the coordinates of the points $(2, 2)$ and $(-4, 1)$ from Example 2 for the coordinates (x_1, y_1) and (x_2, y_2), respectively, in the two-point formula, we obtain

$$y - 2 = \frac{1 - 2}{-4 - 2}(x - 2)$$

which simplifies to Equation (5) in Example 2,

$$y - 2 = \frac{1}{6}(x - 2)$$

Slope-Intercept Form

Now consider the equation of the line passing through a given point on the y-axis with coordinates $(0, b)$ and slope m, as shown in Figure 7.11. Substituting $(0, b)$ in the point-slope form of a linear equation,

$$y - y_1 = m(x - x_1)$$

we obtain

$$y - b = m(x - 0)$$

from which we get Equation (7).

$$y = mx + b \qquad\qquad (7)$$

Equation (7) is called the **slope-intercept form** for a linear equation. Note that b is the y-intercept of the graph of the equation.

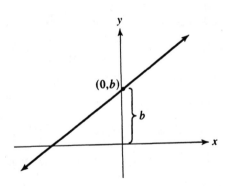

Figure 7.11

EXAMPLE 3   Write $3x + 4y = 6$ in slope-intercept form, and specify the slope of the line and the y-intercept.

Solution   First solve the equation explicitly for y.

$$4y = -3x + 6 \qquad \textbf{Divide each side by 4.}$$

$$y = \frac{-3}{4}x + \frac{3}{2}$$

Hence, the slope is $-\frac{3}{4}$, the coefficient of x, and the y-intercept is $\frac{3}{2}$.

Intercept Form　If the x- and y-intercepts are a and b (a, $b \neq 0$), respectively, as shown in Figure 7.12, then　$m = -b/a$.　Replacing m in the point-slope formula, we have

$$y = -\frac{b}{a}x + b \qquad \text{Multiply each side by } a.$$

$$ay = -bx + ab \qquad \text{Add } bx \text{ to each side.}$$

$$bx + ay = ab$$

Then dividing each member by ab, we obtain Equation (8), called the **intercept form** for a linear equation.

$$\frac{x}{a} + \frac{y}{b} = 1 \qquad\qquad (8)$$

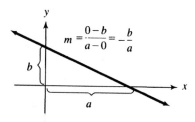

Figure 7.12

EXAMPLE 4　Given that the x- and y-intercepts of a line are 2 and -3, respectively, write an equation of the line in standard form.

Solution　Substituting **2** and **-3** for a and b, respectively, in the intercept form, we obtain

$$\frac{x}{2} + \frac{y}{-3} = 1$$

from which, by multiplying each member by the LCD, -6,

$$-3x + 2y = -6$$

Then multiplying each member by -1, we obtain

$$3x - 2y = 6$$

The next example shows how we can write an equation of a line that is parallel to or perpendicular to a given line.

EXAMPLE 5　Write the equation of the line that is parallel to, and the line that is perpendicular to, the graph of　$2x + 3y = 6$　and passes through $(3, 3)$.

Solution　First find the slope of the graph of　$2x + 3y = 6$.

$$3y = -2x + 6$$

$$y = \frac{-2}{3}x + 2$$

Hence, the slope is $-\dfrac{2}{3}$ and the slope m_1 of the line parallel to this line is also $-\dfrac{2}{3}$.

The slope m_2 of the line perpendicular to the given line is

$$m_2 = \frac{-1}{m_1} = -\frac{1}{\dfrac{-2}{3}} = \frac{3}{2}$$

Use the point-slope formula to get the two equations of the lines passing through the point $(3,3)$ with slopes $m_1 = -\dfrac{2}{3}$ and $m_2 = \dfrac{3}{2}$.

a.
$$y - 3 = \frac{-2}{3}(x - 3)$$
$$3y - 9 = -2x + 6$$
$$2x + 3y = 15$$

b.
$$y - 3 = \frac{3}{2}(x - 3)$$
$$2y - 6 = 3x - 9$$
$$3x - 2y = 3$$

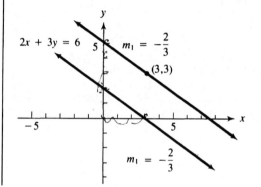

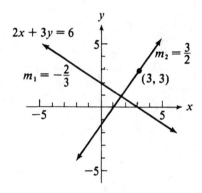

E X E R C I S E   S E T   7.4

▲ *Find an equation of the line that goes through each of the given points and has the given slope. Write the equation in standard form. See Example 1.*

1. $(-1, 3)$; $m = 2$

2. $(2, -5)$; $m = -3$

3. $(-2, 6)$; $m = -1$

4. $(-6, -1)$; $m = 4$

5. $(0, 3)$; $m = \dfrac{1}{2}$

6. $(2, 0)$; $m = -\dfrac{1}{3}$

7. $(-1, 2)$; $m = -\dfrac{3}{2}$

8. $(2, -1)$; $m = \dfrac{5}{3}$

9. $(-3, -5)$; $m = 0$

10. $(0, -6)$; $m = 0$

11. $(-3, 2)$; parallel to y-axis

12. $(0, 0)$; $m = 1$

▲ *Find an equation of the line whose graph includes the two given points. Write the equation in the form $ax + by = c$ or $ax + by + c = 0$. See Example 2.*

13. $(-4, 2), (3, 3)$

14. $(5, -1), (2, -3)$

15. $(-1, -3), (2, 0)$

16. $(0, 5), (3, -4)$

17. $(-3, -4), (2, -2)$

18. $(-1, 4), (-3, -3)$

19. $(0, -4), (3, 0)$

20. $(-1, 0), (0, -4)$

▲ **a.** *Write each equation in slope-intercept form.*

 b. *Specify the slope of the line and the y-intercept. See Example 3.*

21. $x + y = 3$

22. $2x + y = -1$

23. $3x + 2y = 1$ **24.** $3x - y = 7$

25. $x - 3y = 2$ **26.** $2x - 3y = 0$

27. $8x - 3y = 0$ **28.** $-x = 2y - 5$

29. $y + 2 = 0$ **30.** $y - 3 = 0$

▲ *Write an equation in standard form of the line with x-intercept a and y-intercept b. See Example 4.*

31. $a = 3$ and $b = -2$

32. $a = -4$ and $b = 1$

33. $a = -2$ and $b = 4$

34. $a = 5$ and $b = -3$

35. $a = -3$ and $b = -6$

36. $a = -4$ and $b = -2$

37. $a = -\dfrac{1}{2}$ and $b = \dfrac{3}{4}$

38. $a = \dfrac{2}{3}$ and $b = -\dfrac{1}{4}$

▲ *For Exercises 39–42, see Example 5.*

39. Write an equation of the line that is parallel to the graph of $x - 2y = 5$ and passes through the origin. Draw the graphs of both equations.

40. Write an equation of the line that passes through $(0, 5)$ parallel to $2y - 3x = 5$. Draw the graphs of both equations.

41. Write an equation of the line that is perpendicular to the graph of $x - 2y = 5$ and passes through the origin. Draw the graphs of both equations.

42. Write an equation of the line that is perpendicular to the graph of $2y - 3x = 5$ and passes through $(0, 5)$. Draw the graphs of both equations.

Miscellaneous Exercises

43. Write an equation of the line that passes through the origin and the point (a, b) when (a) $a = b$ and (b) $a = -b$.

44. Write an equation of the line that passes through the origin and the point (a, b) when (a) $a = 2b$ and (b) $b = 2a$.

45. Write the equation $\dfrac{x}{a} + \dfrac{y}{b} = 1$ in slope-intercept form.

46. Write the equation $\dfrac{x}{a} + \dfrac{y}{b} = 1$ in point-slope form.

47. Write an equation of the line with slope m and x-intercept a.

48. Show that the graphs of $ax + by = c$ and $bx - ay = c$ are perpendicular for all a, b, and c, $a \neq 0$, $b \neq 0$.

7.5 | APPLICATIONS OF LINEAR EQUATIONS

Many relationships can be modeled by linear equations, and their graphs may be helpful in obtaining information that may not be immediately evident from the statement of the relationship.

EXAMPLE 1 Yumiko's long-distance telephone company charges a $3 access fee for a call to Tokyo and $2 for each minute of the call. (A fraction of a minute is charged as the corresponding fraction of $2.)

a. Write an equation that expresses the cost of a call to Tokyo in terms of the length of the call.

b. Graph the equation in part a.

Solutions **a.** Let t represent the length of the call in minutes, and let C represent the cost of the call. Then

$$C = 3 + 2t \qquad (t \geqslant 0)$$

Since the equation is linear, we need only two points to graph the equation.

b. Choose any two nonnegative values for t and calculate the corresponding values for C to obtain the following ordered pairs:

t	C	(t, C)
0	3	$(0, 3)$
3	9	$(3, 9)$

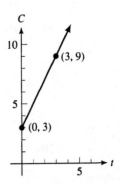

The graphs of these points lie on a straight line, as shown in the figure. Note that the line extends infinitely in only one direction, since negative values of t do not make sense here.

To draw a graph that is useful in analyzing a problem, we must choose scales for the axes that reflect the magnitudes of the variables involved.

EXAMPLE 2   In 1960 a three-bedroom house in Midville cost \$30,000. The price of a home has increased linearly by an average of \$4000 per year since then.

a. Write an equation that expresses the price of a three-bedroom house in Midville in terms of the number of years since 1960.

b. Graph the equation in part a.

c. Estimate the cost of a three-bedroom house in 1990.

Solutions   **a.** Let P represent the price of the house t years after 1960. Then
$$P = 30,000 + 4000t \qquad (t \geqslant 0) \tag{1}$$

b. Since the equation is linear, choose two values for t and calculate the corresponding values for P to obtain the following ordered pairs.

t	P	(t, P)
0	30,000	$(0, 30,000)$
10	70,000	$(10, 70,000)$

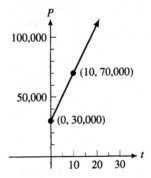

To graph the equation, we scale the horizontal axis, or t-axis, in 5-year intervals and the vertical axis, or P-axis, in intervals of \$10,000, then plot the points found in the table.

c.   In 1990, $t = 30$,   so substitute $t = 30$ into Equation (1) to obtain

$$P = 30{,}000 + 4000(30)$$
$$= 150{,}000$$

A three-bedroom house cost $150,000 in 1990.

EXAMPLE 3

Phil and Ernie buy a used photocopier for $800 and set up a copy service on their campus. For each hour that the copier runs continuously, Phil and Ernie make $40.

a.   Write an equation that relates Phil and Ernie's profit (or loss) to the number of hours they run the copier.

b.   Find the intercepts and sketch the graph.

c.   What is the significance of the intercepts to the problem?

Solutions

a.   Let t represent the number of hours that Phil and Ernie run the copier, and let P represent their net profit or loss. Then

$$P = -800 + 40t \qquad (t \geqslant 0)$$

b.   If $t = 0$,   then

$$P = -800 + 40(0)$$
$$P = -800$$

If $P = 0$,   then

$$0 = -800 + 40t$$
$$-40t = -800$$
$$t = 20$$

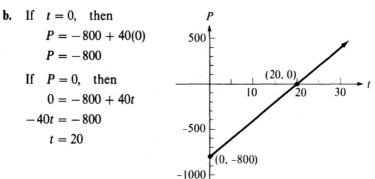

The P-intercept is -800 and the t-intercept is 20. Graph the points $(0, -800)$ and $(20, 0)$ and draw a line through them. Note that we do not include points with negative t-coordinates in the graph.

c.   The P-intercept, -800, is the value of P when $t = 0$,   that is, the initial, or starting, value of the profit variable. Phil and Ernie start out $800 in debt.

The t-intercept, 20, is the value of t when $P = 0$,   the number of hours of operation required for Phil and Ernie to break even.

Slope as a Rate of Change

The following example illustrates how the slope of a line represents a rate of change.

EXAMPLE 4

A driver for a cross-country trucking firm travels at a constant speed of 50 miles per hour.

a.   Write an equation that expresses the distance traveled in terms of the number of hours driven.

b.   Graph the equation.

c. Find the slope of the graph, and interpret it as a rate of change.

Solutions   a. Let t represent the number of hours driven and D the distance traveled. Then
$$D = 50t \quad (t \geqslant 0)$$

b. Choose several values for t and calculate the corresponding values for D to obtain the graph.

c. Note that if you move from one point to another on the graph, then
$$\frac{\Delta D}{\Delta t} = \frac{50 \text{ miles}}{1 \text{ hour}}$$

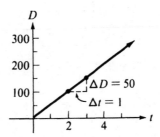

so the slope is 50. It represents the change in distance with respect to time traveled, or the speed of the truck in miles per hour.

EXAMPLE 5   Ms. Randolph bought a new car in 1980. In 1982 the car was worth $9000, and in 1985 it was valued at $4500.

a. Assuming that the depreciation is linear, that is, that the value of the car decreases by the same amount each year, write an equation that expresses the value of Ms. Randolph's car in terms of the number of years she has owned it.

b. Interpret the slope as a rate of change.

c. Find the value of the car when it was new.

Solutions   a. Let t represent the number of years that Ms. Randolph has owned her car, and let V represent its value after t years. Then the two ordered pairs $(2, 9000)$ and $(5, 4500)$ represent points on the graph of V versus t. To find its equation, first compute the slope.
$$m = \frac{V_2 - V_1}{t_2 - t_1} = \frac{9000 - 4500}{2 - 5}$$
$$= \frac{4500}{-3} = -1500$$

Then use the point-slope formula with either point, say $(2, 9000)$, and $m = -1500$.
$$V - V_1 = m(t - t_1)$$
$$V - 9000 = -1500(t - 2)$$
$$V - 9000 = -1500t + 3000$$
$$V + 1500t = 12,000$$

b. The slope represents the change in the value of the car per year. Thus,

$$m = \frac{\Delta V}{\Delta t} = \frac{-1500 \text{ dollars}}{1 \text{ year}}$$

so the car depreciated at a rate of $1500 per year.

c. The car was new when $t = 0$, so

$$V + 1500(0) = 12,000$$

from which

$$V = 12,000$$

The car was worth $12,000 when new.

EXERCISE SET 7.5

▲ *Solve. See Examples 1–3.*

1. Frank plants a dozen corn seedlings, each 6 inches tall. With plenty of water and sunlight they will grow approximately 2 inches per day.
   a. Write an equation that expresses the height of the seedlings in terms of the number of days since they were planted.
   b. Graph the equation.
   c. How tall is the corn after 3 weeks?
   d. How long will it be before the corn is 6 feet tall?

2. In the desert the temperature at 6 A.M., just before sunrise, was 65°F. The temperature rose about 5 degrees every hour until it reached its maximum value at about 5 P.M.
   a. Write an equation that expresses the temperature in the desert in terms of the number of hours since 6 A.M.
   b. Graph the equation.
   c. How hot is it at noon?
   d. When will the temperature be 110°F?

3. On October 31, Betty and Paul fill their 250-gallon heating fuel oil tank. Beginning in November, they use an average of 15 gallons per week in heating fuel oil.
   a. Write an equation that relates the amount of oil in the tank to the number of weeks since October 31.
   b. Graph the equation.
   c. How much fuel oil is left in the tank 8 weeks later?
   d. When will there be only 70 gallons of fuel oil left?

4. Leon's camper has a 20-gallon gas tank, and he gets 12 miles to the gallon.
   a. Write an equation that relates the amount of gasoline in Leon's fuel tank to the number of miles he has driven.
   b. Graph the equation.
   c. How much gas does Leon have after driving 100 miles?
   d. If Leon's gas gauge registers one-fourth of a tank, how far has he driven?

5. Sandra works for the post office. She is assigned to sort and stack mail for 2 hours in the morning. After that, she delivers mail to 15 houses per hour.
   a. Write an equation that expresses the number of hours in Sandra's shift in terms of the number of houses on her route.
   b. Graph the equation.
   c. How long is Sandra's shift if there are 60 houses on her route?
   d. How many houses can she cover in an 8-hour workday?

6. Jim works at the blood bank. It takes him $2\frac{1}{2}$ hours in the morning to collect samples from the patients and to set up the chemicals for the tests. He can then process an average of 20 samples per hour.
   a. Write an equation that expresses the number of samples Jim processes in terms of the number of hours he works.
   b. Graph the equation.
   c. How many samples can Jim process on a 7-hour shift?
   d. How long will it take Jim to process 125 samples?

7. Here is a formula for calculating the daily calorie intake for a woman that will result in a weight loss of 1 pound per week. First, determine the woman's ideal weight (lean weight at age 22). For each pound of ideal weight, allow 15 calories per day. Now subtract 500 calories.
   a. Write an equation that relates a woman's daily calorie allowance to her ideal weight.
   b. Graph the equation.
   c. What is the calorie intake recommended for a woman whose ideal weight is 125 pounds?
   d. What is the ideal weight of a woman who should consume 1300 calories per day on this diet?

8. Repeat Exercise 7 to determine a diet program for a man. A man's ideal weight is his lean weight at age 25, and he is allowed 17 calories for each pound of ideal weight.
   a. Write an equation that relates a man's daily calorie allowance to his ideal weight.
   b. Graph the equation.
   c. What calorie intake is recommended for a man whose ideal weight is 175 pounds?
   d. What is the ideal weight of a man who should consume 2200 calories per day on this diet?

9. The owner of a gas station has $4800 to spend on unleaded gasoline this month. Regular unleaded costs him $0.60 per gallon, and premium unleaded costs $0.80 per gallon.
   a. Write an equation that relates the amount of regular unleaded gasoline he can buy to the amount of premium unleaded he can buy.
   b. Graph the equation.
   c. If the owner buys 3000 gallons of premium unleaded, how many gallons of regular unleaded can he buy?

10. Five pounds of body fat is equivalent to 16,000 calories. Carol can burn 600 calories per hour bicycling and 400 calories per hour swimming.
    a. Write an equation that relates the number of hours of each activity Carol needs to perform to lose 5 pounds.
    b. Graph the equation.
    c. If Carol bicycles for 10 hours, how many hours must she swim?

11. A real estate agent receives a salary of $10,000 plus 3% of her total sales for the year.
    a. Write an equation that relates the agent's salary to her total annual sales.

    b. Graph the equation.
    c. If the agent sells $500,000 worth of property, what will her salary be?
    d. How much property must the agent sell to make a yearly salary of $40,000?

12. Under a proposed graduated income tax system, a single taxpayer whose taxable income is between $13,920 and $16,190 would pay taxes of $1706.30 plus 20% of the amount of his income over $13,920.
    a. Write an equation that relates the taxes owed to the amount of income over $13,920.
    b. Graph the equation.
    c. How much does a single taxpayer with a taxable income of $15,000 pay in taxes?
    d. If Everett paid $1800 in taxes last year, what was his taxable income?

▲ For Exercises 13–24, find the intercepts of the graphs in Exercises 1–12. In each case, explain what the intercepts represent in the terms of the problem. Do the intercepts make sense in the context of the problem? See Example 3.

▲ For Exercises 25 and 26, see Example 4.

25. The distance covered by a cross-country competitor is given by $d = 6t$, where t is the number of hours she runs.
    a. Graph the equation.
    b. Using two points on the graph, compute the slope $\Delta d / \Delta t$ (including units).
    c. What is the significance of the slope in terms of the problem?

26. A temporary typist's paycheck (before deductions) is given by $S = 8t$, where t is the number of hours she worked.
    a. Graph the equation.
    b. Using two points on the graph, compute the slope $\Delta S / \Delta t$ (including units).
    c. What is the significance of the slope in terms of the problem?

▲ For Exercises 27–32, do the following.
    a. Find a linear equation relating the variables.
    b. Graph the equation.
    c. State the slope of the line, including units, and explain its meaning in the context of the problem.
    See Example 5.

27. It cost a bicycle company $9000 to make 50 touring bikes in its first month of operation and $15,000 to make 125 bikes during its second month. Express its production costs in terms of the number of bicycles made.

28. Under ideal conditions, Andrea's Porsche can travel 312 miles on a full tank (12 gallons of gasoline) and 130 miles on 5 gallons. Express the distance Andrea can drive in terms of the amount of gasoline she buys.

29. On an international flight a passenger may check two bags weighing 70 pounds, or 154 kilograms, each and one carry-on bag weighing 50 pounds, or 110 kilograms. Express the weight of a bag in kilograms in terms of its weight in pounds.

30. A radio station in Detroit, Michigan, reports the high and low temperatures in the Detroit/Windsor area as 59°F and 23°F, respectively. A station in Windsor, Ontario, reports the high and low temperatures as 15°C and −5°C, respectively. Express the Fahrenheit temperature in terms of the Celsius temperature.

31. When Harold and Nancy leave their motel at 8 A.M. on the second day of their summer vacation, they are 265 miles from Los Angeles. When they stop for lunch at 1 P.M., they are 590 miles from Los Angeles. Express their distance from Los Angeles on the second day in terms of the time they have driven.

32. Flying lessons cost $645 for an 8-hour course and $1425 for a 20-hour course. Both prices include a fixed insurance fee. Express the cost of flying lessons in terms of the length of the course.

CHAPTER SUMMARY

[7.1] The **solution** of an equation or inequality in two variables is an **ordered pair** of numbers.

[7.2] We can use a **Cartesian** (or **rectangular**) **coordinate system** to graph ordered pairs of numbers on a plane. The components of a given ordered pair are called the **coordinates** of its graph.

    The graph of a first-degree (linear) equation in two variables is a straight line. The x-coordinate of a point of intersection of a graph with the x-axis is the **x-intercept** of the graph, and the y-coordinate of a point of intersection of a graph with the y-axis is the **y-intercept** of the graph. These intercepts are obtained by setting $y = 0$ and $x = 0$, respectively, in the equation.

[7.3] For any two points in a geometric plane corresponding to (x_1, y_1) and (x_2, y_2), the distance d between the points is given by the **distance formula**,

$$d = \sqrt{(x_2 - x_1)^2 + (y_2 - y_1)^2}$$

The **slope** m of the line containing the points (x_1, y_1) and (x_2, y_2) is given by

$$m = \frac{y_2 - y_1}{x_2 - x_1} \qquad (x_2 \neq x_1)$$

The slopes of parallel lines are equal ($m_1 = m_2$), and the nonzero slopes of perpendicular lines are the negative reciprocals of each other ($m_1 = -1/m_2$).

[7.4] Any of the forms of linear equations discussed in this section may be used in working with their graphs.

Form	Data Required	Equation
Point-slope	Slope, m Point, (x_1, y_1)	$y - y_1 = m(x - x_1)$
Two-point	Two points, (x_1, y_1) and (x_2, y_2)	$y - y_1 = \dfrac{y_2 - y_1}{x_2 - x_1}(x - x_1)$
Slope-intercept	Slope, m y-intercept, b	$y = mx + b$
Intercept	x-intercept, a y-intercept, b	$\dfrac{x}{a} + \dfrac{y}{b} = 1$

[7.5] Linear equations and their graphs can be used to model relationships in which one quantity varies with another quantity at a constant rate.

REVIEW EXERCISES

[7.1]

1. Find the missing component in each solution of
$2x - 6y = 12$.
   a. $(0, ?)$ **b.** $(?, 0)$ **c.** $(3, ?)$

2. List the solutions of $y = 2x - 3$, where x is 2, 4, and 6.

3. In the equation $xy = 2x^2y + 3$, express y explicitly in terms of x.

4. In the equation $x^2 - 9y^2 = 4$, express y explicitly in terms of x.

[7.2]

▲ *Graph each equation.*

5. $y = 3x + 1$

6. $y = 2x - 5$

7. $3x - y = 6$

8. $3x - y = 0$

9. $x + y = 0$

10. $x - 2y = 6$

11. $2x = y - 8$

12. $3x = y - 6$

13. $2x = -4$

14. $3x - 6 = 0$

[7.3]

15. **a.** Find the distance between the points $(3, -5)$ and $(6, 8)$.
    b. Find the slope of the line segment joining the points in part a.

16. **a.** Find the distance between the points $(4, 2)$ and $(7, -4)$.
    b. Find the slope of the line segment joining the points in part a.

17. **a.** Given points $P_1(2, 2)$, $P_2(-2, -2)$, $P_3(0, 4)$, and $P_4(-3, 1)$, show that the line segments $P_1 P_2$ and $P_3 P_4$ are parallel.
    b. Show that the line segments $P_1 P_2$ and $P_1 P_3$ are perpendicular.

[7.4]

18. Find the equation in standard form of the line through $(3, 5)$ with slope 2.

19. Find the equation in standard form of the line through $(-4, 2)$ with slope $-\dfrac{1}{2}$.

20. **a.** Write $3x - y = 4$ in slope-intercept form.
    b. Specify the slope and the y-intercept of its graph.

21. **a.** Write $2x + 3y = 6$ in slope-intercept form.
    b. Specify the slope and the y-intercept of its graph.

22. Write an equation in standard form of the line through $(3, -1)$ and $(4, 5)$.

23. Write an equation of the line that passes through $(-4, 2)$ and $(0, 3)$.

24. Write an equation of the line with x-intercept -5 and y-intercept 2.

[7.5]

25. Last year, Pinwheel Industries introduced a new model calculator. It cost $2000 to develop the calculator and $20 to manufacture each one.

    a. Write an equation that expresses the total costs in terms of the number of calculators produced.

    b. Graph the equation.

    c. What is the cost of producing 1000 calculators?

    d. How many calculators can be produced for $10,000?

26. An interior decorator charges a consulting fee of $500 plus 10% of the cost of the remodeling.

    a. Write an equation that relates the decorator's fee to the cost of the remodeling.

    b. Graph the equation.

    c. How much is the decorator's fee on a $12,000 remodeling job?

27. Auto registration fees in Connie's home state are $35 plus 2% of the value of the automobile.

    a. Write an equation that relates the registration fee to the value of the automobile.

    b. Graph the equation.

    c. How much is the registration fee on a $20,000 sports car?

28. The world's copper reserves were 500 million tons in 1976; total annual consumption is 8 million tons.

    a. Write an equation that expresses the remaining copper reserves in terms of time.

    b. Graph the equation.

    c. How much copper will be left in the year 2000?

    d. When will the world's copper reserves be completely depleted?

29. The owner of a movie theater needs to bring in $1000 at each screening to stay in business. He sells adult tickets at $5 apiece and children's tickets at $2 each.

    a. Write an equation that relates the number of adult tickets he must sell to the number of children's tickets he must sell.

    b. Graph the equation.

    c. If the owner sells 120 adult tickets, how many children's tickets must he sell?

    d. In the context of the problem, what is the significance of the x- and y-intercepts of the graph?

30. Megan weighed 5 pounds at birth and gained 18 ounces per month during her first year.

    a. Write an equation that expresses Megan's weight in terms of her age.

    b. Graph the equation.

    c. How much did Megan weigh at 9 months?

    d. When did Megan weigh 9 pounds?

▲ *The numbers in brackets refer to the sections in which such problems are first considered.*

▲ *Simplify each expression.*

1. $\dfrac{(a^2b)^3(bc)^2}{b^2c(ac^2)^3}$ **[5.1]**

2. $\sqrt[9]{64}$ **[5.4]**

3. $\dfrac{y^2 - 4y + 4}{2y^2 - 8}$ **[4.1]**

4. $2[x^2 - (x + 1)(x - 1) - 3]$ **[3.3]**

▲ *Write each expression as a single fraction.*

5. $\dfrac{1}{x - 1} - \dfrac{2}{x^2 - 1}$ **[4.5]**

6. $1 - \dfrac{1}{1 - \dfrac{1}{x}}$ **[4.6]**

7. Solve $(ax - b)^2 = 4$ for x in terms of a and b. **[6.1]**

8. Graph $2x - y = 6$.   **[7.2]**

9. Write $(2 - \sqrt{-3})(-1 + \sqrt{-3})$ in the form $a + bi$. **[5.8]**

10. Write $\dfrac{xy^{-1}}{x^{-1} - y^{-1}}$ as a single fraction in which all exponents are positive.   **[5.2]**

11. Determine k so that the solutions of $x^2 - 2x - k + 1 = 0$ are real numbers.   **[6.2]**

12. Find an equation in standard form of the line that passes through the points $(4, -1)$ and has slope -2. **[7.4]**

13. Factor $\sqrt{18} - 2\sqrt{6} + \sqrt{3} = \sqrt{3}(?).$ **[5.7]**

14. Factor completely $9x^2 - 12x + 4 - 4y^2$.   **[3.7]**

▲ *Solve.*

15. $0.20(x - 1) + 0.30(x + 2) = 4.40$ **[2.3]**

16. $(x - 1)(x + 2) = 4$ **[3.5]**

17. $4 - \dfrac{3}{x - 2} = \dfrac{15}{x}$ **[4.6]**

18. $\sqrt[3]{x - 2} = -2$ **[6.3]**

19. $(x - 1)^{1/2} - (x - 1)^{1/4} - 6 = 0$ **[6.3]**

20. $x^2 + 3 = 2x$ **[5.8]**

21. An investment broker promises her client a 5% return on his funds. If the broker invests $3000 in bonds paying 4% interest, how much must she invest in stocks paying 8% interest to keep her promise?   **[2.5]**

22. The size of a rectangular computer monitor screen is the length of its diagonal. If the length of the rectangle is 3 inches greater than the width, what are the dimensions of a 15-inch monitor?   **[3.6]**

23. The school district receives $320,000 to be divided between maintenance and new equipment in the ratio of 4 to 5. How much should be allocated to maintenance?   **[4.8]**

24. Gene's motorboat travels 20 miles per hour in still water. It took him 3 hours longer to go 90 miles upriver on a fishing trip than it took to return 75 miles downriver. How fast was the current in the river?   **[6.2]**

25. The reprographics department has a choice of two new copying machines. One costs $20,000 and $0.02 per copy to operate. The other sells for $17,000, but operating costs are $0.025 per copy. How many copies must the repro department make before the more expensive copier is a better value than the cheaper one?   **[7.5]**

8 FUNCTIONS

DEFINITIONS AND NOTATIONS

In Chapter 7 we studied a number of relationships between two variables; in particular, we considered equations that define linear relationships. For example, the equation

$$C = 30t + 800 \qquad (t \geqslant 0) \tag{1}$$

relates the variables t and C. To each value of $t \geqslant 0$ we associate the value of C given by Equation (1). Thus,

when $t = 0$, $\qquad C = 30(0) + 800 = 800$

when $t = 4$, $\qquad C = 30(4) + 800 = 920$

when $t = 10$, $\qquad C = 30(10) + 800 = 1100$

We can represent an association between the values of two variables by a chart or by ordered pairs, as follows:

t	C	(t, C)
0	800	$(0, 800)$
4	920	$(4, 920)$
10	1100	$(10, 1100)$

Notice that for the relationship defined by Equation (1) we can always determine one and only one value of C associated with each value of t. Such a relationship between variables is called a **function**. The variable t in Equation (1) is called the **independent** variable; C is the **dependent** variable because its values are determined by the values of t. In general, we use the following definition:

> A **function** *is a relation between two variables for which a unique value of the* **dependent** *variable can be determined from a value of the* **independent** *variable.*

Note that Equation (1) defines a function because there is exactly one value of C corresponding to each value of t. However, not all equations in two variables define functions.

EXAMPLE 1

a. $y = 2x + 1$ defines a function because exactly one value of y is paired with each real number replacement for x.

b. $x^2 + y^2 = 1$,   or, equivalently, $y = \pm\sqrt{1 - x^2}$,   does not define a function because two values of y are paired with each real number replacement for x.

c. $y = x^2 - 4$ defines a function because exactly one value of y is paired with each real number replacement for x.

The graphs of the three equations in Example 1 are shown in Example 2.

Geometric Test for a Function

There is an easy way of checking to see whether a particular graph does or does not represent a function. If we imagine a line parallel to the y-axis passing across the graph, we can see whether or not it ever intersects the graph at more than one point; that is, *whether or not there are two or more different y-coordinates for any given x-coordinate.* If there are, the graph is not the graph of a function.

EXAMPLE 2

Graphs a and c in the figure are graphs of functions. Graph b does not represent a function because a vertical line intersects the graph in more than one point.

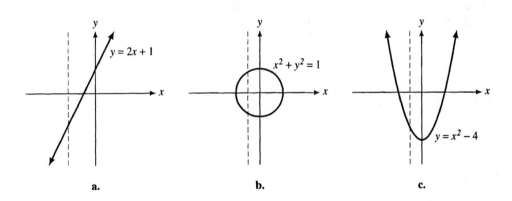

Domain and Range

The set of all values for the independent variable is called the **domain** of a function. The set of all values for the dependent variable is called the **range** of the function. For the function defined by Equation (1),

$$C = 30t + 800 \qquad (t \geqslant 0)$$

the domain is the set of real numbers such that $t \geqslant 0$, and the range is the set of real numbers such that $C \geqslant 800$. In this case the domain is given to us explicitly.

Let us make the following agreement concerning functions defined by equations:

▲ *If the domain of a function is not specified, we shall assume that the domain is the set of all real numbers that produce real numbers in the range.*

Thus values of the variable that make a denominator zero or result in an imaginary value for y are excluded from the domain. Since imaginary values are excluded from the domain, radicands of even roots cannot be negative numbers, as shown in Examples 3c and 3d.

EXAMPLE 3

Specify the domain (the set of replacements for x) for each function.

a. $y = x + 5$ b. $y = \dfrac{3}{x - 4}$ c. $y = \sqrt{x - 2}$ d. $y = \sqrt{3 - x}$

Solutions

a. The entire set of real numbers, because y is a real number for all real numbers x.

b. The set of real numbers except $x = 4$, because $3/(x - 4)$ is undefined for this value of x.

c. The set of real numbers $x \geqslant 2$, because $\sqrt{x - 2}$ is a real number, provided $x - 2 \geqslant 0$. (If $x < 2$, then $x - 2$ is negative and $\sqrt{x - 2}$ is imaginary.)

d. The set of real numbers $x \leqslant 3$, because $\sqrt{3 - x}$ is a real number for these values only. (If $x > 3$, then $3 - x$ is negative and $\sqrt{3 - x}$ is imaginary.

Function Notation

Functions are usually designated by means of a single symbol, P, R, f, g, or some other letter. The symbol $f(x)$ represents the value in the range of function f that is associated with the value x in its domain. Thus, we shall use $f(x)$ (read "f of x" or "the value of f at x") in precisely the same way that we used $P(x)$ in Section 2.1 when we discussed expressions and, in particular, polynomial expressions. This notation is commonly called **function notation**.

EXAMPLE 4

a. If f is the function defined by the equation

$$y = x - 3$$

then we can just as well write

$$f(x) = x - 3$$

where $f(x)$ plays the same role as y.

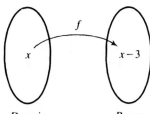

Domain   Range

b. If $f(x) = x - 3$, then

$$f(6) = (6) - 3 = 3$$
$$f(-2) = (-2) - 3 = -5$$
$$f(t) = (t) - 3 = t - 3$$

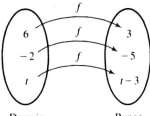

Domain   Range

In function notation, each point on the graph of a function f has coordinates of the form $(x, f(x))$, where $f(x)$ is the name of the dependent variable corresponding to the independent variable x.

EXAMPLE 5   Consider the following graph of a function f:

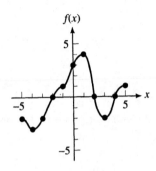

Solutions

a.   Find $f(-2)$, $f(0)$, and $f(5)$.

b.   For what value(s) of x is $f(x) = -2$?   For what value(s) of x is $f(x) = 0$?

c.   What is the largest, or maximum, value of $f(x)$? For what value of x does the function take on its maximum value?

a.   The points $(-2, 0)$, $(0, 3)$, and $(5, 1)$ lie on the graph of f. Therefore, $f(-2) = 0$, $f(0) = 3$,   and $f(5) = 1$.

b.   Since the point $(-3, -2)$ lies on the graph, $f(-3) = -2$.   (The x-value is -3.)
Since the points $(-2, 0)$, $(2, 0)$, and $(4, 0)$ lie on the graph, $f(-2) = 0$, $f(2) = 0$, and $f(4) = 0$.   (The x-values are -2, 2, and 4.)

c.   The maximum value of $f(x)$ is the second coordinate of the highest point on the graph, $(1, 4)$. Thus, the maximum value of $f(x)$ is 4, and it occurs when $x = 1$.

We can also use function notation when the elements in the domain are represented by algebraic expressions.

EXAMPLE 6   Find   **a.** $f(a)$;   **b.** $f(b)$;   **c.** $f(a + b)$

for the function

$$f(x) = x^2 - 2x$$

Solutions

a. $f(a) = (a)^2 - 2(a) = a^2 - 2a$

b. $f(b) = (b)^2 - 2(b) = b^2 - 2b$

c. $f(a + b) = (a + b)^2 - 2(a + b) = a^2 + 2ab + b^2 - 2a - 2b$

EXAMPLE 7 Find **a.** $f(x + h)$; **b.** $f(x + h) - f(x)$; **c.** $\dfrac{f(x + h) - f(x)}{h}$

for the function

$$f(x) = x^2 + 1$$

Solutions

a. $f(x + h) = (x + h)^2 + 1 = x^2 + 2xh + h^2 + 1$

b. $f(x + h) - f(x) = (x^2 + 2xh + h^2 + 1) - (x^2 + 1) = 2xh + h^2$

c. $\dfrac{f(x + h) - f(x)}{h} = \dfrac{2xh + h^2}{h} = 2x + h$

Zeros of Functions

For any function f, the solutions of the equation $f(x) = 0$ are called **zeros** of the function. These values of x are also the x-intercepts of the graph of f. Thus, we have three different names for related concepts. In particular, for a quadratic equation the following three statements all describe the same x-values:

1. The solutions of the equation

$$ax^2 + bx + c = 0$$

2. The zeros of the function

$$f(x) = ax^2 + bx + c$$

3. The x-intercepts of the graph of

$$f(x) = ax^2 + bx + c$$

EXAMPLE 8

a. The zeros of the function f in Example 5 on page 207 are -2, 2, and 4, because $f(-2) = 0$, $f(2) = 0$, and $f(4) = 0$.

b. The zeros of

$$f(x) = x^2 + 3x - 10 = (x + 5)(x - 2)$$

are -5 and 2 because $f(-5) = 0$ and $f(2) = 0$.

EXERCISE SET 8.1

▲ **a.** *Solve each equation explicitly for y in terms of x.*
  b. *State whether the equation defines a function. See Example 1.*

1. $2x + y = 6$
3. $x - 2y = 8$
5. $(x - 2)y = 4$
7. $xy - 4y = 6$
9. $2x^2 + y^2 = 8$
11. $4x^2 - y^2 = 16$

2. $2x + 3y = 12$
4. $3x - 2y = 8$
6. $(x + 3)y = 6$
8. $xy + 2y = 8$
10. $x^2 + 2y^2 = 8$
12. $y^2 - 4x^2 = 16$

▲ *Which of the following graphs represent functions? See Example 2.*

13.

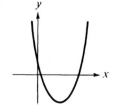

14.

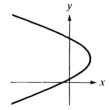

15.

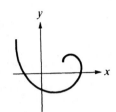

16.

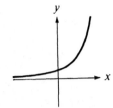

17.

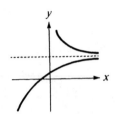

18.

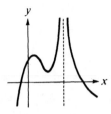

19.

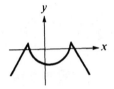

20.

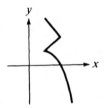

21.

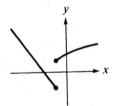

22.

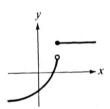

▲ *Consider the following graphs of functions. See Example 5.*

41. **a.** Find $h(-3)$, $h(1)$, and $h(3)$.
  b. For what value(s) of z is $h(z) = 3$?
  c. Find the x- and y-intercepts of the graph.
  d. What is the maximum value of $h(z)$?
  e. For what value(s) of z does h take on its maximum value?

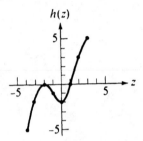

42. **a.** Find $G(-5)$, $G(-1)$, and $G(3)$.
  b. For what value(s) of s is $G(s) = 3$?
  c. Find the x- and y-intercepts of the graph.
  d. What is the minimum value of $G(s)$?
  e. For what value(s) of s does G take on its minimum value?

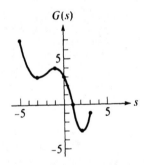

▲ *Specify the domain for each function. See Example 3.*

23. $y = 6x - 2$

24. $y = x^2 - 2x + 3$

25. $y = \dfrac{4}{x - 5}$

26. $y = \dfrac{x}{x + 3}$

27. $y = \dfrac{x}{2x + 1}$

28. $y = \dfrac{3x}{3x - 2}$

29. $y = \sqrt{x + 5}$

30. $y = -\sqrt{x - 3}$

31. $y = \dfrac{\sqrt{x - 1}}{x - 2}$

32. $y = \dfrac{\sqrt{x - 2}}{x - 4}$

33. $xy - y = 6$

34. $2xy - 4y = 7$

▲ *Find the value of each expression. See Example 4.*

35. $f(4)$, if $f(x) = x^2 - 2x + 1$

36. $g(3)$, if $g(x) = 2x^2 + 3x - 1$

37. $g(5) - g(2)$, if $g(x) = x + 3$

38. $f(2) - f(0)$, if $f(x) = 3x - 1$

39. $f(3) - f(-3)$, if $f(x) = x^2 - x + 1$

40. $f(0) - f(-2)$, if $f(x) = x^2 + 3x - 2$

43. **a.** Find $R(1)$ and $R(3)$.
  b. For what value(s) of p is $R(p) = 2$?
  c. Find the x- and y-intercepts of the graph.
  d. Find the maximum and minimum values of $R(p)$.
  e. Find what value(s) of p does R take on its maximum and minimum values?

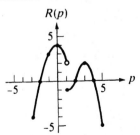

44. **a.** Find $f(-1)$ and $f(3)$.
  b. For what value(s) of t is $f(t) = 5$?
  c. Find the x- and y-intercepts of the graph.
  d. Find the maximum and minimum values of $f(t)$.
  e. For what value(s) of t does f take on its maximum and minimum values?

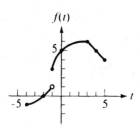

45. **a.** Find $S(0)$, $S(\pi/6)$, and $S(-\pi)$.
  b. Estimate the value of $S(\pi/3)$ from the graph.
  c. For what value(s) of x is $S(x) = -\dfrac{1}{2}$?
  d. Find the maximum and minimum values of $S(x)$.
  e. For what value(s) of x does S take on its maximum and minimum values?

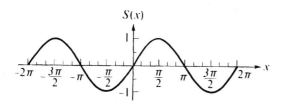

46. **a.** Find $C(0)$, $C(-\pi/3)$, and $C(\pi)$.
  b. Estimate the value of $C(\pi/6)$ from the graph.
  c. For what value(s) of x is $C(x) = \dfrac{1}{2}$?
  d. Find the maximum and minimum values of $C(x)$.
  e. For what value(s) of x does C take on its maximum and minimum values?

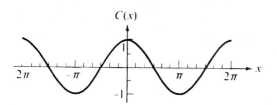

▲ *In Exercises 47–50, find:*
  a. $f(a)$;   **b.** $f(b)$;   **c.** $f(a + b)$
  for each function. See Example 6.

47. $f(x) = 5x - 3$ **48.** $f(x) = 3x + 2$
49. $f(x) = x^2 + 3x$ **50.** $f(x) = x^2 - 2x$

▲ *In Exercises 51–56, find:*
  a. $f(x + h)$;   **b.** $f(x + h) - f(x)$;
  c. $\dfrac{f(x + h) - f(x)}{h}$

  for each function. See Examples 6 and 7.

51. $f(x) = 3x - 4$
52. $f(x) = 2x + 5$
53. $f(x) = x^2 - 3x + 5$
54. $f(x) = x^2 + 2x$
55. $f(x) = x^3 + 2x - 1$
56. $f(x) = x^3 + 3x^2 - 1$

▲ *Find the zeros of each function. See Example 8.*

57. $f(x) = 3x + 6$
58. $f(x) = 2x - 8$
59. $f(x) = x^2 - 5x + 4$
60. $f(x) = x^2 - 6x + 8$
61. $f(x) = -x^2 + x + 6$
62. $f(x) = -x^2 + 2x + 15$

Miscellaneous Exercises

▲ *For each pair of functions, do the following:*
  a. *Compute $f(0)$ and $g(0)$*
  b. *Find all values of x for which $f(x) = 0$.*
  c. *Find all values of x for which $g(x) = 0$.*
  d. *Find all values of x for which $f(x) = g(x)$.*

63. $f(x) = 2x^2 + 3x$, $g(x) = 5 - 6x$
64. $f(x) = 3x^2 - 6x$, $g(x) = 8 + 4x$
65. $f(x) = \sqrt{x + 2}$, $g(x) = 3x - 4$
66. $f(x) = \sqrt{x - 3}$, $g(x) = 2x - 7$

8.2 | FUNCTIONS AS MATHEMATICAL MODELS; VARIATION

In applications of mathematics to other sciences, mathematical models are often used to answer questions or to make predictions. Mathematical models generally involve one or more functions. There are two types of widely used functional relationships to which custom has assigned special names.

Direct Variation

First, any function defined by the equation

$$y = kx \qquad (k \text{ a positive constant}) \qquad (1)$$

is an example of **direct variation**. The variable y is said to **vary directly** as the variable x. Another example of direct variation is

$$y = kx^2 \qquad (k \text{ a positive constant}) \qquad (1a)$$

where we say that y varies directly as the square of x. In general,

$$y = kx^n \qquad (k \text{ a positive constant and } n > 0) \qquad (1b)$$

asserts that y varies directly as the nth power of x.

EXAMPLE 1

a. The circumference of a circle varies directly as the radius, since

$$C = 2\pi r \qquad (2)$$

b. The area of a circle varies directly as the square of the radius, since

$$A = \pi r^2 \qquad (3)$$

Since for each r, Equations (2) and (3) associate only one value of C or A, both of these equations define functions—Equation (2) a linear function and Equation (3) a quadratic function.

Inverse Variation

The second important type of function is defined by the equation

$$y = \frac{k}{x} \qquad (4)$$

where y is said to **vary inversely** as x. Similarly, if

$$y = \frac{k}{x^2} \qquad (4a)$$

y is said to vary inversely as the square of x, and so on.

EXAMPLE 2

The quantity q demanded by consumers for a certain product varies inversely with its selling price p. Hence,

$$q = \frac{k}{p}$$

Thus q increases as p decreases.

The names "direct" and "inverse," as applied to variation, arise from the fact that in direct variation an assignment of increasing absolute values of x results in an association with increasing absolute values of y, whereas in inverse variation an assignment of increasing absolute values of x results in an association with decreasing absolute values of y.

Constant of Variation

The constant involved in an equation defining a direct or inverse variation is called the **constant of variation**. For example, $C = 2\pi r$ has 2π as the constant of variation. Also, for constant V, $h = V/\pi r^2$ has V/π as the constant of variation.

If we know that one variable varies directly or inversely as another, and if we have one set of associated values for the variables, we can find the constant of variation involved. We can then use this constant to express one of the variables as a function of the other.

EXAMPLE 3

The speed (v) at which a particle falls in a certain medium varies directly with the time (t) it falls. A particle is falling at a speed of 20 feet per second 4 seconds after being dropped. Express v as a function of t.

Solution

Since v varies directly with t, we know that there is a positive constant to k, so

$$v = kt$$

Since $v = 20$ when $t = 4$, we have

$$20 = k(4)$$

from which

$$k = 5$$

Thus, the functional relationship between v and t is given by

$$v = 5t$$

Solving for Unknown Values

Once we have constructed a model, values for one of the variables can readily be obtained for known values of the other variable. For example, in Example 3 we can obtain the velocity of the particle at any time by substituting for t in the equation $v = 5t$. Thus, for $t_1 = 6$ seconds

$$v_1 = 5(6)$$
$$= 30$$

for $t_2 = 8$ seconds

$$v_2 = 5(8)$$
$$= 40$$

for $t_3 = 10$ seconds

$$v_3 = 5(10)$$
$$= 50$$

EXAMPLE 4

The weight of an object varies inversely with the square of its distance from the center of the Earth. How much would a 120-pound astronaut weigh on a spaceship 500 miles above the Earth? (The radius of the Earth is 3963 miles.)

Solution

If w represents the weight of the astronaut and d is her distance from the center of the Earth, then

$$w = \frac{k}{d^2}$$

Since $w = 120$ when $d = 3963$,

$$120 = \frac{k}{(3963)^2}$$

so $k \approx 1{,}885{,}000{,}000$. Thus, w can be expressed as a function of d by

$$w \approx \frac{1{,}885{,}000{,}000}{d^2}$$

To find the astronaut's weight 500 miles above the Earth, substitute for $3963 + 500$ or 4463 for d and find

$$w \approx \frac{1{,}885{,}000{,}000}{(4463)^2}$$

$$\approx 94.6$$

The astronaut would weigh approximately 94.6 pounds.

Two types of variation may take place concurrently. For example, y may vary directly as x and inversely as z, giving rise to the equation

$$y = k\frac{x}{z} \tag{5}$$

The word *variation* as used in this section has a technical meaning, and when the term direct, inverse, or joint variation is encountered, we should always think of equations of the form (1), (4), or (5). For instance, the equations

$$y = 2x + 1, \qquad y = \frac{1}{x} - 2, \qquad \text{and} \qquad y = xz + 2$$

do not describe examples of variation because of the constant terms.

Proportions

An alternative expression—**proportional to**—is used to describe the relationships discussed in this section. To say that "y is directly proportional to x" or "y is inversely proportional to x" is another way of describing direct and inverse variation. The use of the word *proportion* arises from the fact that any two solutions (a_1, b_1) and (a_2, b_2) of an equation expressing a direct variation satisfy the proportion

$$\frac{a_1}{b_1} = \frac{a_2}{b_2} = k$$

where k is the constant of variation. Consider the following example in which the volume (V) of a gas varies directly with the absolute temperature (T) and inversely as the pressure (P).

EXAMPLE 5   If V varies directly as T and inversely as P, and $V = 40$ when $T = 300$ and $P = 30$, find V when $T = 324$ and $P = 24$.

Solution   Write an equation expressing the relationship between the variables.

$$V = \frac{kT}{P} \qquad \text{Solve for } k.$$

$$k = \frac{VP}{T}$$

Since k is constant for different values of $V, P,$ and T, write a proportion relating the variables for two different sets of conditions.

$$\frac{V_1 P_1}{T_1} = \frac{V_2 P_2}{T_2}$$

Substitute the known values of the variables and solve for V_2.

$$\frac{(40)(30)}{300} = \frac{V_2(24)}{324}$$

$$V_2 = \frac{(324)(40)(30)}{300(24)} = 54$$

The previous examples of functional relationships involved direct and inverse variation. The following examples illustrate several other functional relationships and equations that model them.

EXAMPLE 6   A company that produces computer chips finds that after a start-up cost of $10,000, each new chip costs $200 to manufacture.

a.   Express the cost C of producing x new chips as a function of x.

b.   If the company can sell the chips for $250 each, express the revenue R from the sale of x chips as a function of x.

c.   Express the company's profit P from producing and selling x chips as a function of x.

Solution   **a.**   The cost C is the sum of the start-up cost and the cost of manufacturing x chips. Since the cost of manufacturing x chips is

$$\$200 \cdot x$$

(cost per chip) · (number of chips)

and the start-up cost is $10,000, we have

$$C(x) = 10,000 + 200x$$

Since the company cannot produce a negative number of chips, $x \geqslant 0$.

b.   The total revenue R is given by the product of the selling price per chip times the number of chips sold. Thus,

$$R(x) = 250x \qquad (x \geqslant 0)$$

The graphs of the functions C and R are shown in Figure a.

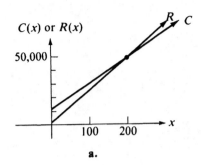

a.

c. In general,

$$\text{profit} = \text{revenue} - \text{cost}$$

so

$$P(x) = R(x) - C(x)$$
$$= 250x - (10,000 + 200x)$$
$$= 50x - 10,000$$

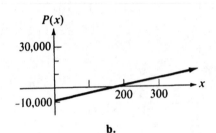

b.

The graph of P is shown in Figure b.

In Example 6 the three functions C, R, and P together with their graphs constitute a model for the company's production and marketing efforts. When $x > 200$, $R(x)$ is greater than $C(x)$, and the company earns a profit. When $x < 200$, $R(x)$ is less than $C(x)$, so the company experiences a loss. The value $x = 200$, where $R(x) = C(x)$, is called the **break-even point**.

EXAMPLE 7

A wire of 12 feet long is to be cut into two pieces of unequal length, and each piece is to be bent into a square. Express the total area A enclosed by both pieces as a function of the length x of the shorter piece.

Solution

Draw and label a figure as shown.

Length of short piece: x
Length of long piece: $12 - x$
Smaller area: A_1
Larger area: A_2
Total area enclosed: $A_1 + A_2$

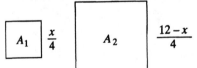

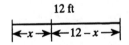

Since the perimeter of the smaller square is x, the side length of this square is $x/4$, as shown in the figure. Similarly, the side length of the larger square is $(12 - x)/4$.

Since the area of a square is the square of the length of its side,

$$A_1 = \left(\frac{x}{4}\right)^2 \quad \text{and} \quad A_2 = \left(\frac{12 - x}{4}\right)^2$$

and the total area is given by

$$A(x) = \left(\frac{x}{4}\right)^2 + \left(\frac{12 - x}{4}\right)^2$$

We can now find the total area enclosed for any specified length x simply by evaluating the function at the given x-value.

E X E R C I S E   S E T   8.2

▲ *Find the constant of variation for each of the stated conditions. See Examples 1–3.*

1. y varies directly as x, and $y = 6$ when $x = 2$.
2. y varies directly as x, and $y = 2$ when $x = 5$.
3. u varies inversely as the square of v, and $u = 2$ when $v = 10$.
4. r varies inversely as the cube of t, and $r = 8$ when $t = 10$.
5. z varies directly as the product of x and y, and $z = 8$ when $x = 2$ and $y = 2$.
6. p varies directly as the product of q and r, and $p = 5$ when $q = 2$ and $r = 7$.
7. z varies directly as the square of x and inversely as the cube of y, and $z = 4$ when $x = 3$ and $y = 2$.
8. z varies directly as the cube of x and inversely as the square of y, and $z = 2$ when $x = 2$ and $y = 4$.
9. z varies inversely as the sum of x^2 and y, and $z = 12$ when $x = 4$ and $y = 6$.
10. z varies directly as the sum of x and y and inversely as their product, and $z = 8$ when $x = 3$ and $y = 4$.

▲ *Solve by first obtaining the constant of variation. See Examples 1–4.*

11. y varies directly with the square of x, and $y = 24$ when $x = 6$. Find y when $x = 2$.
12. y varies directly with the cube of x, and $y = 120$ when $x = 2$. Find y when $x = 20$.
13. y varies inversely with x, and $y = 56$ when $x = 200$. Find y when $x = 8$.
14. y varies inversely with the square of x, and $y = 3.6$ when $x = 25$. Find y when $x = 0.4$.
15. If we neglect the effect of air resistance, the distance s that an object falls varies directly with the square of the time t it falls. If a pebble falls 400 feet from the southern rim of the Grand Canyon in 5 seconds, how far will it fall in 10 seconds?

16. The length L of a pendulum varies directly with the square of its period T, the time required for the pendulum to make one complete swing back and forth. The pendulum on a grandfather clock is $3\frac{1}{4}$ feet long and has a period of 2 seconds. How long is the Foucault pendulum in the Panthéon in Paris, which has a period of 17 seconds?

17. At constant temperature, the pressure P of a sample of gas varies inversely with its volume V. A cylinder contains 500 cubic centimeters of gas at a pressure of 15 kilograms per square centimeter, and the gas is compressed by a piston. What is the pressure of the gas when the volume inside the cylinder is reduced to 62.5 cubic centimeters?

18. The amount of force F that one must exert on a lever to raise a heavy object varies inversely with the length L of the lever. If it takes 100 pounds of force to lift a large stone planter using a 3-foot lever, how much force is necessary to lift the planter using a 4-foot lever?

19. Water pressure p varies directly with the depth d beneath the surface of the water. The pressure at the bottom of a 12-foot swimming pool is 748.8 pounds per square foot. What is the water pressure on a skin diver at a depth of 100 feet?

20. Distant galaxies are receding from us at a rate V that varies directly with their distance D. (The speeds of these galaxies are measured by using a phenomenon called red-shifting.) If a galaxy in Ursa Major is 980,000,000 light-years away and is receding at 15,000 kilometers per second, how far away is a galaxy in the constellation Hydra, which is receding at 61,000 kilometers per second?

21. The frequency f of a guitar string at a given tension varies inversely with its length. The fifth string is 65

centimeters long and is tuned to *A* (with frequency of 220 vibrations per second). How far from the bridge should the fret for C (256 vibrations per second) be placed?

22. The current *I* that flows through an electrical wire varies inversely with the resistance *R* of the wire. If an iron with a resistance of 12 ohms draws 10 amperes of current, how much current does a toaster with a resistance of 9.6 ohms draw?

▲ *For each exercise cited,*
  a. *write an equation by eliminating the constant of variation;*
  b. *solve for the required variable. See Example 5.*

23.	Exercise 11	**24.**	Exercise 12
25.	Exercise 13	**26.**	Exercise 14
27.	Exercise 15	**28.**	Exercise 16
29.	Exercise 17	**30.**	Exercise 18
31.	Exercise 19	**32.**	Exercise 20
33.	Exercise 21	**34.**	Exercise 22

▲ **a.** *Construct a mathematical model.*
  b. *Solve. See Examples 6 and 7.*

35. The set-up cost for printing a book is $5000, after which it costs $10 for each book printed. Express the printing costs *C* for a book as a function of the number *n* of books printed. Find the printing costs for 640 books.

36. The set-up cost to produce a certain kind of computer chip is $12,000, after which it costs $24 to produce each chip. Express the cost *C* of production as a function of the number *n* of chips produced. Find the cost of producing 8000 chips.

37. The cost of building a brick wall is $15 per running foot, and the cost of fencing material is $7.50 per running foot. A rancher is building a square corral with three sides consisting of brick wall and one side consisting of fencing. Express the cost *C* as a function of the side length *s* of the corral. Find the cost of a square corral with sides that are 60 feet in length.

38. The cost of wire mesh fencing is $5.50 per linear foot. Express as a function of its width *w* the cost *C* of fencing a rectangular field if the length of the field is twice its width. Find the cost of fencing a rectangular field with a width of 140 feet.

39. Fran wants to fence a rectangular area of 3200 square feet to grow vegetables for her family of three. Express the perimeter *P* of the garden as a function of its width *w*. Find the perimeter of the garden if its width is 40 feet.

40. Denise makes a frame for a circular stained glass window from a strip of aluminum. Express the area *A* of the window as a function of the length *l* of the aluminum. Find the area of a window framed by a 72-inch length of aluminum.

41. Express the radius *r* of a cylindrical water tank as a function of its circumference *C*. What is the radius of a cylindrical water tank with a circumference of 47 meters?

42. A round bucket just fits inside the square shaft of a well. Express the radius *r* of the bucket as a function of the side *s* of the well. How large a bucket will fit in a well measuring 30 inches on a side?

43. The radius of a cylindrical can should be one-half its height. Express the volume *V* of such a can as a function of its height. What is the volume of a can with a height of 10 centimeters? $(V = \pi r^2 h.)$

44. The Twisty-Freez machine dispenses soft ice cream in a cone-shaped peak with a height of three times the radius of its base. Express the volume *V* of Twisty-Freez that comes in a round dish with diameter *d* as a function of *d*. How much Twisty-Freez comes in a 3-inch dish? $(V = \frac{1}{3}\pi r^2 h.)$

Miscellaneous Exercises

▲ *Solve.*

45. The intensity of illumination *I* from a light source varies inversely with the square of the distance. If you double your distance from a reading lamp, what happens to the illumination?

46. The resistance *R* of a wire varies inversely with the square of its diameter *d*. If you replace an old wire with a new one whose diameter is two-thirds of the old one, what happens to the resistance?

47. The wind resistance *R* experienced by a vehicle on the freeway varies directly with the square of its speed *v*. If you decrease your speed by 10%, what happens to the wind resistance?

48. The power *P* generated by a battery varies directly with its electrical potential *V*. If a battery loses 30% of its potential, what happens to the power it generates?

49. A UFO is hovering directly over your head at an altitude of 700 feet. It begins descending at a rate of 10 feet per second. At the same time, you start to run at 25 feet per second. Express the distance *D* between you and the UFO as a function of time *t* in seconds after its descent begins. How far are you from the UFO 1 minute later?

50. An owl at an altitude of 100 feet spots a mouse directly below it and swoops at a rate of 40 feet per second. At the same time, the mouse begins to run at 15 feet per second. Express the distance D between the owl and the mouse as a function of time t in seconds after the owl swoops. How far is the owl from the mouse after 2 seconds?

8.3 | QUADRATIC FUNCTIONS

In Chapter 7 we considered properties of linear equations and observed that their graphs were straight lines. Except for an equation of the form $x = k$, whose graph is a vertical line, all other linear equations

$$y = f(x) = mx + b$$

define functions. In this section we investigate another important function, one that does not have a straight-line graph.

A function of the form

$$f(x) = ax^2 + bx + c \qquad (a \neq 0) \tag{1}$$

is called a **quadratic function**. The graphs of quadratic functions are called **parabolas**. The constants a, b, and c in Equation (1) determine the relative size and position of the graph. Some examples of parabolas are shown in Figure 8.1.

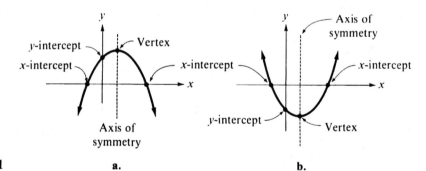

Figure 8.1   **a.**   **b.**

The highest point on the graph in Figure 8.1a is called the **vertex** of the parabola. It corresponds to the *maximum* value of the function. If the parabola opens upward, as in Figure 8.1b, then the vertex is the lowest point on the graph and it corresponds to the *minimum* function value. A parabola is symmetric about a vertical line through its vertex called the **axis of symmetry**. The **y-intercept** is the point where the parabola intersects the y-axis. We shall see that a parabola may intersect the x-axis in zero, one, or two points called the **x-intercepts**. If there are two x-intercepts, they are equidistant from the axis of symmetry.

The intercepts and the vertex of a parabola can be found by analyzing the coefficients a, b, and c. Once these points are found, it is fairly easy to sketch an accurate graph. We begin by considering some special cases.

The Graphs of $y = ax^2$ **and** $y = x^2 + c$

First, consider the graphs of $f(x) = 2x^2$ and $g(x) = -3x^2$ shown in Figure 8.2.

x	$f(x)$	$g(x)$
-2	8	-12
-1	2	-3
0	0	0
1	2	-3
2	8	-12

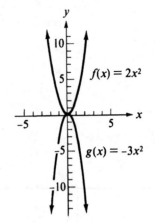

Figure 8.2

In general, the graph of $y = ax^2$ opens upward if $a > 0$ and opens downward if $a < 0$. The magnitude of a determines how "wide" or "narrow" the parabola is. For functions of the form $y = ax^2$ the vertex, the x-intercept, and the y-intercept all coincide at the origin.

Now consider the graphs of $f(x) = x^2 + 4$ and $g(x) = x^2 - 4$ shown in Figure 8.3.

x	$f(x)$	$g(x)$
-2	8	0
-1	5	-3
0	4	-4
1	5	-3
2	8	0

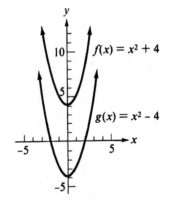

Figure 8.3

The graph of $f(x) = x^2 + 4$ is shifted *upward* four units as compared with the graph of $y = x^2$, and the graph of $g(x) = x^2 - 4$ is shifted *downward* four units. Thus, the vertex of the graph of f is the point $(0, 4)$, and the vertex of the graph of g is the point $(0, -4)$. The x-intercepts of the graph of g can be found by setting $g(x)$ equal to zero and solving for x:

$$0 = x^2 - 4$$
$$= (x - 2)(x + 2)$$

so the x-intercepts are 2 and -2. The graph of f has no x-intercepts, since the equation

$$0 = x^2 + 4$$

(obtained by setting $g(x)$ equal to zero) has no real solutions.

EXAMPLE 1 Graph the following functions:

    a. $g(x) = x^2 - 3$ **b.** $h(x) = -2x^2$

Solutions   **a.** The graph of $g(x) = x^2 - 3$ is shifted downward by three units. The vertex is the point $(0, -3)$, and the x-intercepts are the solutions of the equation

$$0 = x^2 - 3$$

or $\sqrt{3}$ and $-\sqrt{3}$.

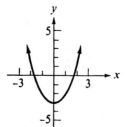

  b. The graph of $h(x) = -2x^2$ opens downward and is narrower than the graph of $y = x^2$. Its vertex is the point $(0,0)$.

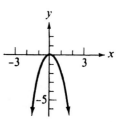

The Graph of We next consider quadratic functions of the form
$y = ax^2 + bx$

$$y = ax^2 + bx$$

We can find the x-intercepts of the graph by setting y equal to zero and solving for x:

$$0 = ax^2 + bx$$
$$0 = x(ax + b)$$

Thus,

$$x = 0 \qquad \text{or} \qquad ax + b = 0$$
$$x = 0 \qquad\qquad\qquad x = -\frac{b}{a}$$

Figure 8.4

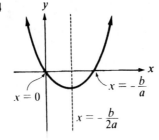

The x-intercepts are 0 and $-b/a$. The axis of symmetry is located halfway between the intercepts, so, taking their average, we have

$$x = \frac{0 + \left(\dfrac{-b}{a}\right)}{2} = \frac{-b}{2a}$$

Thus, the axis of symmetry is the vertical line $x = -b/2a$. (See Figure 8.4.) Since the vertex of the parabola lies on the axis of symmetry, its x-coordinate must be $-b/(2a)$. We find the y-coordinate of the vertex by evaluating the given function at $x = -b/2a$.

EXAMPLE 2

Graph the following functions:

a. $f(x) = 2x^2 + 8x$ **b.** $g(x) = -x^2 + 5x$

Solutions

a. Since $a = 2$ and $2 > 0$, the parabola opens upward. Determine the x-intercepts by setting $f(x)$ equal to zero.

$$0 = 2x^2 + 8x$$
$$= 2x(x + 4)$$

Thus,

$$2x = 0 \quad \text{or} \quad x + 4 = 0$$
$$x = 0 \qquad\qquad x = -4$$

The x-intercepts are 0 and -4. The vertex has x-coordinate

$$x = \frac{-b}{2a} = \frac{-8}{2(2)}$$
$$= \frac{-8}{4} = -2$$

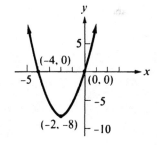

The y-coordinate of the vertex is
$$y = f(-2) = 2(-2)^2 + 8(-2)$$
$$= 8 - 16 = -8$$

Thus, the vertex is the point $(-2, -8)$. The graph of $f(x) = 2x^2 + 8x$ is shown in the figure.

b. Since $a = -1$ and $-1 < 0$, the parabola opens downward. Determine the x-intercepts by setting $g(x)$ equal to zero.

$$0 = -x^2 + 5x$$
$$= -x(x - 5)$$

Thus,

$$-x = 0 \quad \text{or} \quad x - 5 = 0$$
$$x = 0 \qquad\qquad x = 5$$

The x-intercepts are 0 and 5. The vertex has x-coordinate

$$x = \frac{-b}{2a} = \frac{-5}{2(-1)}$$

$$= \frac{-5}{-2} = \frac{5}{2}$$

The y-coordinate of the vertex is

$$y = g\left(\frac{5}{2}\right) = -\left(\frac{5}{2}\right)^2 + 5\left(\frac{5}{2}\right)$$

$$= -\frac{25}{4} + \frac{25}{2} = \frac{25}{4}$$

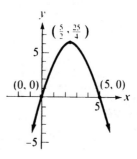

Thus, the vertex is the point $\left(\frac{5}{2}, \frac{25}{4}\right)$. The graph of $g(x) = -x^2 + 5x$ is shown in the figure.

The General Case:
$y = ax^2 + bx + c$

As an example of the general case $y = ax^2 + bx + c$, consider the function

$$y = 2x^2 + 8x + 6 \tag{2}$$

The graph of $y = 2x^2 + 8x + 6$ is shifted six units upward from the graph of $y = 2x^2 + 8x$, which was considered in Example 2a. (See Figure 8.5.) Notice that the x-coordinate of the vertex will not be affected by an upward shift, so the formula $x = -b/2a$ for the x-coordinate of the vertex still holds. The y-coordinate of the vertex can still be found by evaluating the function at $x = -b/2a$. We have

$$x = \frac{-b}{2a} = \frac{-8}{2(2)} = -2$$

and

$$y = 2(-2)^2 + 8(-2) + 6$$
$$= 8 - 16 + 6 = -2$$

so the vertex is the point $(-2, -2)$. (Notice that this point is shifted six units upward from the vertex of $y = 2x^2 + 8x$.)

We find the x-intercepts of the graph by setting y equal to zero.

$$0 = 2x^2 + 8x + 6$$
$$= 2(x + 1)(x + 3)$$

Thus,

$$x + 1 = 0 \qquad \text{or} \qquad x + 3 = 0$$
$$x = -1 \qquad\qquad x = -3$$

The x-intercepts are -1 and -3.

The y-intercept of the graph is found by setting x equal to zero:

$$y = 2(0)^2 + 8(0) + 6$$
$$= 6$$

Note that the y-intercept, 6, is just the constant term in Equation (2).

Because of the symmetry of the parabola about its axis, we can locate another point symmetric to the y-intercept. Since the y-intercept lies two units to the right of the axis of symmetry, there will be another point with y-coordinate 6 that is two units to the left of that axis; its coordinates are $(-4, 6)$.

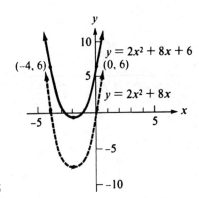

Figure 8.5

EXAMPLE 3   **a.**   Locate the vertex of $y = -x^2 + 5x - 4$.

b.   Graph the equation.

Solutions   **a.**   The x-coordinate of the vertex is

$$x = \frac{-b}{2a} = \frac{-5}{2(-1)} = \frac{5}{2}$$

and the y-coordinate is

$$y = -\left(\frac{5}{2}\right)^2 + 5\left(\frac{5}{2}\right) - 4$$
$$= \frac{-25}{4} + \frac{25}{2} - \frac{16}{4}$$
$$= \frac{-25 + 50 - 16}{4} = \frac{9}{4}$$

Thus, the vertex is the point $\left(\frac{5}{2}, \frac{9}{4}\right)$.

b.   To find the x-intercepts of the graph, set y equal to zero.

$$0 = -x^2 + 5x - 4$$
$$= -(x^2 - 5x + 4)$$
$$= -(x - 4)(x - 1)$$

Thus,

$$x - 4 = 0 \quad \text{or} \quad x - 1 = 0$$
$$x = 4 \qquad\qquad x = 1$$

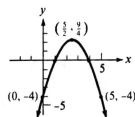

The x-intercepts are 4 and 1. Set x equal to zero to find the y-intercept.

$$y = -0^2 + 5(0) - 4 = -4$$

The y-intercept is -4. Since the y-intercept is $\dfrac{5}{2}$ units to the left of the axis of symmetry, there will be another point $\dfrac{5}{2}$ units to the right, at $(5, -4)$. The graph of $y = -x^2 + 5x - 4$ is shown in the figure.

Number of
x-Intercepts

The graph of a quadratic function f may have two, one, or no x-intercepts, according to the number of real solutions of the quadratic equation $f(x) = 0$. Consider the three functions graphed in Figure 8.6. The graph of $f(x) = x^2 - 4x + 3$ has two x-intercepts, since the equation

$$x^2 - 4x + 3 = 0$$

has two real solutions. The graph of $g(x) = x^2 - 4x + 4$ has only one x-intercept, since the equation

$$x^2 - 4x + 4 = 0$$

has one repeated real solution. The solutions of the equation

$$x^2 - 4x + 6 = 0$$

are imaginery and hence do not appear on the graph, so the graph of the function $h(x) = x^2 - 4x + 6$ has no x-intercepts.

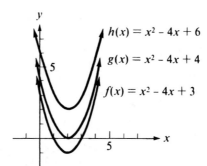

Figure 8.6

Graphing Parabolas

Once we have located the vertex of the parabola, the x-intercepts, the y-intercept, and its symmetric point, we can sketch a reasonably accurate graph. If the graph has no x-intercepts, it may be necessary to locate one or two additional points by evaluation in order to sketch the graph. We summarize this procedure as follows.

> **Graphing** $f(x) = ax^2 + bx + c$
>
> 1. Determine whether the parabola opens upward (if $a > 0$) or downward (if $a < 0$).
> 2. Locate the vertex.
>   a. The x-coordinate of the vertex is $x = -b/2a$.
>   b. The y-coordinate of the vertex is $y = f(-b/2a)$.
> 3. Locate the x-intercepts (if any) by setting $f(x)$ equal to zero and solving for x.
> 4. Locate the y-intercept by evaluating $f(0)$. Locate the point symmetric to the y-intercept with respect to the axis of symmetry.
> 5. If necessary, locate one or two additional points on the graph by evaluation.

EXAMPLE 4   Graph $f(x) = -2x^2 + x - 1$.

Solution
1. Since $a = -2$ and $-2 < 0$, the parabola opens downward.
2. Compute the coordinates of the vertex.

$$x = \frac{-b}{2a} = \frac{-1}{2(-2)} = \frac{1}{4}$$

$$y = -2\left(\frac{1}{4}\right)^2 + \left(\frac{1}{4}\right) - 1$$

$$= -2\left(\frac{1}{16}\right) + \frac{1}{4} - 1$$

$$= \frac{-1 + 2 - 8}{8} = \frac{-7}{8}$$

The vertex has coordinates $\left(\frac{1}{4}, -\frac{7}{8}\right)$.

3. Set y equal to zero to find the x-intercepts.

$$0 = -2x^2 + x - 1$$

$$x = \frac{-1 \pm \sqrt{(1)^2 - 4(-2)(-1)}}{2(-2)}$$

$$= \frac{-1 \pm \sqrt{-7}}{-4}$$

The solutions are imaginary, so there are no x-intercepts. (Or note that there are no x-intercepts because the parabola opens downward from a vertex whose y-coordinate is negative.)

4. Since $f(0) = -1$, the y-intercept is the point $(0, -1)$. The y-intercept lies $\frac{1}{4}$ unit

to the left of the axis of symmetry $\left(\text{the line } x = \dfrac{1}{4}\right)$, so its symmetric point lies $\dfrac{1}{4}$ unit to the right of the axis, at $\left(\dfrac{1}{2}, -1\right)$.

5. Since the three points located so far are not sufficient to provide a good picture of the graph, locate two additional points by evaluation, setting $x = 1$ and $x = -1$.

$$f(1) = -2(1)^2 + (1) - 1 = -2$$

so $(1, -2)$ lies on the graph;

$$f(-1) = -2(-1)^2 + (-1) - 1 = -4$$

so $(-1, -4)$ lies on the graph.
Use symmetry to sketch the graph as shown.

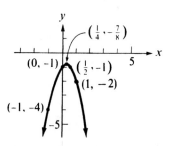

EXAMPLE 5

Graph $f(x) = x^2 + 3x + 1$.

Solution

1. Since $a = 1$ and $1 > 0$, the parabola opens upward.
2. Compute the coordinates of the vertex.

$$x = \frac{-b}{2a} = \frac{-3}{2(1)} = \frac{-3}{2}$$

$$y = \left(\frac{-3}{2}\right)^2 + 3\left(\frac{-3}{2}\right) + 1$$

$$= \frac{9}{4} - \frac{9}{2} + 1$$

$$= \frac{9 - 18 + 4}{4} = \frac{-5}{4}$$

The vertex has coordinates $\left(\dfrac{-3}{2}, \dfrac{-5}{4}\right)$.

3. Set y equal to zero to find the x-intercepts.

$$0 = x^2 + 3x + 1$$

$$x = \frac{-3 \pm \sqrt{3^2 - 4(1)(1)}}{2(1)}$$

$$= \frac{-3 \pm \sqrt{5}}{2}$$

The solutions are irrational, so find decimal approximations for the x-intercepts.

$$\frac{-3 + \sqrt{5}}{2} \approx -0.4$$

$$\frac{-3 - \sqrt{5}}{2} \approx -2.6$$

Plot the x-intercepts at $(-2.6, 0)$ and $(-0.4, 0)$.

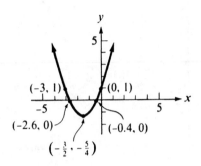

4. Since $f(0) = 1$, the y-intercept is the point $(0, 1)$. The y-intercept lies $\frac{3}{2}$ units to the right of the axis of symmetry $\left(\text{the line } x = \frac{-3}{2}\right)$, so its symmetric point lies $\frac{3}{2}$ units to the left of the axis, at $(-3, 1)$. These points are sufficient to give a reasonable picture of the graph.

Maximum or Minimum Values

Many applied problems involve finding the largest or smallest value for a particular function. For example, the owner of a cannery might want to build a container that holds a certain volume but has the smallest possible surface area and hence the least cost for materials. A theater manager, knowing that attendance is inversely related to ticket price, might want to calculate the ticket price that will maximize the theater's total revenue.

In general, the methods of calculus are needed to solve such problems. However, if the problem can be modeled by a quadratic function, we need only compute the coordinates of the vertex to find the maximum or minimum value of the function.

EXAMPLE 6

a. Find the dimensions of the largest rectangular area that can be enclosed by 36 yards of fence.

b. Sketch the graph of the function used to model the problem.

Solutions

a. The length of the fence is the perimeter of the enclosed rectangle. Which rectangle with perimeter 36 yards has the largest area? First, note that rectangles with the same perimeter can have different areas! Consider the examples in the following table:

Width	Length	Perimeter	Area
2	16	36	32
4	14	36	56
6	12	36	72
8	10	36	80

Let x represent the width of the rectangle so that its length is $18 - x$. The area A of the rectangle is then given by

$$A(x) = x(18 - x)$$
$$= 18x - x^2$$

a quadratic function of x. Since the coefficient of x^2 is -1 and $-1 < 0$, the graph of the function opens downward, and the vertex is the point with the largest value of A. To find the coordinates of the vertex, set

$$x = \frac{-b}{2a} = \frac{-18}{2(-1)} = 9$$

and then evaluate

$$A(9) = 18(9) - (9)^2$$
$$= 162 - 81 = 81$$

Thus, the largest area that can be enclosed is 81 square yards, by forming a rectangle of width 9 yards and length $18 - 9 = 9$ yards.

b.

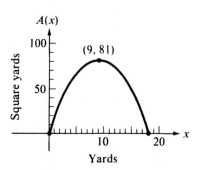

EXERCISE SET 8.3

▲ *Graph. See Example 1.*

1. $y = 3x^2$

2. $y = -2x^2$

3. $y = x^2 - 9$

4. $y = x^2 + 3$

5. $y = \frac{-1}{8}x^2$

6. $y = \frac{2}{3}x^2$

7. $y = x^2 + 6$

8. $y = x^2 - 3$

▲ *See Example 2.*

9. $y = x^2 - 4x$

10. $y = x^2 + 2x$

11. $y = 3x^2 + 6x$

12. $y = 2x^2 - 6x$

13. $y = -2x^2 + 5x$

14. $y = -3x^2 - 8x$

▲ *Find the coordinates of the vertex. See Example 3.*

15. $y = 3x^2 - 6x + 4$

16. $y = -2x^2 + 5x - 1$

17. $y = 3 - 5x + x^2$

18. $y = 2 + 3x - x^2$

19. $y = \frac{1}{2}x^2 - \frac{2}{3}x + \frac{1}{3}$

20. $y = \frac{-3}{4}x^2 + \frac{1}{2}x - \frac{1}{4}$

21. $y = 2.3 - 7.2x - 0.8x^2$
22. $y = 5.1 - 0.2x + 4.6x^2$

▲ *Graph. Specify the coordinates of the vertex and the intercepts. See Examples 3–5.*

23. $y = x^2 - 5x + 4$
24. $y = x^2 + x - 6$
25. $y = -2x^2 + 7x + 4$
26. $y = -3x^2 + 2x + 8$
27. $y = 0.6x^2 + 0.6x - 1.2$
28. $y = 0.5x^2 - 0.25x - 0.75$
29. $y = x^2 + 4x + 7$
30. $y = x^2 - 6x + 10$
31. $y = -2x^2 + x - 3$
32. $y = -3x^2 + x - 2$
33. $y = x^2 + 2x - 1$
34. $y = x^2 - 6x + 2$
35. $y = -2x^2 + 6x - 3$
36. $y = -2x^2 - 8x - 5$

▲ *For Exercises 37–44, do the following.*
   a. *Find the maximum or minimum value.*
   b. *Sketch the graph. See Example 6.*

37. The equation $d = 64t - 16t^2$ gives the distance d in feet above the ground of a toy water rocket t seconds after it is launched. When will the rocket reach its greatest height, and what will that height be?

38. The equation $h = -12 + 32t - 16t^2$ gives the height h in feet of an object tossed into the air from the bottom of a trench 12 feet deep. When will the object reach its greatest height, and what will that height be?

39. What is the area A of the largest rectangle that can be enclosed by 100 inches of twine? (*Hint:* Let x represent the width of the rectangle.)

40. Find the dimensions of the rectangle of greatest area that can be roped off with 80 yards of rope. (*Hint:* Let x represent the width of the rectangle.)

41. A farmer plans to fence a grazing area along a river with 300 yards of fence as shown. What is the largest area he can enclose?

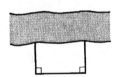

Exercise 41

42. A breeder of horses wants to fence two grazing areas along a river with 600 meters of fence as shown. What is the largest area she can enclose?

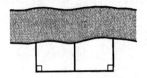

Exercise 42

43. An entrepreneur buys a motel with 40 units. The previous owner charged $24 per night for a room and on the average filled 32 rooms per night at that price. The entrepreneur discovers that for every $2 he raises the price, another room stands vacant. What price should the entrepreneur charge for a room to maximize his revenue? (*Hint:* Let x represent the *number* of $2 price increases.)

44. A travel agent offers a group rate of $2400 per person for a week in London if 16 people sign up for the tour. For each additional person who signs up, the price per person is reduced by $100. How many people must sign up for the tour in order for the travel agent to maximize her revenue?

Miscellaneous Exercises

45. Find the equations of two different parabolas with vertex $(0, 2)$.

46. Find the equations of two different parabolas with vertex $(0, -3)$.

47. Find the equations of two different parabolas with y-intercept $(0, -5)$.

48. Find the equations of two different parabolas with y-intercept $(0, 4)$.

49. Find the equations of two different parabolas with x-intercepts $(2, 0)$ and $(-3, 0)$.

50. Find the equations of two different parabolas with x-intercepts $(-1, 0)$ and $(4, 0)$.

Graphing Parabolas

The graph of the equation $y = ax^2 + bx + c$ is a parabola.

1. If $a > 0$, then the graph is concave upward with an absolute minimum y-value

   that occurs at the point where $x = -\dfrac{b}{2a}$.

2. If $a < 0$, then the graph is concave downward with an absolute maximum y-value

   that occurs at the point where $x = -\dfrac{b}{2a}$.

Example 1. Graph $y = 3x^2 - 6x + 2$.

Vertex: $x = -\dfrac{b}{2a} = -\dfrac{-6}{2(3)} = 1$. Then $y = 3(1)^2 - 6(1) + 2 = -1$. The vertex is $(1, -1)$.

Additional Points: $(0, 2)$, $(2, 2)$, $(-1, 11)$, $(3, 11)$

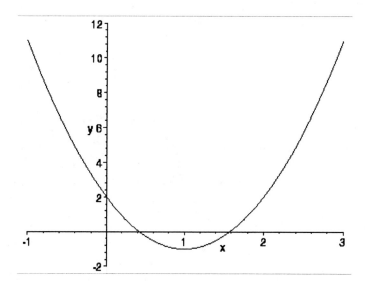

Example 2: Graph $y = -x^2 + 6x - 5$.

Vertex: $x = -\dfrac{b}{2a} = -\dfrac{6}{2(-1)} = 3$. Then $y = -(3)^2 + 6(3) - 5 = 4$. The vertex is $(3, 4)$.

Additional Points: $(0, -5), (6, -5)$

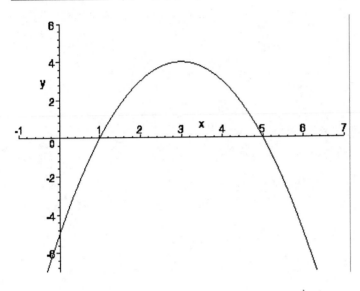

Example 3: Graph $y = 4x^2 - 12x + 9$.

Vertex: $x = -\dfrac{b}{2a} = -\dfrac{-12}{2(4)} = \dfrac{3}{2}$. Then $y = 4\left(\dfrac{3}{2}\right)^2 - 12\left(\dfrac{3}{2}\right) + 9 = 0$. The vertex is $\left(\dfrac{3}{2}, 0\right)$.

Additional Points: $(0, 9), (3, 9)$

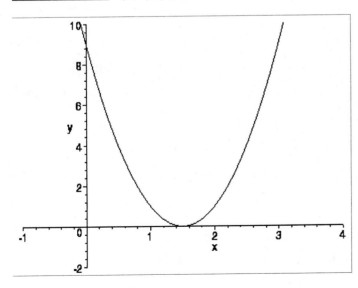

Parabolas

Graph the following equations.

1. $y = 2x^2 - 4x - 1$

2. $y = 2x^2 + 12x + 19$

3. $y = -x^2 + 4x - 4$

4. $y = x^2 + 4x + 4$

5. $y = x^2 - 6x + 11$

6. $y = x^2 + 2x - 1$

7. $y = -2x^2 + 4x + 1$

8. $y = -2x^2 + 4x + 3$

9. $y = 2x^2 - 8x + 7$

10. $y = 2x^2 + 12x + 14$

Answers

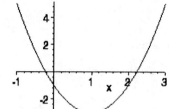

1.

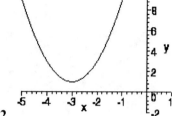

2.

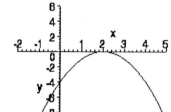

3.

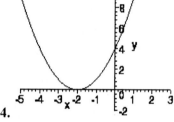

4.

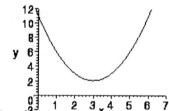

5.

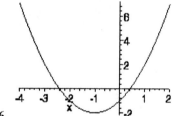

6.

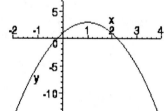

7.

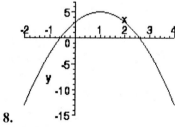

8.

9.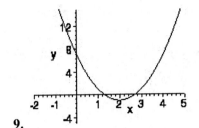

10.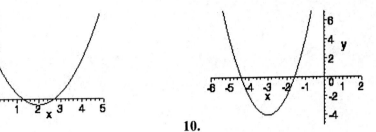

| 8.4 | **EXPONENTIAL FUNCTIONS** |

Powers b^x, x a Real Number

In this section we consider powers b^x $(b > 0)$ for any real number x and functions involving such powers. First recall that in Chapter 5 we defined powers with integer exponents such as those included in Example 1.

EXAMPLE 1

a. $2^{-3} = \dfrac{1}{2^3} = \dfrac{1}{8}$ b. $3^{-2} = \dfrac{1}{3^2} = \dfrac{1}{9}$ c. $4^0 = 1$

Also recall that we extended the definition of powers to include rational exponents such as those included in Example 2.

EXAMPLE 2

a. $25^{1/2} = 5$ b. $4^{3/2} = (4^{1/2})^3$ c. $\left(\dfrac{1}{8}\right)^{2/3} = \left[\left(\dfrac{1}{8}\right)^{1/3}\right]^2$

$$= 2^3 = 8 \qquad\qquad = \left(\dfrac{1}{2}\right)^2 = \dfrac{1}{4}$$

In Section 5.6 we obtained approximations to powers with rational exponents by using a scientific calculator.

EXAMPLE 3

Find an approximation for each power to four places.

a. $2^{1.2}$ b. $2.4^{1.7}$ c. $1.6^{-1.3}$

Solutions

The following keystrokes can be used:

a. $2\ \boxed{x^y}\ 1.2\ \boxed{=}$ b. $2.4\ \boxed{x^y}\ 1.7\ \boxed{=}$ c. $1.6\ \boxed{x^y}\ 1.3\ \boxed{+/-}\ \boxed{=}$

ans. 2.2974   *ans.* 4.4295   *ans.* 0.5428

We can also use a scientific calculator to obtain approximations to powers with irrational exponents.

EXAMPLE 4

Find an approximation for each power to four decimal places.

a. $2^{\sqrt{3}}$ b. $3^{\sqrt{2}}$

Solutions

The following keystrokes can be used:

a. $2\ \boxed{x^y}\ 3\ \boxed{\sqrt{\ }}\ \boxed{=}$ b. $3\ \boxed{x^y}\ 2\ \boxed{\sqrt{\ }}\ \boxed{=}$

ans. 3.3220   *ans.* 4.7288

Exponential Functions

Since for each real x there is one and only one number b^x, the equation

$$f(x) = b^x \qquad (b > 0) \tag{1}$$

defines a function. Because $1^x = 1$ for all real values of x, Equation (1) defines a constant function if $b = 1$. If $b \neq 1$, we say that (1) defines an **exponential function**.

Note that b is restricted to be greater than 0. One reason is that if $b < 0$, b^x is *imaginary* for $x = 1/n$, n even. For example, $(-4)^{1/2}$, $(-9)^{1/2}$, and $(-16)^{1/2}$ are imaginary numbers.

Graphs of Exponential Functions

Exponential functions can be visualized more clearly by considering their graphs. We illustrate two typical examples in which $0 < b < 1$ and $b > 1$, respectively. Assigning values to x in the equations

$$f(x) = \left(\frac{1}{2}\right)^x \quad \text{and} \quad g(x) = 2^x$$

we find ordered pairs in each function and sketch the graphs in Figure 8.7.

If $f(x) = \left(\frac{1}{2}\right)^x$, then   If $g(x) = 2^x$, then

$$f(-3) = \left(\frac{1}{2}\right)^{-3} = 8 \qquad g(-3) = 2^{-3} = \frac{1}{8}$$

$$\vdots \qquad \vdots \qquad \vdots \qquad\qquad \vdots \qquad \vdots \qquad \vdots$$

$$f(0) = \left(\frac{1}{2}\right)^0 = 1 \qquad g(0) = 2^0 = 1$$

$$\vdots \qquad \vdots \qquad \vdots \qquad\qquad \vdots \qquad \vdots \qquad \vdots$$

$$g(3) = 2^3 = 8$$

$$f(3) = \left(\frac{1}{2}\right)^3 = \frac{1}{8}$$

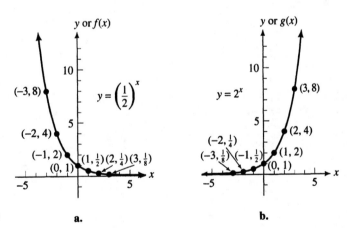

Figure 8.7   a.   b.

Additional ordered pairs can be obtained by using a calculator to obtain function values for nonintegral values in the domain.

Notice that the graph of the function determined by $f(x) = (\frac{1}{2})^x$ goes *down* to the right and the graph of the function determined by $g(x) = 2^x$ goes *up* to the right. For this reason we say that the former function is a **decreasing function** and the latter is an **increasing function**. In each case the domain is the set of real numbers, and the range is the set of positive real numbers. In general, both b and b^x are positive for any exponential function

$$f(x) = b^x$$

These properties are summarized as follows.

The Exponential Function $f(x) = b^x$ ($b > 0$, $b \neq 1$)

1. Domain: x a real number.
2. Range: $b^x > 0$.
3. If $b > 1$, the function is strictly increasing;
   if $0 < b < 1$, the function is strictly decreasing.

EXAMPLE 5

Graph $y = 3^x$. Use selected integral values for x.

Solution

For convenience, arbitrarily select integral values of x, say, -2, -1, 0, 1, 2, and 3. Determine the y-components of each ordered pair.

$$\left(-2, \frac{1}{9}\right), \quad \left(-1, \frac{1}{3}\right), \quad (0, 1), \quad (1, 3), \quad (2, 9), \quad (3, 27)$$

Plot the points and connect them with a smooth curve.

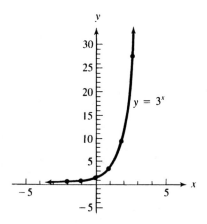

EXAMPLE 6

Graph $f(x) = 2.31^x$.

Solution

Use a calculator with arbitrarily selected integral values of x—say, -2, -1, 0, 1, 2, and 3—to obtain an approximation for each corresponding function value.

$$(-2, 0.2), \quad (-1, 0.4), \quad (0, 1.0), \quad (1, 2.3), \quad (2, 5.3), \quad (3, 12.3)$$

Plot the points and connect them with a smooth curve.

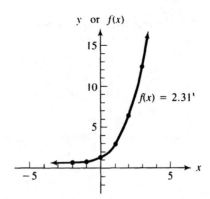

Exponential Growth

Exponential functions are used to model relationships in many fields. Because these models often involve powers with rational exponents, a scientific calculator may be necessary to perform the computations in this section.* We first consider an example of population growth.

EXAMPLE 7
c

In a laboratory experiment a colony of 100 bacteria is established, and the growth of the colony is monitored. The experimenters discover that the colony triples in population every day.

a. Write a function that gives the population of the colony at any time t in days.

b. How many bacteria are present after 5 days? After 36 hours?

c. Graph the function found in part a.

Solutions

a. The population of the colony is 100 when the experiment starts (at $t = 0$) and triples every day thereafter. If P represents the population of the colony after t days, then

$$\begin{array}{lll} \text{when} & t = 0, & P = 100 \\ \text{when} & t = 1, & P = 100 \cdot 3 \\ \text{when} & t = 2, & P = (100 \cdot 3) \cdot 3 = 100 \cdot 3^2 \\ \text{when} & t = 3, & P = (100 \cdot 3^2) \cdot 3 = 100 \cdot 3^3 \end{array}$$

In general, on the tth day the original population, 100, has been multiplied by 3 t times, so the population on day t is $100 \cdot 3^t$, or

$$P(t) = 100 \cdot 3^t$$

b. To find the population at any particular time, evaluate the function for the appropriate value of t. Thus, after 5 days the population is

$$P(5) = 100 \cdot 3^5$$
$$= 100(243) = 24{,}300$$

After 36 hours, or 1.5 days, the population is

$$P(1.5) = 100 \cdot 3^{1.5}$$
$$\approx 100(5.196) = 519.6$$

---

*In Chapter 9 we consider ways to make these computations using tables.

(Calculator sequence for $3^{1.5}$:

$$3 \boxed{x^y} 1.5 \boxed{=} 5.1961524)$$

Since there will never be a fraction of a bacterium, the population of the colony after 36 hours is 519 bacteria. (The 520th bacterium is not formed yet.)

c. To graph the function $P(t) = 100 \cdot 3^t$, tabulate several function values. Then connect the points with a smooth curve to obtain the graph shown in the figure.

t	$P(t)$
0	100
1	300
2	900
3	2,700
4	8,100
5	24,300

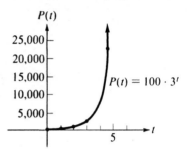

The function $P(t) = 100 \cdot 3^t$ found in Example 7 describes **exponential growth**. The coefficient 100 is called the **initial value** (the initial number of bacteria), and 3 is called the **growth factor** (the factor by which the bacteria population grows every day) of the function.

EXAMPLE 8

Under ideal conditions the number of rabbits in a certain area can double every 3 months. A rancher estimates that there are 60 rabbits living on her land.

a. Write a function that gives the rabbit population after t months.

b. How many rabbits are present after 2 years? After 8 months?

c. Graph the function found in part a.

Solutions

a. If P presents the population of rabbits after t months, then

$$\text{when} \quad t = 0, \qquad P = 60$$
$$\text{when} \quad t = 3, \qquad P = 60 \cdot 2$$
$$\text{when} \quad t = 6, \qquad P = (60 \cdot 2) \cdot 2 = 60 \cdot 2^2$$
$$\text{when} \quad t = 9, \qquad P = (60 \cdot 2^2) \cdot 2 = 60 \cdot 2^3$$

In general, the original population of 60 is multiplied by 2 every 3 months, so the population in month t is $60 \cdot 2^{t/3}$, or $P = 60 \cdot 2^{t/3}$.

b. To find the population at any particular time, evaluate the function for the appropriate value of t. Thus, after 2 years, or 24 months, the population is

$$P(24) = 60 \cdot 2^{24/3}$$
$$= 60 \cdot 2^8 = 15,360$$

After 8 months the population is

$$P(8) = 60 \cdot 2^{8/3}$$
$$\approx 60(6.350) = 381$$

(Calculator sequence for $2^{8/3}$:

$$2 \boxed{x^y} 8 \boxed{=} \boxed{x^y} 3 \boxed{1/x} \boxed{=} 6.3496042)$$

c. To graph the function $P(t) = 60 \cdot 2^{t/3}$, tabulate several function values and plot points. Connect them with a smooth curve to obtain the graph shown in the figure.

t	$P(t)$
0	60
1	76
2	95
3	120
4	151
5	190
6	240

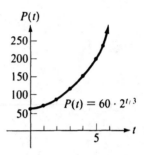

Exponential Decay

In Examples 7 and 8, exponential growth was modeled by increasing functions of the form

$$P(t) = P_0 a^t$$

when $a > 1$. The function $P(t) = P_0 a^t$ is a *decreasing* function if we have $0 < a < 1$. In this case the function is said to describe **exponential decay**, and the constant a is called the **decay factor**.

EXAMPLE 9

A small coal-mining town has been losing population since 1930, when there were 5000 inhabitants. At each census thereafter (taken at 10-year intervals) the population has been approximately $\dfrac{9}{10}$ of its earlier figure.

a. Write a function that gives the population of the town t years after 1930.

b. What was the population of the town in 1980? In 1985?

c. Graph the function found in part a.

Solutions

a. If P represents the population t years after 1930, then

$$\begin{aligned} \text{when} \quad t = 0, \quad & P = 5000 \\ \text{when} \quad t = 10, \quad & P = 5000(0.9) \\ \text{when} \quad t = 20, \quad & P = 5000(0.9)^2 \\ \text{when} \quad t = 30, \quad & P = 5000(0.9)^3 \end{aligned}$$

In general, we find that after t years the original population of 5000 has been multiplied by $0.9^{t/10}$ times, so the population t years after 1930 is $5000 \cdot (0.9)^{t/10}$, or $P(t) = 5000(0.9)^{t/10}$.

b. In 1980, 50 years had elapsed since 1930, so the population was
$$P(50) = 5000(0.9)^{50/10}$$
$$= 5000(0.9)^5 = 2952.45$$

or 2952. In 1985 (55 years after 1930) the population was
$$P(55) = 5000(0.9)^{55/10}$$
$$= 5000(0.9)^{5.5} = 2800.94$$

or 2801.

(Calculator sequence for $5000(0.9)^{5.5}$:

$$0.9 \boxed{x^y} 5.5 \boxed{=} \boxed{\times} 5000 \boxed{=} 2800.94)$$

c. To graph the function $P(t) = 5000(0.9)^{t/10}$, tabulate several function values. Then connect the points to obtain the graph shown in the figure.

t	$P(t)$
0	5000
10	4500
20	4050
30	3645
40	3280

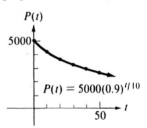

Solving $y = b^x$ for x In this section we evaluated exponential functions $y = b^x$ for b^x $(b > 0)$ for given values of x. We need some additional mathematical tools to be able to find values of x for given values of b^x. The required mathematics is developed in detail in the next chapter.

EXERCISE SET 8.4

▲ *Evaluate the power for each given x. See Examples 1 and 2.*

1. 3^x; 0, 1, and 2 **2.** 2^x; $-3, 0,$ and 3

3. 10^x; 0, 1, and 2

4. 10^x; $-2, -1,$ and 0

5. 4^x; $-\dfrac{1}{2}, 0,$ and $\dfrac{1}{2}$ **6.** 8^x; $-\dfrac{1}{3}, 0,$ and $\dfrac{1}{3}$

7. $\left(\dfrac{1}{2}\right)^x$; 2, 3, and 4

8. $\left(\dfrac{1}{2}\right)^x$; $-2, -3,$ and -4

9. 9^x; $\dfrac{3}{2}$ and $-\dfrac{3}{2}$ **10.** 27^x; $\dfrac{2}{3}$ and $-\dfrac{2}{3}$

▲ *Evaluate the power to the nearest hundredth for each given x. See Examples 3 and 4.*

11. 2.7^x; -2 and 3 **12.** 1.8^x; -3 and 2

13. 0.4^x; 0.2 and 2.3 **14.** 0.3^x; 0.3 and 1.6

15. 3^x; $\sqrt{3}$ and $\sqrt{5}$ **16.** 5^x; $\sqrt{2}$ and $\sqrt{3}$

17. 4^x; $\sqrt{3}$ and $-\sqrt{3}$ **18.** 2^x; $\sqrt{5}$ and $-\sqrt{5}$

▲ *Graph each equation. Use selected integral values for x. See Example 5.*

19. $y = 4^x$ **20.** $y = 6^x$ **21.** $y = 10^x$

22. $y = 2^{-x}$ **23.** $y = 3^{-x}$ **24.** $y = -3^x$

25. $y = -2^x$ **26.** $y = \left(\dfrac{1}{3}\right)^x$

27. $y = \left(\dfrac{1}{4}\right)^x$ 28. $y = \left(\dfrac{1}{10}\right)^x$

29. $y = \left(\dfrac{1}{2}\right)^{-x}$ 30. $y = \left(\dfrac{1}{3}\right)^{-x}$

▲ *Graph each equation. See Example 6.*

31. $f(x) = 1.3^x$ 32. $f(x) = 2.4^x$

33. $f(x) = 0.8^x$ 34. $f(x) = 0.7^x$

▲ *For Exercises 35–42, do the following.*

     a. *Write a function that describes exponential growth or decay.*

     c **b.** *Evaluate the function at the given values.*

     c. *Graph the function.*

▲ *See Examples 7 and 8.*

35. A colony of bacteria starts with 300 organisms and doubles every week. How many bacteria will there be after 8 weeks? After 5 days?

36. A population of 24 fruit flies triples every month. How many fruit flies will there be after 6 months? After 3 weeks? (Assume that a month equals 4 weeks.)

37. A typical beehive contains 20,000 insects. The population can increase in size by a factor of 2.5 every 6 weeks. How many bees will there be after 4 weeks? After 20 weeks?

38. A rancher who started with 800 head of cattle finds that his herd increases by a factor of 1.8 every 3 years. How many head of cattle will he have after 1 year? After 10 years?

▲ *See Example 9.*

39. During a vigorous spraying program the mosquito population was reduced to three-fourths of its previous size every 2 weeks. If the mosquito population was originally estimated at 250,000, how many mosquitos remained after 3 weeks of spraying? After 8 weeks?

40. The number of perch in Hidden Lake has declined to half of its previous value every 5 years since 1960, when the perch population was estimated at 8000. How many perch were there in 1970? In 1988?

41. Scuba divers find that the water in Emerald Lake filters out 15% of the sunlight for each 4 feet that they descend. How much sunlight penetrates to a depth of 20 feet? To a depth of 45 feet?

42. Arline's motorboat cost $15,000 in 1980 and has depreciated by 10% every 3 years. How much was the boat worth in 1989? In 1990?

Miscellaneous Exercises

▲ *In Exercises 43 and 44, use graphical methods to estimate the solutions of the exponential equations.*

43. $2^x = 5$ [*Hint:* Graph $y_1 = 2^x$ and $y_2 = 5$, and approximate the value of x at their point of intersection.]

44. $3^x = 4$ [See the hint for Exercise 43.]

45. For what set of positive real numbers a will $y = a^x$ define an increasing function? A decreasing function?

46. For what set of positive real numbers a will $y = a^{-x}$ define an increasing function? A decreasing function?

8.5   THE INVERSE OF A FUNCTION

One-to-One Functions

In a function f, each element in the domain is associated with just one element in its range. If each element in its range is also associated with just one element in its domain, the function f is called a **one-to-one function**.

     Whether or not a function is a one-to-one function can be readily determined from its graph. Recall (page 205) that any vertical line will intersect the graph of a function in at most one point. If the function f is one-to-one, any horizontal line will also intersect its graph in at most one point, as shown in Figure 8.8a. If it is not one-to-one, a horizontal line will intersect the graph at more than one point, as shown in Figure 8.8b. A function is one-to-one provided each of its y-values maps back to exactly one x-value.

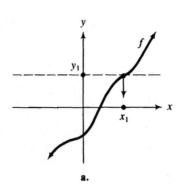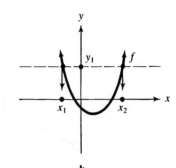

Figure 8.8   a.   b.

Inverse Functions   If the components of each ordered pair in a one-to-one function f are interchanged, the result will be another function called the **inverse function** of f. The inverse function of f is denoted by f^{-1} (read "f inverse" or "the inverse of f"). If f is not one-to-one, then interchanging the components of f will result in an **inverse relation** but *not* a function.

EXAMPLE 1
a. If $f = \{(1,2),(3,4),(5,6)\}$, then $f^{-1} = \{(2,1),(4,3),(6,5)\}$ is a function.

b. If $f = \{(1,2),(2,5),(3,5)\}$, then its inverse relation $\{(2,1),(5,2),(5,3)\}$ is not a function because there are two different range values associated with the domain value 5. Note that f is not a one-to-one function, since *two* ordered pairs have a second component 5.

Note that the domain of f^{-1} is the range of f and the range of f^{-1} is the domain of f. If a one-to-one function f is defined by an equation in two variables, an equation for the inverse f^{-1} can be obtained by interchanging the variables.

EXAMPLE 2   The inverse of the function defined by
$$y = 4x - 3 \tag{1}$$
is defined by
$$x = 4y - 3 \tag{2}$$
where the variables in Equation (1) have been interchanged. When y is expressed in terms of x,
$$y = \frac{1}{4}(x + 3) \tag{2a}$$

Equations (2) and (2a) are equivalent.

Graphs of Inverse Functions   The graphs of a function and its inverse are related in an interesting way. To see this, we first observe in Figure 8.9 that the graphs of the ordered pairs (a,b) and (b,a) are always located symmetrically with respect to the graph of $y = x$. Therefore, because for every ordered pair (a,b) in f, the ordered pair (b,a) is in f^{-1}, the graphs of $y = f^{-1}(x)$ and $y = f(x)$ are reflections of each other about the graph of the equation $y = x$. Figure 8.10 shows the graphs of

$$y = 4x - 3$$

and its inverse,

$$x = 4y - 3 \quad \text{or} \quad y = \frac{1}{4}(x + 3)$$

together with the graph of $y = x$.

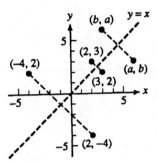

Figure 8.9

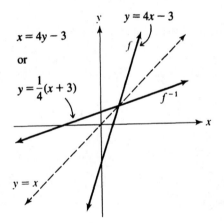

Figure 8.10

In Example 3 we graph the inverse of a function that is not one-to-one.

E X A M P L E 3 The figure on page 240 shows the graph of the function

$$y = x^2$$

together with the graph of its inverse relation,

$$x = y^2 \quad \text{or} \quad y = \pm\sqrt{x}$$

Since for all but one value in its domain $(x = 0)$ the inverse relation associates two different values of y with each x, the inverse relation is not a function.

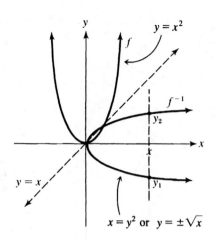

$x = y^2$ or $y = \pm\sqrt{x}$

$f^{-1}(f(x)) = x$;
$f(f^{-1}(x)) = x$

If f and f^{-1} are both functions, f associates the number a with the *unique* number b, and f^{-1} associates the number b with the *unique* number a. Therefore, it must be true that for every x in the domain of f,

$$f^{-1}[f(x)] = x$$

(read "f inverse of f of x is equal to x"). And for every x in the domain of f^{-1},

$$f[f^{-1}(x)] = x$$

(read "f of f inverse of x is equal to x"). For example, if $f(2) = 5$, then $f^{-1}(5) = 2$, so

$$f^{-1}[f(2)] = f^{-1}(5) = 2$$

and

$$f[f^{-1}(5)] = f(2) = 5$$

EXAMPLE 4

Consider Equation (1) on page 238, and note that if f is the linear function defined by
$$f(x) = 4x - 3$$
then f is a one-to-one function. Now f^{-1} is defined by
$$f^{-1}(x) = \frac{1}{4}(x + 3)$$
[Equation (2a) on page 238], and we see that
$$f^{-1}[f(x)] = \frac{1}{4}[(4x - 3) + 3] = x$$
and
$$f[f^{-1}(x)] = 4\left[\frac{1}{4}(x + 3)\right] - 3 = x$$

EXERCISE SET 8.5

▲ *Find the inverse relation of each function, and state whether it is also a function. See Example 1.*

1. $f = \{(-2, -2), (2, 2)\}$
2. $f = \{(-5, 1), (5, 2)\}$
3. $q = \{(1, 3), (2, 3), (3, 4)\}$
4. $q = \{(2, 2), (3, 3), (4, 3)\}$
5. $g = \{(1, 1), (2, 3), (3, 3)\}$
6. $g = \{(-2, 0), (0, 0), (4, -2)\}$

▲ *In Exercises 7–16, each equation defines a function, f.*

   a. *Write the equation defining its inverse relation.*

   b. *Sketch the graphs of f and its inverse relation on the same set of axes.*

   c. *State whether the inverse relation is a function.*

   See Examples 2 and 3.

7. $2x + 4y = 7$
8. $3x - 2y = 5$
9. $x - 3y = 6$
10. $4x + y = 4$
11. $y = x^2 - 4x$
12. $y = x^2 - 4$
13. $y = \sqrt{4 + x^2}$
14. $y = -\sqrt{x^2 - 4}$
15. $y = |x|$
16. $y = |x| + 1$

▲ *Sketch the graph of the inverse of the function whose graph is given. See Example 3.*

17.

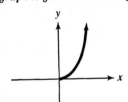

18.

19.

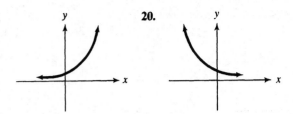

20.

21.

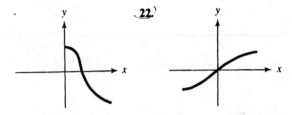

22.

▲ *In Exercises 23–28 each equation defines a one-to-one function f. Find the equation defining f^{-1}, and show that*

$$f[f^{-1}(x)] = f^{-1}[f(x)] = x$$

[Hint: Solve explicitly for y, and let $y = f(x)$.] See Example 4.

23. $y = x$
24. $y = -x$
25. $2x + y = 4$
26. $x - 2y = 4$
27. $3x - 4y = 12$
28. $3x + 4y = 12$

CHAPTER SUMMARY

[8.1] A **function** is a relationship between two variables for which a unique value of the dependent variable can be determined from a value of the independent variable. The **domain** of a function is the set of all first components in the function; the **range** is the set of all second components. Symbols such as $f(x)$, $P(x)$, and $R(x)$ are expressions in **function notation**.

The solutions of the equation $f(x) = 0$ are the x-intercepts of the graph of f and are called the zeros of the function f.

[8.2]   Many functional relationships can be modeled by equations. Two such relationships are given special names. The equation $y = kx$ (k a positive constant) defines a function called a **direct variation**. The equations $xy = k$ (k a positive constant) and $y = \dfrac{k}{x}$ define a function called an **inverse variation**. In each case the constant k is called the **constant of variation**.

[8.3]   The graphs of quadratic functions

$$f(x) = ax^2 + bx + c \qquad (a \neq 0)$$

are **parabolas**. The following procedure can be used to graph a quadratic function:

---

1. Determine whether the parabola opens upward (if $a > 0$) or downward (if $a < 0$).
2. Locate the vertex.
   a. The x-coordinate of the vertex is $x = -b/2a$.
   b. The y-coordinate of the vertex is $y = f(-b/2a)$.
3. Locate the x-intercepts (if any) by setting $f(x)$ equal to zero and solving for x.
4. Locate the y-intercept by evaluating $f(0)$. Locate the point symmetric to the y-intercept with respect to the axis of symmetry.
5. If necessary, locate one or two additional points on the graph by evaluation.

The maximum or minimum value of a quadratic function is the y-coordinate of the vertex of its graph.

[8.4]   A function defined by an equation of the form

$$f(x) = b^x \qquad (b > 0, b \neq 1)$$

is called an **exponential function**. If $b > 1$, it is an **increasing function**; if $0 < b < 1$, it is a **decreasing function**. The domain of the function is the set of real numbers; the range is the set of positive real numbers.

[8.5]   If each element in the range of a function f is associated with just one element in its domain, the function is called a **one-to-one function**. The **inverse** of the function f can be obtained by interchanging the components of each ordered pair in f. If f is a one-to-one function, then the inverse f^{-1} is also a function. The graphs of f^{-1} and f are reflections of each other in the graph of $y = x$.

REVIEW EXERCISES

[8.1]

▲ **a.** *Solve each equation explicitly for y in terms of x.*
   b. *State whether the equation defines a function.*
   c. *Specify the domain of each function.*

1. $3x + 4y = 6$
2. $xy - 5y = 2$
3. $\sqrt{x + 4} - y = 0$
4. $y^2 - 2x^2 = 6$

▲ *Which of the following graphs represent functions?*

5.
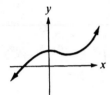

6.
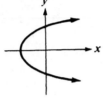

7.
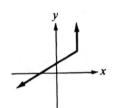

8.
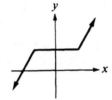

9. Given that $f(x) = x - 4$, find each of the following:
   a. $f(6)$
   b. $f(x + h) - f(x)$

10. Given that $f(x) = 2x^2 - 3x + 1$, find each of the following:
    a. $f(3)$
    b. $\dfrac{f(x + h) - f(x)}{h}$

▲ *Consider the following graphs for Exercises 11 and 12:*

11. **a.** Find $f(-2)$ and $f(2)$.
    b. For what value(s) of t is $f(t) = 4$?
    c. Find the intercepts of the graph.
    d. What is the maximum value of f? For what value(s) of t does f take on its maximum value?

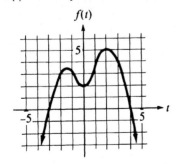

$f(t)$

12. **a.** Find $P(-3)$ and $P(3)$.
    b. For what value(s) of z is $P(z) = 2$?
    c. Find the intercepts of the graph.
    d. What is the minimum value of P? For what value(s) of z does P take on its minimum value?

$P(z)$

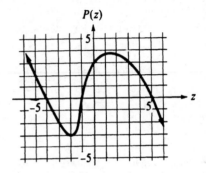

▲ *Find the zeros of each function.*

13. $f(x) = x^2 - 7x + 6$
14. $g(x) = 4x^2 - 6x$

[8.2]

15. If y varies inversely with t^2 and $y = 16$ when $t = 3$, **a.** express y as a function of t; **b.** find y when $t = 8$.

16. If y varies directly with s^2 and inversely with t and $y = 4$ when $s = 2$ and $t = 5$, **a.** express y as a function of s and t; **b.** find y when $s = 3$ and $t = 4$.

17. The distance s a particle falls in a certain medium varies directly with the square of the length of time t it falls. If the particle falls 28 centimeters in 4 seconds, **a.** express the distance a particle will fall as a function of time it falls; **b.** find the distance a particle falls in 6 seconds.

18. The volume V of a gas varies directly with the absolute temperature T and inversely with the pressure P of the gas. If $V = 40$ when $T = 300$ and $P = 30$, **a.** express the volume of the gas as a function of the absolute temperature and pressure of the gas; **b.** find the volume when $T = 320$ and $P = 40$.

19. **a.** Express the area (A) of an equilateral triangle as a function of the length of a side (s); **b.** Find the area of an equilateral triangle with sides that are 4 centimeters in length.

20. The hypotenuse (c) of a right triangle is 12 centimeters long. **a.** Express the area (A) of the triangle as a function of the shortest side;

b. Find the area of a right triangle with a short side that is 4 centimeters in length.

[8.3]

▲ *Graph. Specify the coordinates of the vertex and the intercepts.*

21. $y = \dfrac{1}{2}x^2$

22. $y = x^2 - 4$

23. $y = x^2 - 9x$

24. $y = -2x^2 - 4x$

25. $y = x^2 - x - 12$

26. $y = -2x^2 + x - 4$

27. $y = -x^2 + 2x + 4$

28. $y = x^2 - 3x + 4$

▲ *Find the maximum value. Sketch the graph.*

29. A farmer inherits an apple orchard on which 60 trees are planted. Each tree yields 12 bushels of apples. Experimentation has shown that for each additional tree planted per acre, the yield per tree decreases by $\frac{1}{2}$ bushel. How many trees should be planted per acre to maximize the total apple harvest?

30. A small company manufactures radios. When it charges $20 for a radio, it sells 500 radios per month. For each dollar the price is increased, 10 fewer radios are sold per month. What should the company charge for a radio to maximize its monthly revenue?

[8.4]

▲ *Find each value.*

31. 10^x for x equal to $-3, -1, 0, 1, 3$.

32. $\left(\dfrac{1}{2}\right)^x$ for x equal to $-3, -1, 0, 1, 3$.

▲ *Sketch each graph.*

33. $y = 5^x$

34. $y = 5^{-x}$

[8.5]

▲ *Which of the following functions have inverses that are also functions?*

35. **a.** 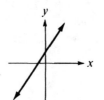 **b.**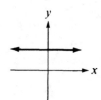

c. 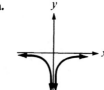 **d.**

36. **a.** 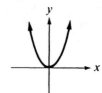 **b.**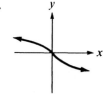

c.  **d.**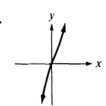

37. Graph the function defined by $y = 2x + 6$ and its inverse on the same set of axes.

38. Graph the function defined by $y = x^2 + 1$ and its inverse on the same set of axes.

▲ *The numbers in brackets refer to the sections in which such problems are first considered.*

▲ *Simplify.*

1. $2x - x(3 - x) - (x + 1)^2$ **[3.3]**

2. $\left(\dfrac{-ab}{s^2 t}\right)^3 \left(\dfrac{s^3 t}{a^2 b}\right)^2$ **[5.1]**

▲ *Factor completely.*

3. $2(x - 3)(x - 2) + 4(x - 3)^2$ **[3.2]**

4. $27a^6 + b^3$ **[3.7]**

▲ *Write as a single fraction in lowest terms.*

5. $\dfrac{x - 2}{x^2 - 4x + 3} - \dfrac{2x - 1}{x^2 - x - 6}$ **[4.4]**

6. $\dfrac{\dfrac{a}{a - 2}}{\dfrac{2}{a^2} - \dfrac{2}{a}}$ **[4.6]**

7. Divide $\dfrac{3t^3 - 7t + 3}{t - 2}$.   **[4.2]**

8. Write $\sqrt[4]{3x} + x\sqrt[3]{y^2}$ with exponential notation.   **[5.5]**

9. Solve $A = 2a^2 + 4lw$ for l.   **[2.3]**

10. Solve $0.10x + 0.90(20) = 0.50(x + 20)$.   **[2.5]**

11. Solve $x^2 + kx + k - 4 = 0$ for x in terms of k.   **[6.2]**

12. $x^{-2} - 2x^{-1} - 15 = 0$.   **[6.4]**

▲ *Graph each equation in the plane.*

13. $2x - 6y = 12$ **[7.2]**

14. $4x - 8 = 0$ **[7.2]**

15. Show that the triangle whose vertices are $(1, 1)$, $(-6, 2)$, and $(-2, 5)$ is an isosceles triangle.   **[7.3]**

16. Find an equation in standard form that includes the points $(-2, 5)$ and $(1, 3)$.   **[7.4]**

17. Find the equation in standard form for the line with x-intercept $a = \dfrac{1}{3}$ and y-intercept $b = -\dfrac{3}{2}$.   **[7.4]**

18. Write an equation in standard form for the line perpendicular to the graph of $3x + y = 6$ that passes through the point $(-2, -4)$.   **[7.4]**

19. Calculate $\dfrac{f(x + h) - f(x)}{h}$ for the function $f(x) = x^2 - 3x$.   **[8.1]**

20. Graph $f(x) = 2x^2 + 5x - 3$.   **[8.3]**

21. The length of a rectangle is 5 feet greater than its width. A square whose side is equal to the length of the rectangle has an area that is 60 square feet greater than the area of the rectangle. Find the dimensions of the rectangle.   **[2.4]**

22. A small sign is 11 inches tall and 8 inches wide. The margin must be twice as wide at the top and bottom as it is at the sides. If 25 square inches are needed for the printed message, how wide should the margin be?   **[3.6]**

23. If a typical household in the Midwest uses 83 million BTUs of electricity annually and pays $1236, how much will a household that uses 70 million BTUs annually spend for energy?   **[4.8]**

24. A computer programmer is paid $15 per hour.

    a. Write an equation that expresses the programmer's wages (W) in terms of the number (n) of hours she works.

    b. Graph the equation.   **[7.5]**

25. Find the maximum area of a rectangle whose perimeter is 80 inches.   **[8.3]**

9 LOGARITHMIC FUNCTIONS

In Section 8.4 we considered exponential equations

$$y = b^x \qquad (b > 0, \quad b \neq 1)$$

and obtained values of b^x or y for given values of x. In this chapter we will see how we can obtain values for x for given values of y by using either tables or a scientific calculator.

Recall that it was necessary to use a scientific calculator in Section 8.4 to obtain values of b^x for noninteger values of x. In this chapter we will see how we can also obtain such values using tables.

9.1 DEFINITIONS AND NOTATIONS

In this section we shall first consider the inverse of the exponential function $y = b^x$; then we shall see how this inverse will enable us to find the exponent x for given values of the power b^x.

Inverse of the Exponential Function

Recall from Section 8.5 that we can obtain the inverse of a function by interchanging the components in each ordered pair of the function or by interchanging the variables in the defining equation of the function. Recall also that the graph of the inverse of a function is symmetric to the graph of the function about the line with equation $y = x$.

Because the exponential function

$$y = f(x) = b^x \qquad (b > 0, \quad b \neq 1) \tag{1}$$

is a one-to-one function, there is exactly one y associated with each x value as well as only one x value associated with each y. Therefore, the inverse of Function (1) is also a function, given by the equation

$$x = b^y \qquad (b > 0 \quad b \neq 1) \qquad \qquad (2)$$

At this point we do not know how to solve $x = b^y$ for y in terms of x, but we can still find out a lot about the function defined by Equation (2). Since the domain of Equation (1) is the same as the range of Equation (2) and the range of Equation (1) is the same as the domain of Equation (2), we have the positive real numbers for the domain of Equation (2), whereas the range is the set of real numbers.

The graphs of functions of the form in Equation (2) can be illustrated by the example

$$x = 10^y \qquad (x > 0)$$

We assign arbitrary values to y, say, $-2, -1, 0, 1$, and 2, and obtain the ordered pairs that can be plotted and connected with a smooth curve, as in Figure 9.1a.

$$
\begin{aligned}
&\text{If} \quad y = -2, \quad &\text{then} \quad &x = 10^{-2} = 0.01 \\
&\text{If} \quad y = -1, \quad &\text{then} \quad &x = 10^{-1} = 0.1 \\
&\text{If} \quad y = 0, \quad &\text{then} \quad &x = 10^{0} = 1 \\
&\text{If} \quad y = 1, \quad &\text{then} \quad &x = 10^{1} = 10 \\
&\text{If} \quad y = 2, \quad &\text{then} \quad &x = 10^{2} = 100
\end{aligned}
$$

Alternatively, we can reflect the graph of $y = 10^x$ about the graph of $y = x$ and obtain the same result, as shown in Figure 9.1b.

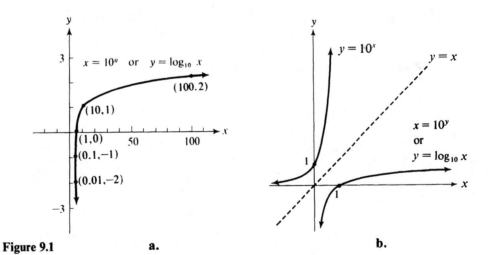

Figure 9.1   **a.**   **b.**

Logarithmic Notation   It is always useful to be able to write an equation in the two variables x and y so that the variable y is expressed explicitly in terms of the variable x. To do this in equations such as Equation (2), we use the notation

$$y = \log_b x \qquad (x > 0, \quad b > 0, \quad b \neq 1) \qquad \qquad (3)$$

where $\log_b x$ is read "logarithm to the base b of x" or "logarithm of x to the base b." The functions defined by such equations are called **logarithmic functions**.

This means that

$$x = b^y \quad \text{and} \quad y = \log_b x \qquad (4)$$

are equivalent equations.

In Section 8.4 we noted that the power $x = b^y$ and the base b were both restricted to *positive* numbers and also that $b \neq 1$. Hence, we have similar restrictions for $\log_b x$ in Equation (3).

Note that because $x = b^y$ and $y = \log_b x$ are equivalent equations, $\log_b x$ (equal to y) is an **exponent**. In particular, $\log_b x$ is the exponent on b such that the power equals x. Thus,

$$b^{\log_b x} = x$$

EXAMPLE 1

Express each logarithm as an integer.

a. $\log_{10} 100$ **b.** $\log_2 16$

Solutions

a. $\log_{10} 100$ is the *exponent* on 10 such that the power equals 100. Hence,

$$\log_{10} 100 = 2$$

$\log_2 16$ is the *exponent* on 2 such that the power equals 16. Hence,

$$\log_2 16 = 4$$

The two equations in (4) enable us to write exponential equations in logarithmic form.

EXAMPLE 2

a. $5^2 = 25$ is equivalent to $\log_5 25 = 2$.

b. $8^{1/3} = 2$ is equivalent to $\log_8 2 = \dfrac{1}{3}$.

c. $3^{-2} = \dfrac{1}{9}$ is equivalent to $\log_3 \dfrac{1}{9} = -2$.

Also, logarithmic statements may be written in exponential form.

EXAMPLE 3

a. $\log_{10} 100 = 2$ is equivalent to $10^2 = 100$.

b. $\log_3 81 = 4$ is equivalent to $3^4 = 81$.

c. $\log_2 \dfrac{1}{2} = -1$ is equivalent to $2^{-1} = \dfrac{1}{2}$.

Note that because $b^0 = 1$,

$$\log_b 1 = 0 \qquad (b > 0, \quad b \neq 1)$$

Furthermore, because $b^1 = b$,

$$\log_b b = 1 \qquad (b > 0, \quad b \neq 1)$$

For example,

$$\log_{10} 1 = 0, \qquad \log_5 1 = 0$$

$$\log_5 5 = 1, \quad \text{and} \quad \log_{10} 10 = 1$$

If two of the three variables in an equation of the form $y = \log_b x$ are known, we can determine the third variable either directly by using the definition of a logarithm or by first writing the equation in exponential form.

EXAMPLE 4   Solve for the unknown value in each equation.

a. $\log_2 x = 3$ **b.** $\log_b 2 = \dfrac{1}{2}$

Solutions   **a.** Write in exponential form.

$$2^3 = x$$

Solve for the variable.

$$x = 8$$

b. Write in exponential form.

$$b^{1/2} = 2$$

Solve for the variable.

$$(b^{1/2})^2 = 2^2$$

$$b = 4$$

E X E R C I S E   S E T   9.1

▲ *Find the value of each logarithm, using the fact that* $\log_b x$ *is the exponent on b such that the power is equal to x. See Example 1.*

1. $\log_7 49$

2. $\log_2 32$

3. $\log_4 64$

4. $\log_3 27$

5. $\log_3 \sqrt{3}$

6. $\log_5 \sqrt{5}$

7. $\log_5 \dfrac{1}{5}$

8. $\log_3 \dfrac{1}{3}$

9. $\log_2 2$

10. $\log_{10} 10$

11. $\log_{10} 100$

12. $\log_{10} 1$

13. $\log_{10} 0.1$

14. $\log_{10} 0.01$

▲ *Express each equation in logarithmic notation. See Example 2.*

15. $4^2 = 16$

16. $5^3 = 125$

17. $3^3 = 27$

18. $8^2 = 64$

19. $\left(\dfrac{1}{2}\right)^2 = \dfrac{1}{4}$

20. $\left(\dfrac{1}{3}\right)^2 = \dfrac{1}{9}$

21. $8^{-1/3} = \dfrac{1}{2}$

22. $64^{-1/6} = \dfrac{1}{2}$

23. $10^2 = 100$

24. $10^0 = 1$

25. $10^{-1} = 0.1$

26. $10^{-2} = 0.01$

▲ *Express each equation in exponential notation. See Example 3.*

27. $\log_2 64 = 6$

28. $\log_5 25 = 2$

29. $\log_3 9 = 2$

30. $\log_{16} 256 = 2$

31. $\log_{1/3} 9 = -2$

32. $\log_{1/2} 8 = -3$

33. $\log_{10} 1000 = 3$

34. $\log_{10} 1 = 0$

35. $\log_{10} 0.01 = -2$

36. $\log_{10} 0.0001 = -4$

▲ *Solve for the unknown value. See Example 4.*

37. $\log_3 9 = y$

38. $\log_5 125 = y$

39. $\log_b 8 = 3$

40. $\log_b 625 = 4$

41. $\log_4 x = 3$

42. $\log_{1/2} x = -5$

43. $\log_2 \dfrac{1}{8} = y$

44. $\log_5 \dfrac{1}{5} = y$

45. $\log_b 10 = \dfrac{1}{2}$

46. $\log_b 0.1 = -1$

47. $\log_2 x = 2$

48. $\log_{10} x = -3$

Miscellaneous Exercises

▲ *Simplify each expression.*

49. $\log_2(\log_4 16)$

50. $\log_5(\log_5 5)$

51. $\log_{10}[\log_3(\log_5 125)]$

52. $\log_{10}[\log_2(\log_3 9)]$

53. $\log_2[\log_2(\log_2 16)]$

54. $\log_4[\log_2(\log_3 81)]$

55. $\log_b(\log_b b)$ **56.** $\log_b(\log_a a^b)$

57. For what values of x is $\log_b(x - 9)$ defined?

58. For what values of x is $\log_b(x^2 - 4)$ defined?

▲ *Graph each logarithmic function.*

59. $y = \log_2 x$ **60.** $y = -\log_2 x$

61. $y = \log_3(x + 1)$ **62.** $y = \log_3(x - 2)$

9.2 | PROPERTIES OF LOGARITHMS

Because a logarithm is an exponent by definition, the three laws given here are valid for positive real numbers b $(b \neq 1)$, x_1, x_2, and all real numbers m.

$$\log_b(x_1 x_2) = \log_b x_1 + \log_b x_2 \tag{1}$$

For example,

$$\log_2 32 = \log_2(4 \cdot 8) = \log_2 4 + \log_2 8$$
$$\downarrow \qquad\qquad \downarrow \qquad \downarrow$$
$$5 \qquad\qquad = 2 \ + \ 3$$

The validity of (1) is established as follows: Since

$$x_1 = b^{\log_b x_1} \quad \text{and} \quad x_2 = b^{\log_b x_2}$$

then

$$x_1 x_2 = b^{\log_b x_1} \cdot b^{\log_b x_2}$$
$$= b^{\log_b x_1 + \log_b x_2}$$

and by the definition of a logarithm,

$$\log_b(x_1 x_2) = \log_b x_1 + \log_b x_2$$

The validity of Laws (2) and (3) can be established in a similar way.

$$\log_b \frac{x_2}{x_1} = \log_b x_2 - \log_b x_1 \tag{2}$$

For example,

$$\log_2 8 = \log_2 \frac{16}{2} = \log_2 16 - \log_2 2$$
$$\downarrow \qquad\qquad \downarrow \qquad \downarrow$$
$$3 \qquad\qquad = 4 \ - \ 1$$

$$\log_b(x_1)^m = m \log_b x_1 \qquad\qquad (3)$$

For example,

$$\log_2 64 = \log_2 (4)^3 = 3 \log_2 4$$

$$\downarrow \qquad\qquad\qquad \downarrow \ \ \downarrow$$

$$6 \qquad\qquad\qquad\qquad = 3 \cdot 2$$

We shall refer to the preceding equations as the first, second, and third laws of logarithms, respectively. These laws can be applied to rewrite expressions involving products, quotients, powers, and roots in forms that are sometimes more useful.

EXAMPLE 1 Expand $\log_b\left(\dfrac{x^3 y^{1/2}}{z}\right)^{1/5}$ in terms of simpler logarithmic expressions.

Solution First write

$$\frac{1}{5}\log_b\left(\frac{x^3 y^{1/2}}{z}\right)$$

by using the third law of logarithms. Then, by using the first and second laws,

$$\frac{1}{5}\log_b\left(\frac{x^3 y^{1/2}}{z}\right) = \frac{1}{5}\left[\log_b x^3 + \log_b y^{1/2} - \log_b z\right]$$

from which, by using the third law again,

$$\log_b\left(\frac{x^3 y^{1/2}}{z}\right)^{1/5} = \frac{1}{5}\left[3\log_b x + \frac{1}{2}\log_b y - \log_b z\right]$$

EXAMPLE 2 Expand $\log_b\sqrt{\dfrac{xy}{z}}$ in terms of simpler logarithmic expressions.

Solution First express $\sqrt{\dfrac{xy}{z}}$ using a fractional exponent.

$$\log_b\sqrt{\frac{xy}{z}} = \log_b\left(\frac{xy}{z}\right)^{1/2}$$

By the third law of logarithms,

$$\log_b\left(\frac{xy}{z}\right)^{1/2} = \frac{1}{2}\log_b\left(\frac{xy}{z}\right)$$

Now, by the first and second laws of logarithms,

$$\frac{1}{2}\log_b\left(\frac{xy}{z}\right) = \frac{1}{2}(\log_b x + \log_b y - \log_b z)$$

Therefore,

$$\log_b\sqrt{\frac{xy}{z}} = \frac{1}{2}(\log_b x + \log_b y - \log_b z)$$

EXAMPLE 3   Given that $\log_b 2 = 0.3010$ and $\log_b 3 = 0.4771$,   find the value of:

a. $\log_b 9$ **b.** $\log_b 12$

Solutions   First express $\log_b 9$ and $\log_b 12$ in terms of the known logarithmic quantities.

a. $\log_b 9 = \log_b 3^2$ **b.** $\log_b 12 = \log_b 4 + \log_b 3$
$\qquad\quad = 2\log_b 3$ $\qquad\qquad\quad = \log_b 2^2 + \log_b 3$
$\qquad\quad = 2(0.4771)$ $\qquad\qquad\quad = 2\log_b 2 + \log_b 3$
$\qquad\quad = 0.9542$ $\qquad\qquad\quad = 2(0.3010) + 0.4771$
$\qquad\qquad\qquad\qquad\qquad\qquad\qquad\qquad\quad = 1.0791$

We can also use the three laws of logarithms to write sums and differences of logarithmic quantities as a single term.

EXAMPLE 4   Express $\dfrac{1}{2}(\log_b x - \log_b y)$ as a single logarithm with a coefficient of 1.

Solution   By the second law of logarithms,

$$\frac{1}{2}(\log_b x - \log_b y) = \frac{1}{2}\log_b\left(\frac{x}{y}\right)$$

By the third law of logarithms,

$$\frac{1}{2}\log_b\left(\frac{x}{y}\right) = \log_b\left(\frac{x}{y}\right)^{1/2}$$

Therefore,

$$\frac{1}{2}(\log_b x - \log_b y) = \log_b\left(\frac{x}{y}\right)^{1/2}$$

COMMON ERRORS   *Note that*

$$\log_b(x + y) \neq \log_b x + \log_b y$$

and

$$\log_b\frac{x}{y} \neq \frac{\log_b x}{\log_b y}$$

Solving Logarithmic Equations   We sometimes may want to use the laws of logarithms to write the sum or difference of two logarithms as a single term in the solution of an equation, as illustrated in the following example.

EXAMPLE 5   Solve $\log_{10}(x + 1) + \log_{10}(x - 2) = 1$.

Solution   Using the first law of exponents to rewrite the left-hand member, we obtain
$$\log_{10}(x + 1)(x - 2) = 1$$
Then, writing this equation in exponential form, we have

$$(x + 1)(x - 2) = 10^1$$

from which

$$x^2 - x - 2 = 10$$
$$x^2 - x - 12 = 0$$
$$(x - 4)(x + 3) = 0$$

Thus,

$$x = 4 \quad \text{or} \quad x = -3$$

The number -3 is not a solution of the original equation: The terms $\log_{10}(x + 1)$ and $\log_{10}(x - 2)$ are not defined for $x = -3$ because $x + 1$ and $x - 2$ are *negative* for $x = -3$.

So far in this chapter, we have generalized the discussion of the properties of the exponential and logarithmic functions for any base $b > 0$, $b \neq 1$. In Sections 9.3 and 9.4 we shall find values for the powers and logarithms with base 10 and base e that occur most often in applied problems. In Section 9.3 we shall use tables to find such values, and in Section 9.4 we shall see how a scientific calculator can be used for the same purpose.

EXERCISE SET 9.2

▲ *Use Properties (1), (2), and (3) on pages 250–251 to write each expression in terms of simpler logarithmic quantities. Assume that all variables denote positive real numbers. See Examples 1 and 2.*

1. $\log_b (2x)$
2. $\log_b (xy)$
3. $\log_b (3xy)$
4. $\log_b (4yz)$
5. $\log_b \left(\dfrac{x}{y} \right)$
6. $\log_b \left(\dfrac{y}{x} \right)$
7. $\log_b \left(\dfrac{xy}{z} \right)$
8. $\log_b \left(\dfrac{x}{yz} \right)$
9. $\log_b x^3$
10. $\log_b x^{1/3}$
11. $\log_b \sqrt{x}$
12. $\log_b \sqrt[5]{y}$
13. $\log_b \sqrt[3]{x^2}$
14. $\log_b \sqrt{x^3}$
15. $\log_b (x^2 y^3)$
16. $\log_b (x^{1/3} y^2)$
17. $\log_b \left(\dfrac{x^{1/2} y}{z^2} \right)$
18. $\log_b \left(\dfrac{xy^3}{z^{1/2}} \right)$
19. $\log_{10} \sqrt[3]{\dfrac{xy^2}{z}}$
20. $\log_{10} \sqrt[5]{\dfrac{x^2 y}{z^3}}$
21. $\log_{10} \left(x \sqrt{\dfrac{x}{y}} \right)$
22. $\log_{10} \left(2y \sqrt[3]{\dfrac{x}{y}} \right)$
23. $\log_{10} \left(2\pi \sqrt{\dfrac{l}{g}} \right)$
24. $\log_{10} \sqrt{\dfrac{2L}{R^2}}$
25. $\log_{10} \sqrt{(s - a)(s - b)}$
26. $\log_{10} \sqrt{s^2(s - a)^3}$

▲ *Given that* $\log_b 2 = 0.3010$, $\log_b 3 = 0.4771$, *and* $\log_b 5 = 0.6990$, *find the value of each expression. See Example 3.*

27. $\log_b 6$
28. $\log_b 10$
29. $\log_b \dfrac{2}{5}$
30. $\log_b \dfrac{3}{2}$
31. $\log_b 9$
32. $\log_b 25$
33. $\log_b \dfrac{15}{2}$
34. $\log_b \dfrac{6}{5}$
35. $\log_b (0.002)^3$
36. $\log_b \sqrt{50}$
37. $\log_b 75$
38. $\log_b \dfrac{0.08}{15}$

▲ *Express as a single logarithm with a coefficient of 1. See Example 4.*

39. $\log_b 8 - \log_b 2$
40. $\log_b 5 + \log_b 2$
41. $\dfrac{1}{2} \log_b 16 + 2 \log_b 2 - \log_b 8$
42. $\dfrac{1}{2} (\log_b 6 + 2 \log_b 4 - \log_b 2)$
43. $2 \log_b x - 3 \log_b y$
44. $\dfrac{1}{4} \log_b x + \dfrac{3}{4} \log_b y$

45. $3 \log_b x + \log_b y - 2 \log_b z$

46. $\dfrac{1}{3}(\log_b x + \log_b y - 2 \log_b z)$

47. $\dfrac{1}{2}(\log_{10} y + \log_{10} x - 2 \log_{10} z)$

48. $\dfrac{1}{2}(\log_{10} x - 3 \log_{10} y - \log_{10} z)$

49. $-2 \log_b x$ **50.** $-\log_b x$

▲ *Solve each logarithmic equation. See Example 5.*

51. $\log_{10} x + \log_{10} 2 = 3$
52. $\log_{10}(x - 1) - \log_{10} 4 = 2$
53. $\log_{10} x + \log_{10}(x + 21) = 2$
54. $\log_{10}(x + 3) + \log_{10} x = 1$
55. $\log_{10}(x + 2) + \log_{10}(x - 1) = 1$
56. $\log_{10}(x + 3) - \log_{10}(x - 1) = 1$

Miscellaneous Exercises

57. Show by a numerical example that $\log_{10}(x + y)$ is not equivalent to $\log_{10} x + \log_{10} y$.

58. Show by a numerical example that $\log_{10} \dfrac{x}{y}$ is not equivalent to $\dfrac{\log_{10} x}{\log_{10} y}$.

▲ *Verify that each statement is true.*

59. $\log_b 4 + \log_b 8 = \log_b 64 - \log_b 2$
60. $\log_b 24 - \log_b 2 = \log_b 3 + \log_b 4$
61. $2 \log_b 6 - \log_b 9 = 2 \log_b 2$
62. $4 \log_b 3 - 2 \log_b 3 = \log_b 9$
63. $\dfrac{1}{2} \log_b 12 - \dfrac{1}{2} \log_b 3 = \dfrac{1}{3} \log_b 8$
64. $\dfrac{1}{4} \log_b 8 + \dfrac{1}{4} \log_b 2 = \log_b 2$

9.3 | **USING TABLES***

For $b > 0$ and $b \neq 1$, values for $b^x (x$ a real number$)$ and $\log_b x$ $(x > 0)$ can be obtained by using prepared tables in conjunction with the laws of logarithms. Because we are familiar with the number 10 as the base of our numeration system, we shall first give our attention to logarithms and powers to the base 10. This was the base that was first used in the invention of logarithms to perform computations in astronomy and navigation.

Common Logarithms

Recall from Equation (4) on page 248 that $\log_{10} x$ is the exponent that must be placed on 10 so that the resulting power is x. Values for $\log_{10} x$ are sometimes called **common logarithms**.

Values for $\log_{10} 10^k$, k an Integer

Some values of $\log_{10} x$ can be obtained simply by considering the definition of a logarithm, while other values require tables. Let us first consider values of $\log_{10} x$ for all values of x that are integral powers of 10. These can be obtained by inspection.

$$
\begin{array}{lll}
\text{Since} & 10^3 = 1000, & \log_{10} 1000 = 3 \\
\text{since} & 10^2 = 100, & \log_{10} 100 = 2 \\
\text{since} & 10^1 = 10, & \log_{10} 10 = 1 \\
\text{since} & 10^0 = 1, & \log_{10} 1 = 0 \\
\text{since} & 10^{-1} = 0.1, & \log_{10} 0.1 = -1 \\
\text{since} & 10^{-2} = 0.01, & \log_{10} 0.01 = -2 \\
\text{since} & 10^{-3} = 0.001, & \log_{10} 0.001 = -3
\end{array}
$$

---

*The topics covered in this section are also covered in Section 9.4 using a calculator instead of tables.

Notice that the logarithm of a power of 10 is simply the exponent on the base 10. For example,

$$\log_{10} 100 = \log_{10} 10^2 = 2$$
$$\log_{10} 0.01 = \log_{10} 10^{-2} = -2$$

and so on.

EXAMPLE 1

Find each logarithm.

a. $\log_{10} 10^6$ **b.** $\log_{10} 10^{-5}$

Solutions

By definition:

a. $\log_{10} 10^6$ is the exponent on 10 so that the power equals 10^6. Hence
$$\log_{10} 10^6 = 6$$

b. $\log_{10} 10^{-5}$ is the exponent on 10 so that the power equals 10^{-5}. Hence,
$$\log_{10} 10^{-5} = -5$$

Values for $\log_{10} x$, $1 < x < 10$

Table II in Appendix D gives values for $\log_{10} x$ for $1 < x < 10$. Consider the following excerpt from the table. Each number in the column headed x represents the first two digits of the numeral for x, while each of the other column-head numbers represents the third significant digit of the numeral for x. The number located at the intersection of a row and a column forms the logarithm of x. For example, to find $\log_{10} 4.25$, we look at the intersection of the row containing 4.2 under x and the column containing 5. Thus,

$$\log_{10} 4.25 = 0.6284$$

Similarly,

$$\log_{10} 4.02 = 0.6042$$
$$\log_{10} 4.49 = 0.6522$$

and so on.

x	0	1	2	3	4	5	6	7	8	9
3.8	.5798	.5809	.5821	.5832	.5843	.5855	.5866	.5877	.5888	.5899
3.9	.5911	.5922	.5933	.5944	.5955	.5966	.5977	.5988	.5999	.6010
4.0	.6021	.6031	.6042	.6053	.6064	.6075	.6085	.6096	.6107	.6117
4.1	.6128	.6138	.6149	.6160	.6170	.6180	.6191	.6201	.6212	.6222
4.2	.6232	.6243	.6253	.6263	.6274	.6284	.6294	.6304	.6314	.6325
4.3	.6335	.6345	.6355	.6365	.6375	.6385	.6395	.6405	.6415	.6425
4.4	.6435	.6444	.6454	.6464	.6474	.6484	.6493	.6503	.6513	.6522
4.5	.6532	.6542	.6551	.6561	.6571	.6580	.6590	.6599	.6609	.6618
4.6	.6628	.6637	.6646	.6656	.6665	.6675	.6684	.6693	.6702	.6712

The values in the tables are rational-number approximations of irrational numbers. We shall follow customary usage and write = instead of ≈.

EXAMPLE 2 | Find an approximation for each logarithm.

a. $\log_{10} 1.68$ **b.** $\log_{10} 4.3$

Solutions | Use Table II in Appendix D.

a. $\log_{10} 1.168 = 0.2253$ **b.** $\log_{10} 4\,3 = .0.6335$

Values for $\log_{10} x$, $x > 10$

Now suppose we wish to find $\log_{10} x$ for values of x outside the range of the table—that is, for $x > 10$ or $0 < x < 1$ (see Figure 9.2). This can be done quite readily by first representing the number in scientific notation and then applying the first law of logarithms.

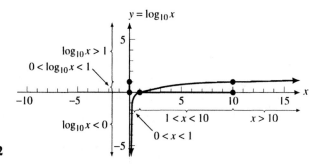

Figure 9.2

EXAMPLE 3 |
a. $\log_{10} 42.5$
$= \log_{10}(4.25 \times 10^1)$
$= \log_{10} 4.25 + \log_{10} 10^1$
$= 0.6284 + 1$
$= 1.6284$

b. $\log_{10} 425$
$= \log_{10}(4.25 \times 10^2)$
$= \log_{10} 4.25 + \log_{10} 10^2$
$= 0.6284 + 2$
$= 2.6284$

c. $\log_{10} 4250$
$= \log_{10}(4.25 \times 10^3)$
$= \log_{10} 4.25 + \log_{10} 10^3$
$= 0.6284 + 3$
$= 3.6284$

d. $\log_{10} 42{,}500$
$= \log_{10}(4.25 \times 10^4)$
$= \log_{10} 4.25 + \log_{10} 10^4$
$= 0.6284 + 4$
$= 4.6284$

Observe that the decimal portion of the logarithms in Examples 3a–d is always 0.6284 and *the integral portion is the exponent on 10 when the number is written in scientific notation*. This process can be reduced to a mechanical one by considering $\log_{10} x$ to consist of two parts, an *integral part* (called the **characteristic**) and a *nonnegative decimal fraction part* (called the **mantissa**). Thus, the table of values for $\log_{10} x$ for $1 < x < 10$ can be looked upon as a table of mantissas for $\log_{10} x$ for all $x > 0$.

In Examples 3a, 3b, 3c, and 3d, where $x > 10$, the mantissa in each case is 0.6284 and the characteristics are 1, 2, 3, and 4, respectively.

Values for $\log_{10} x$, $0 < x < 1$

Now consider an example of the form $\log_{10} x$ for $0 < x < 1$ (see Figure 9.2). To find $\log_{10} 0.00425$, we write

$$\log_{10} 0.00425 = \log_{10}(4.25 \times 10^{-3})$$
$$= \log_{10} 4.25 + \log_{10} 10^{-3}$$

We find from the table that $\log_{10} 4.25 = 0.6284$. Upon adding 0.6284 to the characteristic -3, we obtain

$$\log_{10} 0.00425 = 0.6284 + (-3)$$
$$= -2.3716$$

where the decimal part of the logarithm is no longer 0.6284. The decimal part is -0.3716, a negative number.

If we want to use the table, which contains only positive entries, it is customary to write the logarithm in a form in which the decimal part is positive. In the preceding example, we write

$$\log_{10} 0.00425 = 0.6284 - 3$$

where the decimal part is positive. Because -3 can be written $1 - 4$, $2 - 5$, $3 - 6$, $7 - 10$, and so on, the forms $1.6284 - 4$, $2.6284 - 5$, $3.6284 - 6$, $7.6284 - 10$, and so on, are equally valid representations of the desired logarithm. It will sometimes be convenient to use these alternative forms. We can add the positive decimal and negative integer in any of these forms to obtain -2.3716, in which the integer and decimal parts are both negative.

E X A M P L E 4

a. $\log_{10} 0.294$
$= \log_{10}(2.94 \times 10^{-1})$
$= \log_{10} 2.94 + \log_{10} 10^{-1}$
$= 0.4683 - 1$
$= -0.5317$

b. $\log_{10} 0.00294$
$= \log_{10}(2.94 \times 10^{-3})$
$= \log_{10} 2.94 + \log_{10} 10^{-3}$
$= 0.4683 - 3$
$= -2.5317$

Antilog$_{10}$ N

Given a value for an exponent, $\log_{10} x$, we can use Table II in Appendix D to find the power x by reversing the process described to find the logarithm of a number. In this case the power x is called the **antilogarithm** of $\log_{10} x$. For example, if

$$\log_{10} x = 0.4409$$

then

$$x = \text{antilog}_{10} 0.4409$$

which can be obtained by locating 0.4409 in the body of Table II and observing that

$$\log_{10} 2.76 = 0.4409$$

or

$$\text{antilog}_{10}\, 0.4409 = 2.76$$

If the $\log_{10} x$ is greater than 1, it can first be written as the sum of a positive decimal (the **mantissa**) and a positive integer (the **characteristic**). Antilog$_{10}\, x$ can then be written as the product of a number between 1 and 10 and a power of 10.

EXAMPLE 5

a. If $\log_{10} x = 2.7364$,   then

$$x = \text{antilog}_{10}\, 2.7364 = \text{antilog}_{10}(0.7364 + 2)$$

Locate the mantissa 0.7364 in the body of Table II in Appendix D and determine the associated antilog$_{10}$ (a number between 1 and 10). Write the characteristic 2 as an exponent on the factor with base 10.

$$x = \text{antilog}_{10}(\underbrace{0.7364} + 2)$$
$$= 5.45 \times 10^2$$
$$= 545$$

b. If $\log_{10} x = 0.4409 - 3$,   then

$$x = \text{antilog}_{10}(\underbrace{0.4409} - 3)$$
$$= 2.76 \times 10^{-3}$$
$$= 0.00276$$

If the decimal part of $\log_{10} x$ is negative and we wish to use the table to obtain x, we cannot use the table directly. However, we can first write $\log_{10} x$ equivalently with a positive decimal part. For example, to find

$$\text{antilog}_{10}(-0.4522) \qquad \text{or} \qquad \text{antilog}_{10}(-2.4522)$$

we can first add $(+1 - 1)$ to write -0.4522 as

$$-0.4522 + 1 - 1 = 0.5478 - 1$$

and add $(+3 - 3)$ to write -2.4522 as

$$-2.4522 + 3 - 3 = 0.5478 - 3$$

and then use the tables. Thus,

$$\text{antilog}_{10}(-0.4522) = \text{antilog}_{10}(0.5478 - 1)$$
$$= 3.53 \times 10^{-1} = 0.353$$

and

$$\text{antilog}_{10}(-2.4522) = \text{antilog}_{10}(0.5478 - 3)$$
$$= 3.53 \times 10^{-3} = 0.00353$$

EXAMPLE 6 Use Table II in Appendix D to find the value of x.

a. $\log_{10} x = -0.7282$

b. $\log_{10} x = -1.4634$

Solutions

a. $x = \text{antilog}_{10}(-0.7282)$
$= \text{antilog}_{10}(-0.7282 + 1 - 1)$
$= \text{antilog}_{10}(0.2718 - 1)$
$= 1.87 \times 10^{-1} = 0.187$

b. $x = \text{antilog}_{10}(-1.4634)$
$= \text{antilog}_{10}(-1.4634 + 2 - 2)$
$= \text{antilog}_{10}(0.5366 - 2)$
$= 3.44 \times 10^{-2} = 0.0344$

In Example 6 the mantissas, 0.2718 and 0.5366, were listed in Table II of Appendix D. If we seek the common logarithm of a number that is not an entry in the table (for example, $\log_{10} 23.42$) or if we seek x when $\log_{10} x$ is not an entry in the table, we shall simply use the entry in the table that is closest to the value that we seek.

Powers to the Base 10 By the definition of a logarithm,

$$P = 10^E$$

can be written in logarithmic form as

$$\log_{10} P = E$$

from which we see that the power P is the antilogarithm of the exponent E,

$$P = \text{antilog}_{10} E$$

Since $P = 10^E$,

$$10^E = \text{antilog}_{10} E$$

and we can obtain a power 10^E simply by finding the antilogarithm of the exponent E.

EXAMPLE 7 Compute each power.

a. $10^{0.2148}$

b. $10^{-1.6345}$

Solutions

a. $10^{0.2148}$
$= \text{antilog}_{10} 0.2148$
$= 1.64$

b. $10^{-1.6345}$
$= \text{antilog}_{10}(-1.6345)$
$= \text{antilog}_{10}(-1.6345 + 2 - 2)$
$= \text{antilog}_{10}(0.3645 - 2)$
$= 2.32 \times 10^{-2}$

Powers to the Base e The number $e \approx 2.7182818$ is an irrational number that has applications in business, biological and physical sciences, and engineering. Because of its importance, special tables have been prepared for both e^x and $\log_e x$. Table III in Appendix D gives approximations for powers e^x and e^{-x} for $0 \leqslant x \leqslant 1.00$ in 0.01 intervals and for $1.00 < x \leqslant 10.00$ in 0.1 intervals.

EXAMPLE 8 Find an approximation for each power.

a. $e^{2.4}$ **b.** $e^{-4.7}$

Solutions Use Table III in Appendix D.

a. $e^{2.4} = 11.023$ **b.** $e^{-4.7} = 0.0091$

Although we can obtain values for e^x and e^{-x} outside the interval 0 to 10 by using the table along with the first law of exponents, at this time the function values in the table over this interval will be adequate for our work.

Natural Logarithms, ln x

The most-used values for $\log_e x$ $(x > 0)$ are printed in Table IV of Appendix D. These values, like those for e^x, e^{-x}, and $\log_{10} x$, are *approximations* that are accurate to the number of decimals shown. The symbol $\log_e x$ is often written as **ln x** and read as "**natural logarithm of x**." Unlike Table II for common logarithms, which provides only the decimal part of $\log_{10} x$, the table for natural logarithms gives the entire value for ln x, both the integral and decimal portions.

EXAMPLE 9 Use Table IV in Appendix D.

a. $\ln 6.6 = 1.8871$ **b.** $\ln 0.7 = -0.3567$

If we seek a value for e^x or ln x for a value of x between two entries in the tables, we shall simply use the entry in the table that is closest to the value that we seek.

Powers to the Base e, Antilogarithms

We noted on page 259 that

$$\text{antilog}_{10} x = 10^x$$

Similarly,

$$\text{antilog}_e x = e^x$$

Hence we can obtain values for x for given values of ln x by using Table III in Appendix D.

EXAMPLE 10 **a.** $\ln x = 1.3$ **b.** $\ln x = -0.47$

Solutions **a.** $\ln x = 1.3$ is equivalent to   **b.** $\ln x = -0.47$ is equivalent to

$$x = e^{1.3}$$ $$x = e^{-0.47}$$
$$= 3.6693$$ $$= 0.6250$$

As was noted earlier in this section, a power to the base b is called the antilog$_b$ of the exponent. Thus in Example 10a,

$$x = e^{1.3} = \text{antilog}_e 1.3$$
$$= 3.6693$$

E X E R C I S E   S E T   9.3

▲ *Find each logarithm by inspection. See Example 1.*

1. $\log_{10} 10^2$
2. $\log_{10} 10^4$
3. $\log_{10} 10^{-4}$
4. $\log_{10} 10^{-6}$
5. $\log_{10} 10^0$
6. $\log_{10} 10^n$

▲ *Find an approximation for each logarithm using Table II in Appendix D. See Examples 2–4.*

7. $\log_{10} 6.73$
8. $\log_{10} 891$
9. $\log_{10} 83.7$
10. $\log_{10} 21.4$
11. $\log_{10} 317$
12. $\log_{10} 219$
13. $\log_{10} 0.813$
14. $\log_{10} 0.00214$
15. $\log_{10} 0.08$
16. $\log_{10} 0.000413$
17. $\log_{10}(2.48 \times 10^2)$
18. $\log_{10}(5.39 \times 10^{-3})$

▲ *Solve for x using Table II in Appendix D. See Example 5.*

19. $\log_{10} x = 0.6128$
20. $\log_{10} x = 0.2504$
21. $\log_{10} x = 1.5647$
22. $\log_{10} x = 3.9258$
23. $\log_{10} x = 0.8075 - 2$
24. $\log_{10} x = 0.9722 - 3$
25. $\log_{10} x = 7.8562 - 10$
26. $\log_{10} x = 1.8155 - 4$

▲ *For Exercises 27–32, see Example 6.*

27. $\log_{10} x = -0.5272$
28. $\log_{10} x = -0.4123$
29. $\log_{10} x = -1.2984$
30. $\log_{10} x = -1.0545$
31. $\log_{10} x = -2.6882$
32. $\log_{10} x = -2.0670$

▲ *Compute each power. See Example 7.*

33. $10^{0.8762}$
34. $10^{1.6405}$
35. $10^{2.8943}$
36. $10^{4.3766}$
37. $10^{-1.4473}$
38. $10^{-2.0958}$

▲ *Find an approximation for each power. See Example 8.*

39. $e^{0.43}$
40. $e^{0.62}$
41. $e^{-0.57}$
42. $e^{-0.08}$
43. $e^{1.5}$
44. $e^{2.6}$
45. $e^{-2.4}$
46. $e^{-1.2}$

▲ *Find each logarithm. See Example 9.*

47. $\ln 3.9$
48. $\ln 6.3$
49. $\ln 16$
50. $\ln 55$
51. $\ln 0.4$
52. $\ln 0.7$

▲ *Find each value of x. See Example 10.*

53. $\ln x = 0.16$
54. $\ln x = 0.25$
55. $\ln x = 1.8$
56. $\ln x = 2.4$
57. $\ln x = 4.5$
58. $\ln x = 6.0$

Miscellaneous Exercises

▲ *Find each antilogarithm to the nearest hundredth.*

59. $\text{antilog}_{10} 0.4518$
60. $\text{antilog}_{10}(-0.9263)$
61. $\text{antilog}_{10} 2.8543$
62. $\text{antilog}_{10}(-1.5888)$
63. $\text{antilog}_e 1.0942$
64. $\text{antilog}_e(-2.1170)$

9.4   USING CALCULATORS

c Scientific calculators enable us to obtain function values for exponential and logarithmic functions more efficiently than we could obtain them by using tables.

A great variety of calculators exist. We shall need one that has at least one of the keys $\boxed{\text{LOG}}$, $\boxed{\text{LN}}$, $\boxed{e^x}$ and the inverse operation connected with that key. Many scientific calculators contain all three keys and may contain $\boxed{10^x}$ and $\boxed{y^x}$ keys also.

$\log_{10} 10^k$, k an integer Values of $\log_{10} x$, called **logarithms to the base 10** or **common logarithms**, can readily be obtained for all $x > 0$ by using a calculator. However, values for $\log_{10} x$, where *x is an integral power* of 10, can be obtained directly from the definition of a logarithm. You should obtain such values *without using your calculator.*

$$\begin{array}{lll} \text{since} & 10^3 = 1000, & \log_{10} 1000 = 3 \\ \text{since} & 10^2 = 100, & \log_{10} 100 \;\;= 2 \\ \text{since} & 10^1 = 10, & \log_{10} 10 \;\;\;\;= 1 \\ \text{since} & 10^0 = 1, & \log_{10} 1 \;\;\;\;\;= 0 \\ \text{since} & 10^{-1} = 0.1, & \log_{10} 0.1 \;\;= -1 \\ \text{since} & 10^{-2} = 0.01, & \log_{10} 0.01 \;= -2 \\ \text{since} & 10^{-3} = 0.001, & \log_{10} 0.001 = -3 \end{array}$$

Notice that the logarithm of a power of 10 is simply the exponent on the base 10. For example,

$$\log_{10} 100 = \log_{10} 10^2 = \mathbf{2}$$
$$\log_{10} 0.01 = \log_{10} 10^{-2} = \mathbf{-2}$$

and so on. More generally, we have that

$$\log_b b^x = x$$

EXAMPLE 1   Find each logarithm.

a. $\log_{10} 10^6$ **b.** $\log_{10} 10^{-5}$

Solutions   By definition,

a. $\log_{10} 10^6$ is the exponent on 10 so that the power equals 10^6. Hence
$$\log_{10} 10^6 = 6$$

b. $\log_{10} 10^{-5}$ is the exponent on 10 so that the power equals 10^{-5}. Hence,
$$\log_{10} 10^{-5} = -5$$

Your ability to determine the logarithms of powers of 10 by inspection will help you estimate function values $\log_{10} x$ when x is not a power of 10. Note from Figure 9.2, which is reproduced here from Section 9.3, that

if	$0 < x \leqslant 1,$	then	$\log_{10} x \leqslant 0$
if	$1 < x \leqslant 10,$	then	$0 < \log_{10} x \leqslant 1$
if	$10 < x \leqslant 100,$	then	$1 < \log_{10} x \leqslant 2$
if	$100 < x \leqslant 1000,$	then	$2 < \log_{10} x \leqslant 3$

and so on.

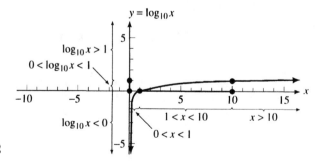

Figure 9.2

$\log_{10} x,\ x > 0$ On a calculator the function key $\boxed{\text{LOG}}$ is ordinarily used to find values for $\log_{10} x$ ($x > 0$). Some calculators do not have a $\boxed{\text{LOG}}$ key but do have a $\boxed{\text{LN}}$ key. In such cases, function values for $\log_{10} n$ can be obtained by finding the quotient $\ln n / \ln 10$. The reason why this is valid is discussed in Section 9.5.

EXAMPLE 2

Find each logarithm.

a. $\log_{10} 23.4$ **b.** $\log_{10} 0.00402$

Solutions

a. Using the $\boxed{\text{LOG}}$ key, we obtain

$$23.4 \boxed{\text{LOG}} = 1.3692$$

Or, using the fact that $\log_{10} 23.4 = \ln 23.4/\ln 10$, we obtain

$$23.4 \boxed{\text{LN}} \boxed{\div} 10 \boxed{\text{LN}} \boxed{=} 1.3692$$

b. Using the $\boxed{\text{LOG}}$ key, we obtain

$$0.00402 \boxed{\text{LOG}} = -2.3958$$

Or, using the fact that $\log_{10} 0.00402 = \ln 0.00402/\ln 10$, we obtain

$$0.00402 \boxed{\text{LN}} \boxed{\div} 10 \boxed{\text{LN}} \boxed{=} -2.3958$$

Note that in Example 2b the integer part of the logarithm (-2) is negative and *the decimal part (-0.3958) is also negative.* Contrary to our procedure when using tables, when we use a calculator, it is not necessary to maintain a positive decimal part of a logarithm.

Furthermore, it should be understood that the values obtained by using a calculator are, in general, approximations for irrational numbers even though we shall, as is customary, use the "$=$" sign.

Power, 10^x

Some calculators have a $\boxed{10^x}$ key. In this case the power is readily computed. If a calculator does not have this key, the power can be computed by using the $\boxed{\text{LOG}}$ key in conjunction with the $\boxed{\text{INV}}$ key (or $\boxed{\text{2ND}}$ function key). This is possible because the logarithmic function is the inverse of the exponential function. Alternatively, the $\boxed{y^x}$ key can be used. In this case the $\boxed{=}$ key must be pressed as shown in the following example. We shall round off readings of powers of 10^x to five significant digits.

EXAMPLE 3

Compute $10^{2.34}$.

Solution

Use the $\boxed{10^x}$ key to obtain

$$2.34 \boxed{10^x} = 218.78$$

or use the $\boxed{\text{INV}}$ (or second function) key to obtain

$$2.34 \boxed{\text{INV}} \boxed{\text{LOG}} = 218.78$$

or use the $\boxed{y^x}$ key to obtain

$$10 \boxed{y^x} 2.34 \boxed{=} 218.78$$

Note that in Example 3 we could use different keystrokes because "raising to the power of" and "taking the logarithm base of" are inverse operations.

Given a value for $\log_{10} x$, we can find x by first expressing the logarithm in exponential form.

EXAMPLE 4   If $\log_{10} x = 2.34$, then, by the definition of a logarithm,
$$x = 10^{2.34} = 218.78$$

A power to the base b is sometimes called the **antilog,** of the exponent. Hence, in Example 4,
$$x = 10^{2.34} = \text{antilog}_{10} 2.34$$

EXAMPLE 5   Find each value of x.

a. $\log_{10} x = 2.4211$ b. $\log_{10} x = -1.2147$

Solutions

a. $\log_{10} x = 2.4211$
is equivalent to $x = 10^{2.4211}$;
$\text{antilog}_{10} 2.4211 = 263.69$.

b. $\log_{10} x = -1.2147$
is equivalent to $x = 10^{-1.2147}$;
$\text{antilog}_{10}(-1.2147) = 0.06100$.

Base e   The second base in general use with exponential and logarithmic functions is the irrational number $e \approx 2.7182818$. This number has applications in business, biological and physical sciences, and engineering.

ln x, $x > 0$ Approximations for $\log_e x$, commonly written as **ln x**, are called **natural logarithms** and can be obtained on most calculators by using the $\boxed{\text{LN}}$ key. We shall round off the readings to five significant digits.

EXAMPLE 6   Find each logarithm.

a. $\ln 6.6$ b. $\ln 0.7$

Solutions   a. $6.6 \boxed{\text{LN}} = 1.8871$ b. $0.7 \boxed{\text{LN}} = -0.35667$

Power, e^x   Some calculators have a special key for e^x. If your calculator does not, this power can be obtained by using the $\boxed{\text{LN}}$ key in conjunction with the $\boxed{\text{INV}}$ key (or $\boxed{\text{2ND}}$ function key).

EXAMPLE 7   Find each power.

a. $e^{2.4}$ b. $e^{-4.7}$

Solution

a. $2.4 \boxed{e^x} = 11.023$
or
$2.4 \boxed{\text{INV}} \boxed{\text{LN}} = 11.023$

b. $-4.7 \boxed{e^x} = 0.0090953$
or
$-4.7 \boxed{\text{INV}} \boxed{\text{LN}} = 0.0090953$

Given a value for an exponent in the form of a natural logarithm, we can obtain the power by first expressing the logarithm in exponential form. This procedure is the same one we used in examples 4 and 5 for exponents that were written as common logarithms.

EXAMPLE 8 | Find each value of x.

a. $\ln x = 2.4$ **b.** $\ln x = -4.7$

Solutions   **a.** $\ln x = 2.4$ is equivalent to   **b.** $\ln x = -4.7$ is equivalent to
             $x = e^{2.4} = 11.023$. $x = e^{-4.7} = 0.0090953$.

E X E R C I S E   S E T   9.4

▲ *Find each logarithm by inspection. See Example 1.*

1. $\log_{10} 10^2$
2. $\log_{10} 10^4$
3. $\log_{10} 10^{-4}$
4. $\log_{10} 10^{-6}$
5. $\log_{10} 10$
6. $\log_{10} 1$
7. $\log_{10} 10{,}000$
8. $\log_{10} 0.001$

▲ *Use a calculator in all of the following exercises.*
🄲 *Round off each reading to five significant digits.*

▲ *Find each logarithm. See Example 2.*

9. $\log_{10} 54.3$
10. $\log_{10} 27.9$
11. $\log_{10} 2344$
12. $\log_{10} 1476$
13. $\log_{10} 0.073$
14. $\log_{10} 0.00614$
15. $\log_{10} 0.6942$
16. $\log_{10} 0.0104$

▲ *Find each power. See Example 3.*

17. $10^{1.62}$
18. $10^{0.43}$
19. $10^{-0.87}$
20. $10^{-1.31}$
21. $10^{2.113}$
22. $10^{3.141}$
23. $10^{-0.2354}$
24. $10^{-2.0413}$

▲ *Solve for x. See Examples 4 and 5.*

25. $\log_{10} x = 1.41$
26. $\log_{10} x = 2.3$
27. $\log_{10} x = 0.52$
28. $\log_{10} x = 0.8$
29. $\log_{10} x = -1.3$
30. $\log_{10} x = -1.69$

▲ *Find each logarithm. See Example 6.*

31. $\ln 3.9$
32. $\ln 6.3$
33. $\ln 16$
34. $\ln 55$
35. $\ln 6.4$
36. $\ln 0.7$

▲ *Find each power. See Example 7.*

37. $e^{0.4}$
38. $e^{0.73}$
39. $e^{2.34}$
40. $e^{3.16}$
41. $e^{-1.2}$
42. $e^{-2.3}$
43. $e^{-0.4}$
44. $e^{-0.62}$

▲ *Solve for x. See Example 8.*

45. $\ln x = 1.42$
46. $\ln x = 2.03$
47. $\ln x = 0.63$
48. $\ln x = 0.59$
49. $\ln x = -2.6$
50. $\ln x = -3.4$

Miscellaneous Exercises

▲ *Find each antilogarithm.*

51. $\text{antilog}_{10} 0.7312$
52. $\text{antilog}_{10}(-0.6314)$
53. $\text{antilog}_{10} 2.6141$
54. $\text{antilog}_{10}(-1.7421)$
55. $\text{antilog}_e 1.6342$
56. $\text{antilog}_e(-2.4231)$

9.5 | SOLVING EXPONENTIAL EQUATIONS

We can now use the definition of a logarithm and Table II or Table IV in Appendix D or a calculator to obtain solutions to some simple exponential equations in which the variable is part of the exponent.

EXAMPLE 1 | Solve each equation.

a. $10^x = 2.73$ **b.** $e^x = 0.24$

Solutions   **a.** $10^x = 2.73$ is equivalent to   **b.** $e^x = 0.24$ is equivalent to
             $x = \log_{10} 2.73 = 0.436$ $x = \ln 0.24 = -1.43$

In more complicated equations it is sometimes necessary to rewrite the equation first in an equivalent form so that the power is the only term in one member and has a coefficient of one. We can then write the equation in logarithm form.

EXAMPLE 2

Solve $4.31 = 1.73 + 2 \cdot 10^{1.2x}$.

Solution

Adding -1.73 to each member, we have

$$2.58 = 2 \cdot 10^{1.2x}$$

from which, by dividing each member by 2, we get

$$1.29 = 10^{1.2x}$$

The equivalent logarithmic equation is

$$1.2\,x = \log_{10} 1.29$$

Hence, by dividing each member by 1.2 and using Table II in Appendix D or a scientific calculator, we get

$$x = \frac{\log_{10} 1.29}{1.2} = 0.0922$$

We may obtain this result on some calculators as follows:

$$1.29 \boxed{\text{LOG}} \boxed{\div} 1.2 \boxed{=} 0.092158 \approx 0.0922$$

EXAMPLE 3

Solve $140 = 20e^{0.4x}$.

Solution

We first divide each member by 20 to obtain

$$7 = e^{0.4x}$$

from which the equivalent logarithmic equation is

$$0.4x = \ln 7$$

Hence, by dividing each member by 0.4 and using Table IV in Appendix D or a scientific calculator, we get

$$x = \frac{\ln 7}{0.4} = 4.86$$

We may obtain this result on some calculators as follows:

$$7 \boxed{\text{LN}} \boxed{\div} 0.4 \boxed{=} 4.8648 \approx 4.86$$

Changing Bases

A similar procedure applies to any exponential equation involving the base e or the base 10 because values for $\ln x$ and $\log_{10} x$ can be obtained from tables or a scientific calculator. However, the solution of an exponential equation that involves a base other than e or 10 requires other methods.

One method involves writing a logarithm to one base in terms of logarithms to a different base. To obtain a formula for $\log_b N$ in terms of another base, say a, we first let

$$y = \log_b N \tag{1}$$

Then, from the definition of a logarithm, we have that

$$N = b^y$$

Equating the logarithm of each member using the base a, we have

$$\log_a N = \log_a b^y$$

From the third law of logarithms,

$$\log_a N = y \log_a b$$

from which

$$y = \frac{\log_a N}{\log_a b}$$

Hence, substituting $\log_b N$ for y from Equation (1), we obtain the following equation:*

$$\log_b N = \frac{\log_a N}{\log_a b} \tag{2}$$

EXAMPLE 4

Compute a value for $\log_5 16$.

Solution

From Equation (2), with $a = 10$,

$$\log_5 16 = \frac{\log_{10} 16}{\log_{10} 5}$$

$$= \frac{1.2041}{0.69897} = 1.72$$

Calculator sequence:

$$16 \boxed{\text{LOG}} \div 5 \boxed{\text{LOG}} \boxed{=} 1.7227 \approx 1.72$$

Alternatively, with $a = e$,

$$\log_5 16 = \frac{\ln 16}{\ln 5}$$

$$= \frac{2.7726}{1.6094} = 1.72$$

Calculator sequence:

$$16 \boxed{\text{LN}} \div 5 \boxed{\text{LN}} \boxed{=} 1.7227 \approx 1.72$$

Equation (2) can be used to solve exponential equations in which the base is a positive number other than 10 or e.

---

*A special case of Equation (2) with $b = 10$ is the relationship that we used on page 263 to find values of $\log_{10} N$ when we used a calculator that did not have a $\boxed{\text{LOG}}$ key.

EXAMPLE 5 | Solve $5^x = 7$.

Solution | We can first write this equation in logarithmic form as
$$x = \log_5 7$$

Now, from Equation (2) and using the base 10, we have
$$x = \log_5 7$$
$$= \frac{\log_{10} 7}{\log_{10} 5} = \frac{0.84510}{0.69897} = 1.21$$

The use of natural logarithms will yield the same result.

Note that we could have obtained the quotient $\log_{10} 7/\log_{10} 5$ in Example 5 by first equating the logarithm of each member of $5^x = 7$ to the base 10 to obtain
$$\log_{10} 5^x = \log_{10} 7$$

Then, from the third law of logarithms,
$$x \log_{10} 5 = \log_{10} 7$$

from which
$$x = \frac{\log_{10} 7}{\log_{10} 5}$$

COMMON ERROR | *The quotient shows the division of the log values, which differs from finding the log of a quotient.*
$$\frac{\log_{10} 7}{\log_{10} 5} \neq \log_{10} 7 - \log_{10} 5$$

Equations with Several Variables

We can use the definition of a logarithm in exponential equations and logarithmic equations of more than one variable to solve for one of the variables in terms of the others.

EXAMPLE 6 | **a.** Solve $P = Cb^{kt}$ for t.   **b.** Solve $N = N_0 \log_b(ks)$ for s.

Solutions | **a.** First express the power b^{kt} in terms of the other variables.
$$b^{kt} = \frac{P}{C} \quad (C \neq 0)$$

Write the exponential equation in logarithmic form.
$$kt = \log_b \frac{P}{C}$$

b. First express $\log_b(ks)$ in terms of the other variables.
$$\log_b(ks) = \frac{N}{N_0} \quad (N_0 \neq 0)$$

Write the logarithmic equation in exponential form.
$$ks = b^{N/N_0}$$

Multiply each member by $\frac{1}{k}$. Multiply each member by $\frac{1}{k}$.

$$t = \frac{1}{k}\log_b \frac{P}{C} \quad (k \neq 0)$$ $$s = \frac{1}{k}b^{N/N_0} \quad (k \neq 0)$$

EXERCISE SET 9.5

▲ *Compute solutions of Exercises 1–30. A calculator was used to obtain the answers for this section. Answers obtained by using tables may differ slightly from those given.*

▲ *Solve each exponential equation. See Example 1.*

1. $10^x = 4.93$ 2. $10^x = 8.07$
3. $10^x = 23.4$ 4. $10^x = 182.4$
5. $10^x = 6832.3$ 6. $10^x = 9480.2$
7. $e^x = 1.9$ 8. $e^x = 2.1$ 9. $e^x = 45$
10. $e^x = 60$ 11. $e^x = 0.3$ 12. $e^x = 0.9$

▲ *For Exercises 13–20, see Example 2.*

13. $26.1 = 1.4(10^{1.3x})$ 14. $140 = 63.1(10^{0.2x})$
15. $14.8 = 1.72 + 10^{-0.3x}$
16. $180 = 64 + 10^{-1.3x}$
17. $12.2 = 2(10^{1.4x}) - 11.6$
18. $163 = 3(10^{0.7x}) - 49.3$
19. $3(10^{-1.5x}) - 14.7 = 17.1$
20. $4(10^{-0.6x}) + 16.1 = 28.2$

▲ *For Exercises 21–30, see Example 3.*

21. $6.21 = 2.3e^{1.2x}$ 22. $22.26 = 5.3e^{0.4x}$
23. $7.74 = 1.72e^{0.2x}$ 24. $14.105 = 4.03e^{1.4x}$
25. $6.4 = 20e^{0.3x} - 1.8$ 26. $4.5 = 4e^{2.1x} + 3.3$
27. $46.52 = 3.1e^{1.2x} + 24.2$
28. $1.23 = 1.3e^{2.1x} - 17.1$

29. $16.24 = 0.7e^{-1.3x} - 21.7$
30. $55.68 = 0.6e^{-0.7x} + 23.1$

▲ *Use Equation (2) on page 267 to find the value of each of the following logarithms to the nearest hundredth. Use base 10 or base e. See Example 4.*

31. $\log_3 18$ 32. $\log_3 24$ 33. $\log_2 7.43$
34. $\log_2 14.3$ 35. $\log_4 17.3$ 36. $\log_4 28.1$

▲ *Solve using logarithms to the base 10. See Example 5.*

37. $2^x = 7$ 38. $3^x = 4$ 39. $3^{x+1} = 8$
40. $2^{x-1} = 9$ 41. $4^{x^2} = 15$ 42. $3^{x^2} = 21$
43. $3^{-x} = 10$ 44. $2.13^{-x} = 8.1$

Miscellaneous Exercises

▲ *Solve each exponential or logarithmic equation for the specified variable. Leave the results in the form of an equation equivalent to the given equation.*

45. $y = e^{kt}$ for t using the base e
46. $y = k(1 - e^{-t})$ for t using the base e
47. $\dfrac{T}{R} = e^{t/2}$ for t using the base e
48. $B - 2 = (A + 3)e^{-t/3}$ for t using the base e
49. $T = T_0 \ln(k + 10)$ for k
50. $P = P_0 + \ln 10k$ for k
51. Show that $\ln N \approx 2.303 \log_{10} N$.
52. Show that $\ln 10 = \dfrac{1}{\log_{10} e}$.

| 9.6 | **APPLICATIONS** |

Exponential equations involving powers with base 10 or base e can be used as models for a variety of real-world phenomena. In equations such as

$$A = Be^{kt} + C \quad \text{or} \quad A = B \cdot 10^{kt} + C$$

we may want to find values for a particular variable in an expression that may or may not be "part" of the exponent.

The first case, in which we want to find a value for a variable that is *not* part of the exponent, is illustrated by the following example. In this case we merely evaluate an exponential function.

EXAMPLE 1   A scientist starts an experiment with 25 grams of a radioactive element. The number of grams remaining at any time t is given by $y = 25e^{-0.5t}$, where t is in seconds. How much of the element (to the nearest hundredth of a gram) is remaining after three seconds?

Solution   Substituting 3 for t, we have

$$y = 25e^{-0.5(3)}$$
$$= 25e^{-1.5} = 5.57825$$

There are approximately 5.58 grams of material remaining after three seconds.

The second case, in which we want to find a value for a variable that is in the exponent, is illustrated by the following example. In this case we must use logarithms to solve an exponential equation.

EXAMPLE 2   The atmospheric pressure P, in inches of mercury, is given approximately by

$$P = 30(10)^{-0.09a} \qquad \qquad (1)$$

where a is the altitude in miles above sea level. How high above the Earth (to the nearest hundredth of a mile) is the atmospheric pressure 26.4 inches of mercury?

Solution   Substituting 26.4 for P, we obtain

$$26.4 = 30(10)^{-0.09a}$$

which is equivalent to

$$\frac{26.4}{30} = 10^{-0.09a}$$

Writing the equation in logarithmic form, we have

$$-0.09a = \log_{10} \frac{26.4}{30}$$

from which

$$a = -\frac{1}{0.09} \log_{10} \frac{26.4}{30}$$
$$= 0.61686$$

Hence, the pressure is 26.4 inches of mercury at approximately 0.62 mile above the Earth.

EXERCISE SET 9.6

▲ *A calculator was used to obtain the answers from this section; answers obtained by using tables may differ slightly from those given. See Examples 1 and 2.*

▲ *Solve Exercises 1–6 using the relationship $P = 30(10)^{-0.09a}$ between altitude (a) in miles and atmospheric pressure (P) in inches of mercury. Round off results to the nearest hundredth.*

1. The elevation of Mount Everest, the highest mountain in the world, is 29,028 feet. What is the atmospheric pressure at the top? [*Hint:* One mile equals 5280 feet.]

2. What is the atmospheric pressure at sea level? At 50,000 feet? At 100,000 feet?

3. How high above sea level is the atmospheric pressure 20.2 inches of mercury?

4. How high above sea level is the atmospheric pressure 16.1 inches of mercury?

5. Find the height above sea level at which the pressure is equal to one-half of the pressure at sea level.

6. Find the height above sea level at which the pressure is equal to one-fourth of the pressure at sea level.

▲ *Solve Exercises 7–12 using the fact that population growth is given approximately by $P = P_0 e^{rn}$, where an initial population P_0 increases at an annual rate r (expressed as a decimal) to a population P after n years.*

7. The population of the state of California increased from 1960 to 1970 at a rate of approximately 2.39% per year. The population in 1960 was 15,717,000.

   a. Approximately what was the population in 1970?

   b. Assuming the same rate of growth, estimate the population in the years 1980, 1990, and 2000.

8. The population of the state of New York increased from 1960 to 1970 at a rate of approximately 0.83% per year. The population in 1960 was 16,782,000.

   a. Approximately what was the population in 1970?

   b. Assuming the same rate of growth, estimate the population in the years 1980, 1990, and 2000.

9. The population of the state of Texas in 1960 was 9,579,700. In 1970 the population was 11,196,700. What was the annual rate of growth to the nearest hundredth of a percent?

10. The population of the state of Florida in 1960 was 4,951,600. In 1970 the population was 6,789,400. What was the annual rate of growth to the nearest hundredth of a percent?

11. If the annual rate of growth of a country is 3.7%, how long will it take for the population to double?

12. The population of a country doubled in 20 years. What was the annual rate of growth (to the nearest hundredth of a percent)?

13. The amount of a radioactive element present at any time t is given by $y = y_0 e^{-0.4t}$, where t is measured in seconds and y_0 is the amount present initially. How much of the element (to the nearest hundredth of a gram) would remain after 3 seconds if 40 grams were present initially?

14. The number N of bacteria present in a culture is given by $N = N_0 e^{0.04t}$, where N_0 is the number of bacteria present at time $t = 0$ and t is time in hours. If 6000 bacteria were present at $t = 0$, how many were present 10 hours later?

15. The voltage V across a capacitor in a certain circuit is given by $V = 100(1 - e^{-0.5t})$, where t is the time in seconds. What is the voltage (to the nearest tenth of a volt) after 10 seconds?

16. The intensity I (in lumens) of a light beam after passing through a thickness t (in centimeters) of a medium having an absorption coefficient of 0.1 is given by $I = 1000e^{-0.1t}$. What is the intensity (to the nearest tenth) of a light beam passing through 0.6 centimeter of the medium?

17. The voltage V across a capacitor in a certain circuit is given by $V = 100(1 - e^{-0.5t})$, where t is the time in seconds. How much time must elapse (to the nearest hundredth of a second) for the voltage to reach 75 volts?

18. The amount of a radioactive element present at any time t is given by $y = y_0 e^{-0.4t}$, where t is measured in seconds and y_0 is the amount present initially. How much time must elapse (to the nearest hundredth of a second) for 40 grams to be reduced to 12 grams?

▲ *Solve Exercises 19–26 using the following information: P dollars invested at an annual interest rate r (expressed as a decimal) compounded yearly yields an amount A after n years given by $A = P(1 + r)^n$. If the interest is compounded t times yearly, the amount is given by*

$$A = P\left(1 + \frac{r}{t}\right)^{tn}$$

19. One dollar compounded annually for 10 years yields $5.12. What is the rate of interest to the nearest 1/2%?

20. How many years (to the nearest year) will it take for $1000 to grow to $2000 if it is compounded annually at 12%?

21. What rate of interest (to the nearest 1/2%) is required so that $100 would yield $190 after 5 years if the money were compounded semiannually?

22. What rate of interest (to the nearest 1/2%) is required so that $40 would yield $60 after 3 years if the money were compounded quarterly?

23. Find the compounded amount of $5000 invested at 12% for 10 years when it is compounded annually; when it is compounded semiannually.

24. How many years (to the nearest year) will it take for a sum of money to double if it is invested at 10% and compounded quarterly?

25. How many years (to the nearest year) will it take for a sum of money to increase fivefold if it is invested at 10% and compounded quarterly?

26. Two investors, A and B, each invested $10,000 at 8% for 20 years with a bank that computed interest quarterly. Investor A withdrew interest at the end of each 3-month period, but B allowed the investment to be compounded. How much more than A did B earn over the period of 20 years?

CHAPTER SUMMARY

[9.1] The inverse of an exponential function is called a **logarithmic function** and is defined by an equation of the form

$$x = b^y \qquad \text{or} \qquad y = \log_b x \qquad (b > 0, \quad b \neq 1)$$

$\log_b x$ is the **exponent** on b such that the power equals x. The domain of a logarithmic function is the set of positive real numbers; the range is the set of real numbers.

[9.2] The following properties of logarithms follow from the definition of a logarithm and the properties of exponents developed in Chapter 6:

$$\log_b(x_1 x_2) = \log_b x_1 + \log_b x_2 \qquad \textbf{(1)}$$

$$\log_b \frac{x_2}{x_1} = \log_b x_2 - \log_b x_1 \qquad \textbf{(2)}$$

$$\log_b(x_1)^m = m \log_b x_1 \qquad \textbf{(3)}$$

[9.3] Values of $\log_{10} x$, $x > 0$ are known as **common logarithms**. Values of $\log_{10} x$, where x is a power of 10 with an integer exponent, can be obtained by inspection directly from the definition of a logarithm. Values of $\log_{10} x$ $(1 < x < 10)$ are between 0 and 1 and can be obtained directly from Table II in Appendix D. Values of $\log_{10} x$ $(x > 10 \text{ and } 0 < x < 1)$ can be obtained from Table II in Appendix D in conjunction with the first law of logarithms. The *integral part* of a logarithm to the base 10 is the **characteristic** of the logarithm, and the *positive decimal part* is the **mantissa**. Values for e^x can be obtained by using Table III in Appendix D; values for $\log_e x$ or $\ln x$, called **natural logarithms**, can be obtained by using Table IV.

A power b^x is called the **antilogarithm** of x. Thus,

$$10^x = \text{antilog}_{10} x \qquad \text{and} \qquad e^x = \text{antilog}_e x$$

[9.4] A scientific calculator can be used to find values for the powers 10^x and e^x and the exponents $\log_{10} x$ and $\ln x$ ($x > 0$).

[9.5] Exponential equations can be solved by using the properties of logarithms plus a table of logarithms or a calculator.

[9.6] Exponential equations can be used as models for many real-world problems.

The following table summarizes the different ways of finding the exponential and logarithmic function values that have been considered in this chapter.

To find the power for a given value of an exponent:

	10^x (antilog$_{10}$ x)	e^x (antilog$_{10}$ x)	b^x ($b > 0, b \neq 1$)
Table	II*	III	
Calculator	$\boxed{10^x}$ or $\boxed{y^x}$ or $\boxed{\text{INV}}$ $\boxed{\text{2ND}}$ $\boxed{\text{LOG}}$	$\boxed{e^x}$ or $\boxed{y^x}$ or $\boxed{\text{INV}}$ $\boxed{\text{2ND}}$ $\boxed{\text{LN}}$	$\boxed{y^x}$

To find the exponent for a given value of a power:

	$10^x = N$ $x = \log_{10} N$	$e^x = N$ $x = \ln N$	$b^x = N$ ($b > 0, b \neq 1$)
Table	II*	IV*	II* or IV*
Calculator	$\boxed{\text{LOG}}$ or $x = \log_{10} N = \dfrac{\ln N}{\ln 10}$ N $\boxed{\text{LN}}$ $\boxed{\div}$ 10 $\boxed{\text{LN}}$ $\boxed{=}$ x	$\boxed{\text{LN}}$	$x = \log_b N = \dfrac{\ln N}{\ln b}$ N $\boxed{\text{LN}}$ $\boxed{\div}$ b $\boxed{\text{LN}}$ $\boxed{=}$ x

Note: When Table II or IV in Appendix D is used, the decimal part (mantissa) of a logarithm must be positive; the characteristic must be an integer.

REVIEW EXERCISES

[9.1]

1. Write each statement in logarithmic notation.

   a. $9^{3/2} = 27$ **b.** $\left(\dfrac{4}{9}\right)^{1/2} = \dfrac{2}{3}$

2. Write each statement in exponential notation.

   a. $\log_5 625 = 4$ **b.** $\log_{10} 0.0001 = -4$

▲ *Solve for x.*

3. **a.** $\log_4 16 = x$ **b.** $\log_2 x = 3$

4. **a.** $\log_{10} x = -2$ **b.** $\log_3 \dfrac{1}{3} = x$

▲ *Find the value of each logarithm by inspection.*

5. **a.** $\log_3 9$ **b.** $\log_4 \dfrac{1}{4}$

6. **a.** $\log_{10} 1000$ **b.** $\log_{10} 0.001$

[9.2]

7. Express each as the sum or difference of simpler logarithmic quantities.

   a. $\log_b 3x^2 y$ **b.** $\log_b \dfrac{y\sqrt{x}}{z^2}$

8. Given that $\log_b 2 = 0.3010$ and $\log_b 3 = 0.4771$, find the value for each logarithm.

   a. $\log_b 36$ **b.** $\log_b \sqrt{18}$

9. Write each expression as a single logarithm with a coefficient of 1.

   a. $5\log_b x - 2\log_b y$

   b. $\dfrac{1}{3}(\log_b x - 4\log_b y + 2\log_b z)$

10. **a.** Solve $\log_{10}(x + 9) - \log_{10} x = 1$.

   b. Solve $\log_{10} x + \log_{10}(x - 3) = 1$.

▲ *In Exercises 11–26, use the tables or a calculator (round off readings to three significant digits).*

[9.3–9.4]

11. Find a value for each logarithm.

   a. $\log_{10} 0.713$ **b.** $\log_{10} 1810$

12. Solve for x.

   a. $\log_{10} x = 2.6345$ **b.** $\log_{10} x = -1.4214$

13. Compute each power.

   a. $10^{1.2347}$ **b.** $10^{-0.5453}$

14. Find the value of each power.

   a. $e^{0.83}$ **b.** $e^{-1.3}$

15. Find the value of each logarithm.

   a. $\ln 7$ **b.** $\ln 0.4$

16. Solve for x.

   a. $\ln x = 0.73$ **b.** $\ln x = 2.7$

[9.5]

▲ *Solve each exponential equation.*

17. $10^x = 1.3$ 18. $e^x = 62$

19. $7.35 = 2.1(10)^{1.2x}$ 20. $12.4 = 2e^{0.3x} - 4.2$

21. Given that $N = N_0 10^{0.4t}$, find t if $N = 280$ and $N_0 = 4$.

22. Given that $y = y_0 e^{-0.2t}$, find t if $y = 4$ and $y_0 = 20$.

▲ *Use Equation (2) on page 267 to find each logarithm.*

23. $\log_2 23.1$ 24. $\log_3 7.04$

▲ *Solve for x using logarithms to the base 10 or the base e.*

25. $3^x = 15$ 26. $2^{x-4} = 10$

[9.6]

27. The concentration C of a certain drug in the bloodstream at any time t is given by $C(t) = 10 - 10e^{-0.5t}$, where C is in milligrams and t is in minutes. Determine the concentration to the nearest tenth of a milligram at $t = 0$ and $t = 1$.

28. The intensity I of a light beam after passing through a thickness t of a certain medium is given by $I = 500e^{-0.2t}$, where I is in lumens and t is in centimeters. What is the intensity (to the nearest tenth of a lumen) of a light beam passing through 0.4 centimeter of the medium?

29. Using the formula for population growth on page 271, how long (to the nearest tenth of a year) will it take for a city with an annual rate of growth of 3% to grow from a population of 200,000 to 300,000?

30. Using the formula for radioactive decay in Exercise 13 on page 271, how much time (to the nearest tenth of a second) must elapse for 100 grams to be reduced to 50 grams?

CUMULATIVE EXERCISES

▲ *The numbers in brackets refer to the section in which such problems are first considered.*

▲ *Simplify each expression.*

1. $\left(\dfrac{-ab}{s^2t}\right)^3\left(\dfrac{s^3t^5}{a^4bc^2}\right)^2$ **[5.1]**

2. $\dfrac{\sqrt[3]{4x^3y^5z^5}\,\sqrt[3]{10y^4z^{11}}}{\sqrt[3]{8x^2y}}$ **[5.6]**

3. $\dfrac{1}{x+2}-\dfrac{2x-6}{3x^2+5x-2}$ **[4.5]**

4. $\dfrac{\dfrac{a}{a-2}}{\dfrac{2}{a^2}-\dfrac{2}{a}}$ **[4.6]**

5. Factor $a^6b - a^2b^5$ completely.   **[3.4]**

6. Divide $\dfrac{3t^3-7t+3}{t-2}$.   **[4.2]**

7. Rationalize the denominator and simplify:
$\dfrac{1-\sqrt{x-1}}{1+\sqrt{x+1}}$.   **[5.7]**

8. Solve for x in terms of y: $2x^2-2xy+y^2=4$. **[6.2]**

9. Evaluate x^2-4x+5 for $x=2+i$.   **[5.8]**

10. Find the solution to $y=|x-1|+|2x-1|$ for $x=-2$.   **[7.1]**

11. Find the inverse of the function defined by $2x-3y=8$.   **[8.5]**

12. Express as a single logarithm with coefficient 1:
$\dfrac{1}{2}\log_b x - (2\log_b y + 3\log_b z)$.   **[9.2]**

▲ *Solve each equation.*

13. $x^2-2-3\sqrt{x^2-2}-18=0$ **[6.4]**

14. $16.2=3(10^{2.3x})-8.7$ to four decimal places. **[9.5]**

15. $2x^2+kx+k-4=0$ for x in terms of k.   **[6.2]**

16. $4-(x-2)(x+3)=6$ **[6.2]**

▲ *Graph.*

17. $f:4x-y=8$ and f^{-1} **[8.5]**

18. $f:x+3y=6$ and f^{-1} **[8.5]**

19. $f:y=x^2$ $(x\geq 0)$ and f^{-1} **[8.5]**

20. $f:y=2^x$ and f^{-1} **[8.5]**

21. The altitude of an isosceles triangle is 12 inches. Find the base if the perimeter is 36 inches.   **[6.3]**

22. Write an equation for the line perpendicular to the graph of $3x+y=6$ that passes through the point $(-2,-4)$.   **[7.4]**

23. The intensity of illumination from a light source varies inversely with the square of the distance from the source. If a reading lamp has an intensity of 100 lumens at a distance of 3 feet, what is its intensity 8 feet away?   **[8.2]**

24. Find the dimensions of the largest rectangular area that can be enclosed by 36 yards of fence.   **[8.3]**

25. The value of a large tractor originally worth \$30,000 depreciates exponentially according to the formula $V(t)=30,000(10)^{-0.04t}$, where t is in years. When will the tractor be worth half its original value? **[9.6]**

10 SYSTEMS OF LINEAR EQUATIONS

10.1 SYSTEMS IN TWO VARIABLES

In Chapter 7 we considered the solution sets of equations in two variables. These solution sets contain infinitely many ordered pairs of numbers. It is often useful to consider *pairs* of equations and to inquire whether or not their solution sets contain ordered pairs in common.

Consider the two first-degree equations

$$2x - y = 2 \quad \text{and} \quad -x + 2y = 5$$

and their graphs in Figure 10.1. Because their graphs intersect at $P(x_1, y_1)$, the two equations have a common solution (x_1, y_1), the *intersection* of the solution sets of the two equations.

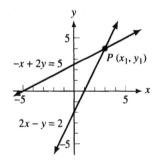

Figure 10.1

In a geometric sense, because the graphs of linear equations are straight lines, we are confronted with three possibilities when we graph two equations, as illustrated in Figure 10.2.

a. The graphs are the same line.

b. The graphs are parallel but distinct lines.

c. The graphs intersect at one and only one point.

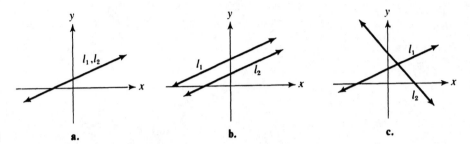

Figure 10.2   a.   b.   c.

From Figure 10.2 we see that for any given system of two such linear equations, one and only one of the following occurs:

a. The solution sets of the equations are equal, and their intersection contains all (an infinite number of) ordered pairs found in either one of the solution sets.

b. The intersection of the two solution sets is the empty set.

c. The intersection of the two solution sets contains one and only one ordered pair.

In case (a) the linear equations in x and y are said to be **dependent**, and in case (b) the equations are said to be **inconsistent**. In case (c) the equations are **consistent** and **independent**, and the system has one and only one solution.

Consider the system

$$x + y = 5$$
$$x - y = 1$$

From the graph of the system in Figure 10.3 it is evident that $(3, 2)$ is the only ordered pair common to the solution sets of both equations. We can verify this by substituting $(3, 2)$ into each equation and observing that a true statement results in each case.

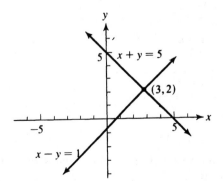

Figure 10.3

As another example, consider the system

$$x + y = 5$$
$$2x + 2y = 3$$

and the graphs of these equations in Figure 10.4, where the lines appear to be parallel. We conclude from this that the solution set of this system is empty.

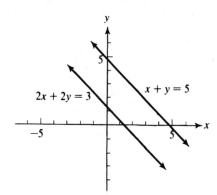

Figure 10.4

Because graphing equations is a time-consuming process and, more importantly, because graphic results are not always precise, solutions to systems of linear equations are usually sought by algebraic methods.

Solution by Linear Combination

One method that can be used to solve a system of the form

$$a_1 x + b_1 y = c_1$$
$$a_2 x + b_2 y = c_2$$

involves choosing multipliers for one or both of these equations so that the coefficients of one of the variables, x or y, are additive inverses of each other. Then the addition of respective sides of the equation results in an equation that is free of one of the variables.

EXAMPLE 1

Solve the system.

$$2x + 3y = 8 \qquad \text{(1)}$$
$$3x - 4y = -5 \qquad \text{(2)}$$

Solution

In this example we obtain the coefficients of x as additive inverses by multiplying each member of Equation (1) by 3 and each member of Equation (2) by -2 to obtain

$$6x + 9y = 24 \qquad \text{(1a)}$$
$$-6x + 8y = 10 \qquad \text{(2a)}$$

Adding the corresponding members of Equations (1a) and (2a), we obtain

$$17y = 34 \qquad \text{(3)}$$
$$y = 2 \qquad \text{(3a)}$$

Equation (3) is called a **linear combination** of Equations (1) and (2). Any solution of (3) or (3a) is of the form $(x, 2)$—that is, it has y-component 2 for any value of x. Now, substituting 2 for y in either Equation (1) or (2), we can determine the x-component for the ordered pair $(x, 2)$ that satisfies both Equations (1) and (2). If we use Equation (1), we have

$$2x + 3(2) = 8$$
$$x = 1$$

and if we use Equation (2), we have

$$3x - 4(2) = -5$$
$$x = 1$$

Since the ordered pair $(1, 2)$ satisfies both Equations (1) and (2), the required solution set is $\{(1, 2)\}$.

It is helpful to rewrite any equation in a system that has fractional coefficients as an equivalent equation without fractions before attempting to use the procedure followed in Example 1.

EXAMPLE 2 Solve the system by linear combinations.

$$\frac{2}{3}x - y = 2 \qquad \qquad \textbf{(4)}$$

$$x + \frac{1}{2}y = 7 \qquad \qquad \textbf{(5)}$$

Solution Multiply each member of Equation (4) by 3 and each member of Equation (5) by 2.

$$2x - 3y = 6 \qquad \qquad \textbf{(4a)}$$
$$2x + \ y = 14 \qquad \qquad \textbf{(5a)}$$

Add -1 times Equation (4a) to 1 times Equation (5a) and solve for y.

$$4y = 8$$
$$y = 2$$

Substitute 2 for y in Equation (4), (5), (4a), or (5a) and solve for x. In this example, Equation (5) is used.

$$x + \frac{1}{2}(2) = 7$$

$$x = 6$$

The solution set is $\{(6, 2)\}$.

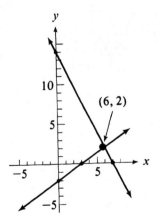

The figure provides a check on the algebraic solution.

Solution by Substitution

Sometimes a system of linear equations can be solved readily by a substitution procedure, particularly if one of the variables is expressed explicitly in terms of the other variable.

EXAMPLE 3

Solve each system.

a.
$$2x - y = 6 \tag{6}$$
$$x = 4 \tag{7}$$

b.
$$x + 3y = 8 \tag{8}$$
$$y = 6 - x \tag{9}$$

Solutions

a. From Equation (7), substitute 4 for x in Equation (6) and solve for y.
$$2(4) - y = 6$$
$$-y = 6 - 8$$
$$y = 2$$

Hence, the solution set is $\{(4, 2)\}$.

b. From Equation (9), substitute $6 - x$ for y in Equation (8) and solve for x.
$$x + 3(6 - x) = 8$$
$$x + 18 - 3x = 8$$
$$-2x = -10$$
$$x = 5$$

Then substitute 5 for x in Equation (9) to obtain
$$y = 6 - (5) = 1$$

Hence, the solution set is $\{(5, 1)\}$.

Test for a Unique Solution

We can determine whether a system has a unique solution or whether the equations are inconsistent or dependent by writing each equation in slope-intercept form. In general we can write the system in standard form

$$a_1 x + b_1 y = c_1$$
$$a_2 x + b_2 y = c_2$$

equivalently as

$$y = \frac{-a_1}{b_1} x + \frac{c_1}{b_1}$$

$$y = \frac{-a_2}{b_2} x + \frac{c_2}{b_2}$$

Now, if the slopes $-a_1/b_1$ and $-a_2/b_2$ are unequal, the graphs will intersect at one point and there will be one and only one solution. If $a_1/b_1 = a_2/b_2$, then the graphs are either the same line (if $c_1/b_1 = c_2/b_2$) or parallel lines (if $c_1/b_1 \neq c_2/b_2$). These conclusions are summarized in the following property in a modified form.

The System	Examples
$a_1 x + b_1 y = c_1$ $a_2 x + b_2 y = c_2$ has one and only one solution if $$\frac{a_1}{a_2} \neq \frac{b_1}{b_2} \qquad \text{(I)}$$	$2x + 3y = 12$ $x - 4y = 6$ has one solution because $\frac{2}{1} \neq \frac{3}{-4}$. (Their graphs intersect.)
has no solution if $$\frac{a_1}{a_2} = \frac{b_1}{b_2} \neq \frac{c_1}{c_2} \qquad \text{(II)}$$	$2x + 3y = 8$ $4x + 6y = 2$ has no solution because $\frac{2}{4} = \frac{3}{6} \neq \frac{8}{2}$. (Their graphs are parallel.)
has an infinite number of solutions if $$\frac{a_1}{a_2} = \frac{b_1}{b_2} = \frac{c_1}{c_2} \qquad \text{(III)}$$	$x - 4y = 6$ $2x - 8y = 12$ has an infinite number of solutions because $\frac{1}{2} = \frac{-4}{-8} = \frac{6}{12}$. (Their graphs are identical.)

EXAMPLE 4

a. To solve the system

$$2x = 2 - 3y$$
$$6y = 7 - 4x$$

we first rewrite it in standard form as

$$2x + 3y = 2$$
$$4x + 6y = 7$$

and then we note that

$$\frac{2}{4} = \frac{3}{6} \neq \frac{2}{7}$$

Hence, from Property (II) the system does not have a solution.

b. To solve the system

$$3y = 5 - 2x$$
$$-4x = 7y - 8$$

we first rewrite it in standard form as

$$2x + 3y = 5$$
$$4x + 7y = 8$$

and then we note that

$$\frac{2}{4} \neq \frac{3}{7}$$

Hence, from Property (I) the system has one and only one solution.

Applications of the systems that we have considered in this section are included in Section 10.6. (In particular, Examples 1 and 2 and Exercises 1–12 in Section 10.6 relate to these systems.)

EXERCISE SET 10.1

▲ *Solve each system by linear combinations or substitution. Sketch the graphs of the equations. See Examples 1–3.*

1. $x - y = 1$
$x + y = 5$

2. $2x - 3y = 6$
$x + 3y = 3$

3. $3x + y = 7$
$2x - 5y = -1$

4. $2x - y = 7$
$3x + 2y = 14$

5. $5x - y = -29$
$2x + 3y = 2$

6. $x + 4y = -14$
$3x + 2y = -2$

7. $3x + 2y = 7$
$x + y = 3$

8. $2x - 3y = 8$
$x + y = -1$

9. $3y = x - 1$
$y = 6x - 6$

10. $3x = 3y - 3$
$2y = 6x + 14$

11. $2x - 3y = -4$
$5x + 2y = 9$

12. $3x + 5y = 1$
$2x - 3y = 7$

13. $5x + 2y = 3$
$x = 0$

14. $2x - y = 0$
$x = -3$

15. $3x - 2y = 4$
$y = -1$

16. $x + 2y = 6$
$x = 2$

17. $\frac{1}{4}x - \frac{1}{3}y = -\frac{5}{12}$
$\frac{1}{10}x + \frac{1}{5}y = \frac{1}{2}$

18. $\frac{2}{3}x - y = 4$
$x - \frac{3}{4}y = 6$

19. $\frac{1}{7}x = \frac{3}{7}y + 1$
$y = 2x + 4$

20. $\frac{1}{3}x = \frac{2}{3}y + 2$
$2y = x - 6$

▲ *Use the properties on page 281 to determine whether each of the following systems has one solution, no solution, or an infinite number of solutions. DO NOT SOLVE. See Example 4.*

21. $x + 3y = 6$
$2x + 6y = 12$

22. $3x - 2y = 6$
$6x - 4y = 8$

23. $2x - y = 1$
$8x - 4y = 3$

24. $6x + 2y = 1$
$12x + 4y = 2$

25. $x - 3y = 4$
$2x + y = 6$

26. $2x + y = 4$
$x - 3y = 2$

27. $x = 2y - 4$
$2x - 4y = 6$

28. $y = 3x + 4$
$6x - 2y = 4$

29. $y - 4 = x$
$2x + 8 = 4y$

30. $x + 2 = y$
$3y - 6 = 3x$

31. $x = 2y + 3$
$y = 2x - 3$

32. $2x - 3 = y$
$2y + 3 = x$

Miscellaneous Exercises

▲ *Solve each system. Hint: Set $u = 1/x$ and $v = 1/y$, solve for u and v, and then solve for x and y.*

33. $\frac{1}{x} + \frac{1}{y} = 7$
$\frac{2}{x} + \frac{3}{y} = 16$

Hint: Set $u = 1/x$ and $v = 1/y$ to yield $u + v = 7$ and $2u + 3v = 16$. Solve for u and v. Then use the fact that $u = 1/x$ and $v = 1/y$ to solve for x and y.]

34. $\frac{1}{x} + \frac{2}{y} = -\frac{11}{12}$
$\frac{1}{x} + \frac{1}{y} = -\frac{7}{12}$

35. $\frac{5}{x} - \frac{6}{y} = -3$
$\frac{10}{x} + \frac{9}{y} = 1$

36. $\frac{1}{x} + \frac{2}{y} = 11$
$\frac{1}{x} - \frac{2}{y} = -1$

37. $\frac{1}{x} - \frac{1}{y} = 4$
$\frac{2}{x} - \frac{1}{2y} = 11$

38. $\frac{2}{3x} + \frac{3}{4y} = \frac{7}{12}$
$\frac{4}{x} - \frac{3}{4y} = \frac{7}{4}$

10.2 | SYSTEMS IN THREE VARIABLES

A solution of an equation in three variables, such as

$$x + 2y - 3z = -4$$

is an ordered triple of numbers (x, y, z) that satisfies the equation. Thus, $(0, -2, 0)$ and $(-1, 0, 1)$ are solutions of this equation, while $(1, 1, 1)$ is not. There are, of course, infinitely many members in the solution set.

The solution set of a system of three linear equations in three variables, such as

$$x + 2y - 3z = -4 \qquad \textbf{(1)}$$

$$2x - y + z = 3 \qquad \textbf{(2)}$$

$$3x + 2y + z = 10 \qquad \textbf{(3)}$$

is the intersection of the solution sets of all three equations in the system. We seek solution sets of systems such as these by methods similar to those used in solving linear systems in two variables.

In the system presented in the preceding paragraph, we might begin by eliminating x from the system. First we multiply Equation (1) by -2 and add the result to 1 times Equation (2) to produce

$$\begin{aligned}
(-2)(x + 2y - 3z) &= (-2)(-4) \\
\underline{(1)(2x - y + z)} &= \underline{(1)(3)} \\
-5y + 7z &= 11
\end{aligned} \qquad \textbf{(4)}$$

Then we add -3 times Equation (1) to 1 times Equation (3) to obtain

$$\begin{aligned}
(-3)(x + 2y - 3z) &= (-3)(-4) \\
\underline{(1)(3x + 2y + z)} &= \underline{(1)(10)} \\
-4y + 10z &= 22
\end{aligned} \qquad \textbf{(5)}$$

We can now argue that any ordered triple satisfying the system (1), (2), and (3) will also satisfy the system

$$-5y + 7z = 11 \qquad \textbf{(4)}$$

$$-4y + 10z = 22 \qquad \textbf{(5)}$$

Since the system (4) and (5) does not depend on x, the problem has been reduced to one of finding only the y- and z-components of the solution. The system (4) and (5) can be solved by the method of Section 10.1, which leads to the values $y = 2$ and $z = 3$. Now, since any solution of (1), (2), and (3) must be of the form $(x, 2, 3)$, we can substitute 2 for y and 3 for z in (1) to obtain $x = 1$. The desired solution set is

$$\{(1, 2, 3)\}$$

The process of solving a system of equations can be reduced to a series of mechanical procedures, as illustrated by the following example.

EXAMPLE 1 | Solve the system.

$$x + 2y - z = -3 \qquad (6)$$
$$x - 3y + z = 6 \qquad (7)$$
$$2x + y + 2z = 5 \qquad (8)$$

Solution | To obtain a system of two equations in two variables, we first eliminate x in the system. We multiply Equation (6) by -1 and add the result to 1 times Equation (7) to get

$$(-1)(x + 2y - z) = (-1)(-3)$$
$$\underline{(1)(x - 3y + z) = (1)(6)}$$
$$-5y + 2z = 9 \qquad (9)$$

We multiply Equation (6) by -2 and add the result to 1 times Equation (8) to get

$$(-2)(x + 2y - z) = (-2)(-3)$$
$$\underline{(1)(2x + y + 2z) = (1)5}$$
$$-3y + 4z = 11 \qquad (10)$$

Then we solve the system in two variables formed by Equations (9) and (10). We multiply Equation (9) by -2 and add the result to 1 times Equation (10) to obtain

$$(-2)(-5y + 2z) = (-2)(9) \qquad (9\text{a})$$
$$\underline{(1)(-3y + 4z) = (1)(11)} \qquad (10\text{a})$$
$$7y = -7$$
$$y = -1$$

We substitute -1 for y in either (9) or (10)—here we use (9)—and solve for z.

$$-5(-1) + 2z = 9$$
$$z = 2$$

We substitute -1 for y and 2 for z in (6), (7), or (8)—here we use (6)—and solve for x.

$$x + 2(-1) - 2 = -3$$
$$x = 1$$

The solution set is $\{(1, -1, 2)\}$.

As was suggested in Section 10.1, it is usually helpful to first rewrite any equation that has fractional coefficients as an equivalent equation without fractions.

EXAMPLE 2 | Solve the system.

$$x + 2y - z = -3 \qquad (11)$$
$$\frac{1}{3}x - y + \frac{1}{3}z = 2 \qquad (12)$$
$$x + \frac{1}{2}y + z = \frac{5}{2} \qquad (13)$$

Solution We multiply each member of Equation (12) by 3 and each member of Equation (13) by 2 to obtain the equivalent system.

$$x + 2y - z = -3$$

$$3\left(\frac{1}{3}x\right) - 3(y) + 3\left(\frac{1}{3}z\right) = 3(2)$$

$$2(x) + 2\left(\frac{1}{2}y\right) + 2(z) = 2\left(\frac{5}{2}\right)$$

When the equations are simplified, the system (and its solution) is identical to the system in Example 1.

Graphs in Three Dimensions A three-dimensional Cartesian coordinate system can be established to show a one-to-one correspondence between the points in a three-dimensional space and ordered triples of real numbers. If this is done, it can be shown that the graph of a first-degree equation in three variables is a plane. Hence, the solution set of a system of three such equations consists of the coordinates of the common intersection of three planes. Although it is not practical to solve a system of three first-degree equations in three variables by graphing, it is interesting to see the possibilities for the relative positions of the plane graphs (Figure 10.5).

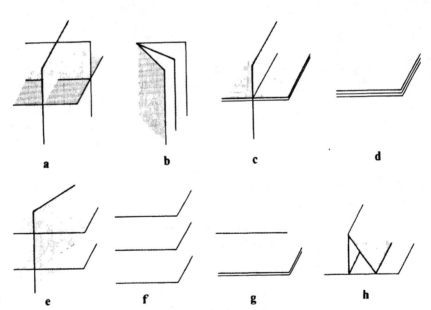

Figure 10.5

In case (a) the common intersection consists of a single point, and hence the solution set of the corresponding system of three equations contains a single member. In cases (b), (c), and (d) the intersection is a line or a plane, and the solution of the corresponding system has infinitely many members. In cases (e), (f), (g), and (h) the three planes have no common intersection, and the solution set of the corresponding system is the null set.

If at any step of the process the resulting linear combination vanishes or yields a contradiction, then the system does not have a unique solution. It has either an infinite number of members or no members in its solution set.

EXAMPLE 3 | Solve the system.

$$3x + y - 2z = 1 \tag{14}$$
$$6x + 2y - 4z = 5 \tag{15}$$
$$-2x - y + 3z = -1 \tag{16}$$

Solution To eliminate y in Equations (14) and (15), we multiply Equation (14) by -2 and add the result to 1 times Equation (15) to obtain

$$
\begin{array}{ll}
6x + 2y - 4z = 5 & \textbf{(15)} \\
\underline{-6x - 2y + 4z = -2} & \textbf{-2 times (14)} \\
\ 0 = 3 &
\end{array}
$$

Since the resulting linear combination yields a contradictory result, $0 = 3$ means $0x + 0y + 0z = 3$, which no ordered triple (x, y, z) satisfies, the system does not have a unique solution.

EXAMPLE 4 | Solve the system.

$$-x + 3y - z = -2 \tag{17}$$
$$2x + y - 4z = 6 \tag{18}$$
$$2x - 6y + 2z = 4 \tag{19}$$

Solution To eliminate x in Equations (17) and (18), we multiply Equation (17) by 2 and add the result to 1 times Equation (18) to obtain

$$
\begin{array}{ll}
2x - 6y + 2z = 4 & \textbf{(18)} \\
\underline{-2x + 6y - 2z = -4} & \textbf{2 times (17)} \\
\ 0 = 0 &
\end{array}
$$

Since the resulting linear combination $0 = 0$ means $0x + 0y + 0z = 0$, which is satisfied by any ordered triple (x, y, z), the system does not have a unique solution.

Applications of the systems that we have considered in this section are included in Section 10.6. (In particular, Examples 3 and 4 and Exercises 13–18 relate to these systems.)

EXERCISE SET 10.2

▲ *Solve. See Example 1.*

1.
$$x + y + z = 2$$
$$2x - y + z = -1$$
$$x - y - z = 0$$

2.
$$x + y + z = 1$$
$$2x - y + 3z = 2$$
$$2x - y - z = 2$$

3.
$$x + y + 2z = 0$$
$$2x - 2y + z = 8$$
$$3x + 2y + z = 2$$

4.
$$x - 2y + 4z = -3$$
$$3x + y - 2z = 12$$
$$2x + y - 3z = 11$$

5. $x - 2y + z = -1$
$2x + y - 3z = 3$
$3x + 3y - 2z = 10$

6. $x + 5y - z = 2$
$3x - 9y + 3z = 6$
$x - 3y - z = -6$

7. $2x - y + z = 6$
$x - 3y - z = 7$
$3x + 2y + z = 6$

8. $x - 2y + 4z = 10$
$2x + 3y - z = -7$
$x - y + 2z = 4$

9. $3x - y = 6$
$x - 2z = -7$
$2y + z = -2$

10. $2x + z = 5$
$3y + 2z = 6$
$x - 2z = 10$

11. $4x + z = 3$
$2x - y = 2$
$3y + 2z = 0$

12. $3y + z = 3$
$-2x + 3y = 7$
$3x - 2z = -6$

21. $2x + 3y - z = -2$
$x - y + \frac{1}{2}z = 2$
$4x - \frac{1}{3}y + 2z = 8$

22. $3x + 6y + 2z = -2$
$\frac{1}{2}x - 3y - z = 1$
$4x + y + \frac{1}{3}z = -\frac{1}{3}$

23. $2x + y = 6$
$x - z = 4$
$3x + y - z = 10$

24. $x - 2y + z = 5$
$-x + y = -2$
$y - z = -3$

25. $x = 2y - 7$
$y = 4z + 3$
$z = 3x + y$

26. $x = y + z$
$y = 2x - z$
$z = 3x - y$

27. $\frac{1}{2}x + y = \frac{1}{2}z$
$x - y = -z - 2$
$-x - 2y = -z + \frac{4}{3}$

28. $x = \frac{1}{2}y - \frac{1}{2}z + 1$
$x = 2y + z - 1$
$x = \frac{1}{2}y - \frac{1}{2}z + \frac{1}{4}$

▲ *Solve. See Example 2.*

13. $x - \frac{1}{2}y - \frac{1}{2}z = 4$
$x - \frac{3}{2}y - 2z = 3$
$\frac{1}{4}x + \frac{1}{4}y + \frac{1}{4}z = 0$

14. $x + 2y + \frac{1}{2}z = 0$
$x + \frac{3}{5}y - \frac{2}{5}z = \frac{1}{5}$
$4x - 7y - 7z = 6$

29. $x - y = 0$
$2x + 2y + z = 5$
$2x + y - \frac{1}{2}z = 0$

30. $x + y = 1$
$2x - y + z = -1$
$x - 3y - z = -\frac{2}{3}$

15. $x + y - z = 2$
$\frac{1}{2}x - y + \frac{1}{2}z = -\frac{1}{2}$
$x + \frac{1}{3}y - \frac{2}{3}z = \frac{4}{3}$

16. $x + y - 2z = 2$
$x - \frac{1}{3}y + \frac{1}{3}z = \frac{5}{3}$
$\frac{1}{2}x - \frac{1}{2}y - z = \frac{3}{2}$

Miscellaneous Exercises

▲ *Solve each system.* [*Hint: Use substitutions* $u = 1/x$, $v = 1/y$, *and* $w = 1/z$; *solve for u, v, and w, then solve for x, y, and z.*]

17. $x = -y$
$x + z = \frac{5}{6}$
$y - 2z = -\frac{7}{6}$

18. $x = y + \frac{1}{2}$
$y = z + \frac{5}{4}$
$2z = x - \frac{7}{4}$

31. $\frac{1}{x} + \frac{1}{y} - \frac{1}{z} = 1$
$\frac{2}{x} - \frac{2}{y} + \frac{1}{z} = 1$
$\frac{-3}{x} + \frac{1}{y} - \frac{1}{z} = -3$

32. $\frac{4}{x} - \frac{2}{y} + \frac{1}{z} = 4$
$\frac{3}{x} - \frac{1}{y} + \frac{2}{z} = 0$
$\frac{-1}{x} + \frac{3}{y} - \frac{2}{z} = 0$

▲ *Solve. If there is no unique solution, so state. See Examples 1–4.*

33. $\frac{1}{x} + \frac{2}{y} - \frac{2}{z} = 3$
$\frac{2}{x} - \frac{4}{y} + \frac{2}{z} = -1$
$\frac{4}{x} - \frac{2}{y} - \frac{4}{z} = 5$

34. $\frac{2}{x} - \frac{1}{y} - \frac{1}{z} = -1$
$\frac{4}{x} - \frac{2}{y} + \frac{1}{z} = -5$
$\frac{2}{x} + \frac{1}{y} - \frac{4}{z} = 4$

19. $3x - 2y + z = 6$
$2x + y - z = 2$
$4x + 2y - 2z = 3$

20. $x + 3y - z = 4$
$-2x - 6y + 2z = 1$
$x + 2y - z = 3$

|10.3| **SOLUTION OF SYSTEMS USING SECOND-ORDER DETERMINANTS**

We now introduce a mathematical tool called a *determinant* that can be used to solve linear systems. In this section we limit our study to the solution of systems of two equations in two variables.

2 x 2 Determinants An expression of the form

$$\begin{vmatrix} a_1 & b_1 \\ a_2 & b_2 \end{vmatrix}$$

is called a **determinant**. The numbers a_1, b_1, a_2, and b_2 are called **elements** of the determinant. Because this determinant has two rows and two columns of elements, it is called a two-by-two (2×2) determinant or a determinant of order two. We define this determinant as follows:

$$\begin{vmatrix} a_1 & b_1 \\ a_2 & b_2 \end{vmatrix} = a_1 b_2 - a_2 b_1$$

This value is obtained by multiplying the elements on the diagonals and subtracting the second product from the first product. The process can be shown schematically as

$$\begin{vmatrix} a_1 & b_1 \\ a_2 & b_2 \end{vmatrix} = a_1 b_2 - a_2 b_1$$

Note that a determinant is a single number.

EXAMPLE 1

a. $\begin{vmatrix} 1 & 2 \\ -1 & 3 \end{vmatrix}$

$= (1)(3) - (-1)(2)$

$= 3 - (-2) = 5$

b. $\begin{vmatrix} 0 & -1 \\ -1 & 7 \end{vmatrix}$

$= (0)(7) - (-1)(-1)$

$= 0 - 1 = -1$

c. $\begin{vmatrix} -2 & 3 \\ 4 & -1 \end{vmatrix}$

$= (-2)(-1) - (4)(3)$

$= 2 - 12 = -10$

d. $\begin{vmatrix} 4 & -2 \\ 1 & 0 \end{vmatrix}$

$= (4)(0) - (1)(-2)$

$= 0 - (-2) = 2$

Solutions of Linear Systems

Determinants can be used to solve linear systems in two variables of the form

$$a_1 x + b_1 y = c_1 \tag{1}$$
$$a_2 x + b_2 y = c_2 \tag{2}$$

If this system is solved by means of a linear combination, we have, upon multiplication of Equation (1) by $-a_2$ and Equation (2) by a_1, the equations

$$-a_1 a_2 x - a_2 b_1 y = -a_2 c_1 \tag{1a}$$
$$a_1 a_2 x + a_1 b_2 y = a_1 c_2 \tag{2a}$$

The sum of the members of (1a) and (2a) is

$$a_1 b_2 y - a_2 b_1 y = a_1 c_2 - a_2 c_1$$

Now, factoring y from each term in the left-hand member, we have

$$(a_1 b_2 - a_2 b_1) y = a_1 c_2 - a_2 c_1$$

from which

$$y = \frac{a_1 c_2 - a_2 c_1}{a_1 b_2 - a_2 b_1} \qquad (a_1 b_2 - a_2 b_1 \neq 0) \tag{3}$$

Now, the numerator of (3) is just the value of the determinant

$$\begin{vmatrix} a_1 & c_1 \\ a_2 & c_2 \end{vmatrix}$$

which we designate as D_y, and the denominator is the value of the determinant

$$\begin{vmatrix} a_1 & b_1 \\ a_2 & b_2 \end{vmatrix}$$

which we designate as D; so Equation (3) can be written as follows:

$$y = \frac{D_y}{D} = \frac{\begin{vmatrix} a_1 & c_1 \\ a_2 & c_2 \end{vmatrix}}{\begin{vmatrix} a_1 & b_1 \\ a_2 & b_2 \end{vmatrix}} \tag{4}$$

The elements of the determinant in the denominator of (4) are the coefficients of the variables in (1) and (2). The elements of the determinant in the numerator of (4) are identical to those in the denominator, except that *the elements in the column containing the coefficients of y have been replaced by c_1 and c_2*, the constant terms of (1) and (2). By exactly the same procedure, we can show the following:

$$x = \frac{D_x}{D} = \frac{\begin{vmatrix} c_1 & b_1 \\ c_2 & b_2 \end{vmatrix}}{\begin{vmatrix} a_1 & b_1 \\ a_2 & b_2 \end{vmatrix}} \tag{5}$$

Equations (4) and (5) together yield the components of the solution of the system. The use of determinants in this way is known as **Cramer's rule** for the solution of a system of linear equations.

If $D = 0$, the equations in the system are either dependent or inconsistent, depending upon whether or not D_y and D_x are both 0. This follows from the discussion on page 281, where these conditions are considered in terms of the coefficients a_1, b_1, a_2, b_2, and the constant terms c_1 and c_2.

EXAMPLE 2 Solve the following system using Cramer's rule:

$$2x - 3y = 6$$
$$2x + y = 14$$

Solution

$$D = \begin{vmatrix} 2 & -3 \\ 2 & 1 \end{vmatrix} = (2)(1) - (2)(-3) = 8$$

We obtain the elements in D_x from the elements in D by replacing the elements in the column containing the coefficients of x with the corresponding constants **6** and **14**.

$$D_x = \begin{vmatrix} \mathbf{6} & -3 \\ \mathbf{14} & 1 \end{vmatrix} = (6)(1) - (14)(-3) = 48$$

We obtain the elements in D_y from the elements in D by replacing the elements in the column containing the coefficients of y with the corresponding constants 6 and 14.

$$D_y = \begin{vmatrix} 2 & \mathbf{6} \\ 2 & \mathbf{14} \end{vmatrix} = (2)(14) - (2)(6) = 16$$

We can now determine the values for x and y by Cramer's rule.

$$x = \frac{D_x}{D} = \frac{48}{8} = 6, \qquad y = \frac{D_y}{D} = \frac{16}{8} = 2$$

The solution set is $\{(6, 2)\}$.

EXERCISE SET 10.3

▲ *Evaluate. See Example 1.*

1. $\begin{vmatrix} 1 & 0 \\ 2 & 1 \end{vmatrix}$

2. $\begin{vmatrix} 3 & -2 \\ 4 & 1 \end{vmatrix}$

3. $\begin{vmatrix} -5 & -1 \\ 3 & 3 \end{vmatrix}$

4. $\begin{vmatrix} 1 & -2 \\ -1 & 2 \end{vmatrix}$

5. $\begin{vmatrix} -1 & 6 \\ 0 & -2 \end{vmatrix}$

6. $\begin{vmatrix} 20 & 3 \\ -20 & -2 \end{vmatrix}$

7. $\begin{vmatrix} -2 & -1 \\ -3 & -4 \end{vmatrix}$

8. $\begin{vmatrix} -1 & -5 \\ -2 & -6 \end{vmatrix}$

15. $x - 2y = 5$
$$\frac{2}{3}x - \frac{4}{3}y = 6$$

16. $\frac{1}{2}x + y = 3$
$$-\frac{1}{4}x - y = -3$$

17. $x - 3y = 1$
$$y = 1$$

18. $2x - 3y = 12$
$$x = 4$$

19. $ax + by = 1$
$$bx + ay = 1$$

20. $x + y = a$
$$x - y = b$$

▲ *Solve each system using Cramer's rule. See Example 2.*

9. $2x - 3y = -1$
$$x + 4y = 5$$

10. $3x - 4y = -2$
$$x - 2y = 0$$

11. $3x - 4y = -2$
$$6x + 12y = 36$$

12. $2x - 4y = 7$
$$x - 2y = 1$$

13. $\frac{1}{3}x - \frac{1}{2}y = 0$
$$\frac{1}{2}x + \frac{1}{4}y = 4$$

14. $\frac{2}{3}x + y = 1$
$$x - \frac{4}{3}y = 0$$

Miscellaneous Exercises

▲ *Show that each statement is true for every real value of each variable.*

21. $\begin{vmatrix} a & a \\ b & b \end{vmatrix} = 0$

22. $\begin{vmatrix} a_1 & b_1 \\ a_2 & b_2 \end{vmatrix} = -\begin{vmatrix} a_2 & b_2 \\ a_1 & b_1 \end{vmatrix}$

23. $\begin{vmatrix} a_1 & b_1 \\ a_2 & b_2 \end{vmatrix} = -\begin{vmatrix} b_1 & a_1 \\ b_2 & a_2 \end{vmatrix}$

24. $\begin{vmatrix} ka_1 & b_1 \\ ka_2 & b_2 \end{vmatrix} = k \begin{vmatrix} a_1 & b_1 \\ a_2 & b_2 \end{vmatrix}$

25. $\begin{vmatrix} ka & a \\ kb & b \end{vmatrix} = 0$

26. $\begin{vmatrix} a_1 & b_1 \\ ka_2 & kb_2 \end{vmatrix} = k \begin{vmatrix} a_1 & b_1 \\ a_2 & b_2 \end{vmatrix}$

27. Show that if both $D_y = 0$ and $D_x = 0$, it follows that $D = 0$ when c_1 and c_2 are not both 0, and the equations in the system

$$a_1 x + b_1 y = c_1$$
$$a_2 x + b_2 y = c_2$$

are dependent. [*Hint:* Show that the first two determinant equations imply that $a_1 c_2 = a_2 c_1$ and $b_1 c_2 = b_2 c_1$ and that the rest follows from the formation of a proportion with these equations.]

28. Show that for the system given in Exercise 27, if $D = 0$ and $D_x = 0$, then $D_y = 0$.

10.4   SOLUTION OF SYSTEMS USING THIRD-ORDER DETERMINANTS

A third-order determinant is defined as follows:

$$\begin{vmatrix} a_1 & b_1 & c_1 \\ a_2 & b_2 & c_2 \\ a_3 & b_3 & c_3 \end{vmatrix} = a_1 b_2 c_3 - a_1 b_3 c_2 + a_3 b_1 c_2 - a_2 b_1 c_3 + a_2 b_3 c_1 - a_3 b_2 c_1 \quad (1)$$

Again, we note that a 3×3 determinant is simply a number, namely, that number represented by the expression in the right-hand member of Equation (1). We can rewrite Equation (1) in a simpler form in terms of 2×2 determinants formed from the elements of the 3×3 determinant.

Minor of a Determinant

The **minor** of an element in a determinant is defined as the determinant that remains after deleting the row and column in which the element appears. In the determinant (1), for example,

the minor of the element a_1 is $\begin{vmatrix} b_2 & c_2 \\ b_3 & c_3 \end{vmatrix}$

the minor of the element b_1 is $\begin{vmatrix} a_2 & c_2 \\ a_3 & c_3 \end{vmatrix}$

the minor of the element c_1 is $\begin{vmatrix} a_2 & b_2 \\ a_3 & b_3 \end{vmatrix}$

Expansion by Minors

If, by suitably factoring pairs of terms in the right-hand member, we rewrite Equation (1) in the form

$$\begin{vmatrix} a_1 & b_1 & c_1 \\ a_2 & b_2 & c_2 \\ a_3 & b_3 & c_3 \end{vmatrix} = a_1(b_2 c_3 - b_3 c_2) - b_1(a_2 c_3 - a_3 c_2) + c_1(a_2 b_3 - a_3 b_2) \quad (2)$$

we observe that the sums enclosed in parentheses in the right-hand member of Equation (2) are the respective minors (second-order determinants) of the elemnts a_1, b_1, and c_1. Therefore, we can write Equation (2) as

$$\begin{vmatrix} a_1 & b_1 & c_1 \\ a_2 & b_2 & c_2 \\ a_3 & b_3 & c_3 \end{vmatrix} = a_1 \begin{vmatrix} b_2 & c_2 \\ b_3 & c_3 \end{vmatrix} - b_1 \begin{vmatrix} a_2 & c_2 \\ a_3 & c_3 \end{vmatrix} + c_1 \begin{vmatrix} a_2 & b_2 \\ a_3 & b_3 \end{vmatrix} \tag{3}$$

We call the right-hand member of Equation (3) the **expansion** of the determinant by minors *about the first row.*

Suppose, instead of factoring the right-hand member of (1) into the right-hand member of Equation (2), we factor it as

$$\begin{vmatrix} a_1 & b_1 & c_1 \\ a_2 & b_2 & c_2 \\ a_3 & b_3 & c_3 \end{vmatrix} = a_1(b_2 c_3 - b_3 c_2) - a_2(b_1 c_3 - b_3 c_1) + a_3(b_1 c_2 - b_2 c_1) \tag{4}$$

Then we have the expansion of the determinant by minors *about the first column*:

$$\begin{vmatrix} a_1 & b_1 & c_1 \\ a_2 & b_2 & c_2 \\ a_3 & b_3 & c_3 \end{vmatrix} = a_1 \begin{vmatrix} b_2 & c_2 \\ b_3 & c_3 \end{vmatrix} - a_2 \begin{vmatrix} b_1 & c_1 \\ b_3 & c_3 \end{vmatrix} + a_3 \begin{vmatrix} b_1 & c_1 \\ b_2 & c_2 \end{vmatrix} \tag{5}$$

With the proper use of signs, it is possible to expand a determinant by minors about *any* row or *any* column and obtain an expression equivalent to a factored form of the right-hand member of Equation (1). A helpful device for determining the signs of the terms in an expansion of a third-order determinant by minors is the array of alternating signs

$$\begin{matrix} + & - & + \\ - & + & - \\ + & - & + \end{matrix}$$

which we call the **sign array** for the determinant. To obtain an expansion of Equation (1) about a given row or column, we prefix the appropriate sign from the sign array to each term in the expansion.

EXAMPLE 1   **a.** If we first expand the determinant

$$\begin{vmatrix} 1 & 2 & -3 \\ 0 & 2 & -1 \\ 1 & 1 & 0 \end{vmatrix} \tag{6}$$

about the second row, we have

$$\begin{vmatrix} 1 & 2 & -3 \\ 0 & 2 & -1 \\ 1 & 1 & 0 \end{vmatrix} = -0 \begin{vmatrix} 2 & -3 \\ 1 & 0 \end{vmatrix} + 2 \begin{vmatrix} 1 & -3 \\ 1 & 0 \end{vmatrix} - (-1) \begin{vmatrix} 1 & 2 \\ 1 & 1 \end{vmatrix}$$

$$= 0 + 2(0 + 3) + 1(1 - 2)$$

$$= 6 - 1 = 5$$

b. If we expand (6) about the third row, we have

$$\begin{vmatrix} 1 & 2 & -3 \\ 0 & 2 & -1 \\ 1 & 1 & 0 \end{vmatrix} = 1\begin{vmatrix} 2 & -3 \\ 2 & -1 \end{vmatrix} - 1\begin{vmatrix} 1 & -3 \\ 0 & -1 \end{vmatrix} + 0\begin{vmatrix} 1 & 2 \\ 0 & 2 \end{vmatrix}$$

$$= 1(-2 + 6) - 1(-1 - 0) + 0$$

$$= 4 + 1 = 5$$

You should expand this determinant about the first row and about each column to verify that the result is the same in each expansion.

Cramer's Rule   Consider the following linear system in three variables

$$a_1 x + b_1 y + c_1 z = d_1 \tag{7}$$
$$a_2 x + b_2 y + c_2 z = d_2 \tag{8}$$
$$a_3 x + b_3 y + c_3 z = d_3 \tag{9}$$

By solving this system using the methods of Section 10.3, we can show that Cramer's rule applies to such systems of three equations in three variables.

$$x = \frac{D_x}{D}, \qquad y = \frac{D_y}{D}, \qquad z = \frac{D_z}{D}$$

where

$$D = \begin{vmatrix} a_1 & b_1 & c_1 \\ a_2 & b_2 & c_2 \\ a_3 & b_3 & c_3 \end{vmatrix}, \qquad D_x = \begin{vmatrix} d_1 & b_1 & c_1 \\ d_2 & b_2 & c_2 \\ d_3 & b_3 & c_3 \end{vmatrix}$$

$$D_y = \begin{vmatrix} a_1 & d_1 & c_1 \\ a_2 & d_2 & c_2 \\ a_3 & d_3 & c_3 \end{vmatrix}, \qquad D_z = \begin{vmatrix} a_1 & b_1 & d_1 \\ a_2 & b_2 & d_2 \\ a_3 & b_3 & d_3 \end{vmatrix}$$

Note that the elements of the determinant D in each denominator are the coefficients of the variables in Equations (7), (8), and (9). Note also that the numerators are formed from D by replacing the elements in the x, y, or z column, respectively, by d_1, d_2, and d_3.

EXAMPLE 2   Solve the following system using Cramer's rule:

$$x + 2y - 3z = -4$$
$$2x - y + z = 3$$
$$3x + 2y + z = 10$$

Solution   The determinant D, with elements that are the coefficients of the variables, is given by

$$D = \begin{vmatrix} 1 & 2 & -3 \\ 2 & -1 & 1 \\ 3 & 2 & 1 \end{vmatrix}$$

We can expand the determinant about the first column, obtaining

$$D = \begin{vmatrix} 1 & 2 & -3 \\ 2 & -1 & 1 \\ 3 & 2 & 1 \end{vmatrix} = 1\begin{vmatrix} -1 & 1 \\ 2 & 1 \end{vmatrix} - 2\begin{vmatrix} 2 & -3 \\ 2 & 1 \end{vmatrix} + 3\begin{vmatrix} 2 & -3 \\ -1 & 1 \end{vmatrix}$$

$$= -3 - 16 - 3 = -22$$

Replacing the first column in D with -4, 3, and 10, we obtain

$$D_x = \begin{vmatrix} -4 & 2 & -3 \\ 3 & -1 & 1 \\ 10 & 2 & 1 \end{vmatrix}$$

Expanding D_x about the third column, we have

$$D_x = \begin{vmatrix} -4 & 2 & -3 \\ 3 & -1 & 1 \\ 10 & 2 & 1 \end{vmatrix}$$

$$= -3\begin{vmatrix} 3 & -1 \\ 10 & 2 \end{vmatrix} - 1\begin{vmatrix} -4 & 2 \\ 10 & 2 \end{vmatrix} + 1\begin{vmatrix} -4 & 2 \\ 3 & -1 \end{vmatrix}$$

$$= -48 + 28 - 2 = -22$$

In a similar fashion, we can compute D_y and D_z.

$$D_y = \begin{vmatrix} 1 & -4 & -3 \\ 2 & 3 & 1 \\ 3 & 10 & 1 \end{vmatrix} = -44, \qquad D_z = \begin{vmatrix} 1 & 2 & -4 \\ 2 & -1 & 3 \\ 3 & 2 & 10 \end{vmatrix} = -66$$

We then have

$$x = \frac{D_x}{D} = \frac{-22}{-22} \qquad y = \frac{D_y}{D} = \frac{-44}{-22} \quad \text{and} \quad z = \frac{D_z}{D} = \frac{-66}{-22}$$

$$= 1, \qquad\qquad = 2, \qquad\qquad\qquad = 3$$

The solution set of the system is therefore $\{(1, 2, 3)\}$.

As was noted on page 289 for a linear system in two variables, if $D = 0$ for a linear system in three variables, the system does not have a unique solution.

E X E R C I S E   S E T   10.4

▲ *Evaluate each determinant. See Example 1.*

1. $\begin{vmatrix} 2 & 0 & 1 \\ 1 & 1 & 2 \\ -1 & 0 & 1 \end{vmatrix}$

2. $\begin{vmatrix} 1 & 3 & 1 \\ -1 & 2 & 1 \\ 0 & 2 & 0 \end{vmatrix}$

5. $\begin{vmatrix} 1 & 2 & 3 \\ 3 & -1 & 2 \\ 2 & 0 & 2 \end{vmatrix}$

6. $\begin{vmatrix} 1 & 0 & 0 \\ 0 & 1 & 2 \\ 0 & 3 & 4 \end{vmatrix}$

3. $\begin{vmatrix} 2 & -1 & 0 \\ -3 & 1 & 2 \\ 1 & -3 & 1 \end{vmatrix}$

4. $\begin{vmatrix} 2 & 4 & -1 \\ -1 & 3 & 2 \\ 4 & 0 & 2 \end{vmatrix}$

7. $\begin{vmatrix} -1 & 0 & 2 \\ -2 & 1 & 0 \\ 0 & 1 & -3 \end{vmatrix}$

8. $\begin{vmatrix} 2 & 1 & 4 \\ 3 & 2 & 6 \\ 5 & -3 & 10 \end{vmatrix}$

Another Method to Evaluate a 3 by 3 Determinant

Another method for expanding a 3×3 determinant is to reproduce the first two columns, find the sums of the products along the upward arrows, and subtract these sums of products of upward arrows as shown below. This method works *only* for 3×3 determinants.

Example 1. Find the determinant: $\begin{vmatrix} 1 & 3 & -2 \\ -1 & -2 & -3 \\ 1 & 1 & 2 \end{vmatrix}$.

$$[-4 + (-9) + 2] \quad - \quad [4 + (-3) + (-6)] = -11 - (-5) = -11 + 5 = \boxed{-6}$$

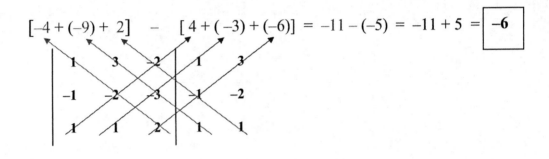

Example 2. Find the determinant: $\begin{vmatrix} 0 & -1 & 0 \\ 2 & 4 & 2 \\ 3 & 1 & 5 \end{vmatrix}$.

$$[0 + (-6) + 0] \quad - \quad [0 + 0 + (-10)] = -6 - (-10) = -6 + 10 = \boxed{4}$$

Cramer's Rule for Solving a System of 3 Equations in 3 Variables

Given the system

$$a_1 x + b_1 y + c_1 z = d_1$$
$$a_2 x + b_2 y + c_2 z = d_2$$
$$a_3 x + b_3 y + c_3 z = d_3$$

with

$$D = \begin{vmatrix} a_1 & b_1 & c_1 \\ a_2 & b_2 & c_2 \\ a_3 & b_3 & c_3 \end{vmatrix} \neq 0, \qquad D_x = \begin{vmatrix} d_1 & b_1 & c_1 \\ d_2 & b_2 & c_2 \\ d_3 & b_3 & c_3 \end{vmatrix},$$

$$D_y = \begin{vmatrix} a_1 & d_1 & c_1 \\ a_2 & d_2 & c_2 \\ a_3 & d_3 & c_3 \end{vmatrix}, \qquad D_z = \begin{vmatrix} a_1 & b_1 & d_1 \\ a_2 & b_2 & d_2 \\ a_3 & b_3 & d_3 \end{vmatrix},$$

then

$$x = \frac{D_x}{D}, \qquad y = \frac{D_y}{D}, \qquad \text{and} \qquad z = \frac{D_z}{D}.$$

Note: Determinant D is the determinant of the coefficients of the x, y, and z variables.

Determinant D_x is obtained by replacing the first column $\begin{matrix} a_1 \\ a_2 \\ a_3 \end{matrix}$ of Determinant D with the column of constants $\begin{matrix} d_1 \\ d_2 \\ d_3 \end{matrix}$.

Determinant D_y is obtained by replacing the second column $\begin{matrix} b_1 \\ b_2 \\ b_3 \end{matrix}$ of Determinant D with the column of constants $\begin{matrix} d_1 \\ d_2 \\ d_3 \end{matrix}$.

Determinant D_z is obtained by replacing the third column $\begin{matrix} c_1 \\ c_2 \\ c_3 \end{matrix}$ of Determinant D with the column of constants $\begin{matrix} d_1 \\ d_2 \\ d_3 \end{matrix}$.

Solving Systems of 3 Equations in 3 Variables

Example: Solve the following system of equations by Cramer's Rule using determinants.

$$\begin{cases} x - y + 2z = -3 \\ x + 2y + 3z = 4 \\ 2x + y + z = -3 \end{cases}$$

$$D = \begin{vmatrix} 1 & -1 & 2 \\ 1 & 2 & 3 \\ 2 & 1 & 1 \end{vmatrix} \begin{matrix} 1 & -1 \\ 1 & 2 \\ 2 & 1 \end{matrix} \quad = [2 - 6 + 2] - [8 + 3 - 1] = -2 - 10 = -12$$

$$D_x = \begin{vmatrix} -3 & -1 & 2 \\ 4 & 2 & 3 \\ -3 & 1 & 1 \end{vmatrix} \begin{matrix} -3 & -1 \\ 4 & 2 \\ -3 & 1 \end{matrix} \quad = [-6 + 9 + 8] - [-12 - 9 - 4] = 11 - [-25] = 11 + 25 = 36$$

$$D_y = \begin{vmatrix} 1 & -3 & 2 \\ 1 & 4 & 3 \\ 2 & -3 & 1 \end{vmatrix} \begin{matrix} 1 & -3 \\ 1 & 4 \\ 2 & -3 \end{matrix} \quad = [4 - 18 - 6] - [16 - 9 - 3] = -20 - 4 = -24$$

$$D_z = \begin{vmatrix} 1 & -1 & -3 \\ 1 & 2 & 4 \\ 2 & 1 & -3 \end{vmatrix} \begin{matrix} 1 & -1 \\ 1 & 2 \\ 2 & 1 \end{matrix} \quad = [-6 - 8 - 3] - [-12 + 4 + 3] = -17 - [-5] = -17 + 5 = -12$$

$$x = \frac{D_x}{D} = \frac{36}{-12} = -3 \qquad\qquad y = \frac{D_y}{D} = \frac{-24}{-12} = 2 \qquad\qquad z = \frac{D_z}{z} = \frac{-12}{-12} = 1$$

The solution is $x = -3$, $y = 2$, and $z = 1$, or the ordered triple $(-3, 2, 1)$. You can easily verify that this solution satisfies all three equations in the original system.

9. $\begin{vmatrix} 2 & 5 & -1 \\ 1 & 0 & 2 \\ 0 & 0 & 1 \end{vmatrix}$

10. $\begin{vmatrix} 2 & 3 & 1 \\ 0 & 1 & 0 \\ -4 & 2 & 1 \end{vmatrix}$

11. $\begin{vmatrix} a & b & 1 \\ a & b & 1 \\ 1 & 1 & 1 \end{vmatrix}$

12. $\begin{vmatrix} a & a & a \\ 1 & 2 & 3 \\ 4 & 5 & 6 \end{vmatrix}$

13. $\begin{vmatrix} x & 0 & 0 \\ 0 & x & 0 \\ 0 & 0 & x \end{vmatrix}$

14. $\begin{vmatrix} 0 & 0 & x \\ 0 & x & 0 \\ x & 0 & 0 \end{vmatrix}$

15. $\begin{vmatrix} x & y & 0 \\ x & y & 0 \\ 0 & 0 & 1 \end{vmatrix}$

16. $\begin{vmatrix} 0 & a & b \\ a & 0 & a \\ b & a & 0 \end{vmatrix}$

17. $\begin{vmatrix} a & b & 0 \\ b & 0 & b \\ 0 & b & a \end{vmatrix}$

18. $\begin{vmatrix} 0 & b & 0 \\ b & a & b \\ 0 & b & 0 \end{vmatrix}$

▲ *Solve each system using Cramer's rule. If a unique solution does not exist $(D = 0)$, so state. See Example 2.*

19. $x + y = 2$
$2x - z = 1$
$2y - 3z = -1$

20. $2x - 6y + 3z = -12$
$3x - 2y + 5z = -4$
$4x + 5y - 2z = 10$

21. $x - 2y + z = -1$
$3x + y - 2z = 4$
$y - z = 1$

22. $2x + 5z = 9$
$4x + 3y = -1$
$3y - 4z = -13$

23. $2x + 2y + z = 1$
$x - y + 6z = 21$
$3x + 2y - z = -4$

24. $4x + 8y + z = -6$
$2x - 3y + 2z = 0$
$x + 7y - 3z = -8$

25. $x + y + z = 0$
$2x - y - 4z = 15$
$x - 2y - z = 7$

26. $x + y - 2z = 3$
$3x - y + z = 5$
$3x + 3y - 6z = 9$

27. $x - 2y + 2z = 3$
$2x - 4y + 4z = 1$
$3x - 3y - 3z = 4$

28. $3x - 2y + 5z = 6$
$4x - 4y + 3z = 0$
$5x - 4y + z = -5$

29. $\frac{1}{4}x - z = -\frac{1}{4}$
$x + y = \frac{2}{3}$
$3x + 4z = 5$

30. $2x - \frac{2}{3}y + z = 2$
$\frac{1}{2}x - \frac{1}{3}y - \frac{1}{4}z = 0$
$4x + 5y - 3z = -1$

31. $x + 4z = 3$
$y + 3z = 9$
$2x + 5y - 5z = -5$

32. $2x + y = 18$
$y + z = -1$
$3x - 2y - 5z = 38$

Miscellaneous Exercises

33. Show that for all values of x, y, and z,
$$\begin{vmatrix} x & x & a \\ y & y & b \\ z & z & c \end{vmatrix} = 0$$
[*Hint:* Expand about the elements of the third column.] Make a conjecture about determinants that contain two identical columns.

34. Show that
$$\begin{vmatrix} 0 & 0 & 0 \\ a & b & c \\ d & e & f \end{vmatrix} = 0$$
for all values of a, b, c, d, e, and f. Make a conjecture about determinants that contain a row of 0 elements.

35. Show that
$$\begin{vmatrix} 1 & 2 & 3 \\ 4 & 5 & 6 \\ 0 & 0 & 1 \end{vmatrix} = -\begin{vmatrix} 4 & 5 & 6 \\ 1 & 2 & 3 \\ 0 & 0 & 1 \end{vmatrix}$$
Make a conjecture about the result of interchanging any two rows of a determinant.

36. Show that
$$\begin{vmatrix} 2 & 0 & 1 \\ 4 & 1 & -2 \\ 6 & 1 & 1 \end{vmatrix} = 2\begin{vmatrix} 1 & 0 & 1 \\ 2 & 1 & -2 \\ 3 & 1 & 1 \end{vmatrix}$$
Make a conjecture about the result of factoring a common factor from each element of a column in a determinant.

37. Show that the graph of
$$\begin{vmatrix} x & y & 1 \\ 4 & -1 & 1 \\ 2 & 3 & 1 \end{vmatrix} = 0$$
is a line containing the points $(4, -1)$ and $(2, 3)$.

38. Show that the slope-intercept form of the equation of a line can be written
$$\begin{vmatrix} x & y & 1 \\ 0 & b & 1 \\ 1 & m & 0 \end{vmatrix} = 0$$

10.5 SOLUTION OF SYSTEMS USING MATRICES

In previous sections we solved linear systems by using linear combinations and determinants. In this section we consider another mathematical tool called a *matrix* (plural: matrices) that has wide applications in mathematics. In particular, we will see how it can be used to solve linear systems.

A **matrix** is a rectangular array of elements or **entries** (in this book, real numbers). These entries are ordinarily displayed by using brackets or parentheses (we shall use brackets). Thus,

$$\begin{bmatrix} 1 & 2 & 3 \\ 4 & 5 & 6 \\ 7 & 8 & 9 \end{bmatrix}, \quad \begin{bmatrix} 2 & -1 & 3 \\ 4 & 0 & 2 \end{bmatrix}, \quad \begin{bmatrix} 4 \\ 5 \\ 6 \end{bmatrix}$$

are matrices with real-number elements. The **order**, or **dimension**, of a matrix is an ordered pair having as its first component the number of (horizontal) rows and as its second component the number of (vertical) columns in the matrix. Thus, the three preceding matrices are 3×3 (read "three-by-three"), 2×3 (read "two-by-three"), and 3×1 (read "three-by-one"), respectively. Note that the first matrix—in which the number of rows is equal to the number of columns—is an example of a **square** matrix.

Elementary Transformations

We can transform one matrix into another in a variety of ways. However, here we are concerned only with the following kinds of transformations:

1. Multiplying the entries of any row by a nonzero real number.
2. Interchanging two rows.
3. Multiplying the entries of any row by a real number and adding the results to the corresponding elements of another row.

Such transformations are called **elementary transformations** or **row operations**, and if a matrix A is transformed into a matrix B by a finite succession of such transformations, we say that A and B are **row-equivalent**. We represent this by writing $A \sim B$ (read "A is row-equivalent to B"). For example,

$$A = \begin{bmatrix} 1 & 3 & -1 \\ 2 & 1 & 4 \\ 6 & 2 & -1 \end{bmatrix} \quad \text{and} \quad B = \begin{bmatrix} 1 & 3 & -1 \\ 6 & 3 & 12 \\ 6 & 2 & -1 \end{bmatrix}$$

are row-equivalent, because we can multiply each entry in row 2 of A by 3 to obtain B;

$$A = \begin{bmatrix} 3 & -1 & 2 \\ 2 & 1 & 4 \\ 3 & 1 & 9 \end{bmatrix} \quad \text{and} \quad B = \begin{bmatrix} 3 & 1 & 9 \\ 2 & 1 & 4 \\ 3 & -1 & 2 \end{bmatrix}$$

are row-equivalent, because we can interchange rows 1 and 3 of A to obtain B; and

$$A = \begin{bmatrix} 1 & 2 & 1 \\ 2 & 0 & -1 \\ 3 & 1 & 2 \end{bmatrix} \quad \text{and} \quad B = \begin{bmatrix} 1 & 2 & 1 \\ 0 & -4 & -3 \\ 3 & 1 & 2 \end{bmatrix}$$

are row-equivalent, because we can multiply each entry in row 1 of A by -2 and add the results to the corresponding entries in row 2 of A to obtain B.

It is often convenient to perform more than one elementary transformation on a given matrix. For example, if in the matrix

$$\begin{bmatrix} 1 & -2 & 1 \\ 2 & 1 & 3 \\ -3 & 0 & 0 \end{bmatrix}$$

we add $-2 \cdot$ (row 1) to row 2, and $3 \cdot$ (row 1) to row 3, we obtain the row-equivalent matrix

$$\begin{bmatrix} 1 & -2 & 1 \\ 0 & 5 & 1 \\ 0 & -6 & 3 \end{bmatrix}$$

EXAMPLE 1 Use row operations on the first matrix to form an equivalent matrix with the given elements.

$$\begin{bmatrix} 1 & -4 \\ 3 & 6 \end{bmatrix} \sim \begin{bmatrix} 1 & -4 \\ 0 & ? \end{bmatrix}$$

Solution $-3(\text{row 1}) + \text{row 2}$ $\begin{bmatrix} 1 & -4 \\ 3 & 6 \end{bmatrix} \rightarrow \begin{bmatrix} 1 & -4 \\ 0 & 18 \end{bmatrix}$

EXAMPLE 2 Use row operations on the first matrix to form an equivalent matrix with the given elements.

$$\begin{bmatrix} 1 & -3 & 1 \\ 3 & 1 & -1 \\ 2 & -2 & 3 \end{bmatrix} \sim \begin{bmatrix} 1 & -3 & 1 \\ 0 & ? & ? \\ 0 & ? & ? \end{bmatrix}$$

Solution
$\begin{array}{l} -3(\text{row 1}) + \text{row 2} \\ -2(\text{row 1}) + \text{row 3} \end{array}$ $\begin{bmatrix} 1 & -3 & 1 \\ 3 & 1 & -1 \\ 2 & -2 & 3 \end{bmatrix} \rightarrow \begin{bmatrix} 1 & -3 & 1 \\ 0 & 10 & -4 \\ 0 & 4 & 1 \end{bmatrix}$

EXAMPLE 3 Use row operations on the first matrix to form an equivalent matrix with the given elements.

$$\begin{bmatrix} 1 & -3 & 1 \\ 0 & 10 & -4 \\ 0 & 4 & 1 \end{bmatrix} \sim \begin{bmatrix} 1 & -3 & 1 \\ 0 & 5 & -2 \\ 0 & 0 & 13/5 \end{bmatrix}$$

Solution We first obtain a row-equivalent matrix with second row $\begin{bmatrix} 0 & 5 & -2 \end{bmatrix}$.

$-\dfrac{1}{2}(\text{row 2})$ $\begin{bmatrix} 1 & -3 & 1 \\ 0 & 10 & -4 \\ 0 & 4 & 1 \end{bmatrix} \rightarrow \begin{bmatrix} 1 & -3 & 1 \\ 0 & 5 & -2 \\ 0 & 4 & 1 \end{bmatrix}$

We then obtain a row-equivalent matrix with third row $[0 \quad 0 \quad 13/5]$.

$$-\frac{4}{5}(\text{row 2}) + \text{row 3} \begin{bmatrix} 1 & -3 & 1 \\ 0 & 5 & -2 \\ 0 & 4 & 1 \end{bmatrix} \rightarrow \begin{bmatrix} 1 & -3 & 1 \\ 0 & 5 & -2 \\ 0 & 0 & 13/5 \end{bmatrix}$$

Solution of Linear Systems

In a system of linear equations of the form

$$a_1 x + b_1 y + c_1 z = d_1$$
$$a_2 x + b_2 y + c_2 z = d_2$$
$$a_3 x + b_3 y + c_3 z = d_3$$

the matrices

$$\begin{bmatrix} a_1 & b_1 & c_1 \\ a_2 & b_2 & c_2 \\ a_3 & b_3 & c_3 \end{bmatrix} \quad \text{and} \quad \begin{bmatrix} a_1 & b_1 & c_1 & \vdots & d_1 \\ a_2 & b_2 & c_2 & \vdots & d_2 \\ a_3 & b_3 & c_3 & \vdots & d_3 \end{bmatrix}$$

are called the **coefficient matrix** and the **augmented matrix**, respectively.

By performing elementary transformations on the augmented matrix of a system of equations, we can obtain a matrix from which the solution set of the system is readily determined. The validity of the method, as illustrated in Examples 4 and 5, stems from the fact that performing elementary row operations on the augmented matrix of a system corresponds to forming equivalent systems of equations.

For example, the augmented matrix of

$$\begin{array}{c} x + 2y = 7 \\ 2x - y = 4 \end{array} \quad \text{is} \quad \begin{bmatrix} 1 & 2 & \vdots & 7 \\ 2 & -1 & \vdots & 4 \end{bmatrix}$$

Performing elementary transformations, we have

$$-2(\text{row 1}) + \text{row 2} \begin{bmatrix} 1 & 2 & \vdots & 7 \\ 0 & -5 & \vdots & -10 \end{bmatrix}$$

This matrix corresponds to the system

$$\begin{array}{c} x + 2y = 7 \\ -5y = -10 \end{array}$$

From the last equation, $y = 2$. Substituting 2 for y in the first equation, we obtain $x = 3$. Hence, the solution set is $\{(3, 2)\}$.

Note that in this example the elements $[0 \quad -5 \quad -10]$ in the second row of the final augmented matrix corresond to an equation in one variable $-5y = -10$. In general, to solve a system using matrices, we perform elementary transformations to obtain a coefficient matrix with only one nonzero element in the last row.

EXAMPLE 4

Use matrices to solve the system

$$\begin{array}{c} x - 2y = -5 \\ 2x + 3y = 11 \end{array}$$

Solution The augmented matrix is

$$\begin{bmatrix} 1 & -2 & | & -5 \\ 2 & 3 & | & 11 \end{bmatrix}$$

We perform elementary operations to obtain a coefficient matrix with only one non-zero element in the second row.

$$-2(\text{row 1}) + \text{row 2} \begin{bmatrix} 1 & -2 & | & -5 \\ 2 & 3 & | & 11 \end{bmatrix} \rightarrow \begin{bmatrix} 1 & -2 & | & -5 \\ 0 & 7 & | & 21 \end{bmatrix}$$

The last matrix corresponds to the system

$$x - 2y = -5 \quad . \tag{1}$$
$$7y = 21 \tag{2}$$

From Equation (2), $y = 3$. We substitute 3 for y in Equation (1):

$$x - 2(3) = 5$$
$$x = 1$$

The solution set is $\{(1, 3)\}$.

The next example involves a system of three equations in three variables.

EXAMPLE 5 Solve the system

$$x - 3y + z = -2$$
$$3x + y - z = 8$$
$$2x - 2y + 3z = -1$$

Solution The augmented matrix of the system is

$$\begin{bmatrix} 1 & -3 & 1 & | & -2 \\ 3 & 1 & -1 & | & 8 \\ 2 & -2 & 3 & | & -1 \end{bmatrix}$$

We perform elementary row operations to obtain a coefficient matrix with only one nonzero element in the third row.

$$\begin{array}{c} \\ -3(\text{row 1}) + \text{row 2} \\ -2(\text{row 1}) + \text{row 3} \end{array} \begin{bmatrix} 1 & -3 & 1 & | & -2 \\ 3 & 1 & -1 & | & 8 \\ 2 & -2 & 3 & | & -1 \end{bmatrix}$$

$$\downarrow$$

$$\frac{1}{2}(\text{row 2}) \begin{bmatrix} 1 & -3 & 1 & | & -2 \\ 0 & 10 & -4 & | & 14 \\ 0 & 4 & 1 & | & 3 \end{bmatrix} \quad \begin{array}{r} x - 3y + z = -2 \\ 0x + 10y - 4z = 14 \\ 0x + 4y + z = 3 \end{array}$$

$$\downarrow$$

$$-\frac{4}{5}(\text{row 2}) + \text{row 3} \begin{bmatrix} 1 & -3 & 1 & | & -2 \\ 0 & 5 & -2 & | & 7 \\ 0 & 4 & 1 & | & 3 \end{bmatrix} \quad \begin{array}{r} x - 3y + z = -2 \\ 0x + 5y - 2z = 7 \\ 0x + 4y + z = 3 \end{array}$$

$$\downarrow$$

$$\begin{array}{c} \\ \\ 5(\text{row } 3) \end{array} \begin{bmatrix} 1 & -3 & 1 & \vdots & -2 \\ 0 & 5 & -2 & \vdots & 7 \\ 0 & 0 & \dfrac{13}{5} & \vdots & -\dfrac{13}{5} \end{bmatrix} \qquad \begin{array}{l} x - 3y + \quad z = -2 \\ 0x + 5y - \quad 2z = 7 \\ 0x + 0y + \left(\dfrac{13}{5}\right)z = -\dfrac{13}{5} \end{array}$$

$$\downarrow$$

$$\begin{bmatrix} 1 & -3 & 1 & \vdots & -2 \\ 0 & 5 & -2 & \vdots & 7 \\ 0 & 0 & 13 & \vdots & -13 \end{bmatrix} \qquad \begin{array}{l} x - 3y + \quad z = -2 \\ 0x + 5y - \quad 2z = 7 \\ 0x + 0y + \quad 13z = -13 \end{array}$$

The last matrix corresponds to the system

$$\begin{array}{l} x - 3y + \quad z = -2 \\ \quad\quad 5y - 2z = 7 \\ \quad\quad\quad\quad 13z = -13 \end{array}$$

Since, from the last equation, $z = -1$, we can substitute -1 for z in the second equation to obtain $y = 1$. Finally, substituting -1 for z and 1 for y in the first equation, we have $x = 2$. The solution set is $\{(2, 1, -1)\}$.

If any step in this procedure results in the equation $0x + 0y + 0z = 0$ or a contradiction such as $0x + 0y + 0z = 2$, then the system contains dependent or inconsistent equations, and it has either an infinite number of members or no members in its solution set. In either case we say that the system has no unique solution.

E X E R C I S E   S E T   1 0 . 5

▲ *Use row operations on the first matrix to form an equivalent matrix with the given elements. See Examples 1, 2, and 3.*

1. $\begin{bmatrix} 1 & -3 \\ 2 & 1 \end{bmatrix} \sim \begin{bmatrix} 1 & -3 \\ 0 & ? \end{bmatrix}$

2. $\begin{bmatrix} -2 & 3 \\ 4 & 1 \end{bmatrix} \sim \begin{bmatrix} -2 & 3 \\ 0 & ? \end{bmatrix}$

3. $\begin{bmatrix} 2 & 6 \\ 5 & 3 \end{bmatrix} \sim \begin{bmatrix} 2 & 6 \\ ? & 0 \end{bmatrix}$

4. $\begin{bmatrix} 6 & 4 \\ -1 & -2 \end{bmatrix} \sim \begin{bmatrix} 6 & 4 \\ ? & 0 \end{bmatrix}$

5. $\begin{bmatrix} 1 & -2 & 2 \\ 2 & 3 & -1 \\ 4 & 1 & -3 \end{bmatrix} \sim \begin{bmatrix} 1 & -2 & 2 \\ 0 & ? & ? \\ 0 & ? & ? \end{bmatrix}$

6. $\begin{bmatrix} 2 & -1 & 3 \\ -4 & 0 & 4 \\ 6 & 2 & -1 \end{bmatrix} \sim \begin{bmatrix} 2 & -1 & 3 \\ 0 & ? & ? \\ 0 & ? & ? \end{bmatrix}$

7. $\begin{bmatrix} -1 & 4 & 3 \\ 2 & -2 & -4 \\ 1 & 2 & 3 \end{bmatrix} \sim \begin{bmatrix} -1 & 4 & 3 \\ ? & 0 & ? \\ ? & 0 & ? \end{bmatrix}$

8. $\begin{bmatrix} 3 & -2 & 4 \\ 2 & 2 & 1 \\ -1 & 1 & 5 \end{bmatrix} \sim \begin{bmatrix} 3 & -2 & 4 \\ ? & ? & 0 \\ ? & ? & 0 \end{bmatrix}$

9. $\begin{bmatrix} -2 & 1 & -3 \\ 4 & 2 & 0 \\ -6 & -1 & 2 \end{bmatrix} \sim \begin{bmatrix} -2 & 1 & -3 \\ 0 & ? & ? \\ 0 & 0 & ? \end{bmatrix}$

10. $\begin{bmatrix} -1 & 2 & 3 \\ 4 & 0 & 1 \\ -2 & 2 & -3 \end{bmatrix} \sim \begin{bmatrix} -1 & 2 & 3 \\ 0 & ? & ? \\ 0 & 0 & ? \end{bmatrix}$

▲ *Use row operations on the augmented matrix to solve each system. For Exercises 11–18, see Example 4.*

11. $\begin{array}{l} x + 3y = 11 \\ 2x - y = 1 \end{array}$

12. $\begin{array}{l} x - 5y = 11 \\ 2x + 3y = -4 \end{array}$

13. $x - 4y = -6$
    $3x + y = -5$

14. $x + 6y = -14$
    $5x - 3y = -4$

15. $2x + y = 5$
    $3x - 5y = 14$

16. $3x - 2y = 16$
    $4x + 2y = 12$

17. $x - y = -8$
    $x + 2y = 9$

18. $4x - 3y = 16$
    $2x + y = 8$

▲ *For Exercises 19–26, see Example 5.*

19. $x + 3y - z = 5$
    $3x - y + 2z = 5$
    $x + y + 2z = 7$

20. $x - 2y + 3z = -11$
    $2x + 3y - z = 6$
    $3x - y - z = 3$

21. $2x - y + z = 5$
    $x - 2y - 2z = 2$
    $3x + 3y - z = 4$

22. $x - 2y - 2z = 4$
    $2x + y - 3z = 7$
    $x - y - z = 3$

23. $2x - y - z = -4$
    $x + y + z = -5$
    $x + 3y - 4z = 12$

24. $x - 2y - 5z = 2$
    $2x + 3y + z = 11$
    $3x - y - z = 11$

25. $2x - y = 0$
    $3y + z = 7$
    $2x + 3z = 1$

26. $3x - z = 7$
    $2x + y = 6$
    $3y - z = 7$

Miscellaneous Exercises

▲ *Solve.*

27. $r + s + t - u = 7$
    $2s + 3t - 2u = 7$
    $t + 3u = 9$
    $3t - u = 7$

28. $2r - s - t + 3u = 14$
    $r + 2t + u = 2$
    $3r - u = 0$
    $r + u = 4$

29. $a + 2b - c + d = 3$
    $b - 2c + d = 3$
    $3c + 2d = -6$
    $2b - 3d = -2$

30. $2a - b + 3c - d = -5$
    $a - b + 2d = 6$
    $2a - d = -1$
    $3a - 2d = -3$

10.6 | APPLICATIONS

In previous sections we solved a variety of applied problems by constructing first-degree equations in one variable. This required us to express each of the quantities we wished to find in terms of one variable.

It is generally easier to assign different variables to represent different quantities. However, we must then construct two or more equations from the stated conditions in a problem.

In writing systems of equations, we must be careful that the conditions giving rise to one equation are independent of the conditions giving rise to any other equation. Note that the approach we use to solve equations in the following examples is similar to the five-step procedure we used to solve word problems using one variable.

In the following Examples 1 and 2, only two numbers are to be found. Hence, it is necessary to use only two variables and a system of two independent equations.

EXAMPLE 1

The sum of two numbers is 17, and one of the numbers is 4 less than 2 times the other. Find the numbers.

Solution

We represent each number by a separate variable.

One number: x

Other number: y

We represent the two independent conditions stated in the problem by two equations.

$$x + y = 17$$
$$x = 2y - 4$$

We rewrite the equations in the form

$$x + y = 17$$
$$x - 2y = -4$$

We can use any one of the procedures that we considered in the previous sections to solve this system. The numbers are 10 and 7.

E X A M P L E 2   A company offers split-rail fencing for sale in two options. One option consists of four posts and six rails for $31; the other consists of three posts and four rails for $22. What are the costs of one post and one rail?

Solution   We represent each quantity by a separate variable.

Cost of one post: p

Cost of one rail: r

We represent the two independent conditions stated in the problem by two equations.

$$4p + 6r = 31 \tag{1}$$
$$3p + 4r = 22 \tag{2}$$

Again, we can here use any one of the procedures that we have used to solve systems. One post costs $4.00, and one rail costs $2.50.

The following examples illustrate how a system in three variables can be constructed when we want to find three quantities. Again in writing such systems, we must be careful that the conditions giving rise to one equation are independent of the conditions giving rise to any other equation.

E X A M P L E 3   The sum of three numbers is 12. Twice the first number is equal to the second, and the third is equal to the sum of the other two. Find the numbers.

Solution   We represent each number by a separate variable.

First number: x

Second number: y

Third number: z

We write the three conditions stated in the problem as three equations.

$$x + y + z = 12$$
$$2x = y$$
$$x + y = z$$

We rewrite the equations in the form

$$x + y + z = 12$$
$$2x - y = 0$$
$$x + y - z = 0$$

Solving the system by any of the methods in the preceding sections gives $x = 2$, $y = 4$, and $z = 6$. Hence, the first number is 2, the second number is 4, and the third number is 6.

EXAMPLE 4

Three solutions of $ax + by + cz = 1$ are $(0, 3, -2)$, $(3, -4, 0)$, and $(1, 0, 0)$. Find the coefficients a, b, and c.

Solution

In this case we want to solve for a, b, and c. Substituting the coordinates of the given values of x, y, and z in

$$ax + by + cz = 1$$

we obtain

$$a(0) + b(3) + c(-2) = 1$$
$$a(3) + b(-4) + c(0) = 1$$
$$a(1) + b(0) + c(0) = 1$$

We can now write the system as

$$3b - 2c = 1$$
$$3a - 4b = 1$$
$$a = 1$$

Solving the system we have $a = 1$, $b = \dfrac{1}{2}$, and $c = \dfrac{1}{4}$.

EXERCISE SET 10.6

▲ *Solve each problem using a system of equations. See Examples 1 and 2.*

1. The sum of two numbers is 24, and one of the numbers is 6 less than the other. Find the numbers.

2. The difference of two numbers is 14, and one of the numbers is 1 more than 2 times the other. Find the numbers.

3. If $\frac{1}{3}$ of an integer is added to $\frac{1}{2}$ the next consecutive integer, the sum is 33. Find the integers.

4. If $\frac{1}{2}$ of an integer is added to $\frac{1}{3}$ the next consecutive integer, the sum is 17. Find the integers.

5. The admission at a baseball game was $1.50 for adults and $0.85 for children. The receipts were $93.10 for 82 paid admissions. How many adults and how many children attended the game?

6. In an election, 7179 votes were cast for two candidates. If 6 votes had switched from the winner to the loser, the loser would have won by 1 vote. How many votes were cast for each candidate?

7. A sum of $2000 is invested, part at 10% and the remainder at 8%. Find the amount invested at each rate if the yearly income from the two investments is $184.

8. A woman has $1200 invested in two stocks; one returns 8% per year and the other returns 12% per year. How much has she invested in each stock if the income from the 8% stock is $3 more than the income from the 12% stock?

9. On an airplane flight for which first-class fare is $80 and tourist fare is $64 there were 42 passengers. If receipts for the flight totaled $2880, how many first-class and how many tourist passengers were on the flight?

10. A hardware retailer bought 50 machine screws— 1-inch screws at 18¢ each and 3/4-inch screws at 15¢ each. If the total cost was $8.10, how many screws of each length did the retailer purchase?

11. An airplane travels 1260 miles in the same time that an automobile travels 420 miles. If the rate of the airplane is 120 miles per hour greater than the rate of the automobile, find the rate of each.

12. Two cars start together and travel in the same direction, one going twice as fast as the other. At the end of 3 hours, they are 96 miles apart. How fast is each traveling?

▲ *Solve each problem using a system of equations. See Examples 3 and 4.*

13. The sum of three numbers is 15. The second number equals 2 times the first number, and the third number equals the second number. Find the numbers.

14. The sum of three numbers is 2. The first number is equal to the sum of the other two, and the third number is the result of subtracting the first from the second. Find the numbers.

15. A box contains $6.25 in nickels, dimes, and quarters. There are 85 coins in all with 3 times as many nickels as dimes. How many coins of each kind are there?

16. A man has $446 in ten-dollar, five-dollar, and one-dollar bills. There were 94 bills in all and 10 more five-dollar bills than ten-dollar bills. How many bills of each kind did he have?

17. The perimeter of a triangle is 155 inches. Side x is 20 inches shorter than side y, and side y is 5 inches longer than side z. Find the lengths of the sides of the triangle.

18. One angle of a triangle measures 10° more than a second angle, and the third angle is 10° more than six times the measure of the smallest angle. Find the measure of each angle.

Miscellaneous Exercises

19. In 1986 a vintner had a white wine that was 4 years older than a certain red wine. In 1976 the white wine was 2 times as old as the red wine. In what years were the wines produced?

20. In 1984, Mr. Evans died, leaving a will saying that when his son was 2 times as old as his daughter, both would receive the funds from a trust. If the boy was 3 times as old as his sister in 1984 and they received

their funds in 1989, how old was each when their father died?

21. A record company determines that each production run to manufacture a record involves an initial set-up cost of $20 and $0.40 for each record produced. The records sell for $1.20 each.

   a. Express the cost C of production in terms of the number x of records produced.

   b. Express the revenue R in terms of the number of records sold.

   c. How many records must be sold for the record company to break even (no profit and no loss) on a particular production?

22. How many records must the record company in Exercise 21 sell to break even if the price of each record is lowered to $0.60?

23. Find a and b so that the graph of $ax + by + 3 = 0$ passes through the points $(-1, 2)$ and $(-3, 0)$. [*Hint:* If the graph of the equation passes through the points, the components of each ordered pair must be valid replacements for x and y. Substitute -1 for x and 2 for y and -3 for x and 0 for y to obtain a system in a and b.]

24. Find a and b so that the solution set of the following system is $\{(1, 2)\}$:

$$ax + by = 4$$
$$bx - ay = -3$$

25. Three solutions of the equation $ax + by + cz = 1$ are $(-2, 0, 4)$, $(6, -1, 0)$, and $(0, 3, 0)$. Find the coefficients a, b, and c.

26. Three solutions of the equation $ax + by + bz = 1$ are $(0, 4, 2)$, $(-1, 3, 0)$, and $(-1, 0, 2)$. Find the coefficients a, b, and c.

CHAPTER SUMMARY

[**10.1**] The system of linear equations (in standard form)

$$a_1 x + b_1 y = c_1$$
$$a_2 x + b_2 y = c_2$$

has no solution if the equations are **inconsistent**, infinitely many solutions if the equations are **dependent**, and exactly one solution if the equations are **consistent** and **independent**.

The system has exactly one solution if $\dfrac{a_1}{a_2} \neq \dfrac{b_1}{b_2}$.

The equations are inconsistent if $\dfrac{a_1}{a_2} = \dfrac{b_1}{b_2} \neq \dfrac{c_1}{c_2}$.

The equations are dependent if $\dfrac{a_1}{a_2} = \dfrac{b_1}{b_2} = \dfrac{c_1}{c_2}$.

A unique solution of a system can be found by using a linear combination of two independent equations to obtain one equation in one variable.

[10.2] The solution of a system of three linear equations in three variables (if a solution exists) can be obtained by first using linear combinations to form a system of two equations in two variables. The solution to this latter system contains components that are the respective components of the solution of the original system in three variables. The third component can be obtained by substituting these two values into any one of the equations of the original system.

[10.3] The order of a **determinant** is the number of rows or columns in the determinant. A second-order determinant is defined by

$$\begin{vmatrix} a_1 & b_1 \\ a_2 & b_2 \end{vmatrix} = a_1 b_2 - a_2 b_1$$

Cramer's rule can be used to solve systems of two linear equations in two variables. If

$$a_1 x + b_1 y = c_1$$
$$a_2 x + b_2 y = c_2$$

then, for $D \neq 0$,

$$x = \frac{D_x}{D} = \frac{\begin{vmatrix} c_1 & b_1 \\ c_2 & b_2 \end{vmatrix}}{\begin{vmatrix} a_1 & b_1 \\ a_2 & b_2 \end{vmatrix}} \quad \text{and} \quad y = \frac{D_y}{D} = \frac{\begin{vmatrix} a_1 & c_1 \\ a_2 & c_2 \end{vmatrix}}{\begin{vmatrix} a_1 & b_1 \\ a_2 & b_2 \end{vmatrix}}$$

[10.4] A third-order determinant is defined by

$$\begin{vmatrix} a_1 & b_1 & c_1 \\ a_2 & b_2 & c_2 \\ a_3 & b_3 & c_3 \end{vmatrix} = a_1 b_2 c_3 - a_1 b_3 c_2 + a_3 b_1 c_2 - a_2 b_1 c_3 + a_2 b_3 c_1 - a_3 b_2 c_1$$

The **minor** of an element in a determinant D is the determinant that results when the row and column containing the element are deleted. A determinant of an order greater than or equal to three can be evaluated by expansion by minors about any row or column.

Cramer's rule can also be used to solve systems of three linear equations in three variables. If

$$a_1 x + b_1 y + c_1 z = d_1$$
$$a_2 x + b_2 y + c_2 z = d_2$$
$$a_3 x + b_3 y + c_3 z = d_3$$

then, for $D \neq 0$,

$$x = \frac{D_x}{D}, \qquad y = \frac{D_y}{D}, \qquad z = \frac{D_z}{D}$$

[10.5] A **matrix** is a rectangular array of **elements** or **entries**. Two matrices are said to be **row-equivalent** if one matrix can be transformed to the other by one or more of the following transformations:

1. Multiplying the entries of any row by a nonzero real number.
2. Interchanging two rows.
3. Multiplying the entries of any row by a real number and adding the results to the corresponding elements of another row.

We can use these transformations to solve linear systems of equations.

[10.6] Systems of equations in several variables can be used to solve a variety of applied problems. Different variables are used for different unknown quantities, and two or more independent equations involving these variables are constructed.

||| R E V I E W   E X E R C I S E S

[10.1]

▲ *Solve each system by linear combinations.*

1. $x + 5y = 18$
   $x - y = -3$

2. $x + 5y = 11$
   $2x + 3y = 8$

3. $\frac{2}{3}x - 3y = 8$

   $x + \frac{3}{4}y = 12$

4. $3x = 5y - 6$
   $3y = 10 - 11x$

▲ *State whether the equations in each system have a unique solution, are dependent, or are inconsistent.*

5. $2x - 3y = 4$
   $x + 2y = 7$

6. $2x - 3y = 4$
   $6x - 9y = 4$

7. $2x - 3y = 4$
   $6x - 9y = 12$

8. $x - y = 6$
   $x + y = 6$

[10.2]

▲ *Solve each system using linear combinations.*

9. $x + 3y - z = 3$
   $2x - y + 3z = 1$
   $3x + 2y + z = 5$

10. $x + y + z = 2$
    $3x - y + z = 4$
    $2x + y + 2z = 3$

11. $x + z = 5$
    $y - z = -8$
    $2x + z = 7$

12. $x + 4y + 4z = -20$
    $3x - 2y + z = -4$
    $2x - 4y + z = -4$

13. $\frac{1}{2}x + y + z = 3$

    $x - 2y - \frac{1}{3}z = -5$

    $\frac{1}{2}x - 3y - \frac{2}{3}z = -6$

14. $\frac{3}{4}x - \frac{1}{2}y + 6z = 2$

    $\frac{1}{2}x + y - \frac{3}{4}z = 0$

    $\frac{1}{4}x + \frac{1}{2}y - \frac{1}{2}z = 0$

[10.3]

15. Evaluate $\begin{vmatrix} 3 & -2 \\ 1 & -5 \end{vmatrix}$.

16. Evaluate $\begin{vmatrix} -4 & 0 \\ 2 & -6 \end{vmatrix}$.

▲ *Solve each system using Cramer's rule.*

17. $x - 2y = 6$
    $3x + y = 25$

18. $2x + 3y = -2$
    $x - 8y = -39$

19. $\frac{1}{4}x - \frac{1}{3}y = -\frac{5}{12}$

    $\frac{1}{10}x + \frac{1}{5}y = \frac{1}{2}$

20. $\frac{2}{3}x - y = 4$

    $x - \frac{3}{4}y = 6$

[10.4]

▲ *Evaluate each determinant.*

21. $\begin{vmatrix} 2 & 1 & 3 \\ 0 & 4 & -1 \\ 2 & 0 & 3 \end{vmatrix}$

22. $\begin{vmatrix} 3 & -1 & 2 \\ -2 & 1 & 0 \\ 2 & 4 & 1 \end{vmatrix}$

▲ *Solve each system using Cramer's rule.*

23. $\begin{aligned} x + y &= 3 \\ y + z &= 5 \\ x - y + 2z &= 5 \end{aligned}$

24. $\begin{aligned} 2x + 3y - z &= -2 \\ x - y + z &= 6 \\ 3x - y + z &= 10 \end{aligned}$

25. $\begin{aligned} x + y + z &= 2 \\ 2x - y + z &= -1 \\ x - y - z &= 0 \end{aligned}$

26. $\begin{aligned} x - 2y &= -3 \\ y + 3z &= -1 \\ x - z &= 2 \end{aligned}$

[10.5]

▲ *Use row operations on a matrix to solve each system.*

27. $\begin{aligned} x - 2y &= 5 \\ 2x + y &= 5 \end{aligned}$

28. $\begin{aligned} 4x - 3y &= 16 \\ 2x + y &= 8 \end{aligned}$

29. $\begin{aligned} 2x - y &= 7 \\ 3x + 2y &= 14 \end{aligned}$

30. $\begin{aligned} 2x - y + 3z &= -6 \\ x + 2y - z &= 7 \\ 3x + y + z &= 2 \end{aligned}$

31. $\begin{aligned} x + 2y - z &= -3 \\ 2x - 3y + 2z &= 2 \\ x - y + 4z &= 7 \end{aligned}$

32. $\begin{aligned} x + y + z &= 1 \\ 2x - y - z &= 2 \\ 2x - y + 3z &= 2 \end{aligned}$

[10.6]

▲ *Solve each problem using two or three variables.*

33. A collection of coins consisting of dimes and quarters has a value of $4.95. How many dimes are in the collection if there are 25 more dimes than quarters?

34. The first-class fare on an airplane flight is $280, and the tourist fare is $160. If 64 passengers paid a total of $12,160 for the flight, how many of each ticket were sold?

35. A woman has invested $8000, part in a bank at 10% and part in a savings and loan association at 12%. If her annual return is $844, how much has she invested at each rate?

36. A sum of $2400 is split between an investment in a mutual fund paying 14% and one in corporate bonds paying 11%. If the return on the 14% investment exceeds that on the 11% investment by $111 per year, how much is invested at each rate?

37. An airplane travels 840 miles in the same time that an automobile travels 210 miles. If the rate of the airplane is 180 miles per hour greater than the rate of the automobile, find the rate of each.

38. One woman drives 180 miles in the same time that a second woman drives 200 miles. If the second woman drives 5 miles per hour faster than the first woman, find each woman's speed.

39. The perimeter of a triangle is 30 centimeters. The length of one side is 7 centimeters shorter than that of a second side, and the third side is 1 centimeter longer than the second side. Find the length of each side.

40. One angle of a triangle measures 20° more than a second angle, and the third angle has three times the measure of the first angle. Find the measure of each angle.

▲ *The numbers in brackets refer to the sections in which such problems are first considered.*

1. If $Q(x) = -x^4 + 4x^3 - 9x - 2$, find $Q(-2)$. **[2.1]**

2. Write $3\sqrt{xy} - y\sqrt[3]{x^2}$ with exponential notation. **[5.5]**

3. Factor completely
$5(x - 3)(x - 2)^2 - 3(x - 3)^2(x - 2)$. **[3.2]**

4. Evaluate $\begin{vmatrix} a & b & c \\ 0 & a & b \\ 0 & 0 & a \end{vmatrix}$. **[10.4]**

▲ *Simplify.*

5. $\dfrac{3^3(3^2 - 2^2)}{-3(2 + 3)} - \dfrac{(2^2 + 3)^2}{2(2 + 3) - 3}$ **[2.1]**

6. $-2x[2x - x(3 - x) - (x + 1)^2]$ **[3.3]**

▲ *Write as a single fraction in lowest terms.*

7. $\dfrac{x - 2}{x^2 - 4x + 3} - \dfrac{2x + 1}{x^2 - x - 6} + \dfrac{x + 1}{x^2 + x - 2}$ **[4.4]**

8. Write $(yx^{-1} - xy^{-1})^{-1}$ as a single fraction involving only positive exponents. **[5.2]**

▲ *Solve.*

9. $2x^2 + 3 = 3x$ **[6.1]**

10. $3V = (la + lb + c)h$ for l **[2.3]**

11. $y = k(1 - e^{-t})$ for t **[9.5]**

12. $T = T_0 \ln(k + 10)$ for k **[9.5]**

13. $\dfrac{1}{4}x - \dfrac{2}{3}y = 6$ **[10.3]**
$2x + 3y = -2$

14. $x + 3z = 2$ **[10.5]**
$2y - 3z = 5$
$2x - 7y = 3$

15. Find an equation for the line that includes the points $(-2, 5)$ and $(1, 3)$. **[7.4]**

16. Find the equation in standard form for the line with x-intercept $a = 1/3$ and y-intercept $b = -3/2$. **[7.4]**

17. Calculate $\dfrac{f(x + h) - f(x)}{h}$ for $f(x) = 2x^2 - x$. **[8.1]**

18. Given f defined by $y = 2x + 6$, graph f and f^{-1}. **[8.5]**

▲ *Graph.*

19. $y = 2x^2 - 4x$ **[8.3]**

20. $y = -2x^2 + x + 3$ **[8.3]**

▲ *Solve.*

21. One angle of a triangle measures twice the second angle, and the third angle measures 10° more than the larger of the other two. Find the measure of each angle. **[2.3]**

22. A chartered sight-seeing flight over the Grand Canyon is scheduled to return to its departure point in 3 hours. If the plane flies at 100 miles per hour in still air and there is a head wind of 20 miles per hour on the outward journey, how far can the plane go before it must turn around? **[4.8]**

23. The area of an equilateral triangle is given by the formula $A = (\sqrt{3}/4)s^2$, where s is the length of the side. How long (to the nearest hundredth) is the side of an equilateral triangle whose area is 12 square centimeters? **[6.1]**

24. A small company manufactures radios. When it charges $20 for a radio, it sells 500 radios per month. For each dollar the price is increased, 10 fewer radios are sold per month. What should the company charge for a radio to maximize its monthly revenue? **[8.3]**

25. During an introductory advertising campaign in a large city, the makers of Chip-O's corn chips estimated that after t days of advertising the number of people who had heard of Chip-O's was given by $N(t) = 100 \cdot 8^{t/4}$. How many days should they run the campaign in order for Chip-O's to be familiar to 51,200 people? **[9.6]**

QUADRATIC EQUATIONS IN TWO VARIABLES

In Chapter 8 we considered second-degree equations of the form

$$y = ax^2 + bx + c \qquad (a \neq 0) \tag{1}$$

whose graphs are parabolas. Parabolas are one of four classes of second-degree curves called **conic sections**, or simply **conics**, because they can be formed by the intersection of a plane and a cone, as shown in Figure 11.1.

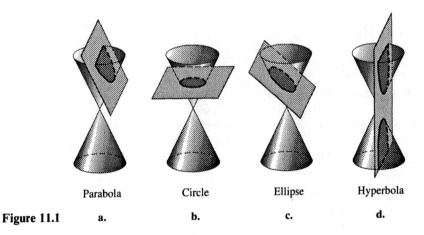

Parabola	Circle	Ellipse	Hyperbola
a.	**b.**	**c.**	**d.**

Figure 11.1

As we noted in Section 8.3, equations of the form of Equation (1) define functions. However, we shall see that the other conic sections—circles, ellipses, and hyperbolas—are not the graphs of functions.

11.1 CENTRAL CONICS

In Chapter 8 we learned that the graph of $y = ax^2$ $(a \neq 0)$ is a parabola whose vertex is located at the origin. In this section we consider the properties of circles, ellipses, and hyperbolas that are centered at the origin. These curves are called **central conics**.

Circles The graph of

$$x^2 + y^2 = r^2 \tag{2}$$

is a **circle** centered at the origin with radius r (see Figure 11.2).

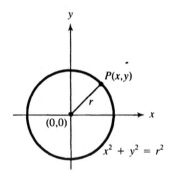

Figure 11.2

EXAMPLE 1 **a.** The graph of $x^2 + y^2 = 16$ is a circle centered at the origin with radius 4.

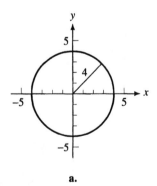

a.

b. The graph of $4y^2 = 15 - 4x^2$, which can be written as

$$x^2 + y^2 = \frac{15}{4} \quad \text{or} \quad x^2 + y^2 = \left(\frac{\sqrt{15}}{2}\right)^2$$

is a circle centered at the origin with radius $\sqrt{15/2}$.

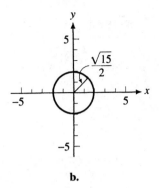

b.

Ellipses The graph of

$$\frac{x^2}{a^2} + \frac{y^2}{b^2} = 1 \tag{3}$$

is centered at the origin and is called an **ellipse**. If $a > b$, the ellipse is elongated along the x-axis, as shown in Figure 11.3a and the graph of

$$\frac{x^2}{b^2} + \frac{y^2}{a^2} = 1 \tag{3a}$$

is an ellipse elongated along the y-axis, as shown in Figure 11.3b.

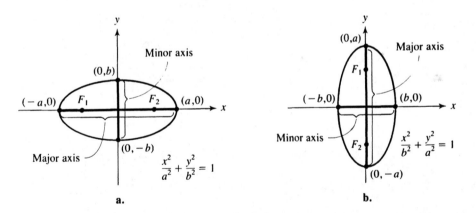

Figure 11.3   **a.**   **b.**

The longer segment indicated by a heavier rule in each figure is called the **major axis** of the ellipse, and the shorter segment is called the **minor axis**. The endpoints of the major axis are called the **vertices** of the ellipse, and the endpoints of the minor axis are called the **covertices**.

Note that if $a = b$, Equation (3) reduces to Equation (2), and its graph is a circle. Thus, a circle is a special case of an ellipse. Whether $a > b$, $a < b$, or $a = b$, the intercepts (vertices and covertices) of an ellipse can readily be obtained by using Equation (3). By setting $y = 0$, we find that the x-intercepts are a and $-a$; by setting $x = 0$, we see that the y-intercepts are b and $-b$. Note that the length of the major axis is $2a$ and the length of the minor axis is $2b$.

EXAMPLE 2 | Graph.

    a. $\dfrac{x^2}{25} + \dfrac{y^2}{4} = 1$ **b.** $4x^2 + y^2 = 12$

Solutions | **a.** The equation can be written as

$$\frac{x^2}{5^2} + \frac{y^2}{2^2} = 1$$

from which we observe that the graph is a central ellipse with x-intercepts 5 and -5 and y-intercepts 2 and -2.

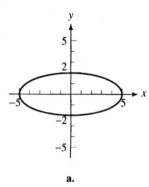

a.

    b. The equation can be written as

$$\frac{x^2}{3} + \frac{y^2}{12} = 1 \quad \text{and then as} \quad \frac{x^2}{(\sqrt{3})^2} + \frac{y^2}{(\sqrt{12})^2} = 1$$

from which we observe that the graph is a central ellipse with x-intercepts $\sqrt{3}$ and $-\sqrt{3}$ and y-intercepts $\sqrt{12}$ and $-\sqrt{12}$.

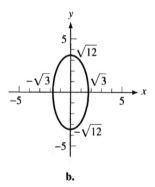

b.

Equations (2) and (3) are called the **standard forms** of the equations of circles and ellipses, respectively. Equations of ellipses are often written as

$$Ax^2 + By^2 = C$$

where $A \neq B$ and A, B, and C have like signs. However, the features of its graph can more easily be seen if the equation is first converted to standard form as in Example 2b.

Hyperbolas The graphs of

$$\frac{x^2}{a^2} - \frac{y^2}{b^2} = 1 \qquad \textbf{(4)} \qquad \text{and} \qquad \frac{y^2}{a^2} - \frac{x^2}{b^2} = 1 \qquad \textbf{(4a)}$$

are centered at the origin and are called **hyperbolas**. The graph of Equation (4) is shown in Figure 11.4a, and the graph of Equation (4a) is shown in Figure 11.4b.

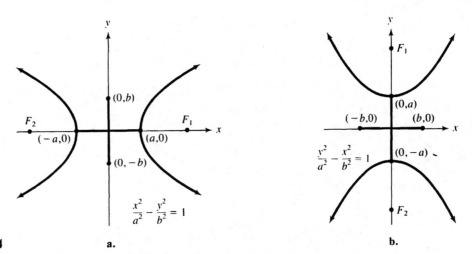

Figure 11.4   **a.**   **b.**

The intercepts of the graphs of both Equations (4) and (4a) are a and $-a$. In both graphs in Figure 11.4, the line segment of length $2a$ is called the **transverse axis,** and the line segment of length $2b$ is called the **conjugate axis.** The endpoints of the transverse axis are called the **vertices.**

Asymptotes of Hyperbolas

We can often simplify the process of graphing a hyperbola by first graphing two straight lines that are approached by the branches of the hyperbola. These lines are called **asymptotes** of the graph. The asymptotes can be obtained by sketching a rectangle centered at the origin with $2a$ as one dimension and $2b$ as the other dimension. Then the asymptotes are the two lines that intersect at the origin and pass through the corners of the rectangle.

EXAMPLE 3   Graph $\dfrac{x^2}{9} - \dfrac{y^2}{16} = 1$.

Solution   The graph is a hyperbola with its center at the origin. Since

$$a^2 = 9 \qquad \text{and} \qquad b^2 = 16$$

then

$$a = 3 \qquad \text{and} \qquad b = 4$$

The x-intercepts are 3 and -3. Sketch the central rectangle with dimensions $2a = 6$ and $2b = 8$. Draw the asymptotes through the vertices of the rectangle, and sketch the hyperbola as shown.

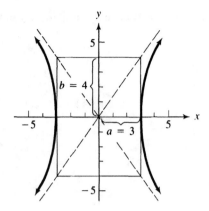

EXAMPLE 4 Graph $\dfrac{y^2}{9} - \dfrac{x^2}{4} = 1$.

Solution The graph is a hyperbola with its center at the origin. Since

$$a^2 = 9 \qquad \text{and} \qquad b^2 = 4$$

then

$$a = 3 \qquad \text{and} \qquad b = 2$$

The y-intercepts are 3 and -3. Sketch the central rectangle with dimensions $2a = 6$ and $2b = 4$. Draw the asymptotes through the vertices of the central rectangle, and sketch the hyperbola as shown.

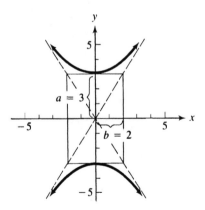

Equations (4) and (4a) are called the **standard forms** of equations of hyperbolas. Equations of hyperbolas are often written as

$$Ax^2 + By^2 = C$$

where A and B have *opposite* signs and $C \neq 0$. However, the features of the graph can be more easily obtained if the equation is first written in standard form.

EXAMPLE 5

Write each equation in standard form and describe the important features of its graph.

a. $4y^2 - x^2 = 16$ **b.** $4x^2 = y^2 + 25$

Solutions

a. First divide each side by 16 to obtain

$$\frac{y^2}{4} - \frac{x^2}{16} = 1 \quad \leftrightarrow \quad \frac{y^2}{(2)^2} - \frac{x^2}{(4)^2} = 1$$

The graph is a central hyperbola with y-intercepts 2 and -2.

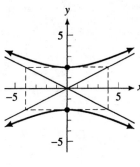

a.

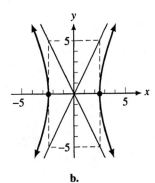

b.

b. We first write the equation as

$$4x^2 - y^2 = 25$$

and then divide each side by 25 to obtain

$$\frac{4x^2}{25} - \frac{y^2}{25} = 1 \quad \leftrightarrow \quad \frac{x^2}{\left(\frac{5}{2}\right)^2} - \frac{y^2}{5^2} = 1$$

The graph is a central hyperbola with x-intercepts $\frac{5}{2}$ and $-\frac{5}{2}$.

Recognizing Central Conic Sections

The standard forms of the central conics are summarized in Table 11.1.

Table 11.1

Name of conic	Equation	Graph
Parabola	$y = ax^2 \quad (a \neq 0)$	
Circle	$x^2 + y^2 = r^2$	
Ellipse a. Major axis on the x-axis b. Major axis on the y-axis	$\dfrac{x^2}{a^2} + \dfrac{y^2}{b^2} = 1$ $Ax^2 + By^2 = C$ $A \neq B$ A, B, C have like signs.	
Hyperbola a. Transverse axis on the x-axis b. Transverse axis on the y-axis	a. $\dfrac{x^2}{a^2} - \dfrac{y^2}{b^2} = 1$ b. $\dfrac{y^2}{a^2} - \dfrac{x^2}{b^2} = 1$ $Ax^2 + By^2 = C$ A and B have opposite signs, $\quad C \neq 0$.	

E X A M P L E 6

Write each equation in standard form and describe its graph.

a. $x^2 = 9y^2 - 9$ **b.** $4x^2 + y = 0$ **c.** $9y^2 = 4 - x^2$

d. $6x^2 = 18 - 6y^2$ **e.** $y^2 = 6x^2 + 8$ **f.** $x^2 = \dfrac{4 - y^2}{2}$

Solutions

a. $x^2 = 9y^2 - 9$ is equivalent to

$$9y^2 - x^2 = 9 \quad \leftrightarrow \quad \frac{y^2}{1^2} - \frac{x^2}{3^2} = 1$$

The graph is a hyperbola with the transverse axis on the y-axis.

b. $4x^2 + y = 0$ is equivalent to

$$y = -4x^2$$

The graph is a parabola that opens downward.

c. $9y^2 = 4 - x^2$ is equivalent to

$$x^2 + 9y^2 = 4 \quad \leftrightarrow \quad \frac{x^2}{2^2} + \frac{y^2}{(4/9)^2} = 1$$

The graph is an ellipse with the major axis on the x-axis because $2 > \dfrac{4}{9}$.

d. $6x^2 = 18 - 6y^2$ is equivalent to

$$6x^2 + 6y^2 = 18 \quad \leftrightarrow \quad x^2 + y^2 = (\sqrt{3})^2$$

The graph is a circle with radius $\sqrt{3}$.

e. $x^2 = 6y^2 + 8$ is equivalent to

$$x^2 - 6y^2 = 8 \quad \leftrightarrow \quad \frac{x^2}{(\sqrt{8})^2} - \frac{y^2}{(2/\sqrt{3})^2} = 1$$

The graph is a hyperbola with the transverse axis on the x-axis.

f. $x^2 = \dfrac{4 - y^2}{2}$ is equivalent to

$$2x^2 + y^2 = 4 \quad \leftrightarrow \quad \frac{x^2}{(\sqrt{2})^2} + \frac{y^2}{2^2} = 1$$

The graph is an ellipse with the major axis on the y-axis because $2 > \sqrt{2}$.

The most general form of a second-degree equation in two variables is

$$Ax^2 + Bxy + Cy^2 + Dx + Ey + F = 0$$

In this section we have considered only equations in which B, D, and E are all zero. Equations that have second-degree *and first-degree* terms are also conic sections, but they are not central conics. Such equations and their graphs are usually considered in more advanced mathematics courses.

Central Conic Sections
(Circles, Ellipses, Hyperbolas)

Graph the following equations. Label all x and y intercepts.

1. $x^2 + y^2 = 4$

2. $x^2 + y^2 = 36$

3. $x^2 + y^2 = 16$

4. $\dfrac{x^2}{36} + \dfrac{y^2}{16} = 1$

5. $x^2 + 9y^2 = 36$

6. $4x^2 + y^2 = 16$

7. $4x^2 + 9y^2 = 36$

8. $25x^2 + 4y^2 = 100$

9. $4x^2 + 25y^2 = 100$

10. $9x^2 + 16y^2 = 144$

11. $25x^2 + 9y^2 = 225$

12. $16x^2 + 9y^2 = 144$

13. $\dfrac{x^2}{9} - \dfrac{y^2}{9} = 1$

14. $\dfrac{x^2}{9} - \dfrac{y^2}{4} = 1$

15. $\dfrac{x^2}{16} - \dfrac{y^2}{9} = 1$

16. $\dfrac{y^2}{25} - \dfrac{x^2}{16} = 1$

17. $\dfrac{y^2}{36} - \dfrac{x^2}{9} = 1$

18. $\dfrac{y^2}{25} - \dfrac{x^2}{9} = 1$

19. $x^2 - 4y^2 = 4$

20. $x^2 - 9y^2 = 36$

21. $y^2 - 4x^2 = 36$

22. $9x^2 - 4y^2 = 36$

Answers

1. $x^2 + y^2 = 4$

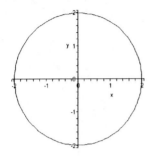

2. $x^2 + y^2 = 36$

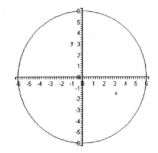

3. $x^2 + y^2 = 16$

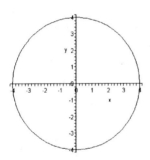

4. $\dfrac{x^2}{36} + \dfrac{y^2}{16} = 1$

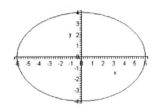

5. $x^2 + 9y^2 = 36$

6. $4x^2 + y^2 = 16$

7. $4x^2 + 9y^2 = 36$

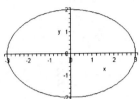

8. $25x^2 + 4y^2 = 100$

9. $4x^2 + 25y^2 = 100$

10. $9x^2 + 16y^2 = 144$

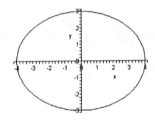

11. $25x^2 + 9y^2 = 225$

12. $16x^2 + 9y^2 = 144$

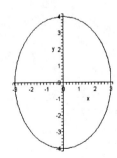

13. $\dfrac{x^2}{9} - \dfrac{y^2}{9} = 1$

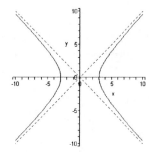

14. $\dfrac{x^2}{9} - \dfrac{y^2}{4} = 1$

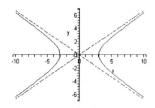

15. $\dfrac{x^2}{16} - \dfrac{y^2}{9} = 1$

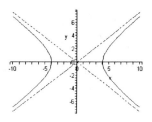

16. $\dfrac{y^2}{25} - \dfrac{x^2}{16} = 1$

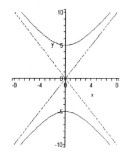

17. $\dfrac{y^2}{36} - \dfrac{x^2}{9} = 1$

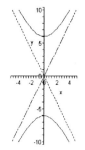

18. $\dfrac{y^2}{25} - \dfrac{x^2}{9} = 1$

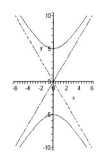

19. $x^2 - 4y^2 = 4$

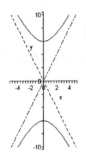

20. $x^2 - 9y^2 = 36$

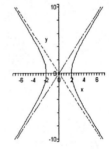

21. $y^2 - 4x^2 = 36$

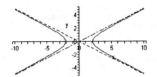

22. $9x^2 - 4y^2 = 36$

EXERCISE SET 11.1

▲ *Graph each equation. See Examples 1 and 2.*

1. $x^2 + y^2 = 25$

2. $x^2 + y^2 = 16$

3. $4x^2 = 16 - 4y^2$

4. $2x^2 = 18 - 2y^2$

5. $\dfrac{x^2}{16} + \dfrac{y^2}{4} = 1$

6. $\dfrac{x^2}{9} + \dfrac{y^2}{16} = 1$

7. $\dfrac{x^2}{10} + \dfrac{y^2}{25} = 1$

8. $\dfrac{x^2}{16} + \dfrac{y^2}{12} = 1$

9. $x^2 + \dfrac{y^2}{14} = 1$

10. $\dfrac{x^2}{8} + y^2 = 1$

11. $3x^2 + 4y^2 = 36$

12. $5x^2 + 2y^2 = 20$

13. $x^2 = 36 - 9y^2$

14. $4x^2 = 36 - y^2$

15. $3y^2 = 30 - 2x^2$

16. $5y^2 = 30 - 3x^2$

▲ *Graph each equation. See Examples 3, 4, and 5.*

17. $\dfrac{x^2}{25} - \dfrac{y^2}{9} = 1$

18. $\dfrac{y^2}{4} - \dfrac{x^2}{16} = 1$

19. $\dfrac{y^2}{12} - \dfrac{x^2}{8} = 1$

20. $\dfrac{x^2}{15} - \dfrac{y^2}{10} = 1$

21. $9x^2 - 4y^2 = 36$

22. $4x^2 - 9y^2 = 36$

23. $y^2 - 9x^2 = 36$

24. $4y^2 - x^2 = 36$

25. $3x^2 = 4y^2 + 24$

26. $4x^2 = 3y^2 + 24$

27. $\dfrac{1}{2}x^2 = y^2 - 12$

28. $y^2 = \dfrac{1}{2}x^2 - 16$

▲ *The graphs of the following equations are circles, ellipses, parabolas, or hyperbolas. Name the graph and describe its main features. See Example 6.*

29. $y^2 = 4 - x^2$

30. $y^2 = 6 - 4x^2$

31. $4y^2 = x^2 - 8$

32. $x^2 + 2y - 4 = 0$

33. $4x^2 = 12 - 2y^2$

34. $6x^2 = 8 - 6y^2$

35. $4x^2 = 6 + 4y$

36. $2x^2 = 5 + 4y^2$

37. $6 + \dfrac{x^2}{4} = y^2$

38. $y^2 = 6 - \dfrac{2x^2}{3}$

39. $\dfrac{1}{2}x^2 - y = 4$

40. $\dfrac{x^2}{4} = 4 + 6y^2$

Miscellaneous Exercises

41. Graph $x^2 - y^2 = 0$. [*Hint:* First write as $(x - y)(x + y) = 0$ and then graph $y = x$ and $y = -x$.]

42. Graph $4x^2 - y^2 = 0$. [See hint for Exercise 41.]

43. Graph $x^2 - y^2 = 4$, $x^2 - y^2 = 1$, and $x^2 - y^2 = 0$ on the same set of axes.

44. Graph $4x^2 - y^2 = 16$, $4x^2 - y^2 = 4$, and $4x^2 - y^2 = 0$ on the same set of axes.

11.2   SOLUTION OF SYSTEMS BY SUBSTITUTION

Real Solutions Obtained from Graphs

Approximate solutions of systems of equations in two variables, where one or both of the equations are quadratic, may often be found by graphing both equations and estimating the coordinates of any points they have in common. For example, to find the solution set of the system

$$x^2 + y^2 = 26 \tag{1}$$

$$x + y = 6 \tag{2}$$

we graph the equations on the same set of axes, as shown in Figure 11.5 and observe that the graphs appear to intersect at $(1, 5)$ and $(5, 1)$. The solution set of the system (1) and (2) is, in fact, $\{(1, 5), (5, 1)\}$.

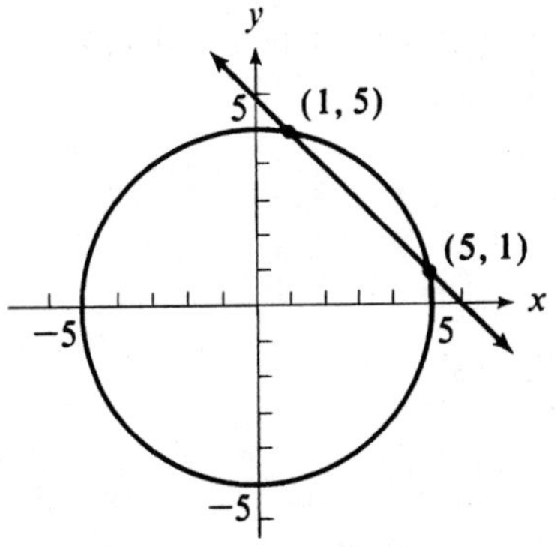

Figure 11.5

However, solving second-degree systems graphically may produce only approximations to real solutions, and we cannot expect to locate solutions in which one or both of the components are imaginary numbers. Therefore, concentrating on algebraic methods of solution is more practical, since the results are exact and we can obtain imaginary solutions. Whenever feasible, sketch the graphs of the equations as a rough check on an algebraic solution.

Solving a System by Substitution

One of the most useful techniques available for finding solution sets for systems of equations is **substitution**. This technique is particularly helpful with systems containing one first-degree and one higher-degree equation.

EXAMPLE 1

Solve

$$x^2 + y^2 = 26 \tag{1}$$
$$x + y = 6 \tag{2}$$

using algebraic methods.

Solution

Equation (2) can be written in the form

$$y = 6 - x \tag{3}$$

and the substitution property may be used to replace y in Equation (1) by its equal, $(6 - x)$, from Equation (3). This will produce

$$x^2 + (6 - x)^2 = 26 \tag{4}$$

Rewriting Equation (4) equivalently, we have

$$x^2 + 36 - 12x + x^2 = 26$$
$$2x^2 - 12x + 10 = 0$$
$$x^2 - 6x + 5 = 0$$
$$(x - 5)(x - 1) = 0$$

from which x is either 1 or 5. Now, by replacing x in Equation (3) with each of these numbers, we have

$$y = 6 - (1) = 5 \quad \text{and} \quad y = 6 - (5) = 1$$

so the solution set of the system (1) and (2) is $\{(1, 5), (5, 1)\}$. Check this solution and notice that these ordered pairs are also solutions of Equation (1).

Note that if we used Equation (1) rather than Equations (2) or (3) in Example 1 to obtain values for the y-component, we would have

$$(1)^2 + y^2 = 26 \qquad (5)^2 + y^2 = 26$$
$$y = \pm 5 \qquad\qquad y = \pm 1$$

and the solutions obtained would be $(1, 5), (1, -5), (5, 1),$ and $(5, -1)$. However, $(1, -5)$ and $(5, -1)$ are not solutions of Equation (2). The solution set is again $\{(1, 5), (5, 1)\}$.

The foregoing example suggests that *if the degrees of equations differ, one component of a solution should be substituted in the equation of <u>lower</u> degree to find <u>only</u> those ordered pairs that are solutions of <u>both</u> equations.*

EXAMPLE 2 | Solve

$$y = x^2 + 2x + 1 \tag{5}$$
$$y - x = 3 \tag{6}$$

using algebraic methods.

Solution | Solve Equation (6) explicitly for y.

$$y = x + 3 \tag{6a}$$

Substitute $(x + 3)$ for y in Equation (5).

$$x + 3 = x^2 + 2x + 1$$

Solve for x.

$$x^2 + x - 2 = 0$$
$$(x + 2)(x - 1) = 0$$
$$x = -2 \quad \text{or} \quad x = 1$$

Substitute each of these values in Equation (6a) to determine values for y. If $x = -2$, then $y = 1$; and if $x = 1$, then $y = 4$. The solution set of the system is $\{(-2, 1), (1, 4)\}$. The graphs of the equations are shown in the figure.

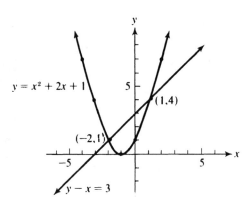

Imaginary Solutions | In Examples 1 and 2 the components of each solution are real numbers, and their graphs are the points of intersection of the graphs of each equation. If one or more of the components of the solutions of a system are imaginary numbers, we can find these solutions, but in such cases the graphs in the real plane do not have points of intersection.

EXAMPLE 3

Solve

$$x^2 + y^2 = 26 \tag{7}$$
$$x + y = 8 \tag{8}$$

Solution

Solving Equation (8) for y, we have

$$y = 8 - x \tag{8a}$$

Substituting $(8 - x)$ for y in Equation (7) and simplifying yield

$$x^2 + (8 - x)^2 = 26$$
$$x^2 + 64 - 16x + x^2 = 26$$
$$2x^2 - 16x + 38 = 0$$
$$x^2 - 8x + 19 = 0$$

Using the quadratic formula to solve for x, we obtain

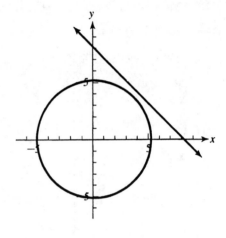

$$x = \frac{8 \pm \sqrt{64 - 76}}{2(1)} = \frac{8 \pm \sqrt{-12}}{2}$$
$$= \frac{8 \pm 2i\sqrt{3}}{2} = \frac{2(4 \pm i\sqrt{3})}{2}$$
$$= 4 \pm i\sqrt{3}$$

Then, substituting $(4 + i\sqrt{3})$ for x in Equation (8a) gives $y = 4 - i\sqrt{3}$, and substituting $(4 - i\sqrt{3})$ for x in Equation (8a) gives $y = 4 + i\sqrt{3}$. Hence, the solution set is

$$\{(4 + i\sqrt{3}, 4 - i\sqrt{3}), (4 - i\sqrt{3}, 4 + i\sqrt{3})\}$$

The graphs of the equations are shown in the figure. Note that the system has no *real-number* solution, which is why the graphs do not intersect.

EXERCISE SET 11.2

▲ *Solve by the method of substitution. In Exercises 1–10, sketch the graphs of the equations. See Examples 1, 2, and 3.*

1. $y = x^2 - 5$
   $y = 4x$

2. $y = x^2 - 2x + 1$
   $y + x = 3$

3. $x^2 + y^2 = 13$
   $x + y = 5$

4. $x^2 + 2y^2 = 12$
   $2x - y = 2$

5. $x + y = 1$
   $xy = -12$

6. $2x - y = 9$
   $xy = -4$

7. $xy = 4$
   $x^2 + y^2 = 8$

8. $x^2 - y^2 = 35$
   $xy = 6$

9. $x^2 + y^2 = 9$
   $y = 4$

10. $2x^2 - 4y^2 = 12$
    $x = 4$

11. $x^2 + y = 4$
    $x - y = -1$

12. $x^2 + 9y^2 = 36$
    $x - 2y = -8$

13. $x^2 - xy - 2y^2 = 4$
    $x - y = 2$

14. $x^2 - 2x + y^2 = 3$
    $2x + y = 4$

15. $2x^2 - 5xy + 2y^2 = 5$ **16.** $2x^2 + xy + y^2 = 9$
         $2x - y = 1$ $-x + 3y = 9$

Miscellaneous Exercises

▲ *Solve each problem using a system of equations.*

17. The sum of the squares of two positive numbers is 13. If 2 times the first number is added to the second, the sum is 7. Find the numbers.

18. The sum of two numbers is 6, and their product is $\frac{35}{4}$. Find the numbers.

19. The perimeter of a rectangle is 26 inches, and the area is 12 square inches. Find the dimensions of the rectangle.

20. The area of a rectangle is 216 square feet. If the perimeter is 60 feet, find the dimensions of the rectangle.

21. The annual income from an investment is $32. If the amount invested were $200 more and the rate were 1/2% less, the annual income would be $35. What are the amount and rate of the investment?

22. At a constant temperature the pressure P and volume V of a gas are related by the equation $PV = K$. The product of the pressure (in pounds per square inch) and the volume (in cubic inches) of a certain gas is 30 inch-pounds. If the temperature remains constant as the pressure is increased by 4 pounds per square inch, the volume is decreased by 2 cubic inches. Find the original pressure and volume of the gas.

11.3 | SOLUTION OF SYSTEMS BY OTHER METHODS

If both the equations in a system are second-degree in both variables, the method of linear combinations often provides a simpler means of solution than does substitution.

EXAMPLE 1 | Solve

$$4x^2 + y^2 = 25 \qquad (1)$$
$$x^2 - y^2 = -5 \qquad (2)$$

Solution | By forming a linear combination using 1 times Equation (1) and 1 times Equation (2), we have

$$5x^2 = 20$$

from which

$$x = 2 \qquad \text{or} \qquad x = -2$$

We now have the x-components of the members of the solution set of the system (1) and (2). Substituting 2 for x in either Equation (1) or Equation (2)—we shall use Equation (1)—we obtain

$$4(2)^2 + y^2 = 25$$
$$y^2 = 25 - 16$$
$$y^2 = 9$$

from which

$$y = 3 \qquad \text{or} \qquad y = -3$$

Thus, the ordered pairs $(2, 3)$ and $(2, -3)$ are in the solution set of the system. Substituting -2 for x in Equation (1) or Equation (2)—this time we shall use Equation (2)—gives us

$$(-2)^2 - y^2 = -5$$
$$-y^2 = -5 - 4$$
$$y^2 = 9$$

from which

$$y = 3 \quad \text{or} \quad y = -3$$

Thus, the ordered pairs $(-2, 3)$ and $(-2, -3)$ are also solutions of the system, and the complete solution set is

$$\{(2, 3), (2, -3), (-2, 3), (-2, -3)\}$$

The graphs of the equations are shown in the figure.

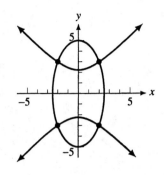

The following example shows another means of solving a system of two second-degree equations.

EXAMPLE 2   Solve

$$x^2 + y^2 = 5 \qquad (3)$$
$$x^2 - 2xy + y^2 = 1 \qquad (4)$$

Solution   By forming a linear combination using 1 times Equation (3) and -1 times Equation (4), we have

$$2xy = 4$$

or

$$xy = 2 \qquad (5)$$

Therefore, by forming the new system

$$x^2 + y^2 = 5 \qquad (3)$$
$$xy = 2 \qquad (5)$$

we can be sure that the solution set of this system is the same as the solution set of the system (3) and (4).

This latter system can be solved by substitution. We have, from Equation (5),

$$y = \frac{2}{x}$$

Replacing y in Equation (3) by $2/x$, we find

$$x^2 + \left(\frac{2}{x}\right)^2 = 5$$

from which

$$x^2 + \frac{4}{x^2} = 5 \qquad (6)$$

Multiplying each member by x^2, we have

$$x^4 + 4 = 5x^2 \qquad\qquad (7)$$
$$x^4 - 5x^2 + 4 = 0 \qquad\qquad (7a)$$

which is quadratic in x^2. Factoring the left-hand member of Equation (7a), we obtain

$$(x^2 - 1)(x^2 - 4) = 0$$

from which

$$x^2 - 1 = 0 \quad \text{or} \quad x^2 - 4 = 0$$

Solving these equations (by factorization), we obtain

$$x = 1, \quad x = -1 \quad \text{and} \quad x = 2, \quad x = -2$$

Since we multiplied Equation (6) by a variable, we are careful to note that these values of x ($x \neq 0$) all satisfy Equation (6).

Now, substituting $1, -1, 2,$ and -2 for x in the equation $xy = 2$ or $y = 2/x$, we have

$$\text{For} \quad x = 1, \quad y = 2 \qquad \text{For} \quad x = -1, \quad y = -2$$
$$\text{For} \quad x = 2, \quad y = 1 \qquad \text{For} \quad x = -2, \quad y = -1$$

The solution set of either system (3) and (5) or system (3) and (4) is

$$\{(1, 2), (-1, -2), (2, 1), (-2, -1)\}$$

The graph of the system is not shown because we have not developed methods to graph Equation (4).

There are other techniques involving substitution in conjunction with linear combinations that are useful in handling systems of higher-degree equations, but they are all similar to those illustrated. Each system should be scrutinized for some means of finding an equivalent system that will lend itself to solution by linear combination or substitution.

EXERCISE SET 11.3

▲ *Solve each system. See Example 1.*

1. $x^2 + y^2 = 10$
$9x^2 + y^2 = 18$

2. $x^2 + 4y^2 = 52$
$x^2 + y^2 = 25$

3. $x^2 + 4y^2 = 17$
$3x^2 - y^2 = -1$

4. $9x^2 + 16y^2 = 100$
$x^2 + y^2 = 8$

5. $x^2 - y^2 = 7$
$2x^2 + 3y^2 = 24$

6. $x^2 + 4y^2 = 25$
$4x^2 + y^2 = 25$

7. $3x^2 + 4y^2 = 16$
$x^2 - y^2 = 3$

8. $4x^2 + 3y^2 = 12$
$x^2 + 3y^2 = 12$

9. $4x^2 - 9y^2 + 132 = 0$
$x^2 + 4y^2 - 67 = 0$

10. $16y^2 + 5x^2 - 26 = 0$
$25y^2 - 4x^2 - 17 = 0$

▲ *For Exercises 11–20, see Example 2.*

11. $2x^2 + xy - 4y^2 = -12$
$x^2 - 2y^2 = -4$

12. $x^2 + 2xy - y^2 = 14$
$x^2 - y^2 = 8$

13. $x^2 + 3xy - y^2 = -3$
$x^2 - xy - y^2 = 1$

14. $2x^2 + xy - 2y^2 = 16$
$x^2 + 2xy - y^2 = 17$

15. $x^2 - xy + y^2 = 7$
$x^2 + y^2 = 5$

16. $3x^2 - 2xy + 3y^2 = 34$
$x^2 + y^2 = 17$

17. $3x^2 + 3xy - y^2 = 35$
$x^2 - xy - 6y^2 = 0$

18. $x^2 - xy + y^2 = 21$
$x^2 + 2xy - 8y^2 = 0$

19. $2x^2 - xy - 6y^2 = 0$
$x^2 + 3xy + 2y^2 = 4$

20. $2x^2 + xy - y^2 = 0$
$6x^2 + xy - y^2 = 1$

Miscellaneous Exercises

21. How many *real* solutions are possible for systems of *independent* equations that consist of:

  a. Two linear equations in two variables?

  b. One linear equation and one quadratic equation in two variables?

  c. Two quadratic equations in two variables?

  Support your answers with sketches.

22. Consider the system

$$x^2 + y^2 = 8 \qquad \textbf{(1)}$$
$$xy = 4 \qquad \textbf{(2)}$$

We can solve this system by substituting $4/x$ for y in Equation (1) to obtain

$$x^2 + \frac{16}{x^2} = 8$$

from which we have $x = 2$ or $x = -2$. Now, if we obtain the y-components of the solution from Equation (2), we find that

For $x = 2$, $y = 2$ For $x = -2$, $y = -2$

But if we seek y-components from Equation (1), we have

For $x = 2$, $y = \pm 2$ For $x = -2$, $y = \pm 2$

Graph Equations (1) and (2) and discuss the fact that we seem to obtain more solutions from Equation (1) than from Equation (2). What is the solution set of the system?

CHAPTER SUMMARY

[11.1] The graphs of second-degree equations in two variables are **conic sections**. A quick sketch of a graph can be made by first writing the equation in standard form (see Table 11.1 on page 316) to identify its form.

[11.2–11.3] Systems of equations in two variables in which either or both equations are second-degree in one or both variables may have solutions with real components, imaginary components, or solutions of both kinds. Such systems can be solved by using substitution methods or by using linear combinations of the members of the equations in the system.

REVIEW EXERCISES

[11.1]

▲ *Graph each conic section.*

1. $\dfrac{x^2}{4} + \dfrac{y^2}{15} = 1$

2. $\dfrac{x^2}{6} - \dfrac{y^2}{12} = 1$

3. $\dfrac{y^2}{8} - \dfrac{x^2}{16} = 1$

4. $4x^2 + 3y^2 = 36$

5. $x^2 + 6y^2 = 24$

6. $x^2 - 8y^2 = 32$

7. $2x^2 = 18 - 2y^2$

8. $\dfrac{1}{2}x^2 = 8 - 3y^2$

9. $\dfrac{1}{2}y^2 = 12 + x^2$

10. $\dfrac{1}{2}y^2 = \dfrac{1}{4}x^2 + 6$

[11.2–11.3]

▲ *Solve each system by substitution or linear combination.*

11. $x + 3y^2 = 4$
    $x = 3$

12. $x^2 + 2y^2 = -8$
    $y = -2$

13. $x^2 + y = 3$
    $5x + y = 7$

14. $x^2 + 3xy + x = -12$
    $2x - y = 7$

15. $6x^2 - y^2 = 1$
    $3x^2 + 2y^2 = 13$

16. $2x^2 + 5y^2 - 53 = 0$
    $4x^2 + 3y^2 - 43 = 0$

17. $x^2 - 2xy + 3y^2 = 17$
    $2x^2 + xy + 6y^2 = 24$

18. $x^2 - xy - y^2 = 1$
    $x^2 + 3xy - y^2 = 9$

Miscellaneous Exercises

▲ *Name the graph of each equation and describe its main features.*

19. $x^2 + 4y^2 = 24$

20. $y^2 - 4x^2 = 12$

21. $x^2 + 48 = 8y$

22. $2y = 4x^2 - 9$

23. $6 + \dfrac{y^2}{2} = x^2$

24. $6x^2 = 12 - y^2$

25. $4x^2 + 4y^2 = 32$

26. $4x^2 - 4y^2 = 32$

27. The perimeter of a rectangle is 34 centimeters long, and the area is 70 square centimeters. Find the dimensions of the rectangle.

28. A rectangle has a perimeter of 18 feet. If the length is decreased by 5 feet and the width is increased by 12 feet, the area is doubled. Find the dimensions of the original rectangle.

▲ The numbers in brackets refer to the sections in which such problems are first considered.

▲ Write as a single fraction in lowest terms.

1. $x - \dfrac{x}{x+3} - \dfrac{x+2}{x^2-9}$ **[4.4]**

2. $\dfrac{x^2 - 8x + 16}{x-4} \div (x^2 - 16)$ **[4.5]**

▲ Simplify.

3. $2x^2 y(xy^2)^{-1}$ **[5.2]**

4. $\sqrt[3]{16x^3 y^2} - x\sqrt[3]{54y^2}$ **[5.8]**

5. Solve $2 = \dfrac{3x}{3y^2 + 1}$ explicitly for y. **[7.1]**

6. State the domain of the function defined by
$x^2 y - 4y = 6$ **[8.1]**

7. Find the zeros of the function $f(x) = 14 + 5x - x^2$. **[8.3]**

8. For what values of x is $\log_3(9 - x^2)$ defined? **[9.1]**

9. Express as a single logarithm with coefficient 1:
$$\frac{1}{2}\log_b x - (2\log_b y + 3\log_b z) \quad \textbf{[9.2]}$$

10. Solve $P = P_0 e^{kt} + c$ for t. **[9.5]**

▲ Solve each system.

11. $\begin{array}{l} 4x = 6 - 2y \\ 3y = 17 + 2x \end{array}$ **[10.1]**

12. $\begin{array}{l} x^2 - 3xy + 2y^2 = 0 \\ 3x + y = 7 \end{array}$ **[11.4]**

13. Solve $2x^2 - kx + 1 = 0$ for x in terms of k. **[6.2]**

14. Write an equation in standard form of the line that is perpendicular to the graph of $2y + x = 6$ and passes through $(2, -3)$. **[7.4]**

15. Find values of a, b, and c such that the graph of $x^2 + y^2 + ax + by + c = 0$ will contain the points $(-2, -2), (-2, 6)$, and $(2, 2)$. **[10.2]**

16. Solve the following system using determinants or matrices:
$$\begin{array}{l} 3x - y + z = 10 \\ 2x + y - 3z = 0 \\ x - 2y - z = 10 \end{array} \quad \textbf{[10.4, 10.5]}$$

▲ Graph each function.

17. $f(x) = x^2 - 4x - 5$ **[8.3]**

18. $f(x) = 2^{x+1}$ **[8.4]**

▲ Approximate the solution of each system by graphing techniques.

19. $\begin{array}{l} y = 2^x \\ x + y = 5 \end{array}$ **[8.4]**

20. $\begin{array}{l} y = \log_{10}(x + 1) \\ x + y = 4 \end{array}$ **[9.1]**

▲ Solve.

21. The scale on a map of Michigan uses $\frac{3}{8}$ inch to represent 10 miles. If Isle Royale is $1\frac{11}{16}$ inches long on the map, what is the actual length of the island? **[4.8]**

22. A photographer plans to enlarge a photograph that measures 8.3 centimeters by 11.2 centimeters to produce a poster that is 36 centimeters wide. How long will the poster be? **[4.8]**

23. The weight of an object varies inversely with the square of its distance from the center of the Earth. How much would a 120-pound astronaut weigh on a spaceship 500 miles above the Earth? Consider the radius of the Earth to be 3963 miles. **[8.2]**

24. The intensity I (in lumens) of a light beam after passing through a thickness t (in centimeters) of a medium having an absorption coefficient of 0.1 is given by $I = 1000e^{-0.1t}$. How many centimeters (to the nearest tenth) of the material would reduce the illumination to 800 lumens? **[9.6]**

25. The number N of bacteria present in a culture is given by $N = N_0 e^{0.04t}$, where N_0 is the number of bacteria present at time $t = 0$, and t is time in hours. How much time must elapse (to the nearest tenth of an hour) for 2500 bacteria to increase to 10,000? **[9.6]**

INEQUALITIES

Order relationships were introduced in Section 1.1, where we also graphed some simple inequalities. In this chapter we will consider some properties that will enable us to solve other inequalities in one variable and systems of inequalities in two variables.

12.1 LINEAR INEQUALITIES

Solution of an Inequality

Any replacement of a variable for which an inequality such as

$$2x + 3 \geqslant x - 5$$

is true is called a **solution**, and the set of all solutions of an inequality is called the **solution set** of the inequality.

Equivalent Inequalities

As in the case of equations, we solve a given inequality by generating a series of equivalent inequalities (inequalities that have the same solution set) until we arrive at one whose solution set is obvious. To do this, we need some fundamental properties of inequalities. Notice that

$$2 < 3$$

$$2 + 5 < 3 + 5$$

and

$$2 - 5 < 3 - 5$$

Figures 12.1a and 12.1b demonstrate that the addition of 5 or -5 to each side of $2 < 3$ simply shifts their graphs the same number of units to the right or left on the number line, with their order left unchanged. This will be the case for the addition

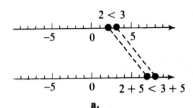

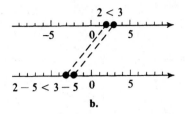

Figure 12.1   a.   b.

of any real number to each side of an inequality. Since any variable represents a real number, we generalize this idea and assert the following:

> **1.** *The addition of the same expression to each side of an inequality produces an equivalent inequality in the* **same sense**.

Next, if we multiply each side of $2 < 3$ by 2, we have

$$4 < 6$$

where the products form an inequality in the same sense. If, however, we multiply each side of $2 < 3$ by -2, we have

$$-4 > -6$$

where the inequality is in the opposite sense. Figure 12.2 illustrates this. Multiplying each side of $2 < 3$ by 2 simply moves their graphs out twice as far in a positive direction (Figure 12.2a). Multiplying by -2 also doubles the absolute value of each

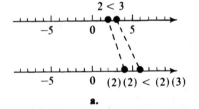

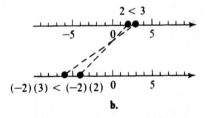

Figure 12.2   a.   b.

side, but the products are negative, so the sense of the inequality is reversed, as shown in Figure 12.2b. In general, we assert the following:

> **2.** *If each side of an inequality is multiplied by the same expression representing a positive number, the result is an equivalent inequality in the* **same sense**.
>
> **3.** *If each side of an inequality is multiplied by the same expression representing a negative number, the result is an equivalent inequality in the* **opposite sense**.

The preceding statements 1, 2, and 3 can be expressed in symbols as follows:

> *The inequality*
>
> $$a < b$$
>
> *is equivalent to*
>
> $$a + c < b + c \tag{1}$$
> $$a \cdot c < b \cdot c \quad \textit{for} \quad c > 0 \tag{2}$$
> $$a \cdot c > b \cdot c \quad \textit{for} \quad c < 0. \tag{3}$$

These relationships are also true with $<$ replaced by $\leqslant$ and $>$ replaced by $\geqslant$. Note that none of these assertions permits multiplying by 0. These properties can be applied to solve first-degree inequalities in the same way the equality properties are applied to solve first-degree equations.

EXAMPLE 1   Solve the inequality

$$3x - 9 < 8 \qquad \textbf{Add 9 to each side.}$$
$$3x < 17 \qquad \textbf{Divide each side by 3.}$$
$$x < \frac{17}{3}$$

Graphs of Solution Sets   The solution set of the inequality in Example 1 can be graphed as shown in Figure 12.3, where the bold line represents the points whose coordinates are in the solution set. The endpoint is shown as an open dot to show that $\frac{17}{3}$ is not included in the set.

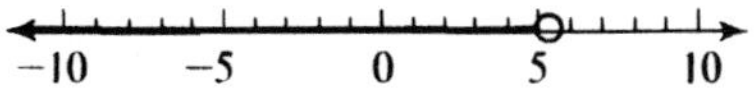

Figure 12.3

EXAMPLE 2   Solve the inequality

$$x + 4 \leqslant 18 + 3x \qquad \textbf{Add } -4 \textbf{ and } -3x \textbf{ to each side.}$$
$$-2x \leqslant 14 \qquad\qquad \textbf{Divide each side by } -2\textbf{; reverse the sense of the inequality.}$$
$$x \geqslant -7$$

The endpoint in the graph is shown as a solid dot to show that -7 is included in the solution set.

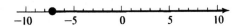

We can use Properties 1, 2, and 3 to solve continued inequalities of the form shown in the following example:

EXAMPLE 3

Solve.

$$4 < x + 4 \leqslant 6 \qquad \text{Add } -4 \text{ to each expression.}$$
$$4 + (-4) < x + 4 + (-4) \leqslant 6 + (-4)$$
$$0 < x \leqslant 2$$

The left endpoint of its graph is an open dot, and the right endpoint is a closed dot.

The suggestions in Section 2.4 for solving word problems in which the mathematical model is an equation are also applicable to problems in which the mathematical model is an inequality, except that symbols such as $\leqslant$ and $<$ replace the symbol $=$.

EXAMPLE 4

A student must have an average of 80% or more and less than 90% on five tests in a course to receive a B. Her grades on the first four tests were 98%, 76%, 86%, and 92%. What grade on the fifth test would give her a B in the course?

Solution

Step 1 We first express the quantity asked for in a simple phrase.

Step 2 Then we represent the quantity symbolically.

$$\boxed{\text{Grade (in percent) on the fifth test:}} \quad x$$

Step 1 ⟶   ⟵ Step 2

Step 3 We then write an inequality expressing the fact that the average of the five tests is greater than or equal to 80 and less than 90.

$$80 \leqslant \frac{98 + 76 + 86 + 92 + x}{5} < 90$$

Step 4 Solving the inequality, we obtain

$$400 \leqslant 352 + x < 450$$
$$48 \leqslant x < 98$$

Step 5 Therefore, any grade equal to or greater than 48 and less than 98 would give the student a B in the course.

EXERCISE SET 12.1

▲ *Solve and graph each solution set. See Examples 1 and 2.*

1. $3x < 6$

2. $x + 7 > 8$

3. $x - 5 \leqslant 7$

4. $2x - 3 < 4$

5. $3x - 2 > 1 + 2x$

6. $2x + 3 \leqslant x - 1$

7. $\dfrac{2x - 6}{3} > 0$

8. $\dfrac{2x - 3}{2} \leqslant 5$

9. $\dfrac{5x - 7x}{3} > 4$

10. $\dfrac{x - 3x}{5} \leqslant 6$

11. $\dfrac{2x - 5x}{2} \leqslant 7$

12. $\dfrac{x - 6x}{2} < -20$

13. $5x + 10 > 3x - 12$

14. $6x + 3 \geqslant 5x - 6$ **15.** $8x + 4 - 4x \geqslant 4$

16. $8 - 2x < 5x + 2$

▲ *Solve and graph each solution set. See Example 3.*

17. $4 < x - 2 < 8$ **18.** $0 \leqslant 2x \leqslant 12$

19. $-3 < 2x + 1 \leqslant 7$ **20.** $2 \leqslant 3x - 4 \leqslant 8$

21. $6 < 4 - x < 10$ **22.** $-3 < 3 - 2x < 9$

23. $-3 < 2x + 1 \leqslant 7$ **24.** $-3 < 3 - 2x < 9$

25. $-2 > \dfrac{3x + 2}{5} > -4$ **26.** $0 \geqslant \dfrac{x + 5}{2} \geqslant -2$

27. $1.5 \leqslant \dfrac{x - 2.5}{3} < 1.8$ **28.** $0.2 < \dfrac{2x - 1.4}{4} \leqslant 2.6$

▲ *Solve each word problem. Example 4.*

29. A student must have an average of 80% or more and less than 90% on five tests to receive a B in a course. What grade on the fifth test would give the student a B if her grades on the first four tests were 78%, 64%, 88%, and 76%?

30. In Exercise 29, what grade on the final examination would give a student a B if her grades on the first four hourly tests were 72%, 68%, 84%, and 70% and the final examination counted for two hourly tests?

31. The Fahrenheit and Celsius temperature scales are related by the formula

$$C = \dfrac{5F - 160}{9}$$

The travel brochure for an Austrian ski resort lists the average temperatures in February as being between $-23°C$ and $-2°C$. What is the average temperature range in degrees Fahrenheit?

32. The Fahrenheit and Celsius temperature scales are related by the formula

$$F = \dfrac{9}{5}C + 32$$

A ski parka has a "comfort range" of $-15°F$ to $25°F$. What is the comfort range in degrees Celsius?

33. Lewis would like to average at least 16 points per game for the remainder of the basketball season. In previous games he scored 12, 15, 19, 17, and 11 points. How many points must he score in the last game to achieve an average of at least 16 points per game?

34. Owen's Market needs to make at least $20,000 per month to stay in business. Over the past 5 months it has made $16,000, $17,600, $19,500, $18,800, and $22,000. How much must it make next month to meet its goal?

35. Barker's Employment Agency charges a commission of $50 plus 15% of the first month's salary for its services. Carter's Career Search charges a commission of $80 plus 12% of the first month's salary. When is it cheaper to use Carter's?

36. Mavis has a choice of two dental insurance plans. Plan A pays 70% of the cost of a regular visit to the dentist after a deductible of $10. Plan B pays 80% of the cost after a deductible of $15. When is plan A cheaper than plan B?

37. In Professor Bunsen's chemistry class, lab projects count as 30% of the grade, tests count as 40%, and the final exam counts as 30%. If Linus has an 86% average on tests and a 73% average on lab projects, what range of scores on the final exam will guarantee Linus a B (greater than or equal to 80% but less than 90%) in the course?

38. A long-distance runner wants to put in 50 training miles per week at an average pace of 6.5 to 7 minutes per mile. If she runs one 12-mile course twice each week at 8 minutes per mile and six 1-mile sprints at 5 minutes per mile, at what pace must she run the remaining 20 training miles?

Miscellaneous Exercises

▲ *Graph the set of numbers that are solutions of the first inequality and also solutions of the second inequality.*

39. $x < 2$ and $x > -2$

40. $x \leqslant 5$ and $x \geqslant 1$

41. $x + 1 \leqslant 3$ and $-x - 1 \leqslant 3$

42. $2x - 3 < 5$ and $-2x + 3 < 5$

43. $x - 7 < 2x$ and $-3x \geqslant 4x + 28$

44. $9 - 3x < 21$ and $-10 < -5x + 15$

12.2 | **SPECIAL NOTATION; SET OPERATIONS**

Set-Builder Notation

One way to describe sets is by a convenient notation called **set-builder notation**. Set-builder notation names a variable and states a condition on the variable. Each replacement value of the variable that satisfies the condition is included in the set. The notation

$$\{x|x \text{ is an integer}\}$$

is read "the set of all x *such that* x is an integer."

This notation is particularly useful in describing a set of numbers defined by an inequality. If the replacement set for a variable is not specified, it is understood to be the set of real numbers. For example,

$$\{y|-2 < y < 6\}$$

is read "the set of all y *such that* -2 is less than y and y is less than 6" or "the set of all y such that y is between -2 and 6," where it is understood that the replacement set for y is the real numbers.

Intersection of Two Sets Sometimes two conditions of inequality are placed on a variable. For example, we may want to consider $\{x|-2 < x \text{ and } x \leqslant 5\}$, that is, the numbers in $\{x|-2 < x\}$ and also in $\{x|x \leqslant 5\}$. Both conditions must be satisfied by a replacement value to be included in the set. We call the resulting set the **intersection** of the two given sets. In general, we have the following.

If A and B are sets, the **intersection** of A and B consists of all those numbers that are in set A and also in set B. We designated this set by $A \cap B$, read "the intersection of sets A and B."

The set $\{x|-2 < x \text{ and } x \leqslant 5\}$ may be written as

$$\{x|-2 < x\} \cap \{x|x \leqslant 5\}$$

The graph of the intersection is shown in Figure 12.4.

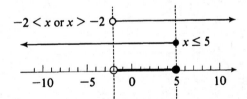

Figure 12.4

EXAMPLE 1 To graph $\{x|x > -4 \text{ and } x + 1 \leqslant 4\}$, which can be written

$$\{x|x > -4\} \cap \{x|x + 1 \leqslant 4\}$$

we first graph each inequality. Then we locate the interval common to both number lines.

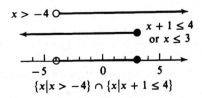

Note that in Example 1 the intersection of the two sets can be written as the single set

$$\{x \mid -4 < x \leqslant 3\}$$

Disjoint Sets   Sets that do not have any numbers in common are called **disjoint sets**. If A and B are sets and

$$A \cap B = \varnothing$$

then A and B are disjoint. For example,

$$\{2,3\} \cap \{4,5\} = \varnothing \quad \text{and} \quad \{x \mid x < 1\} \cap \{x \mid x > 3\} = \varnothing$$

Union of Two Sets   In the preceding discussion we expressed inequalities connected with the word "and" as the intersection of two sets. The set

$$\{x \mid x < -3 \text{ or } x > 3\}$$

combines members of $\{x \mid x < -3\}$ with the members of $\{x \mid x > 3\}$ and is called the **union** of the two sets.

If A and B are sets, the **union** of A and B consists of all those members that are either in set A or in set B or in both. We denote this set by $A \cup B$, read "the union of sets A and B."

The set $\{x \mid x < -3 \text{ or } x > 3\}$ may be written as

$$\{x \mid x < -3\} \cup \{x \mid x > 3\}$$

The graph of the union is shown in Figure 12.5.

Figure 12.5

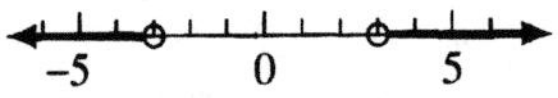

EXAMPLE 2   To graph $\{x \mid -2 \leqslant x < 1 \text{ or } x \geqslant 4\}$, which can be written as
$$\{x \mid -2 \leqslant x < 1\} \cup \{x \mid x \geqslant 4\}$$
we first graph each set. The graph of the union is a combination of the two graphs.

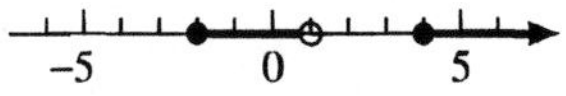

Interval Notation   Another special notation is used sometimes to describe an interval of real numbers. The symbols (a, b) are used for the interval that includes all real numbers *between a and b*, where $a < b$. The symbol "[" is used instead of "(" if a is included in the interval, and "]" is used instead of ")" if b is included in the interval. That is, (a, b) means all x such that $a < x < b$ and $[a, b]$ means all x such that $a \leqslant x \leqslant b$.

EXAMPLE 3 a. $\{x | 3 < x < 5\} = (3, 5)$ b. $\{y | 6 \leqslant y \leqslant 7\} = [6, 7]$

c. $\{z | 1 < z \leqslant 3\} = (1, 3]$ d. $\{x | -2 \leqslant x < 4\} = [-2, 4)$

If an interval includes all real numbers greater than a given real number or less than a given real number, we incorporate the symbols $+\infty$ and $-\infty$ in the notation. These symbols are read "positive infinity" and "negative infinity," respectively. They do not denote specific real numbers.

EXAMPLE 4 a. $\{x | x \geqslant 2\} = [2, +\infty)$ b. $\{y | y > -4\} = (-4, +\infty)$

c. $\{z | z \leqslant 0\} = (-\infty, 0]$ d. $\{t | t < 6\} = (-\infty, 6)$

Because an interval such as $[-5, 8]$ contains both of its endpoints, it is called a **closed interval**. Intervals such as $(3, 18]$ and $[-5, -2)$ are called **half-open intervals**, and intervals such as $(3, 8)$ or $(-\infty, 2)$ are called **open intervals**.

We have now used three different ways to represent the solution set of an inequality, as shown in the following chart:

Set	Interval	Graph
$\{x | -2 < x \leqslant 3\}$	$(-2, 3]$	
$\{x | x < 4\}$	$(-\infty, 4)$	
$\{x | x \geqslant -2\}$	$[-2, +\infty)$	

Parentheses and brackets used in interval notation can also be used when constructing number lines. For example, the three graphs in the chart would appear as follows:

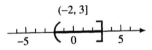
(-2, 3]

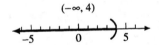
(-∞, 4)

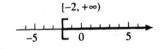
[-2, +∞)

EXERCISE SET 12.2

▲ *Graph each set. See Example 1.*

1. $\{x | x < 2\} \cap \{x | x > -2\}$
2. $\{x | x \leqslant 5\} \cap \{x | x \geqslant 1\}$
3. $\{x | x + 1 \leqslant 3\} \cap \{x | -x - 1 \leqslant 3\}$
4. $\{x | 2x - 3 < 5\} \cap \{x | -2x + 3 < 5\}$
5. $\{x | x - 7 < 2x\} \cap \{x | -3x \geqslant 4x + 28\}$
6. $\{x | 9 \leqslant 3x < 21\} \cap \{x | -10 < 5x \leqslant 15\}$
7. $\{x | x \geqslant -3 \quad \text{and} \quad x < 5\}$

8. $\{x | x < 0 \quad \text{and} \quad x \geqslant -5\}$
9. $\{x | 0 < x < 5 \quad \text{and} \quad x \geqslant 3\}$
10. $\{x | x < 2 \quad \text{and} \quad -2 \leqslant x < 4\}$

▲ *Graph each set. See Example 2.*

11. $\{x | x \leqslant 0\} \cup \{x | x > 3\}$
12. $\{x | x \leqslant -3\} \cup \{x | x > 0\}$
13. $\{x | x - 1 > 3\} \cup \{x + 2 \leqslant 0\}$

14. $\{x|2x + 1 < 3\} \cup \{x|3x - 2 > 10\}$
15. $\{x|-2 < x < 4\} \cup \{x|x > 0\}$
16. $\{x|x \leqslant -2\} \cup \{x|-5 < x < 3\}$
17. $\{x|x < -2 \quad \text{or} \quad x > 3\}$
18. $\{x|x \geqslant 0 \quad \text{or} \quad x < -4\}$
19. $\{x|-2 < x + 2 < 4 \quad \text{or} \quad x > 4\}$
20. $\{x|0 < 2x < 8 \quad \text{or} \quad x \leqslant -3\}$

▲ *Express each set in interval notation. See Examples 3 and 4.*

21. $\{x|-5 < x \leqslant 3\}$
22. $\{x|2 \leqslant x < 6\}$
23. $\{x|-1 \leqslant x \leqslant 6\}$
24. $\{x|-3 < x < 0\}$
25. $\{x|x \geqslant 3\}$
26. $\{x|x < -2\}$
27. $\{x|x \leqslant 0\}$
28. $\{x|x > -4\}$

Miscellaneous Exercises

▲ *Graph the given intervals on the same line graph, and represent the numbers involved using set-builder notation.*

29. $[-8, 2];\quad (3, 7]$
30. $(-4, 0];\quad (2, +\infty)$
31. $[-7, -3];\quad (0, 4]$
32. $(-\infty, 0);\quad (0, +\infty)$
33. $(-5, -3];\quad (-2, 0];\quad (1, 3)$
34. $(-\infty, -4];\quad (-2, 0];\quad (2, +\infty)$

▲ *Write each nonempty interval as a single interval. If the sets are disjoint, so state.*

35. $[-8, -4] \cap [-6, 2)$
36. $(-3, 0] \cap [-1, 4]$
37. $[-5, -3) \cap [-2, 0)$
38. $[-6, 4] \cap (6, 7]$
39. $(0, 3) \cap \emptyset$
40. $(-4, 0] \cap \emptyset$

12.3 | ABSOLUTE-VALUE INEQUALITIES

Equations Involving Absolute Value

Before we study absolute-value inequalities, it will be helpful to consider some simple equations involving absolute values. Recall from Section 1.2 that we define the absolute value of a real number x as follows:

$$|x| = \begin{cases} x & \text{if} \quad x \geqslant 0 \\ -x & \text{if} \quad x < 0 \end{cases}$$

Hence, $|x|$ is always nonnegative. We also noted that $|x|$ can be viewed on a number line as the distance x is from the origin. For example, -7 and 7 are the same distance from the origin (see Figure 12.6) and

$$|-7| = |7| = 7$$

Hence, the equation

$$|x| = 7$$

has two solutions, 7 and -7.

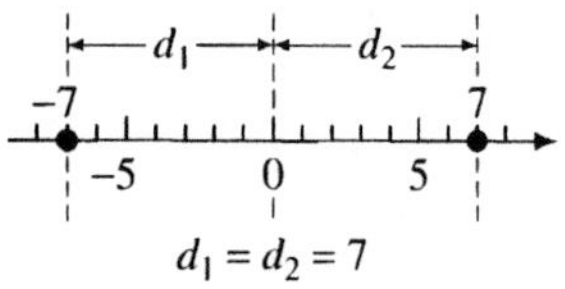

More generally, we have that

Figure 12.6

$$|ax - b| = \begin{cases} ax - b & \text{if} \quad ax - b \geqslant 0 \\ -(ax - b) & \text{if} \quad ax - b < 0 \end{cases}$$

We can solve equations of the form

$$|ax - b| = c$$

by appealing to the definition of absolute value and writing this equation as two equations without absolute-value notation.

$|ax - b| = c \quad (c > 0)$ *is equivalent to the joint statement*

$$ax - b = c \quad or \quad -(ax - b) = c \qquad (1)$$

EXAMPLE 1   Solve $|2x - 3| = 5$.

Solution   This equation implies that

$$2x - 3 = 5 \quad or \quad -(2x - 3) = 5$$
$$2x = 8 \qquad\qquad 2x - 3 = -5$$
$$x = 4 \qquad\qquad 2x = -2$$
$$\qquad\qquad\qquad x = -1$$

Hence, the solution set is $\{4, -1\}$.

Note that in Example 1,

$$\{4\} \cup \{-1\} = \{4, -1\}$$

Inequalities Involving Absolute Value   Consider the graph of the solution set of $|x| < 5$ in Figure 12.7. In this simple case the fact that this is indeed the graph of the inequality can be verified by inspection. Note that if $x \geq 0$,   then $x < 5$,   and if $x < 0$,   then $x > -5$. These two conditions can be expressed as the continued inequality $-5 < x < 5$.

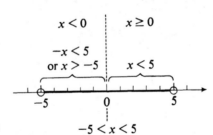

Figure 12.7

The solution set of $|x| < 5$ is $\{x | -5 < x < 5\} = (-5, 5)$.

Now consider the graph of the solution set of $|x| > 5$ in Figure 12.8, which can also be verified by inspection.

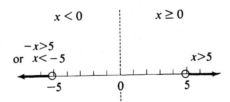

Figure 12.8

The solution set of $|x| > 5$ is $\{x | x < -5 \quad or \quad x > 5\} = (-\infty, -5) \cup (5, \infty)$.

COMMON ERROR   *The two conditions* $x < -5$ *and* $x > 5$ *cannot be written as a continued inequality;* $-5 < x > 5$ *does not make sense.*

The preceding examples suggest the following properties, which can be used to solve inequalities that involve absolute value:

$$|ax - b| < c \quad \text{is equivalent to} \quad -c < ax - b < c \qquad (2)$$

and

$$|ax - b| > c \quad \text{is equivalent to} \quad ax - b > c \quad \text{or} \quad -(ax - b) > c \qquad (3)$$

EXAMPLE 2 Solve $|x + 1| < 3$ and graph the solution set.

Solution From Property 2 this inequality is equivalent to

$$-3 < x + 1 < 3 \qquad \textbf{Add } -1 \textbf{ to each member.}$$
$$-4 < x < 2$$

Hence, the solution set is $\{x \mid -4 < x < 2\} = (-4, 2)$, with the graph as shown.

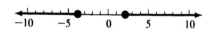

EXAMPLE 3 Solve $|x + 1| \geq 3$ and graph the solution set.

Solution From Property 3 the inequality is equivalent to

$$x + 1 \geq 3 \quad \text{or} \quad -(x + 1) \geq 3$$

from which we have

$$x \geq 2 \quad \text{or} \quad x \leq -4$$

Hence, the solution set is $\{x \mid x \leq -4 \text{ or } x \geq 2\} = (-\infty, -4] \cup [2, +\infty)$, with the graph as shown.

EXERCISE SET 12.3

▲ *Solve. See Example 1.*

1. $|x| = 5$
2. $|x| = 7$
3. $|x - 4| = 9$
4. $|x - 3| = 7$
5. $|2x + 1| = 13$
6. $|3x - 1| = 5$
7. $|4 - 3x| = 1$
8. $|6 - 5x| = 4$
9. $|4x + 3| = 0$
10. $|3x - 7| = 0$
11. $|2x - 3| = 3$
12. $|3x - 2| = 2$

▲ *Solve and graph each solution set. See Example 2.*

13. $|x| < 2$
14. $|x| < 5$

15. $|x + 3| \leq 4$
16. $|x + 1| \leq 8$
17. $|2x - 5| < 3$
18. $|2x + 4| < 6$
19. $|4 - x| \leq 8$
20. $|5 - 2x| \leq 15$
21. $\left| x - \dfrac{1}{4} \right| < \dfrac{7}{4}$
22. $\left| x + \dfrac{1}{3} \right| \leq \dfrac{5}{3}$
23. $\left| 2x + \dfrac{2}{3} \right| \leq 8$
24. $\left| 2x - \dfrac{3}{4} \right| < 6$

▲ *Solve and graph each solution set. See Example 3.*

25. $|x| > 3$
26. $|x| \geq 5$

27. $|x - 2| > 5$

28. $|x + 5| > 2$

29. $|3 - 2x| \geqslant 7$

30. $|4 - 3x| > 10$

31. $\left| x - \dfrac{1}{3} \right| > \dfrac{5}{3}$

32. $\left| x + \dfrac{1}{4} \right| \geqslant \dfrac{9}{4}$

33. $\left| 2x + \dfrac{3}{4} \right| \geqslant 4$

34. $\left| 2x - \dfrac{1}{3} \right| > 6$

▲ *Solve each equation or inequality. See Examples 1–3.*

35. $|x + 1| \leqslant 7$

36. $|x - 2| < 5$

37. $|2x - 6| > 3$

38. $|3x + 5| \geqslant 2$

39. $|5x + 2| = 0$

40. $|2x - 6| = 0$

41. $|4x - 1| \leqslant 6$

42. $|3x + 2| > 5$

Miscellaneous Exercises

▲ *Express by using absolute value.*

43. y is three units from the origin.

44. x is five units from the origin.

45. The distance between x and 5 is three units.

46. The distance between y and -4 is six units.

47. x is within four units of 7.

48. y is within two units of -5.

12.4 | NONLINEAR INEQUALITIES

Properties (1)–(3) and Equations (1)–(3) of Section 12.1 are used to solve linear inequalities. To solve quadratic inequalities, additional procedures are necessary. For example, consider the inequality

$$x^2 + 4x < 5$$

To determine values of x for which this condition holds, we might first rewrite the inequality equivalently as

$$x^2 + 4x - 5 < 0$$

and then as

$$(x + 5)(x - 1) < 0$$

The left-hand side will be negative (less than 0) only for those values of x for which the factors $x + 5$ and $x - 1$ are opposite in sign. There are two ways in which this can happen; either

$$x + 5 < 0 \qquad \text{and} \qquad x - 1 > 0 \tag{1}$$

or

$$x + 5 > 0 \qquad \text{and} \qquad x - 1 < 0 \tag{2}$$

Each of these two cases can be considered separately.

　　Case 1: The inequalities in (1),

$$x + 5 < 0 \qquad \text{and} \qquad x - 1 > 0$$

imply that

$$x < -5 \qquad \text{and} \qquad x > 1$$

a condition that is not satisfied by any value of x. Therefore, the solution set of (1) is $\emptyset$.

Case 2:   The inequalities in (2),

$$x + 5 > 0 \qquad \text{and} \qquad x - 1 < 0$$

imply that

$$x > -5 \qquad \text{and} \qquad x < 1$$

so the solution set for (2) is

$$\{x \mid -5 < x < 1\}$$

The solution set for the inequality is the union of the solution sets for the two cases,

$$\emptyset \cup \{x \mid -5 < x < 1\} \qquad \text{or} \qquad \{x \mid -5 < x < 1\}$$

Sign Arrays   The solution of the inequality $(x + 5)(x - 1) < 0$ can be simplified through the use of an array of signs determined by the factors in the left-hand member. Note that in Figure 12.9 the product is negative (less than zero) whenever the factors have opposite signs.

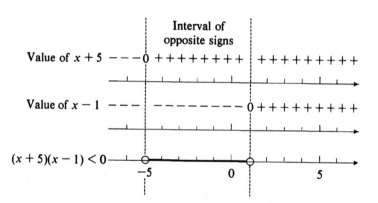

Figure 12.9

Critical Numbers   Sign arrays such as the one shown in Figure 12.9 can be used to solve many nonlinear inequalities. However, the solution of such inequalities can also be simplified further by using the notion of a *critical number*.

Notice in the foregoing solution process that the numbers -5 and 1, which are the solutions of the equation $(x + 5)(x - 1) = 0$,   separate the set of real numbers into the three intervals

$$(-\infty, -5), \quad (-5, 1), \quad \text{and} \quad (1, +\infty)$$

as shown in Figure 12.10. The expression $x^2 + 4x - 5$ cannot change from negative to positive (or vice versa) except at its zeros, the critical numbers -5 and 1. Hence, on each interval the inequality $x^2 + 4x < 5$ is either always positive or always negative. Therefore, each of those intervals either is or is not a part of the solution set.

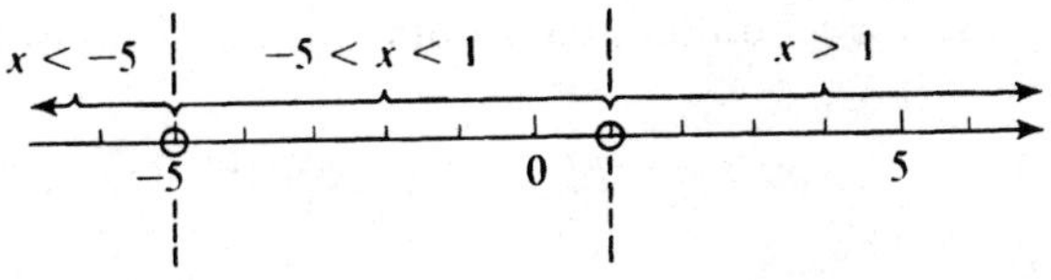

Figure 12.10

To determine which interval is the solution, we need only substitute an arbitrarily selected number from each interval and test it in the inequality. Let us use $-6, 0,$ and $2.$

$$(-6)^2 + 4(-6) \overset{?}{<} 5 \qquad 0^2 + 4(0) \overset{?}{<} 5 \qquad 2^2 + 4(2) \overset{?}{<} 5$$
$$36 - 24 \overset{?}{<} 5 \qquad 0 + 0 \overset{?}{<} 5 \qquad 4 + 8 \overset{?}{<} 5$$
$$12 \overset{?}{<} 5 \qquad 0 \overset{?}{<} 5 \qquad 12 \overset{?}{<} 5$$
$$\text{no} \qquad\qquad \text{yes} \qquad\qquad \text{no}$$

The only interval on which the inequality is true is $(-5, 1)$, and hence this interval is the solution set. The graph is shown in Figure 12.11. If the inequality in this example were $x^2 + 4x - 5 \leqslant 0,$ the endpoints on the graph would be shown as closed dots.

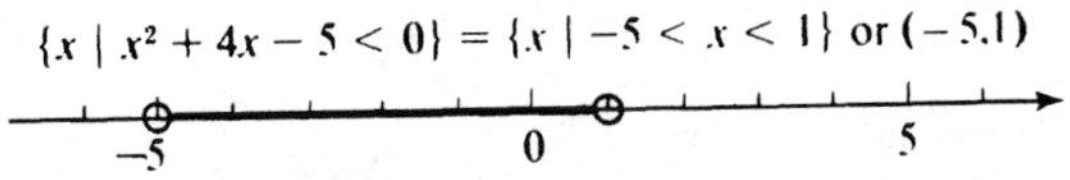

$$\{x \mid x^2 + 4x - 5 < 0\} = \{x \mid -5 < x < 1\} \text{ or } (-5.1)$$

Figure 12.11

Real numbers such as -5 and 1 in the preceding example are called *critical numbers*. In general, we have the following:

The values of x *for which* $P(x) = 0$ *or* $P(x)$ *is undefined are called* **critical numbers** *of* $P(x) < 0$ *or* $P(x) > 0.$

EXAMPLE 1

a. Critical numbers for $2x^2 - x - 1 > 0$ are $-\dfrac{1}{2}$ and $1,$ because

$$2x^2 - x - 1 = (2x + 1)(x - 1) = 0$$

for these values.

b. Critical numbers for $\dfrac{1}{x^2 - 4} < 0$ are 2 and $-2,$ because

$$\frac{1}{x^2 - 4} = \frac{1}{(x - 2)(x + 2)}$$

is not defined for either number.

EXAMPLE 2

Solve and graph the solution set of

$$x^2 - 3x - 4 \geqslant 0 \qquad\qquad (3)$$

Solution

Factoring the left-hand member yields

$$(x + 1)(x - 4) \geqslant 0$$

We note that -1 and 4 are critical numbers because $(x + 1)(x - 4) = 0$ for these values. Hence, we check the intervals on the number line in Figure a. We substitute selected arbitrary values in each interval, say, $-2, 0$, and 5, for the variable in (3).

$$(-2)^2 - 3(-2) - 4 \overset{?}{\geqslant} 0 \qquad (0)^2 - 3(0) - 4 \overset{?}{\geqslant} 0 \qquad (5)^2 - 3(5) - 4 \overset{?}{\geqslant} 0$$

yes   no   yes

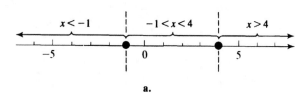

a.

Hence, the solution set is $(-\infty, -1] \cup [4, +\infty)$. The graph is shown in Figure b.

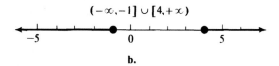

b.

Variable in a Denominator

Inequalities involving fractions must be approached with care if any fraction contains a variable in the denominator. If each member of such an inequality is multiplied by an expression containing the variable, we must be careful either to distinguish between those values of the variable for which the expression denotes a positive and a negative number or to make certain that the expression by which we multiply is always positive. However, we can use the notion of critical numbers to avoid these complications. As shown in the following example, we first obtain an equivalent inequality in which the left side is a single fraction and the right side is zero.

EXAMPLE 3

Solve and graph the solution set of

$$\frac{x}{x - 2} \geqslant 5 \tag{4}$$

Solution

We first write (4) equivalently as

$$\frac{x}{x - 2} - 5 \geqslant 0 \qquad \textbf{Right side is 0.}$$

from which

$$\frac{x - 5(x - 2)}{x - 2} \geqslant 0 \qquad \textbf{Left side is a single fraction.}$$

$$\frac{-4x + 10}{x - 2} \geqslant 0 \tag{4a}$$

In this case the critical numbers are $\dfrac{5}{2}$ and 2, because

$$\frac{-4x + 10}{x - 2}$$

equals 0 for $x = \dfrac{5}{2}$ and is undefined for $x = 2$. Therefore, we want to check the intervals shown on the number line in part (a) of the figure below. Substituting arbitrary values for the variable in (4) or (4a) in each of the three intervals, say, $0, \dfrac{9}{4}$, and 3, we can identify the solution set

$$\left(2, \frac{5}{2}\right]$$

as in Example 2 on page 341. The graph is shown in part (b) of the figure. Note that the left-hand endpoint is an open dot (2 is not a member of the solution set) because the left-hand member of (4) is undefined for $x = 2$.

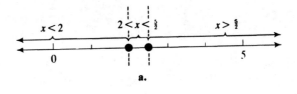

a.

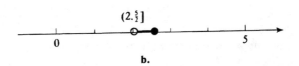

b.

The procedures shown in the preceding examples also apply if more than two critical numbers are associated with an inequality.

It is sometimes possible to determine the solution set of a quadratic inequality simply by inspection. For example, the solution set of

$$4x^2 + 6 > 0$$

is $\{x \mid x \text{ a real number}\}$ because the left side is greater than zero for all real-number replacements of x. For the same reason the solution set of

$$4x^2 + 6 < 0$$

is $\varnothing$.

EXERCISE SET 12.4

▲ *Solve and represent each solution set on a line graph. See Examples 1 and 2.*

1. $(x + 1)(x - 2) > 0$
2. $(x - 3)(x + 2) > 0$
3. $(x + 3)(x - 4) < 0$
4. $(x + 2)(x + 5) \leqslant 0$
5. $x(x - 2) \leqslant 0$
6. $x(x + 4) < 0$
7. $x(x - 5) > 0$
8. $x(x + 3) \geqslant 0$
9. $x^2 - 3x - 4 > 0$
10. $x^2 - 5x - 6 \geqslant 0$
11. $x^2 - x - 6 \leqslant 0$
12. $x^2 + x - 12 < 0$
13. $y(y + 2) \leqslant 15$
14. $y(y - 3) < 10$
15. $y(y - 1) > 12$
16. $y(y + 3) \geqslant 18$
17. $x^2 < 5$
18. $x^2 \leqslant 7$
19. $x^2 + 5 < 0$
20. $4x^2 + 1 < 0$

▲ *Solve and represent each solution set on a line graph. See Example 3.*

21. $\dfrac{x + 3}{x - 2} < 0$ **22.** $\dfrac{x - 1}{x + 4} > 0$

23. $\dfrac{x}{x + 2} - 4 > 0$ **24.** $\dfrac{x + 2}{x - 2} - 6 \geqslant 0$

25. $\dfrac{x - 1}{x} \leqslant 3$ **26.** $\dfrac{x}{x - 1} \geqslant 5$

27. $\dfrac{1}{x - 1} \leqslant 1$ **28.** $\dfrac{x + 1}{x - 1} < 1$

Miscellaneous Exercises

▲ *Solve and represent each solution set on a line graph.*

29. $\dfrac{4}{x + 1} < \dfrac{3}{x}$ **30.** $\dfrac{3}{x - 1} \geqslant \dfrac{1}{x}$

31. $\dfrac{2}{x - 2} \geqslant \dfrac{4}{x}$ **32.** $\dfrac{3}{4x + 1} > \dfrac{2}{x - 5}$

33. $5 < x^2 + 1 < 10$ **34.** $-2 < y^2 - 3 < 13$

35. A fireworks rocket fired from ground level is at a height of $320t - 16t^2$ feet after t seconds. During what interval of time is the rocket higher than 1024 feet?

36. A baseball thrown vertically reaches a height h in feet given by $h = 56t - 16t^2$, where t is measured in

seconds. During what period(s) of time is the ball between 40 and 48 feet high?

37. The cost in dollars of manufacturing x pairs of gardening shears is given by
$C(x) = -0.02x^2 + 14x + 1600$ for $0 \leqslant x \leqslant 700$.
How many pairs of shears can be produced if the total cost must be kept under $2800?

38. The cost in dollars of producing $100x$ cashmere sweaters is given by $C(x) = 100x^2 + 4000x + 9000$. How many sweaters can be produced if the total cost must be kept under $185,000?

39. The Locker Room finds that it sells $1200 - 30p$ sweatshirts each month when it charges p dollars per sweatshirt. If it would like its revenue from sweatshirts to be over $9000 per month, in what range should it keep the price of a sweatshirt? [*Hint:* Recall that $R = xp$, where x is the number of items sold at price p.]

40. Green Valley Nursery sells $120 - 10p$ boxes of rose food per month at a price of p dollars per box. If the nursery would like to keep its monthly revenue from rose food over $350, in what range should it price a box of rose food?

12.5 | INEQUALITIES IN TWO VARIABLES

Linear Inequalities

The solutions of linear inequalities of the form

$$ax + by + c > 0 \qquad \text{or} \qquad ax + by + c < 0$$

where a, b, and c are real numbers, are ordered pairs of real numbers. The solution sets can be graphed on the plane, and the graph will be a region of the plane whose boundary is a straight line. As an example, consider the inequality

$$2x + y - 3 < 0 \qquad\qquad (1)$$

When the inequality is rewritten in the form

$$y < -2x + 3 \qquad\qquad (2)$$

we see that y is less than $-2x + 3$ for each x. The graph of the equation

$$y = -2x + 3 \qquad\qquad (3)$$

is simply a straight line, as illustrated in Figure 12.12. Therefore, to graph (2), we need only observe that any point below this line has x- and y-coordinates that satisfy (2). For example, if $x = 2$, then all ordered pairs of the form $(2, y)$ such that

$$y < -2(2) + 3$$
$$y < -1$$

are in the solution set and their graphs are below the line, as shown in Figure 12.12.

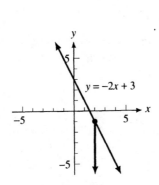

Figure 12.12

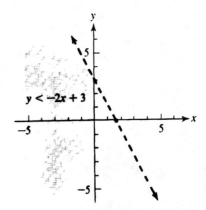

Figure 12.13

The solution set of (2) corresponds to the entire region below the line. The region is indicated on the graph (Figure 12.13) by shading. The dashed line in Figure 12.13 indicates that the points on the line do not correspond to elements in the solution set of the inequality. If the original inequality were

$$2x + y - 3 \leqslant 0$$

the line would be a part of the graph of the solution set and would be shown as a solid line.

The graphs of $ax + by < c$ and $ax + by > c$ are called **open half-planes**. In general, if $b \neq 0$,

$$ax + by + c < 0 \quad \text{or} \quad ax + by + c > 0$$

will have as a solution set all ordered pairs associated with the points in a **half-plane** either above or below the line with equation

$$ax + by + c = 0$$

depending upon the inequality symbols involved. The line $ax + by = c$ is called the **boundary** of the closed half-plane. The graphs of $ax + by \leqslant c$ and $ax + by \geqslant c$ are called **closed half-planes**.

To determine which of the half-planes should be shaded, we can substitute the coordinates of any point that is not on the line into the original inequality and note whether or not they satisfy the inequality. If they do, then the half-plane containing the point should be shaded; if they do not, then the other half-plane should be shaded. A good point to use in this process is the origin, with coordinates $(0,0)$, if the origin does not lie on the line.

EXAMPLE 1

Graph

$$3x - 2y < 6$$

Solution

We first graph $3x - 2y = 6$ using the intercept method. Then, substituting 0 for x and 0 for y in the inequality, we obtain

$$3(0) - 2(0) < 6$$

Since this is a true statement, shade the half-plane that contains the origin. In this case the edge of the half-plane is a dashed line because the original inequality does not contain the "equal to" symbol.

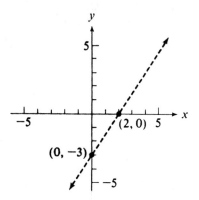

Now, just as we view an equation such as $x = 2$ as representing the equation $x + 0y = 2$, we also view an inequality such as $x > 2$ as representing the inequality $x + 0y > 2$.

EXAMPLE 2

Graph

$$x \geqslant 2$$

Solution

Graph the equality $x = 2$. The solution set consists of all ordered pairs in which x is greater than or equal to 2. Hence, shade the region to the right of the line representing $x = 2$. The line is part of the graph. In this case the edge of the half-plane is a solid line because the original inequality contains the "equal to" symbol.

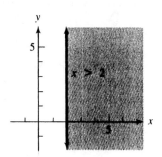

Systems of Linear Inequalities

We sometimes want to find the solutions that are common to two or more inequalities; that is, we want to find the *intersection* of their solution sets. In general, we can obtain good approximations to such solutions by graphical methods.

EXAMPLE 3

Graph the system

$$y > x \quad \text{and} \quad y > 2$$

using double shading.

Solution

Step 1 Graph each equation

$$y = x \quad \text{and} \quad y = 2$$

Step 2 Shade the appropriate half-plane for each inequality. Use dashed lines for the edge of each half-plane.

Step 3 Use a heavy shading to note the region common to both solution sets.

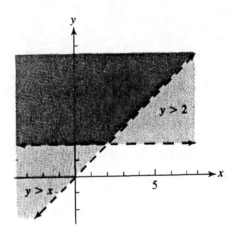

Quadratic Inequalities

Quadratic inequalities in two variables can be graphed in the same way that we graphed linear inequalities. We first graph the associated equation and then shade the appropriate region.

EXAMPLE 4

Graph

$$4x^2 + 9y^2 \leqslant 36 \tag{4}$$

Solution

We first graph $4x^2 + 9y^2 = 36$. In standard form the equation is

$$\frac{x^2}{9} + \frac{y^2}{4} = 1 \tag{5}$$

and we determine that the graph is an ellipse centered at the origin, with x-intercepts 3 and -3 and y-intercepts 2 and -2. Substituting the coordinates of the origin $(0, 0)$ in the original inequality, we obtain

$$4(0)^2 + 9(0)^2 \leqslant 36,$$

which is true. Hence, the part of the plane that includes the origin is shaded. Since the graph of Equation (5) is part of the graph of Equation (4), a solid curve is used.

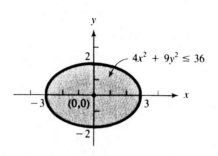

EXERCISE SET 12.5

▲ *Graph each inequality. See Examples 1 and 2.*

1. $y > x + 3$ **2.** $y < x + 4$ **3.** $y \leqslant x + 2$

4. $y \geqslant x - 2$ **5.** $x + y < 5$ **6.** $x - y < 3$

7. $2x + y < 2$ **8.** $x - 2y < 5$

9. $x \leqslant 2y + 4$ **10.** $2x \leqslant y + 1$

11. $0 \geqslant x - y$ **12.** $0 \geqslant x + 3y$

13. $x > 0$ **14.** $y < 0$

15. $y \geqslant 3$ **16.** $x < -2$

17. $-1 < x < 5$ **18.** $-2 \leqslant x < 0$

19. $-4 < y \leqslant 0$ **20.** $0 \leqslant y \leqslant 1$

▲ *Graph each pair of inequalities on the same coordinate system and use double shading to indicate the region common to both. See Example 3.*

21. $x > 0$ and $y > 0$ **22.** $x \leqslant 0$ and $y \geqslant 0$

23. $x > 0$ and $y < 0$ **24.** $x \leqslant 0$ and $y \leqslant 0$

25. $x > 4$ and $y > 2$ **26.** $x < 2$ and $y < 2$

27. $x + y \leqslant 6$ and $x + y \geqslant 4$

28. $2x - y \leqslant 4$ and $x + 2y > 6$

29. $y < x$ and $y \geqslant -3$

30. $y \geqslant -x$ and $y < 2$

31. $x + y < 4$ **32.** $x + y > 6$
$x < 2$ $y < 3$

33. $2x - y \geqslant 6$ **34.** $x + 2y \geqslant 6$
$x + 2y \leqslant 4$ $2x - y \leqslant 4$

35. $2x + 3y - 6 < 0$ **36.** $3x - 2y + 6 \geqslant 0$
$y \geqslant 0$ $x < 0$

▲ *Sketch the graph of each inequality. See Example 4.*

37. $y \leqslant x^2 - 4$ **38.** $y < x^2 + 4$

39. $y < x^2 + x - 6$ **40.** $y \geqslant x^2 + 3x + 2$

41. $x^2 + 4y^2 \leqslant 16$ **42.** $9y^2 - 4x^2 \geqslant 36$

Miscellaneous Exercises

▲ *Graph the region that represents the solution set of the system and find the coordinates of the vertices (approximations as necessary) of the boundary.*

43. $x \geqslant 0$ **44.** $x \geqslant 0$
$y \geqslant 0$ $y \leqslant 0$
$x + y - 4 \leqslant 0$ $x - y - 3 \geqslant 0$

45. $y \leqslant 0$ **46.** $x \geqslant 0$
$x + y \geqslant 0$ $x - y \geqslant 0$
$x - y - 4 \leqslant 0$ $x + y - 4 \leqslant 0$

47. $x \geqslant 0$ **48.** $x \leqslant 0$
$y \geqslant 0$ $y \geqslant 0$
$y - 3 \leqslant 0$ $x + 3 \geqslant 0$
$x - 4 \leqslant 0$ $x + y \leqslant 0$

▲ *Graph each pair of inequalities on the same coordinate system and use double shading to indicate the region common to both.*

49. $y > x^2$ **50.** $y < x^2 + 4$
$y \leqslant x + 2$ $x - y \leqslant 4$

51. $x^2 + y^2 < 25$ **52.** $x^2 + y^2 \geqslant 9$
$y > x$ $y < x$

53. $4x^2 + y^2 \leqslant 36$ **54.** $4x^2 + 3y^2 \leqslant 24$
$x \geqslant 2$ $y \leqslant 0$

55. $4x^2 + y^2 \leqslant 16$ **56.** $x^2 + 2y^2 \geqslant 8$
$y \geqslant x^2$ $y < x^2$

CHAPTER SUMMARY

[12.1] An inequality can be solved by producing equivalent inequalities until one is obtained that can be solved by inspection. The inequality

$$a < b$$

is equivalent to

$$a + c < b + c$$
$$a \cdot c < b \cdot c \quad \text{for} \quad c > 0$$
$$a \cdot c > b \cdot c \quad \text{for} \quad c < 0$$

[12.2] The **intersection** of two sets, $A \cap B$, is the set containing all members that are in both set A *and* set B. If the intersection is $\varnothing$, then A and B are **disjoint sets**. The **union** of two sets, $A \cup B$, consists of all members that are either in set A *or* in set B *or* in both. An **interval** of real numbers is an infinite set. An interval may be **closed** (two endpoints), **half-open** (one endpoint), or **open** (no endpoints).

[12.3] An absolute-value equation or inequality can be solved by first rewriting it in an equivalent form without the absolute-value notation.

$|ax - b| = c$ is equivalent to $ax - b = c$ or $-(ax - b) = c$

$|ax - b| < c$ is equivalent to $-c < ax - b < c$

$|ax - b| > c$ is equivalent to $ax - b > c$ or $-(ax - b) > c$

[12.4] Nonlinear inequalities can be solved by using **sign arrays** to determine the interval of real numbers that satisfy the inequality. Alternatively, solutions for inequalities $P(x) < 0$ or $P(x) > 0$ can be obtained by using **critical numbers**, the values of x for which $P(x) = 0$ or $P(x)$ is undefined.

[12.5] The graph of a first-degree (linear) inequality in two variables,

$$ax + by < c \quad \text{or} \quad ax + by > c$$

is a **half-plane**. The edge of the half-plane is not included; it is shown as a dashed line. The graph of

$$ax + by \leqslant c \quad \text{or} \quad ax + by \geqslant c$$

is also a half-plane; it includes the **boundary**, which is shown as a solid line. Quadratic inequalities in two variables can be graphed by first graphing the equation that has the same members and then shading the appropriate region.

R E V I E W   E X E R C I S E S

[12.1]

▲ *Solve and graph each solution set.*

1. $x - 3 \leqslant 24$
2. $6x - 6 \leqslant 2x$
3. $1 < 2x - 3 \leqslant 7$
4. $-5 < 4 - 3x < 1$
5. $\frac{1}{3}(x - 6) - \frac{1}{2}(x + 1) \leqslant -4$
6. $2(3x - 1) - \frac{1}{3}(x + 2) > \frac{5}{2}$

7. Amir has the following test grades in his algebra class: 72, 67, 84, 78, 82. What grade on the last test will give him a test average of B (less than 90 but greater than or equal to 80)?

8. Irene has a choice of two car rental plans. Plan A costs $15 per day plus $0.30 per mile, and plan B costs $20 per day and $0.25 per mile. If she plans to keep the car for 5 days, how many miles must she drive in order for plan B to be the better bargain?

[12.2]

▲ *Graph.*

9. $\{x|x > -5\} \cap \{x|x < 2\}$
10. $\{x|x + 2 \geqslant -1\} \cap \{x|0 < x < 4\}$
11. $\{x|-2 < x < 5 \text{ and } x \geqslant 3\}$
12. $\{x|x < 0 \text{ and } -3 \leqslant x < 4\}$
13. $\{x|2x \leqslant -2\} \cup \{x|x + 1 > 4\}$
14. $\{x|1 < x \leqslant 4\} \cup \{x|x - 3 > 3\}$
15. $\{x|x - 1 < -4 \text{ or } x \geqslant 0\}$
16. $\{x|-2x > 4 \text{ or } x - 1 \geqslant 3\}$

▲ *Write in interval notation.*

17. $\{x|x \leqslant -4\}$
18. $\{x|x > 3\}$
19. $\{x|-5 < x \leqslant 2\}$
20. $\{x|-4 \leqslant x \leqslant 3\}$

[12.3]

▲ *Solve.*

21. $|2x + 1| = 7$
22. $|3 - 4x| = 8$

▲ *Solve and graph each solution set.*

23. $|x + 3| \geqslant 5$
24. $|x - 2| < 5$
25. $|2x - 1| < 7$
26. $|3x + 2| \geqslant 8$

[12.4]

▲ *Solve each inequality and graph the solution set.*

27. $x^2 - 9x > 0$
28. $x^2 + 5x + 6 < 0$
29. $x(x + 2) \leqslant 8$
30. $x(x - 3) > 4$
31. $\frac{x + 1}{x - 3} \geqslant 0$
32. $\frac{x}{x + 2} \leqslant 2$

[12.5]

▲ *Graph each inequality.*

33. $y > x + 2$
34. $y \leqslant 4x + 4$
35. $x - 2y < 6$
36. $2x - y \geqslant 6$
37. $y > -3$
38. $-2 < x \leqslant 3$

39. Graph $y > -3x$ and $x - 2y \leqslant 6$ on the same coordinate system and use double shading to indicate the region common to both.

40. Graph the region that represents the solution set of the system
$$y \geqslant 0$$
$$x - y \geqslant 0$$
$$x + y - 3 < 0$$

▲ *Graph each inequality.*

41. $y \leqslant x^2 - 9$
42. $y > x^2 - 5x + 4$
43. $x^2 + 9y^2 < 36$
44. $4y^2 - x^2 \geqslant 16$

▲ *The numbers in brackets refer to the sections where such problems are first considered.*

▲ *Simplify.*

1. $2x^2(xy^2)^3 - x^2y^5(-x^3y) + 3y(-x^2y^3)^3$ **[3.1]**

2. $\dfrac{(3 \times 10^{-3})^{-2}(2 \times 10^{-7})}{(6 \times 10^2)^{-2}}$ **[5.3]**

3. $\sqrt[4]{64x^3y^7z^{12}}$ **[5.6]**

▲ *Factor completely.*

4. $6x^2 - x^3 - x^4$ **[3.4]**

5. $2x^3 - x^2 - 2x + 1$ **[3.7]**

▲ *Write as a single fraction in lowest terms.*

6. $\dfrac{x^2 - 8x + 16}{x^2 - 4} \div (x^2 - 16)$ **[4.5]**

7. $x - \dfrac{x}{x + 3} - \dfrac{x + 2}{x^2 - 9}$ **[4.4]**

8. If $f(x) = x^2 - x + 2$, find $f(3) - f(-3)$.   **[8.1]**

▲ *Solve each inequality and graph the solution set.*

9. $\dfrac{2x - 3}{-3} < x - 2$ **[12.1]**

10. $|6x - 9| \geqslant 9$ **[12.2]**

▲ *Solve the systems.*

11. $x^2 - 3xy + 2y^2 = 4$
    $3x + 4y = 18$ **[11.4]**

12. $4x = 6 - 2y$
    $3y = 17 + 2x$ **[10.1]**

13. Write $\dfrac{2 - \sqrt{-5}}{2\sqrt{-3}}$ in the form $a + bi$.   **[5.8]**

14. Reduce $\dfrac{1 - 64x^2}{16x^2 - 2x}$.   **[4.1]**

▲ *Solve.*

15. $\left(x - \dfrac{3}{4}\right)^2 = \dfrac{3}{16}$ **[6.1]**

16. $\sqrt{3x + 1} - \sqrt{x - 4} = 3$ **[6.3]**

17. $\dfrac{8}{x - 3} - \dfrac{5}{x - 2} = \dfrac{19}{x^2 - 5x + 6}$ **[4.7]**

18. $2x^2 + 3x + 3 = 0$ **[5.8]**

19. $\log_{64} x = \dfrac{1}{3}$ **[9.1]**

20. $5^{x+2} = 7$ to the nearest hundredth.   **[9.5]**

▲ *Solve.*

21. Find an equation for the line that contains the points $(-1, -6)$ and $(-3, 5)$.   **[7.4]**

22. z varies directly with x and inversely with the square of y. If $z = 6$ when $x = 72$ and $y = 6$, find z when $x = 80$ and $y = 4$.   **[8.2]**

23. A rectangular tool chest has a square base, and its height is half its length. Express its surface area (S) as a function of its length (x). Find the surface area of a tool chest whose base measures 20 inches on a side. **[8.3]**

24. A radioactive isotope decays exponentially so that the amount present after t years is $N = N_0 e^{-0.002t}$, where N_0 is the initial amount. How long will it take for 90% of the isotope to decay?   **[9.6]**

25. A company ships its product to three cities: Boston, Chicago, and Los Angeles. The cost of shipping is $5 per crate to Chicago, $10 per crate to Boston, and $12 per crate to Los Angeles. The company's shipping bill for April was $445. It shipped 55 crates in all, and twice as many crates went to Boston as to Los Angeles. How many crates were shipped to each destination? **[10.6]**

13 SEQUENCES AND SERIES

Sequences A function whose domain is a set of successive positive integers, for example, a function defined by an equation such as

$$s(n) = 2n - 1 \qquad (n \text{ an element of } \{3, 4, 5\}) \tag{1}$$

or

$$s(n) = n + 3 \qquad (n \text{ an element of } \{1, 2, 3, \dots\}) \tag{2}$$

is called a **sequence function**. The function defined by Equation (1) is called a **finite sequence**, and the function defined by Equation (2) is called an **infinite sequence**. The elements in the range of such functions arranged in the order

$$s(3), s(4), s(5) \qquad \text{or} \qquad s(1), s(2), s(3), \dots$$

are said to form a **sequence**, and the elements are referred to as the **terms** of the sequence. Thus, the sequence associated with Equation (2) is found by successively substituting the numbers **1, 2, 3,** ... for n.

$$s(\mathbf{1}) = (\mathbf{1}) + 3 = 4$$
$$s(\mathbf{2}) = (\mathbf{2}) + 3 = 5$$
$$s(\mathbf{3}) = (\mathbf{3}) + 3 = 6$$

$s(1)$ or 4 is called the first term, $s(2)$ or 5 is called the second term, $s(3)$ or 6 is called the third term, and so on. The expression $n + 3$ is called the **general term** or **nth term**.

EXAMPLE 1

The first three terms of the sequence with the general term $\dfrac{3}{2n-1}$ are

$$s(1) = \frac{3}{2(1)-1} = \frac{3}{1}, \qquad s(2) = \frac{3}{2(2)-1} = \frac{3}{3}, \qquad s(3) = \frac{3}{2(3)-1} = \frac{3}{5}$$

The twenty-fifth term is

$$s(25) = \frac{3}{2(25)-1} = \frac{3}{49}$$

The notation ordinarily used for the terms in a sequence is not function notation as such; rather, it is customary to denote a term in a sequence by means of a subscript. Thus, we will use s_n rather than $s(n)$, and the sequence $s(1), s(2), s(3), \ldots$ will appear as $s_1, s_2, s_3, \ldots$.

EXAMPLE 2

Find the first four terms in a sequence with the given general term.

a. $s_n = \dfrac{n(n+1)}{2}$

b. $s_n = (-1)^n 2^n$

Solutions

a. $s_1 = \dfrac{1(1+1)}{2} = 1$

b. $s_1 = (-1)^1 2^1 = -2$

$s_2 = \dfrac{2(2+1)}{2} = 3$

$s_2 = (-1)^2 2^2 = 4$

$s_3 = \dfrac{3(3+1)}{2} = 6$

$s_3 = (-1)^3 2^3 = -8$

$s_4 = \dfrac{4(4+1)}{2} = 10$

$s_4 = (-1)^4 2^4 = 16$

The first four terms are 1, 3, 6, 10

The first four terms are $-2, 4, -8, 16$.

Series

Associated with any sequence is a **series**; the series is defined as the sum of the terms in the sequence and is denoted by S_n. For example, associated with the sequence

$$4, 7, 10, \ldots, 3n + 1 \tag{3}$$

is the series

$$S_n = 4 + 7 + 10 + \cdots + (3n + 1) \tag{4}$$

Associated with the sequence

$$x, x^2, x^3, x^4, \ldots, x^n$$

is the series

$$S_n = x + x^2 + x^3 + x^4 + \cdots + x^n$$

Since the terms in the series are the same as those in the corresponding sequence, we can refer to the first term or the second term or the general term of a series in the same manner as we do for a sequence.

Sigma Notation A series with a general term that is known can be represented in a very convenient, compact way by using the symbol Σ (the Greek letter **sigma**) in conjunction with the general term in sigma or summation notation; this denotes the sum of all the terms in the series. For example, series (4) can be written

$$S_n = \sum_{i=1}^{n} (3i + 1)$$

maximum value for i

starting value for i

where we understand that S_n is the series with terms obtained by successively replacing i in the expression $3i + 1$ with the numbers, $1, 2, 3, \ldots, n$. Thus,

$$S_6 = \sum_{i=1}^{6} (3i + 1)$$

appears in **expanded form** as

$$[3(1) + 1] + [3(2) + 1] + [3(3) + 1] + [3(4) + 1] + [3(5) + 1] + [3(6) + 1]$$
$$= 4 + 7 + 10 + 13 + 16 + 19$$

The variable used in conjunction with summation notation (in the preceding case, i) is called the **index of summation**; the set of integers over which we sum in this case is $\{1, 2, 3, 4, 5, 6\}$. The use of the symbol i as an index of summation should not be confused with its use as an imaginary unit in the set of complex numbers. Alternatively, the summation index can be any letter such as j, k, l, and so on.

$$\sum_{i=1}^{6} (3i + 1) = \sum_{j=1}^{6} (3j + 1) = \sum_{k=1}^{6} (3k + 1) = \cdots$$

The first member of the replacement set for the index of summation is not necessarily 1. For example,

$$\sum_{i=3}^{6} (3i + 1) = [3(3) + 1] + [3(4) + 1] + [3(5) + 1] + [3(6) + 1]$$
$$= 10 + 13 + 16 + 19$$

where the first replacement for i is 3; the set of integers over which we sum is $\{3, 4, 5, 6\}$. Note that the series in this example contains four terms, which is one more than the difference between the last and the first replacement for i. In general, the series $\sum_{i=a}^{b} s_i$ contains $(b - a + 1)$ terms.

To show that a series has an infinite number of terms—that is, has no last term—we adopt a special notation. For example,

$$S_\infty = \sum_{i=4}^{\infty} (3i + 1)$$

denotes the series that would appear in expanded form as

$$S_\infty = 13 + 16 + 19 + 22 + \cdots \tag{5}$$

where, in this case, i has been replaced by 4, 5, 6, 7, ...

EXAMPLE 3 Write in expanded form.

a. $\displaystyle\sum_{i=2}^{4} (i^2 + 1)$ b. $\displaystyle\sum_{k=1}^{\infty} (-1)^k 2^{k+1}$

Solutions

a. i takes values $2, 3, 4$.
$i = 2, \quad (2)^2 + 1 = 5$
$i = 3, \quad (3)^2 + 1 = 10$
$i = 4, \quad (4)^2 + 1 = 17$

Expanded form: $5 + 10 + 17$.

b. k takes values $1, 2, 3, \ldots$.
$k = 1, \quad (-1)^1 2^{1+1} = (-1)(4) = -4$
$k = 2, \quad (-1)^2 2^{2+1} = (1)(8) = 8$
$k = 3, \quad (-1)^3 2^{3+1} = (-1)(16) = -16$

Expanded form: $-4 + 8 - 16 + \cdots$.

Finding General Terms

As we saw in Example 3, for any given general term s_n, we can obtain the elements of an associated sequence by successively substituting the numbers 1, 2, 3, ... for n. However, it is usually difficult to obtain a general term for a given sequence. In Sections 13.2 and 13.3 we shall consider formulas that will enable us to find general terms for several particular sequences. For now, we might attempt to find general terms by trial and error. A series can be represented in summation notation by various general terms and different ranges. For example, both

$$\sum_{i=5}^{\infty} (3i - 2) \quad \text{and} \quad \sum_{i=6}^{\infty} (3i - 5)$$

also represent series (5). This can be verified by writing the first few terms in each series.

▌▌ E X E R C I S E   S E T   13.1

▲ *Find the first four terms in a sequence with the given general term. See Examples 1 and 2.*

1. $s_n = n - 5$
2. $s_n = 2n - 3$
3. $s_n = \dfrac{n^2 - 2}{2}$
4. $s_n = \dfrac{3}{n^2 + 1}$
5. $s_n = 1 + \dfrac{1}{n}$
6. $s_n = \dfrac{n}{2n - 1}$
7. $s_n = \dfrac{n(n - 1)}{2}$
8. $s_n = \dfrac{5}{n(n + 1)}$
9. $s_n = (-1)^n$
10. $s_n = (-1)^{n+1}$
11. $s_n = \dfrac{(-1)^n (n - 2)}{n}$
12. $s_n = (-1)^{n-1} 3^{n+1}$

▲ *Write in expanded form. See Example 3.*

13. $\displaystyle\sum_{i=1}^{4} i^2$
14. $\displaystyle\sum_{i=1}^{3} (3i - 2)$
15. $\displaystyle\sum_{j=5}^{7} (j - 2)$
16. $\displaystyle\sum_{j=2}^{6} (j^2 + 1)$
17. $\displaystyle\sum_{k=1}^{4} k(k + 1)$
18. $\displaystyle\sum_{i=2}^{6} \dfrac{i}{2}(i + 1)$
19. $\displaystyle\sum_{i=1}^{4} \dfrac{(-1)^i}{2^i}$
20. $\displaystyle\sum_{i=3}^{5} \dfrac{(-1)^{i+1}}{i - 2}$
21. $\displaystyle\sum_{i=1}^{\infty} (2i - 1)$
22. $\displaystyle\sum_{j=1}^{\infty} \dfrac{1}{j}$
23. $\displaystyle\sum_{k=0}^{\infty} \dfrac{1}{2^k}$
24. $\displaystyle\sum_{k=0}^{\infty} \dfrac{k}{1 + k}$

Miscellaneous Exercises

▲ *By trial and error, find a general term for the sequence associated with each series and write each series in sigma notation. (There are no unique solutions.)*

25. $1 + 2 + 3 + 4$ **26.** $2 + 4 + 6 + 8$

27. $x + x^3 + x^5 + x^7$

28. $x^3 + x^5 + x^7 + x^9 + x^{11}$

29. $1 + 4 + 9 + 16 + 25$

30. $1 + 8 + 27 + 64 + 125$

31. $\dfrac{1}{2} + \dfrac{2}{3} + \dfrac{3}{4} + \dfrac{4}{5} + \cdots$ **32.** $\dfrac{2}{1} + \dfrac{3}{2} + \dfrac{4}{3} + \dfrac{5}{4} + \cdots$

33. $\dfrac{1}{1} + \dfrac{2}{3} + \dfrac{3}{5} + \dfrac{4}{7} + \cdots$ **34.** $\dfrac{3}{1} + \dfrac{5}{3} + \dfrac{7}{5} + \dfrac{9}{7} + \cdots$

35. $\dfrac{1}{1} + \dfrac{2}{2} + \dfrac{4}{3} + \dfrac{8}{4} + \cdots$ **36.** $\dfrac{1}{2} + \dfrac{3}{4} + \dfrac{9}{6} + \dfrac{27}{8} + \cdots$

13.2 | ARITHMETIC PROGRESSIONS

Any sequence with a general term that is linear in n has the property that each term except the first can be obtained from the preceding term by adding a common number called the **common difference**. A sequence with this property is called an **arithmetic progression**, or **arithmetic sequence**. We can state the definition for such a sequence symbolically:

$$s_1 = a$$
$$s_{n+1} = s_n + d$$

where d is the common difference. Definitions of this sort are called **recursive definitions**. It is customary to denote the first term in such a sequence by the letter a, the common difference between successive terms by d, the number of terms in the sequence (when finite) by n, and the nth term by s_n.

We can verify that a finite sequence is an arithmetic progression simply by subtracting each term from its successor and noting that the difference in each case is the same. For example, the sequence 7, 18, 29, 40 is an arithmetic progression, because

$$18 - 7 = 11, \qquad 29 - 18 = 11, \qquad \text{and} \qquad 40 - 29 = 11$$

If at least two consecutive terms in an arithmetic progression are known, we can determine the common difference and generate as many terms as we wish.

EXAMPLE 1   The third and fourth terms of an arithmetic progression are 6 and 11, respectively. Write the next three terms of the sequence.

Solution   Given $s_3 = 6$ and $s_4 = 11$,   we can obtain

$$d = s_4 - s_3$$
$$= 11 - 6 = 5$$

Thus, $s_5 = 11 + 5 = 16$, $s_6 = 16 + 5 = 21$,   and $s_7 = 21 + 5 = 26$.   Hence, the next three terms following 6 and 11 are 16, 21, and 26.

nth Term of an Arithmetic Progression   Now consider the general arithmetic progression with first term a and common difference d. The

$$\text{first term is} \qquad a$$
$$\text{second term is} \qquad a + d$$
$$\text{third term is} \qquad a + d + d = a + 2d$$
$$\text{fourth term is} \qquad a + d + d + d = a + 3d$$
$$\vdots \qquad\qquad \vdots$$
$$n\text{th term is} \qquad a + d + d + \cdots + d = a + (n - 1)d$$

Thus, we have the following property:

$$s_n = a + (n - 1)d \qquad\qquad (1)$$

Here we have used an informal inductive process to obtain Equation (1). We shall assume its validity for all natural numbers n.

Equation (1) provides us with a formula to find the nth term of any arithmetic progression when the first term and common difference are known. For example, if the first term of an arithmetic progression is 7 and the common difference is 2, we have from Equation (1) that the nth term is

$$s_n = 7 + (n - 1)2$$
$$= 7 + 2n - 2$$
$$= 2n + 5$$

EXAMPLE 2 Write the next three terms in each arithmetic progression. Find an expression for the general term.

a. $5, 9, \ldots$ **b.** $x, x - a, \ldots$

Solutions **a.** Find the common difference and then continue the sequence.

$$d = 9 - 5 = 4$$
$$13, 17, 21$$

Use $s_n = a + (n - 1)d$ to find an expression for the general term.

$$s_n = 5 + (n - 1)4$$
$$s_n = 4n + 1$$

b. Find the common difference and then continue the sequence.

$$d = (x - a) - x = -a$$
$$x - 2a, x - 3a, x - 4a$$

Use $s_n = a + (n - 1)d$ to find an expression for the general term.

$$s_n = x + (n - 1)(-a)$$
$$s_n = x - a(n - 1)$$

Observe that Equation (1) defines a *linear function* for any values of a and d. As we have noted, the domain (replacement set of n) of this function is the set of natural numbers. Equation (1) can be used directly to find a particular term if the first term and common difference of an arithmetic progression are known.

EXAMPLE 3 Find the fourteenth term of the arithmetic progression $-6, -1, 4, \ldots$.

Solution Find the common difference.

$$d = -1 - (-6) = 5$$

Use $s_n = a + (n-1)d$.

$$s_{14} = -6 + (14-1)5 = 59$$

Equation (1) can also be used to find a particular term in an arithmetic expression in which two terms are known.

EXAMPLE 4 Find the first term in an arithmetic progression in which the third term is 7 and the eleventh term is 55.

Solution A diagram of the situation is helpful here.

$$n: \quad 1, 2, 3, 4, 5, 6, 7, 8, 9, 10, 11$$
$$s_n: \quad \underline{?}, \_\_, \underline{7}, \_\_, \_\_, \_\_, \_\_, \_\_, \_\_, \_\_, \underline{55}$$

Find a common difference by considering an arithmetic progression with first term 7 and ninth term 55. Use $s_n = a + (n-1)d$.

$$s_9 = 7 + (9-1)d$$
$$55 = 7 + 8d$$
$$d = 6$$

Use this difference to find the first term in an arithmetic progression in which the third term is 7. Use $s_n = a + (n-1)d$.

$$s_3 = a + (3-1)6$$
$$7 = a + 12$$
$$a = -5$$

The first term is -5.

Alternative Solution Use $s_n = a + (n-1)d$, with $s_3 = 7$.

$$7 = a + (3-1)d$$
$$7 = a + 2d \tag{2}$$

Use $s_n = a + (n-1)d$, with $s_{11} = 55$.

$$55 = a + (11-1)d$$
$$55 = a + 10d \tag{3}$$

Solve the system (2) and (3) to obtain $a = -5$.

Arithmetic Means Terms between given terms in an arithmetic progression are called **arithmetic means** of the given terms.

EXAMPLE 5   Insert three arithmetic means between 4 and -8.

Solution   If there are three terms between 4 and -8, then the difference between 4 and -8 must be 4 times the common difference (d), as suggested by

Therefore,

$$4d = (-8) - (4) = -12$$
$$d = -3$$

The three requested arithmetic means can then be obtained by successive additions of -3. They are 1, -2, and -5.

Sum of n Terms   The problem of finding an explicit representation for the sum of n terms of a sequence in terms of n is, in general, very difficult. However, we can obtain such a representation for the sum of n terms in an arithmetic progression. Consider the series of n terms associated with the general arithmetic progression

$$a, (a + d), (a + 2d), \ldots, a + (n - 1)d$$

that is,

$$S_n = a + (a + d) + (a + 2d) + \cdots + [a + (n - 1)d] \tag{4}$$

Then consider the same series written as

$$S_n = s_n + (s_n - d) + (s_n - 2d) + \cdots + [s_n - (n - 1)d] \tag{5}$$

where the terms are in reverse order. Adding Equations (4) and (5) term by term, we have

$$S_n + S_n = (a + s_n) + (a + s_n) + (a + s_n) + \cdots + (a + s_n)$$

where the term $(a + s_n)$ occurs **n** times. It follows that

$$2S_n = n(a + s_n)$$

from which we have the following property:

$$S_n = \frac{n}{2}(a + s_n) \tag{6}$$

EXAMPLE 6   The sum of the eight terms of an arithmetic progression with first term -7 and last term 14 is given by

$$S_8 = \frac{8}{2}(-7 + 14) = 28$$

If Equation (6) is rewritten as

$$S_n = n\left(\frac{a + s_n}{2}\right)$$

we observe that the sum is given by the product of the number of terms in the series and the average of the first and last terms. We obtain an alternative form for Equation (6) by substituting in Equation (6) the value for s_n equal to $a + (n-1)d$ as given by Equation (1) to obtain

$$S_n = \frac{n}{2}(a + [a + (n-1)d])$$

from which we have the following property:

$$S_n = \frac{n}{2}[2a + (n-1)d] \qquad (7)$$

In Equation (7) the sum is now expressed in terms of a, n, and d.

EXAMPLE 7 | Compute the sum of the series $\displaystyle\sum_{i=1}^{12} (4i + 1)$.

Solution | Write the first two or three terms in expanded form.

$$5 + 9 + 13 + \cdots$$

By inspection, we find the first term to be 5 and the common difference to be 4. Use

$$S_n = \frac{n}{2}[2a + (n-1)d] \qquad \text{with} \qquad n = 12$$

$$S_{12} = \frac{12}{2}[2(5) + (12 - 1)4] = 324$$

‖ E X E R C I S E   S E T   13.2

▲ *Write the next three terms in each arithmetic progression. Find an expression for the general term. See Examples 1 and 2.*

1. $3, 7, \ldots$
2. $-6, -1, \ldots$
3. $-1, -5, \ldots$
4. $-10, -20, \ldots$
5. $x, x + 1, \ldots$
6. $a, a + 5, \ldots$
7. $x + a, x + 3a, \ldots$
8. $y - 2b, y, \ldots$
9. $2x + 1, 2x + 4, \ldots$
10. $a + 2b, a - 2b, \ldots$
11. $x, 2x, \ldots$
12. $3a, 5a, \ldots$

▲ *Solve. See Example 3.*

13. Find the seventh term in the arithmetic progression $7, 11, 15, \ldots$
14. Find the tenth term in the arithmetic progression $-3, -12, -21, \ldots$
15. Find the twelfth term in the arithmetic progression $2, \frac{5}{2}, 3, \ldots$

16. Find the seventeenth term in the arithmetic progression $-5, -2, 1, \ldots$

17. Find the twentieth term in the arithmetic progression $3, -2, -7, \ldots$

18. Find the tenth term in the arithmetic progression $\dfrac{3}{4}, 2, \dfrac{13}{4}, \ldots$

▲ *Solve. See Example 4.*

19. If the third term in an arithmetic progression is 7 and the eighth term is 17, find the common difference. What is the first term? What is the twentieth term?

20. If the fifth term of an arithmetic progression is -16 and the twentieth term is -46, what is the twelfth term?

21. What term in the arithmetic progression $4, 1, -2, \ldots$ is -77?

22. What term in the arithmetic progression $7, 3, -1, \ldots$ is -81?

▲ *Insert the given number of arithmetic means between the given two numbers. See Example 5.*

23. Two between -6 and 15.

24. Four between 10 and 65.

25. One between 12 and 20.

26. One between -11 and 7.

27. Three between 24 and 4.

28. Six between -12 and 23.

▲ *Find the sum of each finite series. See Examples 6 and 7.*

29. $\displaystyle\sum_{i=1}^{7} (2i + 1)$

30. $\displaystyle\sum_{i=1}^{21} (3i - 2)$

31. $\displaystyle\sum_{j=3}^{15} (7j - 1)$

32. $\displaystyle\sum_{j=10}^{20} (2j - 3)$

33. $\displaystyle\sum_{k=1}^{8} \left(\dfrac{1}{2}k - 3\right)$

34. $\displaystyle\sum_{k=1}^{100} k$

Miscellaneous Exercises

35. Find the sum of all even integers n, where $13 < n < 89$.

36. Find the sum of all integral multiples of 7 between 8 and 110.

37. How many bricks will there be in a stack one brick deep if there are 27 bricks in the first row, 25 in the second row, ..., and 1 in the top row?

38. If there is a total of 256 bricks in a stack arranged like those in Exercise 37, how many bricks are there in the third row from the bottom?

39. Find three numbers that form an arithmetic sequence such that their sum is 21 and their product is 168.

40. Find three numbers that form an arithmetic sequence such that their sum is 21 and their product is 231.

41. Find k if $\displaystyle\sum_{j=1}^{5} kj = 14$.

42. Find p and q if $\displaystyle\sum_{i=1}^{4} (pi + q) = 28$ and $\displaystyle\sum_{i=2}^{5} (pi + q) = 44$.

43. Show that the sum of the first n odd natural numbers is n^2.

44. Show that the sum of the first n even natural numbers is $n^2 + n$.

13.3 GEOMETRIC PROGRESSIONS

Any sequence in which each term except the first is obtained by multiplying the preceding term by a common multiplier is called a **geometric progression**, or **geometric sequence**, and is defined by the recursive equations

$$s_1 = a$$
$$s_{n+1} = rs_n$$

where r is called the **common ratio**. For example the sequence

$$2, 6, 18, 54, \ldots$$

is a geometric progression in which each term except the first is obtained by multiplying the preceding term by 3.

nth Term of a Geometric Progression

If we designate the first term of a geometric progression by a, then the

second term is $\quad ar$

third term is $\quad ar \cdot r = ar^2$

fourth term is $\quad ar^2 \cdot r = ar^3$

and it appears that the nth term will take the following form:

$$s_n = ar^{n-1} \tag{1}$$

EXAMPLE 1

Find the ratio r and general term s_n for the geometric progression

$$2, 6, 18, \dots$$

Solution

By writing the ratio of any term to its predecessor, say, $\dfrac{18}{6}$, we obtain $r = 3$. We can now write a representation for s_n of this sequence in terms of n by substituting 2 for a and 3 for r in Equation (1). Thus,

$$s_n = ar^{n-1} = 2(3)^{n-1}$$

EXAMPLE 2

Write the next three terms in each geometric progression. Find the general term.

a. $3, 6, 12, \dots$ $\qquad$ **b.** $x, 2, \dfrac{4}{x}, \dots$

Solutions

a. Find the common ratio.

$$r = \frac{6}{3} = 2$$

Multiply successively by r to determine the following terms:

$$24, 48, 96$$

Use $\ s = ar^{n-1}\ $ to find the general term.

$$s_n = 3(2)^{n-1}$$

b. Find the common ratio.

$$r = \frac{2}{x}$$

Multiply successively by r to determine the following terms:

$$\frac{8}{x^2}, \frac{16}{x^3}, \frac{32}{x^4}$$

Use $\ s = ar^{n-1}\ $ to find the general term.

$$s_n = x\left(\frac{2}{x}\right)^{n-1} = \frac{2^{n-1}}{x^{n-2}}.$$

We can use Equation (1) to find a particular term in a geometric progression in which two or more terms are known.

EXAMPLE 3 | Find the ninth term of the geometric progression $-24, 12, -6, \ldots$.

Solution | Find the common ratio.

$$r = \frac{12}{-24} = -\frac{1}{2}$$

Use $s_n = ar^{n-1}$.

$$s_9 = -24\left(-\frac{1}{2}\right)^8 = -\frac{3}{32}$$

Observe that Equation (1) defines an *exponential function* for all values of a and r. As we noted, the domain (replacement set of n) of this function is the set of natural numbers.

Geometric Means Terms between given terms in a geometric progression are called **geometric means** of the given terms.

EXAMPLE 4 | Insert two geometric means between 3 and 24.

Solution | Since there are three multiplications by the common ratio between 3 and 24, the quotient when 24 is divided by 3 must be the third power of the common ratio, as suggested by the following:

$$\underset{\times r \;\; \times r \;\; \times r}{\underline{\overline{3 \quad ? \quad ? \quad 24}}}$$

Hence $r^3 = \dfrac{24}{3} = 8$; so $r = \sqrt[3]{8} = 2$. Therefore, the missing terms can be determined by successive multiplications by 2, and we have $3 \times 2 = 6$ and $6 \times 2 = 12$. Thus, the geometric means are 6 and 12.

Sum of n Terms To find an explicit representation for the sum of a given number of terms in a geometric progression in terms of a, r, and n, we employ a device somewhat similar to the one used in finding the sum of an arithmetic series. Consider the geometric series (2) containing n terms and the series (3) obtained by multiplying both members of (2) by r:

$$S_n = a + ar + ar^2 + ar^3 + \cdots + ar^{n-2} + ar^{n-1} \qquad (2)$$
$$rS_n = \quad\;\; ar + ar^2 + ar^3 + ar^4 + \cdots + ar^{n-1} + ar^n \qquad (3)$$

Subtracting Equation (3) from Equation (2), we find that all terms in the right-hand member vanish except the first term in Equation (2) and the last term in Equation (3), and therefore

$$S_n - rS_n = a - ar^n$$

Factoring S_n from the left-hand member yields

$$(1 - r)S_n = a - ar^n$$

from which we have the following property:

$$S_n = \frac{a - ar^n}{1 - r} \qquad (r \neq 1) \qquad \qquad (4)$$

This is a general formula for the sum of n terms of a geometric progression.

EXAMPLE 5 The sum of four terms of a geometric progression with first term 5 and common ratio -3 is given by

$$S_4 = \frac{5 - 5(-3)^4}{1 - (-3)}$$

$$= \frac{5 - 5(81)}{4} = -100$$

It is helpful to rewrite a geometric progression in sigma notation in expanded form before using Equation (4).

EXAMPLE 6 Compute

$$\sum_{i=2}^{7} \left(\frac{1}{3}\right)^i$$

Solution Write the first two or three terms in expanded form.

$$\left(\frac{1}{3}\right)^2 + \left(\frac{1}{3}\right)^3 + \cdots$$

By inspection we find the first term to be $\frac{1}{9}$, the ratio to be $\frac{1}{3}$, and $n = 6$. (Recall from page 354 that the series $\sum_{i=a}^{b}$ contains $(b - a + 1)$ terms.) Use $S_n = \frac{a - ar^n}{1 - r}$.

$$S_6 = \frac{\frac{1}{9} - \frac{1}{9}\left(\frac{1}{3}\right)^6}{1 - \frac{1}{3}} = \frac{\frac{1}{9}\left(1 - \frac{1}{729}\right)}{\frac{2}{3}} = \frac{1}{9} \cdot \frac{728}{729} \cdot \frac{3}{2} = \frac{364}{2187}$$

We can obtain an alternative equation for Equation (4) by first writing it as

$$S_n = \frac{a - r(ar^{n-1})}{1 - r}$$

and since $s_n = ar^{n-1}$, we have the following relationship, where the sum is now given in terms of a, s_n, and r:

$$S_n = \frac{a - rs_n}{1 - r} \qquad (r \neq 1) \qquad (5)$$

EXAMPLE 7 | The sum of the geometric progression

$$6 + 3 + \frac{3}{2} + \frac{3}{4} + \frac{3}{8}$$

with first term 6, common ratio $\frac{1}{2}$, and fifth term $\frac{3}{8}$ is given by

$$S_5 = \frac{6 - \left(\frac{1}{2}\right)\left(\frac{3}{8}\right)}{1 - \frac{1}{2}} = \frac{6 - \frac{3}{16}}{\frac{1}{2}}$$

$$= 2\left(6 - \frac{3}{16}\right) = 12 - \frac{3}{8} = \frac{93}{8}$$

EXERCISE SET 13.3

▲ *Write the next three terms in each geometric progression. Find the general term. See Examples 1 and 2.*

1. $2, 8, 32, \ldots$

2. $4, 8, 16, \ldots$

3. $\frac{2}{3}, \frac{4}{3}, \frac{8}{3}, \ldots$

4. $6, 3, \frac{3}{2}, \ldots$

5. $4, -2, 1, \ldots$

6. $\frac{1}{2}, -\frac{3}{2}, \frac{9}{2}, \ldots$

7. $\frac{a}{x}, -1, \frac{x}{a}, \ldots$

8. $\frac{a}{b}, \frac{a}{bc}, \frac{a}{bc^2}, \ldots$

▲ *Solve. See Example 3.*

9. Find the sixth term in the geometric progression $48, 96, 192, \ldots$.

10. Find the eighth term in the geometric progression $-3, \frac{3}{2}, -\frac{3}{4}, \ldots$.

11. Find the seventh term in the geometric progression $-\frac{1}{3}a^2, a^5, -3a^8, \ldots$.

12. Find the ninth term in the geometric progression $-81a, -27a^2, -9a^3, \ldots$.

13. Find the first term of a geometric progression with fifth term 48 and ratio 2.

14. Find the first term of a geometric progression with fifth term 1 and ratio $-\frac{1}{2}$.

▲ *Insert the given number of geometric means between the two given numbers. See Example 4.*

15. Two between 1 and 27.

16. Two between -4 and -32.

17. One between 36 and 9. (Two answers are possible.)

18. One between -12 and $-\frac{1}{12}$. (Two answers are possible.)

19. Three between 32 and 2. (Two answers are possible.)

20. Three between -25 and $-\frac{1}{25}$. (Two answers are possible.)

▲ *Find each sum. See Examples 5, 6, and 7.*

21. $\sum_{i=1}^{6} 3^i$

22. $\sum_{j=1}^{4} (-2)^j$

23. $\sum_{k=3}^{7} \left(\frac{1}{2}\right)^{k-2}$

24. $\sum_{i=3}^{12} (2)^{i-5}$

25. $\sum_{j=1}^{6} \left(\frac{1}{3}\right)^j$

26. $\sum_{k=1}^{5} \left(\frac{1}{4}\right)^k$

Miscellaneous Exercises

27. Graph the geometric progression defined by $s_n = 2^n$ for $1 \leqslant n \leqslant 4$. Use the horizontal axis for n and the vertical axis for s_n.

28. Graph the geometric progression defined by $s_n = 2^{n-4}$ for $1 \leqslant n \leqslant 7$. Use the horizontal axis for n and the vertical axis for s_n.

29. A culture of bacteria doubles every hour. If there were 10 bacteria in the culture originally, how many are there after 1 hour? After 2 hours? After 3 hours? After 4 hours? After n hours?

30. A certain radioactive substance has a half-life of 2400 years (50% of the original material is present at the end of 2400 years). If 100 grams were produced today, how many grams would be present in 2400 years? In 4800 years? In 7200 years? In 9600 years? In $2400n$ years?

13.4 INFINITE SERIES

Infinite Geometric Series

Consider the infinite geometric series

$$\frac{1}{2} + \frac{1}{4} + \frac{1}{8} + \frac{1}{16} + \cdots$$

and the partial sums of terms of the series,

$$S_1 = \frac{1}{2}$$

$$S_2 = \frac{1}{2} + \frac{1}{4} = \frac{3}{4}$$

$$S_3 = \frac{1}{2} + \frac{1}{4} + \frac{1}{8} = \frac{7}{8}$$

$$S_4 = \frac{1}{2} + \frac{1}{4} + \frac{1}{8} + \frac{1}{16} = \frac{15}{16}$$

Note that the nth term of the sequence of partial sums

$$\frac{1}{2}, \frac{3}{4}, \frac{7}{8}, \frac{15}{16}, \ldots, S_n, \ldots$$

appears to be "approaching" 1. That is, as the number n becomes very large, S_n is very close to 1. In fact, we can make the difference between S_n and 1 as small as we like by using a sufficiently large value for n.

Recall from Section 13.3 that the sum of n terms of a geometric progression is given by

$$S_n = \frac{a - ar^n}{1 - r} \qquad (r \neq 1) \tag{1}$$

If $|r| < 1$, that is, if $-1 < r < 1$, then r^n becomes smaller and smaller for increasingly large n. For example, if $r = \frac{1}{2}$, then

$$r^2 = \left(\frac{1}{2}\right)^2 = \frac{1}{4} \qquad r^3 = \left(\frac{1}{2}\right)^3 = \frac{1}{8} \qquad r^4 = \left(\frac{1}{2}\right)^4 = \frac{1}{16}$$

and so on, and we can make $(\frac{1}{2})^n$ as small as we please by taking n sufficiently large. If we write Equation (1) in the form

$$S_n = \frac{a}{1-r}(1 - r^n) \qquad (2)$$

we see that the value of the factor $(1 - r^n)$ can be made as close as we please to 1, provided that $|r| < 1$ and n is taken large enough. Since this asserts that the sum (2) can be made to approximate

$$\frac{a}{1-r}$$

as closely as we please, we define the sum of an infinite geometric series with $|r| < 1$ as follows:

$$S_\infty = \frac{a}{1-r} \qquad (3)$$

Limit of a Sequence   A sequence that has an nth term (and all terms after the nth) that can be made to approximate a fixed number L as closely as desired by simply taking n large enough is said to *approach the limit L as n increases without bound*. We can indicate this in terms of symbols as

$$\lim_{n \to \infty} S_n = L$$

where S_n is the nth term of the sequence of sums $S_1, S_2, S_3, \ldots, S_n, \ldots$. Thus, Equation (3) might be written as

$$S_\infty = \lim_{n \to \infty} S_n = \frac{a}{1-r}$$

If $|r| \geqslant 1$, then r^n in Equation (2) does not approach 0, and $\lim_{n \to \infty} S_n$ does not exist.

EXAMPLE 1   Find the sum of each series if the sum exists.

a. $3 + 2 + \dfrac{4}{3} + \cdots$ b. $\dfrac{1}{81} - \dfrac{1}{54} + \dfrac{1}{36} + \cdots$

Solutions   a. $r = \dfrac{2}{3}$; the series has a sum, since $|r| < 1$.

$$S_\infty = \frac{a}{1-r} = \frac{3}{1 - \dfrac{2}{3}} = 9$$

b. $r = -\dfrac{1}{54} \div \dfrac{1}{81} = -\dfrac{3}{2}$; the series does not have a sum, since $|r| > 1$.

Repeating Decimals

An interesting application of sum (3) arises in connection with repeating decimals—that is, decimal numerals that, after a finite number of decimal places, have endlessly repeating groups of digits. For example,

$$0.2121\overline{21}, \quad 0.333\overline{3} \quad \text{and} \quad 0.138512512\overline{512}$$

are repeating decimals, where in each case the overbar indicates the repeating digits. Consider the problem of expressing such a decimal numeral as a fraction. We illustrate the process involved with the repeating decimal

$$0.2121\overline{21} \tag{4}$$

This decimal can be written either as

$$0.21 + 0.0021 + 0.000021 + \cdots \tag{5}$$

or as

$$\frac{21}{100} + \frac{21}{10,000} + \frac{21}{1,000,000} + \cdots \tag{6}$$

which are sums with terms that form a geometric progression with a ratio 0.01 (or $\frac{1}{100}$). Since the ratio is less than 1 in absolute value, we can use Equation (3) to find the sum of an infinite number of terms of expression (5) or (6). Thus, using (6), we have

$$S_\infty = \frac{a}{1-r} = \frac{\dfrac{21}{100}}{1 - \dfrac{1}{100}} = \frac{\dfrac{21}{100}}{\dfrac{99}{100}} = \frac{21}{99} = \frac{7}{33}$$

and the given decimal numeral, $0.2121\overline{21}$, is equivalent to $\frac{7}{33}$. If we used the decimal form (5), we would use $S_\infty = \dfrac{a}{1-r}$ with $a = 0.21$ and $r = 0.01$. In the following example, three digits are repeated.

EXAMPLE 2

Find a fraction equivalent to $2.045045\overline{045}$

Solution

Rewrite as a series.

$$2 + \frac{45}{1000} + \frac{45}{1,000,000} + \cdots$$

For series beginning with $\dfrac{45}{1000}$, $r = \dfrac{1}{1000}$. Use $S_\infty = \dfrac{a}{1-r}$.

$$S_\infty = \frac{\dfrac{45}{1000}}{1 - \dfrac{1}{1000}} = \frac{\dfrac{45}{1000}}{\dfrac{999}{1000}} = \frac{45}{999} = \frac{5}{111}$$

Hence,

$$2.045045\overline{045} = 2\frac{5}{111} = \frac{227}{111}$$

The decimal part of the series in Example 2 can be written in decimal notation as $0.045 + 0.000045 + \cdots$, with $a = 0.045$ and $r = 0.001$.

The Number e

The number e that we introduced in Chapter 8 is the limit of the sequence

$$\left(1 + \frac{1}{1}\right)^1, \left(1 + \frac{1}{2}\right)^2, \left(1 + \frac{1}{3}\right)^3, \ldots$$

and the general term is given by

$$\left(1 + \frac{1}{t}\right)^t$$

where t is a natural number. We can use the $\boxed{y^x}$ key on a calculator to obtain a decimal approximation for the expression for different values of t. The first several terms of this sequence, rounded to four decimal places, are

$$2.0000, \quad 2.2500, \quad 2.3704, \quad 2.4414, \quad 2.4883, \quad \ldots$$

and the 1000th term is

$$\left(1 + \frac{1}{1000}\right)^{1000} = 2.7169$$

The question arises as to whether we would approach some number as $t \to \infty$. It is shown in courses in advanced mathematics that

$$\lim_{t \to \infty} \left(1 + \frac{1}{t}\right)^t = e$$

where, as we have noted, e is an irrational number approximately equal to 2.7182818. The expression $[1 + (1/t)]^t$ is a special case of the right-hand member of the formula

$$A = P\left(1 + \frac{r}{t}\right)^{tn} \tag{7}$$

for compound interest. Here, r is the rate and n is the number of compounding periods. It can be shown that if $t \to \infty$ in Equation (7), which implies continuous compounding, we obtain

$$A = Pe^{rn} \tag{8}$$

EXAMPLE 3   Five thousand dollars is invested for 1 year at 10% interest. What is the total value of the investment at the end of the year if the interest is compounded quarterly? If the interest is compounded continuously?

Solution

If the interest is compounded quarterly, then, from Equation (7),

$$A = 5000\left(1 + \frac{0.10}{4}\right)^{4(1)}$$
$$= 5000(1.025)^4$$
$$= 5519.06$$

The total value is \$5519.06. If the interest is compounded continuously, then, from Equation (9),

$$A = 5000e^{0.10(1)} = 5525.85$$

The total value is \$5525.85.

The notion of compounding interest continuously does not provide a practical application of Equation (8). However, different forms of this equation do have wide application in a variety of areas. Some of these applications were included in Exercise set 9.6.

EXERCISE SET 13.4

▲ *Find the sum of each infinite geometric series. If the series has no sum, so state. See Example 1.*

1. $12 + 6 + 3 + \cdots$

2. $2 + 1 + \frac{1}{2} + \cdots$

3. $\frac{1}{36} + \frac{1}{30} + \frac{1}{25} + \cdots$

4. $1 + \frac{2}{3} + \frac{4}{9} + \cdots$

5. $\frac{3}{4} - \frac{1}{2} + \frac{1}{3} - \cdots$

6. $\frac{1}{16} - \frac{1}{8} + \frac{1}{4} - \cdots$

7. $\frac{1}{49} + \frac{1}{56} + \frac{1}{64} + \cdots$

8. $2 - \frac{3}{2} + \frac{9}{8} - \cdots$

9. $\sum_{i=1}^{\infty} \left(\frac{2}{3}\right)^i$

10. $\sum_{i=1}^{\infty} \left(-\frac{1}{4}\right)^i$

▲ *Find a fraction equivalent to each of the given decimal numerals. See Example 2.*

11. $0.3333\overline{3}$

12. $0.6666\overline{6}$

13. $0.3131\overline{31}$

14. $0.4545\overline{45}$

15. $2.4104\overline{10}$

16. $3.0270\overline{27}$

17. $0.12888\overline{8}$

18. $0.8333\overline{3}$

▲ *Use the formulas for compound interest given on page 369. See Example 3.*

19. One hundred dollars is invested for 10 years at 8% interest. What is the total value of the investment if the interest is compounded quarterly? If the interest is compounded continuously?

20. Which investment would produce the greatest annual income: five thousand dollars at 12% compounded semiannually or five thousand dollars at 11% compounded continuously?

Miscellaneous Exercises

21. A force is applied to a particle moving in a straight line in such a fashion that in each second it moves only one-half of the distance it moved in the preceding second. If the particle moves 10 centimeters in the first second, approximately how far will it move before coming to rest?

22. The arc length through which the bob on a pendulum moves is nine-tenths of its preceding arc length. Approximately how far will the bob move before coming to rest if the first arc length is 12 inches?

23. A ball returns two-thirds of its preceding height on each bounce. If the ball is dropped from a height of 6 feet, approximately what is the total distance the ball travels before coming to rest?

24. If a ball is dropped from a height of 10 feet and returns three-fifths of its preceding height on each bounce, approximately what is the total distance the ball travels before coming to rest?

25. If P dollars are invested at an interest rate r *compounded annually*, show that the amount A

present after two years is given by $A = P(1 + r)^2$ and that the amount present after three years is $A = P(1 + r)^3$. Make a conjecture about the amount that is present after n years.

26. If P dollars are invested at an interest rate r, show that the amount A present in one year when the

interest is compounded semiannually for n years is given by $A = P[1 + (r/2)]^{2n}$ and when the interest is compounded quarterly for n years is given by $A = P[1 + (r/4)]^{4n}$. Make a conjecture about the amount that is present if the interest is compounded t times yearly.

13.5 | THE BINOMIAL EXPANSION

Factorial Notation

Sometimes it is necessary to write the product of consecutive positive integers. To do this in some cases, we use the special symbol $n!$ (read "n factorial" or "factorial n"), which is defined as follows:

$$n! = n(n - 1)(n - 2) \cdots \cdot 1$$

For example,

$$5! = 5 \cdot 4 \cdot 3 \cdot 2 \cdot 1 \quad \text{and} \quad 8! = 8 \cdot 7 \cdot 6 \cdot 5 \cdot 4 \cdot 3 \cdot 2 \cdot 1$$

The factorial symbol applies only to the variable or numeral that it follows.

EXAMPLE 1

Write each expression in expanded form.

a. $5n!$ for $n = 4$ **b.** $(2n - 1)!$ for $n = 4$

Solutions

a. $5n! = 5 \cdot (4 \cdot 3 \cdot 2 \cdot 1)$ **b.** $(2n - 1)! = [2(4) - 1]!$
$= 7!$
$= 7 \cdot 6 \cdot 5 \cdot 4 \cdot 3 \cdot 2 \cdot 1$

Since

$$n! = n(n - 1)(n - 2)(n - 3) \cdots \cdot 5 \cdot 4 \cdot 3 \cdot 2 \cdot 1$$

and

$$(n - 1)! = (n - 1)(n - 2)(n - 3) \cdots \cdot 5 \cdot 4 \cdot 3 \cdot 2 \cdot 1$$

we can, for $n > 1$, write the following recursive relationship:

$$n! = n(n - 1)! \tag{1}$$

EXAMPLE 2 Write each expression in expanded form and simplify.

a. $\dfrac{7!}{4!}$ 　　　　　　　　　　b. $\dfrac{4!6!}{8!}$

Solutions a. $\dfrac{7!}{4!} = \dfrac{7 \cdot 6 \cdot 5 \cdot 4!}{4!} = 210$ 　　b. $\dfrac{4!6!}{8!} = \dfrac{4 \cdot 3 \cdot 2 \cdot 1 \cdot 6!}{8 \cdot 7 \cdot 6!} = \dfrac{3}{7}$

EXAMPLE 3 Write each product in factorial notation.

a. $1 \cdot 2 \cdot 3 \cdot 4 \cdot 5 \cdot 6$ 　　　　b. $11 \cdot 12 \cdot 13 \cdot 14$

c. 150 　　　　　　　　　d. $149 \cdot 150$

Solutions a. $1 \cdot 2 \cdot 3 \cdot 4 \cdot 5 \cdot 6 = 6!$ 　　b. $11 \cdot 12 \cdot 13 \cdot 14 = \dfrac{14!}{10!}$

c. $150 = \dfrac{150!}{149!}$ 　　　　　d. $149 \cdot 150 = \dfrac{150!}{148!}$

EXAMPLE 4 Write $(2n + 1)!$ in factored form and show the first three factors and the last three factors.

Solution
$$(2n + 1)! = (2n + 1)(2n)(2n - 1) \cdot \cdots \cdot 3 \cdot 2 \cdot 1$$

If $n = 1$ in Equation (1), we have

$$1! = 1 \cdot (1 - 1)!$$
$$1! = 1 \cdot 0!$$

Therefore, for consistency, we provide the following definition:

$$0! = 1$$

Note that both 1! and 0! are equal to 1.

Binomial Expansion The series obtained by expanding a binomial of the form

$$(a + b)^n$$

is particularly useful in certain branches of mathematics. Starting with familiar examples in which n takes the value 1, 2, 3, 4, and 5, we can show by direct multiplication that

$$(a + b)^1 = a + b$$
$$(a + b)^2 = a^2 + 2ab + b^2$$
$$(a + b)^3 = a^3 + 3a^2b + 3ab^2 + b^3$$
$$(a + b)^4 = a^4 + 4a^3b + 6a^2b^2 + 4ab^3 + b^4$$
$$(a + b)^5 = a^5 + 5a^4b + 10a^3b^2 + 10a^2b^3 + 5ab^4 + b^5$$

We observe that in each case:

1. The first term may be considered to be $a^n b^0$. The exponent on a *decreases* by 1 and the exponent on b *increases* by 1 in each of the following terms. The last term may be considered to be $a^0 b^n$. For example,

$$\underset{\underset{\downarrow}{\dfrac{5}{1!}}}{\quad} \underset{\underset{\downarrow}{\dfrac{5\cdot 4}{2!}}}{\quad} \underset{\underset{\downarrow}{\dfrac{5\cdot 4\cdot 3}{3!}}}{\quad} \underset{\underset{\downarrow}{\dfrac{5\cdot 4\cdot 3\cdot 2}{4!}}}{\quad}$$

$$(a + b)^5 = a^5 + 5a^4 b + 10a^3 b^2 + 10a^2 b^3 + 5ab^4 + b^5.$$

Exponents of a decrease by 1
Exponents of b increase by 1

2. The variable factors of the second term are $a^{n-1}b^1$, and the coefficient is n, which can be written in the form

$$\frac{n}{1!}$$

3. The variable factors of the third term are $a^{n-2}b^2$, and the coefficient can be written in the form

$$\frac{n(n-1)}{2!}$$

4. The variable factors of the fourth term are $a^{n-3}b^3$, and the coefficient can be written in the form

$$\frac{n(n-1)(n-2)}{3!}$$

These results can be generalized to obtain the following **binomial expansion**:

$$(a + b)^n = a^n + \frac{n}{1!}a^{n-1}b + \frac{n(n-1)}{2!}a^{n-2}b^2 + \frac{n(n-1)(n-2)}{3!}a^{n-3}b^3$$
$$+ \cdots + \frac{n(n-1)(n-2)\cdots\cdots(n-r+2)}{(r-1)!}a^{n-r+1}b^{r-1}$$
$$+ \cdots + b^n \tag{2}$$

where r is the number of the term.

EXAMPLE 5

Expand.

a. $(x - 2)^4$ **b.** $(a - 3b)^4$

Solutions

a. In this case, $a = x$ and $b = -2$ in the binomial expansion.

$$(x - 2)^4 = x^4 + \frac{4}{1!}x^3(-2)^1 + \frac{4\cdot 3}{2!}x^2(-2)^2 + \frac{4\cdot 3\cdot 2}{3!}x(-2)^3 + \frac{4\cdot 3\cdot 2\cdot 1}{4!}(-2)^4$$

$$= x^4 - 8x^3 + 24x^2 - 32x + 16$$

b.   In this case, we replace b by $-3b$ in the binomial expansion.

$$(a - 3b)^4 = a^4 + \frac{4}{1!}a^3(-3b) + \frac{4 \cdot 3}{2!}a^2(-3b)^2 + \frac{4 \cdot 3 \cdot 2}{3!}a(-3b)^3 + \frac{4 \cdot 3 \cdot 2 \cdot 1}{4!}(-3b)^4$$

$$= a^4 - 12a^3b + 54a^2b^2 - 108ab^3 + 81b^4$$

rth Term of an Expansion

Note that in Equation (2) the rth term in a binomial expansion is given by

$$\frac{n(n-1)(n-2) \cdot \cdots \cdot (n-r+2)}{(r-1)!}a^{n-r+1}b^{r-1} \tag{3}$$

EXAMPLE 6

a.   Find the fifth term in the expansion $(x - 2)^{10}$.

b.   Find the seventh term in the expansion of $(x - 2)^{10}$.

Solutions

a.   We can use expression (3), where $n = 10$, $r = 5$, $r - 1 = 4$, and $n - r + 2 = 7$.

$$\frac{10 \cdot 9 \cdot 8 \cdot 7}{4 \cdot 3 \cdot 2 \cdot 1}x^6(-2)^4 = 3360x^6$$

b.   We can use expression (3), where $n = 10$, $r = 7$, $r - 1 = 6$, and $n - r + 2 = 5$.

$$\frac{10 \cdot 9 \cdot 8 \cdot 7 \cdot 6 \cdot 5}{6 \cdot 5 \cdot 4 \cdot 3 \cdot 2 \cdot 1}x^4(-2)^6 = 13,440x^4$$

It is helpful to note that when expression (3) is used:

1.   The exponent on b, $(r - 1)$, is one less than r, the number of the term.
2.   The sum of the exponents $(n - r + 1) + (r - 1)$ equals n, the exponent of the power.
3.   The factor $(r - 1)$ in the denominator of the coefficient equals the exponent on b.
4.   The number of factors in the numerator of the coefficient is the same as the number of factors in the denominator.

E X E R C I S E   S E T   13.5

▲ *Write each expression in expanded form. See Example 1.*

1. $(2n)!$ for $n = 4$
2. $(3n)!$ for $n = 4$
3. $2n!$ for $n = 4$
4. $3n!$ for $n = 4$
5. $n(n - 1)!$ for $n = 6$
6. $2n(2n - 1)!$ for $n = 2$

▲ *Write in expanded form and simplify. See Example 2.*

7. $5!$
8. $7!$
9. $\dfrac{9!}{7!}$
10. $\dfrac{12!}{11!}$
11. $\dfrac{5!7!}{8!}$
12. $\dfrac{12!8!}{16!}$

13. $\dfrac{8!}{2!(8-2)!}$

14. $\dfrac{10!}{4!(10-4)!}$

▲ *Write each product in factorial notation. See Example 3.*

15. $1 \cdot 2 \cdot 3$

16. $1 \cdot 2 \cdot 3 \cdot 4 \cdot 5$

17. $3 \cdot 4 \cdot 5 \cdot 6$

18. 7

19. $8 \cdot 7 \cdot 6$

20. $28 \cdot 27 \cdot 26 \cdot 25 \cdot 24$

▲ *Write each expression in factored form and show the first three factors and the last three factors. See Example 4.*

21. $n!$

22. $(n+4)!$

23. $(3n)!$

24. $3n!$

25. $(n-2)!$

26. $(3n-2)!$

▲ *Expand. See Example 5.*

27. $(x+3)^5$

28. $(2x+y)^4$

29. $(x-3)^4$

30. $(2x-1)^5$

31. $\left(2x - \dfrac{y}{2}\right)^3$

32. $\left(\dfrac{x}{3}+3\right)^5$

33. $\left(\dfrac{x}{2}+2\right)^6$

34. $\left(\dfrac{2}{3}-a^2\right)^4$

▲ *Write the first four terms in each expansion. Do not simplify the terms. See Example 5.*

35. $(x+y)^{20}$

36. $(x-y)^{15}$

37. $(a-2b)^{12}$

38. $(2a-b)^{12}$

39. $(x-\sqrt{2})^{10}$

40. $\left(\dfrac{x}{2}+2\right)^8$

▲ *Find each specified term. See Example 6.*

41. $(a-b)^{15}$,   sixth term

42. $(x+2)^{12}$,   fifth term

43. $(x-2y)^{10}$,   fifth term

44. $(a^3-b)^9$,   seventh term

45. $(x^2-y^2)^7$,   third term

46. $\left(x-\dfrac{1}{2}\right)^8$,   fourth term

47. $\left(\dfrac{a}{2}-2b\right)^9$,   fifth term

48. $\left(\dfrac{x}{2}+4\right)^{10}$,   eighth term

Miscellaneous Exercises

▲ *Find each power to the nearest hundredth without using a calculator. [Hint: Write the given power as $(1+x)^n$ and use the first three terms of the binomial expansion.]*

49. $(1.02)^{10}$

50. $(1.01)^{15}$

51. $(0.99)^8$

52. $(0.95)^8$

53. Given that the binomial formula holds for $(1+x)^n$, where n is a negative integer:

   a. Write the first four terms of $(1+x)^{-1}$.

   b. Find the first four terms of the quotient $\dfrac{1}{1+x}$ by dividing $(1+x)$ into 1.

   c. Compare the results of parts a and b.

54. Given that the binomial formula holds as an infinite "sum" for $(1+x)^n$, where n is a noninteger rational number and $|x| < 1$, find to two decimal places without using a calculator:

   a. $\sqrt{1.02}$

   b. $\sqrt{0.99}$

CHAPTER SUMMARY

[13.1] The elements in the range of a function whose domain is a set of successive positive integers form a **sequence**. The sequence is **finite** if it has a last member; otherwise, it is **infinite**. A series is the indicated sum of the terms in a sequence. We can use **sigma**, or **summation**, notation to represent a series.

[13.2] A sequence in which each term after the first is obtained by adding a constant to the preceding term is an **arithmetic progression**. The constant is called the **common difference** of the terms.

The nth term of an arithmetic progression is given by

$$s_n = a + (n-1)d$$

and the sum of n terms is given by

$$S_n = \frac{n}{2}(a + s_n) = \frac{n}{2}[2a + (n - 1)d]$$

where a is the first term, n is the number of terms, and d is the common difference.

[13.3] A sequence in which each term after the first is obtained by multiplying its predecessor by a constant is called a **geometric progression**. The constant is called the **common ratio**.

The nth term of a geometric progression is given by

$$s_n = ar^{n-1}$$

and the sum of n terms is given by

$$S_n = \frac{a - ar^n}{1 - r} = \frac{a - rs_n}{1 - r} \qquad (r \neq 1)$$

where a is the first term, n is the number of terms, and r is the common ratio.

[13.4] An infinite geometric series has a sum if the common ratio has an absolute value less than 1. This sum is given by

$$S_\infty = \lim_{n \to \infty} S_n = \frac{a}{1 - r}$$

The number e is defined by

$$\lim_{t \to \infty} \left(1 + \frac{1}{t}\right)^t$$

[13.5] Factorial notation is convenient to represent special kinds of products. For n a natural number,

$$n! = n(n - 1)(n - 2) \cdots (3)(2)(1)$$
$$= n(n - 1)!$$

Also,

$$0! = 1$$

The binomial power $(a + b)^n$ can be expanded into a series containing $(n + 1)$ terms for n a natural number:

$$(a + b)^n = a^n + \frac{n}{1!}a^{n-1}b + \frac{n(n - 1)}{2!}a^{n-2}b^2 + \frac{n(n - 1)(n - 2)}{3!}a^{n-3}b^3$$

$$+ \cdots + \frac{n(n - 1)(n - 2) \cdots (n - r + 2)}{(r - 1)!}a^{n-r+1}b^{r-1}$$

$$+ \cdots + b^n$$

where r is the number of the term.

REVIEW EXERCISES

[13.1]

▲ *Find the first four terms in a sequence with the general term as given.*

1. $\dfrac{2n-1}{n^2}$

2. $\dfrac{(-1)^{n-1}}{n}$

▲ *Write each series in expanded form.*

3. $\displaystyle\sum_{k=2}^{5} k(k-1)$

4. $\displaystyle\sum_{i=1}^{\infty} \dfrac{1}{i^2+1}$

[13.2]

5. Given that 5 and 9 are the first two terms of an arithmetic progression, find an expression for the general term.

6. Find the twenty-third term of the arithmetic progression $-82, -74, -66, \ldots$.

7. Find the sum of the first twenty-three terms of the arithmetic progression in Exercise 6.

8. The first term of an arithmetic progression is 8, and the twenty-eighth term is 89. Find the twenty-first term.

[13.3]

9. Given that 5 and 9 are the first two terms of a geometric progression, find an expression for the general term.

10. Find the eighth term of the geometric progression $\dfrac{16}{27}$, $-\dfrac{8}{9}, \dfrac{4}{3}, \ldots$.

11. Find the sum of the first four terms of the geometric progression in Exercise 10.

12. Find $\displaystyle\sum_{j=1}^{5} \left(\dfrac{1}{3}\right)^{j}$.

[13.4]

13. Find $\displaystyle\sum_{i=1}^{\infty} \left(\dfrac{1}{3}\right)^{i}$.

14. Find $\displaystyle\sum_{i=1}^{\infty} \left(-\dfrac{3}{4}\right)^{i}$.

15. Find a fraction equivalent to $0.44\overline{4}$.

16. Find a fraction equivalent to $2.63\overline{63}$.

[13.5]

17. Simplify $\dfrac{8!}{3!\,5!}$.

18. Simplify $\dfrac{2n!}{(n-3)!}$.

19. Write the first four terms of the binomial expansion of $(x-2y)^{10}$.

20. Find the eighth term in the expansion of $(x-2y)^{10}$.

▲ *The numbers in brackets refer to the sections in which such problems are first considered.*

1. Multiply $(\sqrt{2} + 2\sqrt{3})(3\sqrt{2} - 2\sqrt{3})$. **[5.7]**

2. Compute to four places $e^{-1.3}$. **[9.3, 9.4]**

3. Solve $2 = \dfrac{3x}{3y^2 + 1}$ explicitly for y. **[7.1]**

4. Solve $-2(x^2 - 7x + 8) = (x + 1)^2 - 3x^2$. **[2.3]**

5. Solve $\dfrac{2}{3}x^2 - x + \dfrac{1}{4} = 0$. **[6.2]**

6. Solve $\log_{10} x + \log_{10}(x - 3) = 1$. **[9.2]**

7. Solve the system
$$2x^2 - 5xy + 2y^2 = 0$$
$$x^2 + xy + y^2 = 28$$
[11.5]

8. Write in expanded form
$$\sum_{k=2}^{6} (-1)^k \frac{2k - 1}{k - 1}.$$
[13.1]

9. Find $\displaystyle\sum_{i=4}^{9} (-3)^{i-4}$. **[13.3]**

10. Find the eighth term of $(2x - y^3)^{11}$. **[13.5]**

11. Solve the system
$$x - 2y = -7$$
$$3x + 2y = -9$$
$$2y - 3z = 4$$
[10.5]

12. Solve $\log_x 8 = -3$. **[9.1]**

13. Solve $\left(\dfrac{a^{1/6}b^{-3/2}c}{a^{3/2}b^{-1}c^2}\right)^{-6}$ as a product or quotient involving only positive exponents. **[5.4]**

14. Write $\dfrac{3 + i}{3 - 2i}$ in the form $a + bi$. **[5.8]**

15. Find the zeros of $f(x) = 2x^2 + 5x - 12$. **[8.1]**

▲ *Graph.*

16. $3x = -4y - 6$ **[7.2]**

17. $3x - 4y \leqslant 0$ **[12.5]**

18. $y = -\left(\dfrac{1}{2}\right)^x$ **[8.4]**

19. $y = -x^2 + 3x + 4$ **[11.2]**

20. $4x^2 = 24 + y^2$ **[11.3]**

▲ *Solve.*

21. Three solutions of the equation $ax + by + cz = 1$ are $(3, 2, 1), (-2, 0, 1)$, and $(1, 3, 4)$. Find the coefficients a, b, and c. **[10.2]**

22. The area of a rectangle is 208 square meters and its perimeter is 58 meters. Find the dimensions of the rectangle. **[10.1]**

23. A certain radioactive isotope decays so that the amount present after t seconds is $N = N_0 e^{-0.2t}$, where N_0 is the initial amount. How long will it be until only 25% of the isotope is left? **[9.6]**

24. Farmer Bob has 48 rows of corn planted in a trapezoidal field. There are 40 stalks of corn in the first row, 43 stalks in the second row, 46 stalks in the third row, and so on, for the 48 rows. How many stalks of corn are in the field? **[13.2]**

25. A ball returns three-fourths of its preceding height on each bounce. If the ball is dropped from a height of 8 feet, approximately what is the total distance the ball travels before coming to rest? **[13.4]**

SYNTHETIC DIVISION

In Section 4.2 we rewrote quotients of polynomials of the form $P(x)/D(x)$ using a long division algorithm (process). If the divisor $D(x)$ is of the form $(x - a)$—*a first-degree polynomial where the coefficient of x is 1 and $a \neq 0$*—this algorithm may be simplified by a procedure known as **synthetic division**. Consider the quotient

$$\frac{x^4 + x^2 + 2x - 1}{x + 3}$$

The division can be accomplished by long division as follows:

$$
\begin{array}{r}
x^3 - 3x^2 + 10x - 28 \\
x + 3 \overline{) x^4 + 0x^3 + x^2 + 2x - 1} \\
\underline{x^4 + 3x^3} \\
-3x^3 + x^2 \\
\underline{-3x^3 - 9x^2} \\
10x^2 + 2x \\
\underline{10x^2 + 30x} \\
-28x - 1 \\
\underline{-28x - 84} \\
83 \quad \text{(remainder)}
\end{array}
$$

We see that, for $x \neq -3$,

$$\frac{x^4 + x^2 + 2x - 1}{x + 3} = x^3 - 3x^2 + 10x - 28 + \frac{83}{x + 3}$$

or, when we clear the fractions,

$$x^4 + x^2 + 2x - 1 = (x^3 - 3x^2 + 10x - 28)(x + 3) + 83$$

379

If we omit the variables, writing only the coefficients of the terms, and use 0 for the coefficient of any missing power, we have

$$
\begin{array}{r}
1 - 3 + 10 - 28 \\
1 + 3 \,\overline{)\, 1 + 0 + 1 + 2 - 1} \\
\mathbf{1} + 3 \\
\hline
-3 + (1) \\
\mathbf{-3} - 9 \\
\hline
10 + (2) \\
\mathbf{10} + 30 \\
\hline
-28 - (1) \\
\mathbf{-28} - 84 \\
\hline
83 \quad \text{(remainder)}
\end{array}
$$

Now observe that the numbers shown in boldface are repetitions of the numbers written immediately above and are also repetitions of the coefficients of the associated variable in the quotient. The numbers shown in parentheses are repetitions of the coefficients of the dividend. Therefore, the whole process can be written in compact form as

$$
\begin{array}{c|rrrrr}
3 & 1 & 0 & 1 & 2 & -1 & \quad\text{(1)} \\
 & & 3 & -9 & 30 & -84 & \quad\text{(2)} \\
\hline
 & 1 & -3 & 10 & -28 & 83 & \quad\text{(remainder: 83)} \quad\text{(3)}
\end{array}
$$

where the repetitions are omitted and where 1, the coefficient of x in the divisor, has also been omitted.

The numbers in line (3), which are the coefficients of the variables in the quotient and the remainder, have been obtained by *subtracting* the **detached coefficients** in line (2) from the detached coefficients of terms of the same degree in line (1). We could obtain the same result by replacing 3 with -3 in the divisor and *adding* instead of subtracting at each step. This is what is done in the *synthetic division* process. The final form then is

$$
\begin{array}{c|rrrrr}
-3 & 1 & 0 & 1 & 2 & -1 & \quad\text{(1)} \\
 & & -3 & 9 & -30 & 84 & \quad\text{(2)} \\
\hline
 & 1 & -3 & 10 & -28 & 83 & \quad\text{(remainder: 83)} \quad\text{(3)}
\end{array}
$$

Note that the numbers in line (2) are obtained by multiplying the preceding number to the left in line (3) by -3.

Comparing the results of using synthetic division with the same process using long division, we observe that the numbers in line (3) are the coefficients of the polynomial

$$
x^3 - 3x^2 + 10x - 28
$$

and that there is a remainder of 83.

As another example, let us write the quotient

$$
\frac{3x^3 - 4x - 1}{x - 2}
$$

in the form $Q(x) + r/(x - a)$. Using synthetic division, we begin by writing

$$2\rfloor \quad 3 \quad 0 \quad -4 \quad -1$$

where 0 has been inserted in the position corresponding to the coefficient of a second-degree term. The divisor is the negative of -2, or 2. Then we have

$$
\begin{array}{r|rrrr}
2\rfloor & 3 & 0 & -4 & -1 \\
 & & 6 & 12 & 16 \\
\hline
 & 3 & 6 & 8 & 15 \\
\end{array}
\quad \text{(remainder: 15)}
$$

(1)
(2)
(3)

This process employs the following steps:

1. 3 is brought down from line (1) to line (3).
2. 6, the product of 2 and 3, is written in the next position on line (2).
3. 6, the sum of 0 and 6, is written on line (3).
4. 12, the product of 2 and 6, is written in the next position on line (2).
5. 8, the sum of -4 and 12, is written on line (3).
6. 16, the product of 2 and 8, is written in the next position on line (2).
7. 15, the sum of -1 and 16, is written on line (3).

We now use the first three numbers on line (3) as coefficients to write a polynomial of degree one less than the degree of the dividend. This polynomial is the quotient lacking the remainder. The last number is the remainder. Thus, for $x - 2 \neq 0$ the quotient of $3x^3 - 4x - 1$ divided by $(x - 2)$ is

$$3x^2 + 6x + 8$$

with a remainder of 15; that is,

$$\frac{3x^3 - 4x - 1}{x - 2} = 3x^2 + 6x + 8 + \frac{15}{x - 2} \qquad (x \neq 2)$$

We will use synthetic division in the following examples to rewrite each quotient in the form $Q(x) + r/(x - a)$, where r is a constant.

EXAMPLE 1

$$\frac{2x^4 + x^3 - 1}{x + 2}$$

Solution

We begin by writing

$$-2\rfloor \quad 2 \quad 1 \quad 0 \quad 0 \quad -1$$

where 0 is the coefficient of any missing power. The divisor is the negative of 2, that is, -2. We proceed by using the following steps:

$$\underline{-2|}\ \ 2\quad 1\quad\ \ 0\quad\ \ 0\quad -1 \qquad (1)$$

$$\longrightarrow -4\ \longrightarrow 6\ \longrightarrow -12\ \longrightarrow 24 \qquad (2)$$

(add)   (add)   (add)   (add)

$$2\quad -3\quad\ \ 6\quad -12\quad 23 \qquad (3)$$

$$(-2)(2)\quad (-2)(-3)\quad (-2)(6)\quad (-2)(-12)$$

We use the first four numbers on line (3) as the coefficients of $Q(x)$. The last number is the remainder.

$$2x^3 - 3x^2 + 6x - 12 + \frac{23}{x+2} \qquad (x \neq -2)$$

EXAMPLE 2 $\dfrac{x^4 - 2x^2 + 3}{x - 2}$

Solution

We begin by writing

$$\underline{2|}\quad 1\quad\ \ 0\quad -2\quad\ \ 0\quad\ \ 3$$

where 0 is the coefficient of any missing power. The divisor is the negative of -2, that is, 2. We proceed by using the following steps:

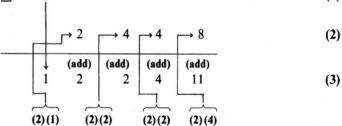

$$\underline{2|}\quad 1\quad\ \ 0\quad -2\quad\ \ 0\quad\ \ 3 \qquad (1)$$

$$\longrightarrow 2\ \longrightarrow 4\ \longrightarrow 4\ \longrightarrow 8 \qquad (2)$$

(add)   (add)   (add)   (add)

$$1\quad\ \ 2\quad\ \ 2\quad\ \ 4\quad\ 11 \qquad (3)$$

$$(2)(1)\quad (2)(2)\quad (2)(2)\quad (2)(4)$$

We use the first four numbers on line (3) as the coefficients of $Q(x)$. The last number is the remainder.

$$x^3 + 2x^2 + 2x + 4 + \frac{11}{x-2} \qquad (x \neq 2)$$

EXERCISE SET APPENDIX A

▲ *Use synthetic division to write each quotient $P(x)/(x - a)$ in the form $Q(x)$ or $Q(x) + r/(x - a)$, where r is a constant. See Examples 1 and 2.*

1. $\dfrac{x^2 - 8x + 12}{x - 6}$

2. $\dfrac{a^2 + a - 6}{a + 3}$

3. $\dfrac{x^2 + 4x + 4}{x + 2}$

4. $\dfrac{x^2 + 6x + 9}{x + 3}$

5. $\dfrac{x^4 - 3x^3 + 2x^2 - 1}{x - 2}$

6. $\dfrac{x^4 + 2x^2 - 3x + 5}{x - 3}$

7. $\dfrac{2x^3 + x - 5}{x + 1}$

8. $\dfrac{3x^3 + x^2 - 7}{x + 2}$

9. $\dfrac{2x^4 - x + 6}{x - 5}$

10. $\dfrac{3x^4 - x^2 + 1}{x - 4}$

11. $\dfrac{x^3 + 4x^2 + x - 2}{x + 2}$

12. $\dfrac{x^3 - 7x^2 - x + 3}{x + 3}$

13. $\dfrac{x^4 - 2x^3 + x^2 - 1}{x - 2}$

14. $\dfrac{x^4 + x^3 - 2x + 3}{x + 1}$

15. $\dfrac{x^5 + x^4 + 2x^2 - 1}{x - 1}$

16. $\dfrac{x^5 - 2x^3 + x^2 - 1}{x + 2}$

17. $\dfrac{x^5 - 3x^2 - 1}{x + 1}$

18. $\dfrac{x^5 - 2x^2 + 1}{x - 2}$

19. $\dfrac{x^6 + x^4 - x}{x - 1}$

20. $\dfrac{x^6 + 3x^3 - 2x - 1}{x - 2}$

21. $\dfrac{x^5 - 1}{x - 1}$

22. $\dfrac{x^5 + 1}{x + 1}$

23. $\dfrac{x^6 - 1}{x - 1}$

24. $\dfrac{x^6 + 1}{x + 1}$

POLYNOMIAL FUNCTIONS

In Section 7.2 we graphed linear functions defined by

$$y = a_1 x + a_0$$

and in Section 8.3 we graphed quadratic functions defined by

$$y = a_1 x^2 + a_1 x + a_0$$

Remainder Theorem   We can graph any **polynomial function** defined by

$$y = a_n x^n + a_{n-1} x^{n-1} + \cdots + a_0$$

where $a_n, a_{n-1}, \cdots + a_0$, and x are real numbers, by obtaining a sufficient number of solutions (ordered pairs) to determine the behavior of its graph. We can obtain the ordered pairs (x, y) by direct substitution of values of x, as we did earlier, or by another method that can sometimes be more efficient. To do this, we first consider an important property of quotients called the **remainder theorem**, which we state without proof as follows:

> *If a polynomial $P(x)$ is divided by $(x - a)$, the remainder r is $P(a)$.*

Since synthetic division offers a means of finding values of $r = P(a)$, we can sometimes find such values more quickly by synthetic division than by direct substitution. For example, if

$$P(x) = 2x^3 - 3x^2 + 2x + 1$$

we can find $P(2)$ by synthetically dividing $2x^3 - 3x^2 + 2x + 1$ by $x - 2$.

$$
\begin{array}{r|rrrr}
\underline{2} & 2 & -3 & 2 & 1 \\
& & 4 & 2 & 8 \\
\hline
& 2 & 1 & 4 & \mathbf{9}
\end{array}
$$

By inspection we note that $r = P(2) = \mathbf{9}$.

EXAMPLE 1

If $P(x) = 4x^4 - 2x^3 + 3x - 2$, find $P(-1)$ and $P(2)$.

Solution

$$
\begin{array}{r|rrrrr}
\underline{-1} & 4 & -2 & 0 & 3 & -2 \\
& & -4 & 6 & -6 & 3 \\
\hline
& 4 & -6 & 6 & -3 & 1 \\
\end{array}
\qquad
\begin{array}{r|rrrrr}
\underline{2} & 4 & -2 & 0 & 3 & -2 \\
& & 8 & 12 & 24 & 54 \\
\hline
& 4 & 6 & 12 & 27 & \mathbf{52} \\
\end{array}
$$
$$P(-1) = \mathbf{1} \qquad\qquad\qquad P(2) = \mathbf{52}$$

Graphs of Polynomial Functions

In the following example we graph a third-degree polynomial by finding a sufficient number of ordered pairs to suggest the appearance of its graph.

EXAMPLE 2

Graph $P(x) = x^3 - 2x^2 - 5x + 6$.

Solution

We obtain solutions of the equation for selected values of x, say, $-3, -2, -1, 0, 1, 2,$ 3, and 4, by dividing $x^3 - 2x^2 - 5x + 6$ by $x + 3$, $x + 2$, and so on. Dividing synthetically by $x + 3$, we obtain

$$
\begin{array}{r|rrrr}
\underline{-3} & 1 & -2 & -5 & 6 \\
& & -3 & 15 & -30 \\
\hline
& 1 & -5 & 10 & \mathbf{-24}
\end{array}
$$

Therefore, $(-3, -\mathbf{24})$ is a solution of the equation. Dividing by $x + 2$, we obtain

$$
\begin{array}{r|rrrr}
\underline{-2} & 1 & -2 & -5 & 6 \\
& & -2 & 8 & -6 \\
\hline
& 1 & -4 & 3 & \mathbf{0}
\end{array}
$$

Therefore, $(-2, \mathbf{0})$ is a solution of the equation. Dividing by $x + 1$ we obtain

$$
\begin{array}{r|rrrr}
\underline{-1} & 1 & -2 & -5 & 6 \\
& & -1 & 3 & 2 \\
\hline
& 1 & -3 & -2 & \mathbf{8}
\end{array}
$$

Therefore, $(-1, \mathbf{8})$ is a solution of the equation. Similarly, $P(0) = 6$, $P(1) = 0$, $P(2) = -4$, $P(3) = 0$, and $P(4) = 18$. Hence, $(0, 6)$, $(1, 0)$, $(2, -4)$, $(3, 0)$, and $(4, 18)$ are solutions, and their graphs are on the graph of the function. Note that $-2, 1,$ and 3 are zeros of the function because

$$f(-2) = 0, \qquad f(1) = 0, \qquad \text{and} \qquad f(3) = 0$$

The points, shown in Figure a, can be connected to give the complete graph as shown in Figure b. Any additional values of x less than -3 and greater than 4 would not change the general appearance of the graph.

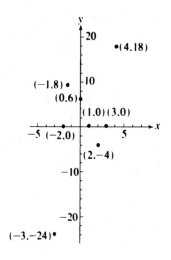

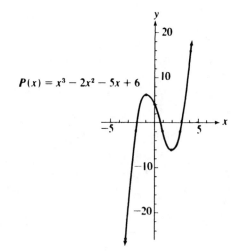

a.

b.

Number of Direction Changes

Note in Example 2 that the graph of this third-degree polynomial function changes direction twice. In fact, it can be shown, although we will not do so, that the *maximum number of direction changes of the graph of a polynomial function is one less than the degree of the polynomial.*

Observe that the high and low points in the graph in Example 2 *do not* exactly correspond with the ordered pairs $(-1, 8)$ and $(2, -4)$, respectively. Finding the exact values of the components of the ordered pairs that are the high and low points of the graphs of polynomial functions of degree greater than 2 requires methods that are considered only in more advanced courses. However, we can obtain approximations for these points by plotting ordered pairs as demonstrated in Example 2.

Factor Theorem

A direct consequence of the remainder theorem is the following result, called the **factor theorem:**

> If $P(a) = 0$, then $(x - a)$ is a factor of $P(x)$; and if $(x - a)$ is a factor, then $P(a) = 0$.

EXAMPLE 3

For the polynomial

$$P(x) = x^3 - 2x^2 - 5x + 6$$

in Example 2 we obtained $P(-2) = 0$, $P(1) = 0$, and $P(3) = 0$. Hence, by the factor theorem, $x + 2$, $x - 1$, and $x - 3$ are factors of the polynomial.

Number of Solutions of P(x) = 0

We note from the factor theorem that a is a solution of $P(x) = 0$ if and only if $(x - a)$ is a factor of $P(x)$. This suggests that *an equation $P(x) = 0$, where $P(x)$ is of nth degree, has n solutions.* This is indeed the case. Note that the third-degree polynomial $x^3 - 2x^2 - 5x + 6$ is equivalent to $(x + 2)(x - 1)(x - 3)$, and that there are exactly three solutions of

$$x^3 - 2x^2 - 5x + 6 = (x + 2)(x - 1)(x - 3) = 0$$

namely, -2, 1, and 3.

Of course, it may be that one or more factors of such an expression are the same. When this happens, we count the solution as many times as the factor involved occurs. Thus, if

$$P(x) = x^4 + 2x^3 - 2x - 1$$
$$= (x + 1)(x + 1)(x + 1)(x - 1)$$

we can see that -1 and 1 are the only solutions of $P(x) = 0$, but we say that -1 is a solution of *multiplicity* three.

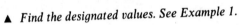

EXERCISE SET APPENDIX B

▲ *Find the designated values. See Example 1.*

1. If $P(x) = 3x^3 - 2x^2 + 5x - 4$, find $P(3)$ and $P(-2)$.

2. If $P(x) = 4x^4 - 2x^3 + 3x^2 - 5$, find $P(1)$ and $P(-1)$.

3. If $P(x) = 2x^5 - 3x^3 + x^2 - x + 2$, find $P(-1)$ and $P(2)$.

4. If $P(x) = x^4 - 10x^3 + 5x^2 - 3x + 6$, find $P(-2)$ and $P(3)$.

▲ *Use synthetic division and the remainder theorem to find sufficient solutions to graph each function. Specify the zeros of the function. See Example 2.*

5. $P(x) = x^3 + x^2 - 6x$
6. $P(x) = x^3 + 5x^2 + 4x$
7. $P(x) = x^3 - 2x^2 + 1$
8. $P(x) = x^3 - 4x^2 + 3x$
9. $P(x) = 2x^3 + 9x^2 + 7x - 6$
10. $P(x) = x^3 - 3x^2 - 6x + 8$
11. $P(x) = x^4 - 4x^2$
12. $P(x) = x^4 - x^3 - 4x^2 + 4x$

▲ *Use the factor theorem to determine whether or not the given binomial is a factor of the given polynomial. See Example 3.*

13. $x - 2$; $x^3 - 3x^2 + 2x + 2$
14. $x - 1$; $2x^3 - 5x^2 + 4x - 1$
15. $x + 3$; $3x^3 + 11x^2 + x - 15$
16. $x + 1$; $2x^3 - 5x^2 + 3x + 3$
17. Verify that 1 is a solution of $x^3 + 2x^2 - x - 2 = 0$, and find the other solutions.
18. Verify that 3 is a solution of $x^3 - 6x^2 - x + 30 = 0$, and find the other solutions.
19. Verify that -3 is a solution of $x^4 - 3x^3 - 10x^2 + 24x = 0$, and find the other solutions.
20. Verify that -5 is a solution of $x^4 + 5x^3 - x^2 - 5x = 0$, and find the other solutions.
21. Graph on the same set of axes the equations $y = kx$, $y = kx^2$, and $y = kx^3$, where $k = 2$ and $x \geqslant 0$. What effect does increasing the degree of the equation $y = kx^n$ have on the graph of the equation?

RATIONAL FUNCTIONS

A function defined by an equation of the form

$$y = \frac{P(x)}{Q(x)}$$

where $P(x)$ and $Q(x)$ are polynomials and $Q(x) \neq 0,$ is called a **rational function**. We can graph such a function by obtaining a sufficient number of solutions (ordered pairs) to determine its behavior by direct substitution of arbitrary values of x. It is also helpful to first obtain any asymptotes to the curve that may exist.

Vertical Asymptotes   Vertical asymptotes can be found by using the following property:

> *The graph of the function defined by* $y = P(x)/Q(x)$ *has a vertical asymptote* $x = a$ *for each value a at which* $Q(x) = 0$ *and* $P(x) \neq 0.$

EXAMPLE 1   Find the vertical asymptotes of the graphs of each function.

   a. $y = \dfrac{2}{x-2}$ **b.** $y = \dfrac{4}{x^2 - x - 6}$

Solutions   **a.** $x - 2 = 0$ if $x = 2$ **b.** $x^2 - x - 6 = (x - 3)(x + 2)$

                                                 $(x - 3)(x + 2) = 0$ if

                                                 $x = 3$ or $x = -2$

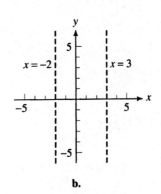

a.

b.

Horizontal Asymptotes The graphs of some rational functions have horizontal asymptotes that can be identified by using the following property:

> *If ax^n is the term of highest degree of a polynomial $P(x)$ and bx^m is the term of highest degree of a polynomial $Q(x)$, then the graph of the function*
> $y = P(x)/Q(x)$ *has a horizontal asymptote*
>
> $$at \quad y = 0 \qquad if \quad n < m$$
> $$at \quad y = a/b \qquad if \quad n = m$$
> $$nowhere \qquad if \quad n > m$$

EXAMPLE 2 Determine any horizontal asymptotes of the graphs of each function.

a. $y = \dfrac{3x}{x^2 - 5x + 4}$ b. $y = \dfrac{4x^2}{2x^2 - x}$ c. $y = \dfrac{x^4 + 1}{x^2 + 2}$

Solutions a. The degree of $3x$ is less than the degree of x^2. Hence, the graph has a horizontal asymptote at $y = 0$.

b. $4x^2$ and $2x^2$ are of the same degree. Hence, the graph has a horizontal asymptote at $y = 4/2 = 2$.

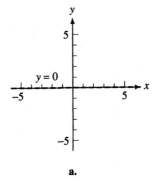

a.

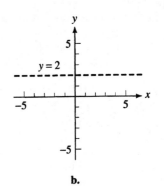

b.

c. The degree of x^4 is greater than the degree of x^2. Hence, the graph does not have a horizontal asymptote.

After vertical and horizontal asymptotes have been found, a few additional ordered pairs associated with points on opposite sides of each asymptote will usually be sufficient to complete the graph.

EXAMPLE 3   Graph $y = \dfrac{2}{x - 2}$.

Solution   Because $x - 2 = 0$ at $x = 2$, the vertical asymptote is $x = 2$. Because the degree of the numerator is less than the degree of the denominator, the horizontal asymptote is $y = 0$. Note that if $x = 0$, the y-intercept is -1. Several additional ordered pairs,

$$\left(-2, -\frac{1}{2}\right), \quad (1, -2), \quad (3, 2), \quad \text{and} \quad (4, 1)$$

can be connected to give the complete graph. Use the asymptotes as a guide for the branches of the curve.

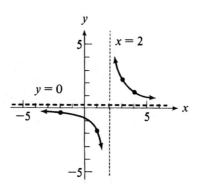

EXAMPLE 4   Graph

$$y = \frac{2x - 4}{x^2 - 9}$$

Solution   Because $x^2 - 9 = (x - 3)(x + 3)$, which is zero for $x = 3$ and $x = -3$, the vertical asymptotes are $x = 3$ and $x = -3$. Because the degree of $2x$ is less than the degree of x^2, the horizontal asymptote is $y = 0$. If $x = 0$, the y-intercept is $\dfrac{4}{9}$. If $y = 0$, $2x - 4 = 0$; hence, the x-intercept is 2. Several additional ordered pairs,

$$\left(-4, -\frac{12}{7}\right), \quad \left(-2, \frac{8}{5}\right), \quad \text{and} \quad \left(4, \frac{4}{7}\right)$$

enable us to complete the graph as we use the asymptotes to direct the branches of the curve.

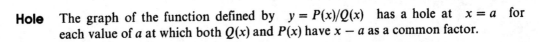

Hole The graph of the function defined by $y = P(x)/Q(x)$ has a hole at $x = a$ for each value of a at which both $Q(x)$ and $P(x)$ have $x - a$ as a common factor.

EXAMPLE 5 Graph $y = \dfrac{x^2 - 4}{x + 2}$.

Solution Since $x + 2$ is a common factor of both the numerator and denominator, it can be divided out. But since the denominator cannot equal 0, $x \neq -2$. Thus,

$$y = \frac{x^2 - 4}{x + 2}$$

$$= \frac{(x + 2)(x - 2)}{x + 2} = x - 2$$

where $x \neq -2$.

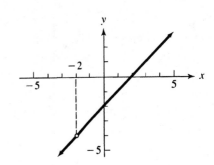

EXERCISE SET APPENDIX C

▲ *Determine the vertical asymptotes of the graph of each function. See Example 1.*

1. $y = \dfrac{2}{x + 3}$

2. $y = \dfrac{1}{x - 4}$

3. $y = \dfrac{3}{(x - 2)(x + 3)}$

4. $y = \dfrac{4}{(x + 1)(x - 4)}$

5. $y = \dfrac{2x}{x^2 - x - 6}$

6. $y = \dfrac{2x + 1}{x^2 - 3x + 2}$

▲ *Determine any vertical or horizontal asymptotes of the graphs of each function. See Examples 1 and 2.*

7. $y = \dfrac{x}{x^2 - 9}$

8. $y = \dfrac{2x - 4}{x^2 + 5x + 4}$

9. $y = \dfrac{x - 4}{2x - 1}$

10. $y = \dfrac{2x + 1}{x - 3}$

11. $y = \dfrac{2x^2}{x^2 - 3x - 4}$

12. $y = \dfrac{x^2}{x^2 - x - 12}$

▲ *Graph each function after first identifying all asymptotes and intercepts. See Examples 3 and 4.*

13. $y = \dfrac{1}{x + 3}$

14. $y = \dfrac{1}{x - 3}$

15. $y = \dfrac{2}{(x - 4)(x + 1)}$

16. $y = \dfrac{4}{(x + 2)(x - 1)}$

17. $y = \dfrac{2}{x^2 - 5x + 4}$

18. $y = \dfrac{4}{x^2 - x - 6}$

19. $y = \dfrac{x}{x + 3}$

20. $y = \dfrac{x}{x - 2}$

21. $y = \dfrac{x + 1}{x + 2}$

22. $y = \dfrac{x - 1}{x - 3}$

23. $y = \dfrac{2x}{x^2 - 4}$

24. $y = \dfrac{x}{x^2 - 9}$

25. $y = \dfrac{x - 2}{x^2 + 5x + 4}$

26. $y = \dfrac{x + 1}{x^2 - x - 6}$

▲ *Graph each function. See Example 5.*

27. $y = \dfrac{x^2 - 9}{x - 3}$

28. $y = \dfrac{x^2 - 1}{x + 1}$

29. $y = \dfrac{x^2 - 5x + 4}{x - 1}$

30. $y = \dfrac{x^2 - x - 6}{x - 3}$

31. $y = \dfrac{(x^2 - 4)(x + 1)}{x + 1}$

32. $y = \dfrac{(x^2 - 1)(x - 3)}{x - 3}$

33. Graph $xy = k$ for $k = 4$ and $k = 12$ on the same set of axes.

34. Graph $xy = k$ for $k = -4$ and $k = -12$ on the same set of axes.

TABLES

Table I   SQUARES, SQUARE ROOTS, AND PRIME FACTORS

Number	Square	Square root	Prime factors	Number	Square	Square root	Prime factors
1	1	1.000		51	2,601	7.141	$3 \cdot 17$
2	4	1.414	2	52	2,704	7.211	$2^2 \cdot 13$
3	9	1.732	3	53	2,809	7.280	53
4	16	2.000	2^2	54	2,916	7.348	$2 \cdot 3^3$
5	25	2.236	5	55	3,025	7.416	$5 \cdot 11$
6	36	2.449	$2 \cdot 3$	56	3,136	7.483	$2^3 \cdot 7$
7	49	2.646	7	57	3,249	7.550	$3 \cdot 19$
8	64	2.828	2^3	58	3,364	7.616	$2 \cdot 29$
9	81	3.000	3^2	59	3,481	7.681	59
10	100	3.162	$2 \cdot 5$	60	3,600	7.746	$2^2 \cdot 3 \cdot 5$
11	121	3.317	11	61	3,721	7.810	61
12	144	3.464	$2^2 \cdot 3$	62	3,844	7.874	$2 \cdot 31$
13	169	3.606	13	63	3,969	7.937	$3^2 \cdot 7$
14	196	3.742	$2 \cdot 7$	64	4,096	8.000	2^6
15	225	3.873	$3 \cdot 5$	65	4,225	8.062	$5 \cdot 13$
16	256	4.000	2^4	66	4,356	8.124	$2 \cdot 3 \cdot 11$
17	289	4.123	17	67	4,489	8.185	67
18	324	4.243	$2 \cdot 3^2$	68	4,624	8.246	$2^2 \cdot 17$
19	361	4.359	19	69	4,761	8.307	$3 \cdot 23$
20	400	4.472	$2^2 \cdot 5$	70	4,900	8.367	$2 \cdot 5 \cdot 7$
21	441	4.583	$3 \cdot 7$	71	5,041	8.426	71
22	484	4.690	$2 \cdot 11$	72	5,184	8.485	$2^3 \cdot 3^2$
23	529	4.796	23	73	5,329	8.544	73
24	576	4.899	$2^3 \cdot 3$	74	5,476	8.602	$2 \cdot 37$
25	625	5.000	5^2	75	5,625	8.660	$3 \cdot 5^2$
26	676	5.099	$2 \cdot 13$	76	5,776	8.718	$2^2 \cdot 19$
27	729	5.196	3^3	77	5,929	8.775	$7 \cdot 11$
28	784	5.292	$2^2 \cdot 7$	78	6,084	8.832	$2 \cdot 3 \cdot 13$
29	841	5.385	29	79	6,241	8.888	79
30	900	5.477	$2 \cdot 3 \cdot 5$	80	6,400	8.944	$2^4 \cdot 5$
31	961	5.568	31	81	6,561	9.000	3^4
32	1,024	5.657	2^5	82	6,724	9.055	$2 \cdot 41$
33	1,089	5.745	$3 \cdot 11$	83	6,889	9.110	83
34	1,156	5.831	$2 \cdot 17$	84	7,056	9.165	$2^2 \cdot 3 \cdot 7$
35	1,225	5.916	$5 \cdot 7$	85	7,225	9.220	$5 \cdot 17$
36	1,296	6.000	$2^2 \cdot 3^2$	86	7,396	9.274	$2 \cdot 43$
37	1,369	6.083	37	87	7,569	9.327	$3 \cdot 29$
38	1,444	6.164	$2 \cdot 19$	88	7,744	9.381	$2^3 \cdot 11$
39	1,521	6.245	$3 \cdot 13$	89	7,921	9.434	89
40	1,600	6.325	$2^3 \cdot 5$	90	8,100	9.487	$2 \cdot 3^2 \cdot 5$
41	1,681	6.403	41	91	8,281	9.539	$7 \cdot 13$
42	1,764	6.481	$2 \cdot 3 \cdot 7$	92	8,464	9.592	$2^2 \cdot 23$
43	1,849	6.557	43	93	8,649	9.644	$3 \cdot 31$
44	1,936	6.633	$2^2 \cdot 11$	94	8,836	9.695	$2 \cdot 47$
45	2,025	6.708	$3^2 \cdot 5$	95	9,025	9.747	$5 \cdot 19$
46	2,116	6.782	$2 \cdot 23$	96	9,216	9.798	$2^5 \cdot 3$
47	2,209	6.856	47	97	9,409	9.849	97
48	2,304	6.928	$2^4 \cdot 3$	98	9,604	9.899	$2 \cdot 7^2$
49	2,401	7.000	7^2	99	9,801	9.950	$3^2 \cdot 11$
50	2,500	7.071	$2 \cdot 5^2$	100	10,000	10.000	$2^2 \cdot 5^2$

Table II **VALUES OF LOG₁₀ x AND ANTILOG₁₀ x OR (10^x)**

x	0	1	2	3	4	5	6	7	8	9
1.0	.0000	.0043	.0086	.0128	.0170	.0212	.0253	.0294	.0334	.0374
1.1	.0414	.0453	.0492	.0531	.0569	.0607	.0645	.0682	.0719	.0755
1.2	.0792	.0828	.0864	.0899	.0934	.0969	.1004	.1038	.1072	.1106
1.3	.1139	.1173	.1206	.1239	.1271	.1303	.1335	.1367	.1399	.1430
1.4	.1461	.1492	.1523	.1553	.1584	.1614	.1644	.1673	.1703	.1732
1.5	.1761	.1790	.1818	.1847	.1875	.1903	.1931	.1959	.1987	.2014
1.6	.2041	.2068	.2095	.2122	.2148	.2175	.2201	.2227	.2253	.2279
1.7	.2304	.2330	.2355	.2380	.2405	.2430	.2455	.2480	.2504	.2529
1.8	.2553	.2577	.2601	.2625	.2648	.2672	.2695	.2718	.2742	.2765
1.9	.2788	.2810	.2833	.2856	.2878	.2900	.2923	.2945	.2967	.2989
2.0	.3010	.3032	.3054	.3075	.3096	.3118	.3139	.3160	.3181	.3201
2.1	.3222	.3243	.3263	.3284	.3304	.3324	.3345	.3365	.3385	.3404
2.2	.3424	.3444	.3464	.3483	.3502	.3522	.3541	.3560	.3579	.3598
2.3	.3617	.3636	.3655	.3674	.3692	.3711	.3729	.3747	.3766	.3784
2.4	.3802	.3820	.3838	.3856	.3874	.3892	.3909	.3927	.3945	.3962
2.5	.3979	.3997	.4014	.4031	.4048	.4065	.4082	.4099	.4116	.4133
2.6	.4150	.4166	.4183	.4200	.4216	.4232	.4249	.4265	.4281	.4298
2.7	.4314	.4330	.4346	.4362	.4378	.4393	.4409	.4425	.4440	.4456
2.8	.4472	.4487	.4502	.4518	.4533	.4548	.4564	.4579	.4594	.4609
2.9	.4624	.4639	.4654	.4669	.4683	.4698	.4713	.4728	.4742	.4757
3.0	.4771	.4786	.4800	.4814	.4829	.4843	.4857	.4871	.4886	.4900
3.1	.4914	.4928	.4942	.4955	.4969	.4983	.4997	.5011	.5024	.5038
3.2	.5051	.5065	.5079	.5092	.5105	.5119	.5132	.5145	.5159	.5172
3.3	.5185	.5198	.5211	.5224	.5237	.5250	.5263	.5276	.5289	.5302
3.4	.5315	.5328	.5340	.5353	.5366	.5378	.5391	.5403	.5416	.5428
3.5	.5441	.5453	.5465	.5478	.5490	.5502	.5514	.5527	.5539	.5551
3.6	.5563	.5575	.5587	.5599	.5611	.5623	.5635	.5647	.5658	.5670
3.7	.5682	.5694	.5705	.5717	.5729	.5740	.5752	.5763	.5775	.5786
3.8	.5798	.5809	.5821	.5832	.5843	.5855	.5866	.5877	.5888	.5899
3.9	.5911	.5922	.5933	.5944	.5955	.5966	.5977	.5988	.5999	.6010
4.0	.6021	.6031	.6042	.6053	.6064	.6075	.6085	.6096	.6107	.6117
4.1	.6128	.6138	.6149	.6160	.6170	.6180	.6191	.6201	.6212	.6222
4.2	.6232	.6243	.6253	.6263	.6274	.6284	.6294	.6304	.6314	.6325
4.3	.6335	.6345	.6355	.6365	.6375	.6385	.6395	.6405	.6415	.6425
4.4	.6435	.6444	.6454	.6464	.6474	.6484	.6493	.6503	.6513	.6522
4.5	.6532	.6542	.6551	.6561	.6571	.6580	.6590	.6599	.6609	.6618
4.6	.6628	.6637	.6646	.6656	.6665	.6675	.6684	.6693	.6702	.6712
4.7	.6721	.6730	.6739	.6749	.6758	.6767	.6776	.6785	.6794	.6803
4.8	.6812	.6821	.6830	.6839	.6848	.6857	.6866	.6875	.6884	.6893
4.9	.6902	.6911	.6920	.6928	.6937	.6946	.6955	.6964	.6972	.6981
5.0	.6990	.6998	.7007	.7016	.7024	.7033	.7042	.7050	.7059	.7067
5.1	.7076	.7084	.7093	.7101	.7110	.7118	.7126	.7135	.7143	.7152
5.2	.7160	.7168	.7177	.7185	.7193	.7202	.7210	.7218	.7226	.7235
5.3	.7243	.7251	.7259	.7267	.7275	.7284	.7292	.7300	.7308	.7316
5.4	.7324	.7332	.7340	.7348	.7356	.7364	.7372	.7380	.7388	.7396
x	0	1	2	3	4	5	6	7	8	9

(*continued next page*)

Table II (*continued*)

x	0	1	2	3	4	5	6	7	8	9
5.5	.7404	.7412	.7419	.7427	.7435	.7443	.7451	.7459	.7466	.7474
5.6	.7482	.7490	.7497	.7505	.7513	.7520	.7528	.7536	.7543	.7551
5.7	.7559	.7566	.7574	.7582	.7589	.7597	.7604	.7612	.7619	.7627
5.8	.7634	.7642	.7649	.7657	.7664	.7672	.7679	.7686	.7694	.7701
5.9	.7709	.7716	.7723	.7731	.7738	.7745	.7752	.7760	.7767	.7774
6.0	.7782	.7789	.7796	.7803	.7810	.7818	.7825	.7832	.7839	.7846
6.1	.7853	.7860	.7868	.7875	.7882	.7889	.7896	.7903	.7910	.7917
6.2	.7924	.7931	.7938	.7945	.7952	.7959	.7966	.7973	.7980	.7987
6.3	.7993	.8000	.8007	.8014	.8021	.8028	.8035	.8041	.8048	.8055
6.4	.8062	.8069	.8075	.8082	.8089	.8096	.8102	.8109	.8116	.8122
6.5	.8129	.8136	.8142	.8149	.8156	.8162	.8169	.8176	.8182	.8189
6.6	.8195	.8202	.8209	.8215	.8222	.8228	.8235	.8241	.8248	.8254
6.7	.8261	.8267	.8274	.8280	.8287	.8293	.8299	.8306	.8312	.8319
6.8	.8325	.8331	.8338	.8344	.8351	.8357	.8363	.8370	.8376	.8382
6.9	.8388	.8395	.8401	.8407	.8414	.8420	.8426	.8432	.8439	.8445
7.0	.8451	.8457	.8463	.8470	.8476	.8482	.8488	.8494	.8500	.8506
7.1	.8513	.8519	.8525	.8531	.8537	.8543	.8549	.8555	.8561	.8567
7.2	.8573	.8579	.8585	.8591	.8597	.8603	.8609	.8615	.8621	.8627
7.3	.8633	.8639	.8645	.8651	.8657	.8663	.8669	.8675	.8681	.8686
7.4	.8692	.8698	.8704	.8710	.8716	.8722	.8727	.8733	.8739	.8745
7.5	.8751	.8756	.8762	.8768	.8774	.8779	.8785	.8791	.8797	.8802
7.6	.8808	.8814	.8820	.8825	.8831	.8837	.8842	.8848	.8854	.8859
7.7	.8865	.8871	.8876	.8882	.8887	.8893	.8899	.8904	.8910	.8915
7.8	.8921	.8927	.8932	.8938	.8943	.8949	.8954	.8960	.8965	.8971
7.9	.8976	.8982	.8987	.8993	.8998	.9004	.9009	.9015	.9020	.9025
8.0	.9031	.9036	.9042	.9047	.9053	.9058	.9063	.9069	.9074	.9079
8.1	.9085	.9090	.9096	.9101	.9106	.9112	.9117	.9122	.9128	.9133
8.2	.9138	.9143	.9149	.9154	.9159	.9165	.9170	.9175	.9180	.9186
8.3	.9191	.9196	.9201	.9206	.9212	.9217	.9222	.9227	.9232	.9238
8.4	.9243	.9248	.9253	.9258	.9263	.9269	.9274	.9279	.9284	.9289
8.5	.9294	.9299	.9304	.9309	.9315	.9320	.9325	.9330	.9335	.9340
8.6	.9345	.9350	.9355	.9360	.9365	.9370	.9375	.9380	.9385	.9390
8.7	.9395	.9400	.9405	.9410	.9415	.9420	.9425	.9430	.9435	.9440
8.8	.9445	.9450	.9455	.9460	.9465	.9469	.9474	.9479	.9484	.9489
8.9	.9494	.9499	.9504	.9509	.9513	.9518	.9523	.9528	.9533	.9538
9.0	.9542	.9547	.9552	.9557	.9562	.9566	.9571	.9576	.9581	.9586
9.1	.9590	.9595	.9600	.9605	.9609	.9614	.9619	.9624	.9628	.9633
9.2	.9638	.9643	.9647	.9652	.9657	.9661	.9666	.9671	.9675	.9680
9.3	.9685	.9689	.9694	.9699	.9703	.9708	.9713	.9717	.9722	.9727
9.4	.9731	.9736	.9741	.9745	.9750	.9754	.9759	.9763	.9768	.9773
9.5	.9777	.9782	.9786	.9791	.9795	.9800	.9805	.9809	.9814	.9818
9.6	.9823	.9827	.9832	.9836	.9841	.9845	.9850	.9854	.9859	.9863
9.7	.9868	.9872	.9877	.9881	.9886	.9890	.9894	.9899	.9903	.9908
9.8	.9912	.9917	.9921	.9926	.9930	.9934	.9939	.9943	.9948	.9952
9.9	.9956	.9961	.9965	.9969	.9974	.9978	.9983	.9987	.9991	.9996
x	0	1	2	3	4	5	6	7	8	9

Table III   VALUES OF e^x

x	e^x	e^{-x}
0.00	1.0000	1.0000
0.01	1.0101	0.9901
0.02	1.0202	0.9802
0.03	1.0305	0.9705
0.04	1.0408	0.9608
0.05	1.0513	0.9512
0.06	1.0618	0.9418
0.07	1.0725	0.9324
0.08	1.0833	0.9231
0.09	1.0942	0.9139
0.10	1.1052	0.9048
0.11	1.1163	0.8958
0.12	1.1275	0.8869
0.13	1.1388	0.8781
0.14	1.1503	0.8694
0.15	1.1618	0.8607
0.16	1.1735	0.8521
0.17	1.1853	0.8437
0.18	1.1972	0.8353
0.19	1.2092	0.8270
0.20	1.2214	0.8187
0.21	1.2337	0.8106
0.22	1.2461	0.8025
0.23	1.2586	0.7945
0.24	1.2712	0.7866
0.25	1.2840	0.7788
0.26	1.2969	0.7711
0.27	1.3100	0.7634
0.28	1.3231	0.7558
0.29	1.3364	0.7483
0.30	1.3499	0.7408
0.31	1.3634	0.7334
0.32	1.3771	0.7261
0.33	1.3910	0.7190
0.34	1.4050	0.7118
0.35	1.4191	0.7047
0.36	1.4333	0.6977
0.37	1.4477	0.6907
0.38	1.4623	0.6839
0.39	1.4770	0.6771
0.40	1.4918	0.6703
0.41	1.5068	0.6636
0.42	1.5220	0.6570
0.43	1.5373	0.6505
0.44	1.5527	0.6440
0.45	1.5683	0.6376
0.46	1.5841	0.6313
0.47	1.6000	0.6250
0.48	1.6160	0.6188
0.49	1.6323	0.6126

x	e^x	e^{-x}
0.50	1.6487	0.6065
0.51	1.6653	0.6005
0.52	1.6820	0.5945
0.53	1.6990	0.5886
0.54	1.7160	0.5827
0.55	1.7333	0.5769
0.56	1.7507	0.5712
0.57	1.7683	0.5655
0.58	1.7860	0.5599
0.59	1.8040	0.5543
0.60	1.8221	0.5488
0.61	1.8404	0.5434
0.62	1.8590	0.5380
0.63	1.8776	0.5326
0.64	1.8965	0.5273
0.65	1.9155	0.5220
0.66	1.9348	0.5169
0.67	1.9542	0.5117
0.68	1.9739	0.5066
0.69	1.9937	0.5016
0.70	2.0138	0.4966
0.71	2.0340	0.4916
0.72	2.0544	0.4868
0.73	2.0751	0.4819
0.74	2.0959	0.4771
0.75	2.1170	0.4724
0.76	2.1383	0.4677
0.77	2.1598	0.4630
0.78	2.1815	0.4584
0.79	2.2034	0.4538
0.80	2.2255	0.4493
0.81	2.2479	0.4449
0.82	2.2705	0.4404
0.83	2.2933	0.4360
0.84	2.3164	0.4317
0.85	2.3396	0.4274
0.86	2.3632	0.4232
0.87	2.3869	0.4190
0.88	2.4109	0.4148
0.89	2.4351	0.4107
0.90	2.4596	0.4066
0.91	2.4843	0.4025
0.92	2.5093	0.3985
0.93	2.5345	0.3946
0.94	2.5600	0.3906
0.95	2.5857	0.3867
0.96	2.6117	0.3829
0.97	2.6379	0.3791
0.98	2.6645	0.3753
0.99	2.6912	0.3716

(continued next page)

Table III (*continued*)

x	e^x	e^{-x}
1.0	2.7183	0.3679
1.1	3.0042	0.3329
1.2	3.3201	0.3012
1.3	3.6693	0.2725
1.4	4.0552	0.2466
1.5	4.4817	0.2231
1.6	4.9530	0.2019
1.7	5.4739	0.1827
1.8	6.0496	0 1653
1.9	6.6859	0 1496
2.0	7.3891	0 1353
2.1	8.1662	0 1225
2.2	9.0250	0.1108
2.3	9.9742	0.1003
2.4	11.023	0.0907
2.5	12.182	0.0821
2.6	13.464	0.0743
2.7	14.880	0.0672
2.8	16.445	0.0608
2.9	18.174	0.0550
3.0	20.086	0.0498
3.1	22.198	0.0450
3.2	24.533	0.0408
3.3	27.113	0.0369
3.4	29.964	0.0334
3.5	33.115	0.0302
3.6	36.598	0.0273
3.7	40.447	0.0247
3.8	44.701	0.0224
3.9	49.402	0.0202
4.0	54.598	0.0183
4.1	60.340	0.0166
4.2	66.686	0.0150
4.3	73.700	0.0136
4.4	81.451	0.0123
4.5	90.017	0.0111
4.6	99.484	0.0101
4.7	109.95	0.0091
4.8	121.51	0.0082
4.9	134.29	0.0074
5.0	148.41	0.0067
5.1	164.02	0.0061
5.2	181.27	0.0055
5.3	200.34	0.0050
5.4	221.41	0.0045

x	e^x	e^{-x}
5.5	244.69	0.0041
5.6	270.43	0.0037
5.7	298.87	0.0034
5.8	330.30	0.0030
5.9	365.04	0.0027
6.0	403.43	0.0025
6.1	445.86	0.0022
6.2	492.75	0.0020
6.3	544.57	0.0018
6.4	601.85	0.0017
6.5	665.14	0.0015
6.6	735.10	0.0014
6.7	812.41	0.0012
6.8	897.85	0.0011
6.9	992.27	0.0010
7.0	1096.6	0.0009
7.1	1212.0	0.0008
7.2	1339.5	0.0007
7.3	1480.3	0.0007
7.4	1636.0	0.0006
7.5	1808.0	0.0006
7.6	1998.2	0.0005
7.7	2208.4	0.0005
7.8	2440.6	0.0004
7.9	2697.3	0.0004
8.0	2981.0	0.0003
8.1	3294.5	0.0003
8.2	3641.0	0.0003
8.3	4023.9	0.0002
8.4	4447.1	0.0002
8.5	4914.8	0.0002
8.6	5431.7	0.0002
8.7	6002.9	0.0002
8.8	6634.2	0.0002
8.9	7332.0	0.0001
9.0	8103.1	0.0001
9.1	8955.3	0.0001
9.2	9897.1	0.0001
9.3	10938	0.0001
9.4	12088	0.0001
9.5	13360	0.0001
9.6	14765	0.0001
9.7	16318	0.0001
9.8	18034	0.0001
9.9	19930	0.0001

Table IV   VALUES OF ln x

x	ln x	x	ln x	x	ln x
		4.5	1.5041	9.0	2.1972
		4.6	1.5261	9.1	2.2083
0.1	−2.3026	4.7	1.5476	9.2	2.2192
0.2	−1.6094	4.8	1.5686	9 3	2.2300
0.3	−1.2040	4.9	1.5892	9.4	2.2407
0.4	−0.9163				
		5.0	1.6094	9.5	2.2513
0.5	−0.6931	5.1	1.6292	9.6	2.2618
0.6	−0.5108	5.2	1.6487	9.7	2.2721
0.7	−0.3567	5.3	1.6677	9.8	2.2824
0.8	−0.2231	5.4	1.6864	9.9	2.2925
0.9	−0.1054				
		5.5	1.7047	10	2.3026
1.0	0.0000	5.6	1.7228	11	2.3979
1.1	0.0953	5.7	1.7405	12	2.4849
1.2	0.1823	5.8	1.7579	13	2.5649
1.3	0.2624	5.9	1.7750	14	2.6391
1.4	0.3365				
		6.0	1.7918	15	2.7081
1.5	0.4055	6.1	1.8083	16	2.7726
1.6	0.4700	6.2	1.8245	17	2.8332
1.7	0.5306	6.3	1.8405	18	2.8904
1.8	0.5878	6.4	1.8563	19	2.9444
1.9	0.6419				
		6.5	1.8718	20	2.9957
2.0	0.6931	6.6	1.8871	25	3.2189
2.1	0.7419	6.7	1.9021	30	3.4012
2.2	0.7885	6.8	1.9169	35	3.5553
2.3	0.8329	6.9	1.9315	40	3.6889
2.4	0.8755				
		7.0	1.9459	45	3.8067
2.5	0.9163	7.1	1.9601	50	3.9120
2.6	0.9555	7.2	1.9741	55	4.0073
2.7	0.9933	7.3	1.9879	60	4.0943
2.8	1.0296	7.4	2.0015	65	4.1744
2.9	1.0647				
		7.5	2.0149	70	4.2485
3.0	1.0986	7.6	2.0281	75	4.3175
3.1	1.1314	7.7	2.0412	80	4.3820
3.2	1.1632	7.8	2.0541	85	4.4427
3.3	1.1939	7.9	2.0669	90	4.4998
3.4	1.2238				
		8.0	2.0794	100	4.6052
3.5	1.2528	8.1	2.0919	110	4.7005
3.6	1.2809	8.2	2.1041	120	4.7875
3.7	1.3083	8.3	2.1163	130	4.8676
3.8	1.3350	8.4	2.1282	140	4.9416
3.9	1.3610				
		8.5	2.1401	150	5.0106
4.0	1.3863	8.6	2.1518	160	5.0752
4.1	1.4110	8.7	2.1633	170	5.1358
4.2	1.4351	8.8	2.1748	180	5.1930
4.3	1.4586	8.9	2.1861	190	5.2470
4.4	1.4816				

FORMULAS FROM GEOMETRY

TRIANGLES

$$P = a + b + c$$
$$\angle A + \angle B + \angle C = 180°$$

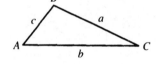

Equilateral triangle with equal sides s:

$$\angle A = \angle B = \angle C = 60°$$
$$h = \frac{s}{2}\sqrt{3}, \quad h \text{ bisects base}$$
$$A = \frac{\sqrt{3}}{4}s^2$$

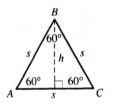

Isosceles triangle with equal sides s:

$$\angle A = \angle B \qquad h \text{ bisects base}$$

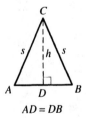

$$AD = DB$$

Right triangle with hypotenuse c:

$$c^2 = a^2 + b^2 \qquad \text{Pythagorean Theorem}$$

QUADRILATERALS

Trapezoid:
exactly two sides parallel

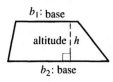

$A = \frac{1}{2}h(b_1 + b_2)$

Parallelogram:
opposite sides parallel

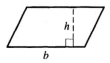

Measures of opposite
angles equal; lengths
of opposite sides
equal
$A = hb$

Rectangle:
parallelogram with one
right angle (other three
angles are also right
angles)

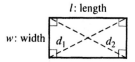

$A = lw$
$p = 2l + 2w$
$d_1 = d_2$

Square:
rectangle with all sides
equal

$A = s^2$
$p = 4s$
$d_1 = d_2 = \sqrt{2}s$
d_1 perpendicular to d_2

CIRCLE

r: **radius** $d = 2r$
d: **diameter** $c = 2\pi r$
c: **circumference** $c = \pi d$
A: **area** $A = \pi r^2$

SOLIDS

Right circular cylinder:
Parallel circular bases;
elements (line segments
perpendicular to the
bases) on the lateral
surface are parallel.

Volume:
$$V = Bh$$
$$= \pi r^2 h$$

Lateral surface area:
$$S = 2\pi r h$$

Pyramid:
Base is a closed
geometric figure.

Volume:
$$V = \tfrac{1}{3} Bh$$

Right circular cone:
Base is a circle.

Volume:
$$V = \tfrac{1}{3} Bh$$
$$= \tfrac{1}{3} \pi r^2 h$$

Lateral surface area:
$$S = \pi r s$$

Sphere:
Points are equidistant
from a given point, the
center.

Volume:
$$V = \tfrac{4}{3} \pi r^3$$

Surface area:
$$S = 4\pi r^2$$

Answers to Odd-Numbered Section Exercises and All Review Exercises

Exercise Set 1.1 (page 6) **1.** $\{3, 4, 5\}$

3. $\{0, 1, 2\}$ **5.** $\{5, 6, 7, \ldots\}$ **7.** $\{5, 7, 9\}$

9. finite **11.** finite **13.** infinite **15.** 6

17. y **19.** r **21.** $8 > 5$ **23.** $-6 < -4$

25. $x + 1 < 0$ **27.** $x - 4 \leqslant 0$ **29.** $-2 < y < 3$

31. $1 \leqslant x < 7$ **33.** $-2 < 8$ **35.** $-7 > -13$

37. $1\frac{1}{2} = \frac{3}{2}$ **39.** $3 > 0 > -4$

41.

43.

45.

47.

49. **51.** $\{0, 8\}$

53. $\{-\sqrt{15}\}$ **55.** $\left\{-5, -\sqrt{15}, -3.44, -\frac{2}{3}\right\}$

57. $\varnothing$ and $\{\ \}$ **59.** $x \geqslant 0$

Exercise Set 1.2 (page 13) **1.** 12 **3.** $3y$

5. $t \cdot 4$ **7.** 1 **9.** 1 **11.** $3x; 3y$ **13.** 5

15. -3 **17.** 3 **19.** $-x$ **21.** 3 **23.** 4

25. -2 **27.** -5 **29.** x if $x \geqslant 0; -x$ if $x < 0$

31. 11 **33.** 6 **35.** 3 **37.** -7 **39.** 5

41. -3 **43.** -9 **45.** 6 **47.** 2 **49.** 11

51. -10 **53.** 10 **55.** 3 **57.** 7 **59.** -12

61. 12 **63.** 24 **65.** -20 **67.** 24 **69.** 0

71. -24 **73.** -4 **75.** -13 **77.** 3

79. 0 **81.** undefined **83.** 4 **85.** $7 \cdot \frac{1}{8}$

87. $3 \cdot \frac{1}{8}$ **89.** $\frac{3}{2}$ **91.** $\frac{3x}{y}$ **93.** x **95.** $x + y$

97. **a.** If $a > -b$ or $b > -a$ **b.** If $a > b$

99. negative **101.** positive **103.** $x \geqslant 0; \ x < 0$

Exercise Set 1.3 (page 16) **1.** 20 **3.** 0

5. -17 **7.** -13 **9.** -2 **11.** 6

13. -44 **15.** 5 **17.** -2 **19.** -2

21. 60 **23.** 10 **25.** 2 **27.** undefined

29. 1 **31.** 0 **33.** 100 **35.** 4

37. 1080 **39.** \$1016

41. **a.** 7.2 cubic meters **b.** 6.2 square centimeters

43. **a.** 2622.5 cubic meters **b.** 1902.5 square inches

Review Exercises (page 19) **1.** $\{-3, 0, 1\}$

2. $\{0, 1\}$ **3.** $a < c$ **4.** $a \leqslant 7$ **5.** $a < b < c$

6. $y \geqslant 6$ **7.**

8. **9.** $2 + x$

10. $18 + t$ **11.** $\frac{1}{3}$ **12.** 1

13. **a.** 14 **b.** 8 **14.** **a.** -6 **b.** 5

15. **a.** -36 **b.** 0 **c.** 21 **d.** 24

16. **a.** -27 **b.** 0 **c.** 24 **d.** -72

17. **a.** 12 **b.** 0 **c.** -8 **d.** -8

18. **a.** $-7 \cdot \frac{1}{5}$ **b.** $24 \cdot \frac{1}{7}$ **c.** $-4 \cdot \frac{1}{5}$ **d.** $8 \cdot \frac{1}{3}$

19. **a.** $\frac{2x}{3}$ **b.** $\frac{3y}{4}$ **c.** $\frac{x}{3}$ **d.** $\frac{y}{4}$

20. **a.** -11 **b.** -12 **c.** -3 **d.** 48

21. **a.** 7 **b.** -24 **c.** 4 **d.** 26

22. **a.** -21 **b.** 2 **c.** -4 **d.** -36

23. **a.** -3 **b.** -2 **c.** -11 **d.** 11

24. **a.** 3 **b.** 6 **25.** **a.** 5 **b.** 1

26. **a.** 16 **b.** -11 **27.** 4 **28.** 44

29. 1080 **30.** 5 **31.** 6 **32.** -26 **33.** 2

34. -3

Exercise Set 2.1 (page 23)

1. binomial; degree 3; 2 and -1

3. monomial; degree 4; 5

5. trinomial; degree 2; 3 and -1

7. trinomial; degree 3; 1, -2, and -1 **9.** -25

11. 9 **13.** -2 **15.** 50 **17.** -2

19. -5 **21.** 7 **23.** 13 **25.** 5 **27.** 0

29. 1 **31.** 64 **33.** 8 **35.** 54

37. $-1; -21$ **39.** $-4; 16$ **41.** $Q(x)$ **43.** -3

45. three **47.** 12; 2 **49.** -10

Exercise Set 2.2 (page 28) 1. $7x^2$ 3. $-3y^2$

5. z^2 **7.** $7x^2y - 2x$ **9.** $6r^2 + 4r$

11. $s^2 - 4s$ **13.** $t^2 + 2t - 1$ **15.** $-2u^2 - u - 3$

17. $-x^2 - 4x + 7$ **19.** $-t^3 - 4t^2 + t + 1$

21. $a^2 - 6a - 3$ **23.** $8x^2y + 3xy^2 - xy$

25. $-2y - 1$ **27.** $2 - x$ **29.** $x - 1$

31. $-x^2 - 3x - 1$ **33.** $2x - y$ **35.** $-4x - 5$

37. 6 **39.** $-2a^2 - 2a$ **41.** $4a + 4$

43. $4a + 4$ **45.** $-4x^2 - 11x$ **47.** $-2x^2 + x - 3$

49. $b^2 + 3b + 1$ **51.** $2x - 1$ **53.** -1

55. $2x - 1$ **57.** -1

59. Let $x = 2$: $-(2 + 1) \neq -2 + 1$

Exercise Set 2.3 (page 34) 1. $\{7\}$ 3. $\{7\}$

5. $\{240\}$ **7.** $\{2890\}$ **9.** $\left\{\frac{8}{3}\right\}$ **11.** $\{4\}$

13. $\left\{-\frac{13}{2}\right\}$ **15.** $\left\{\frac{16}{3}\right\}$ **17.** $\{-6\}$ **19.** $\left\{\frac{8}{3}\right\}$

21. $\{11\}$ **23.** $\{24\}$ **25.** $\{15\}$ **27.** 25.8

29. 73.6 **31.** 4 **33.** $m = \frac{f}{a}$ **35.** $p = \frac{l}{rt}$

37. $w = \frac{P - 2l}{2}$ **39.** $g = \frac{v - k}{t}$

41. $h = \frac{S}{2\pi} - r$ or $h = \frac{S - 2\pi r}{2\pi}$

43. $n = \frac{l - a}{d} + 1$ or $n = \frac{l - a + d}{d}$

45. $t = \frac{A - P}{Pr}$ **47.** 16; -9 **49.** 400; -200

51. $d/t; d/r$ **53.** $180 - B - C$; $180 - A - B$

55. $-4 + x$; $x = 4$

Exercise Set 2.4 (page 39) 1. $3x + 5 = 26$

3. $4x - 6 = 22$ **5.** $2x + x = 21$ **7.** $\frac{x + 2}{4} = 5$

Note: Equations for Exercises 9–33 are not unique. The answers given can be obtained by using different equations.

9. **a.** Number of students that applied: x
   b. $0.75x = 600$
   c. 800 students

11. **a.** Total sales: x
   b. $0.02x = 300$
   c. \$15,000

13. **a.** Number of students enrolled: x
   b. $0.30x = 12$
   c. 40 students

15. **a.** Total number of bats: x
   b. $0.95x = 1710$
   (If 5% of bats are discarded, 95% are not discarded.)
   c. 1800 bats

17. **a.** Total number of employees: x
   b. $0.06x = 9$
   (If 94% were present, 6% were absent.)
   c. 150 employees

19. **a.** Length of shorter piece: x
   Length of longer piece: $x + 6$
   b. $x + (x + 6) = 24$
   c. 9 feet and 15 feet

21. **a.** Number of votes of loser: x
   Number of votes of winner: $x + 140$
   b. $x + (x + 140) = 620$
   c. Loser: 240 votes
   Winner: 380 votes

23. **a.** Number of votes of winner: x
   Number of votes
   of second candidate: $x - 210$
   Number of votes
   of third candidate: $x - 490$

b. $x + (x - 210) + (x - 490) = 6560$

c. Winner: 2420 votes
Second candidate: 2210 votes
Third candidate: 1930 votes

25. a. Measure of smallest angle: x
Measure of second angle: $2x$
Measure of third angle: $3x + 12$

b. $x + 2x + (3x + 12) = 180$

c. Smallest angle: $28°$
Second angle: $56°$
Third angle: $96°$

27. a. Measure of smallest angle: x
Measure of second angle: $x + 10$
Measure of third angle: $2x + 10$

b. $x + (x + 10) + (2x + 10) = 180$

c. Smallest angle: $40°$
Second angle: $50°$
Third angle: $90°$

29. a. Length of smallest side: x
Length of each equal side: $x + 15.6$

b. $x + (x + 15.6) + (x + 15.6) = 66.8$

c. Smallest side: 11.9 centimeters
Each equal side: 27.5 centimeters

31. a. Length of side of original square: x

b. $(x + 5.1)^2 - x^2 = 85.7$

c. 5.85 centimeters

33. a. Width of table: x
Length of table: $x + 4$

b. $2x + 2(x + 4) = 28$

c. Width: 5 feet
Length: 9 feet

35. 2600   **37.** $72.00   **39.** $80°$

Exercise Set 2.5 (page 44)

1. a. Number of quarters: x
Number of dimes: $2x$

b. $0.25x + 0.10(2x) = 3.60$

c. 8 quarters; 16 dimes

3. a. Number of dimes: d
Number of quarters: $d + 12$

b. $10d + 25(d + 12) = 1245$

c. 27 dimes; 39 quarters

5. a. Number of first-class passengers: f
Number of tourist passengers: $42 - f$

b. $80f + 64(42 - f) = 2880$

c. 12 first-class; 30 tourist

7. a. Pounds of less expensive brand: x
Pounds of more expensive brand: $x + 2$

b. $1.20x + 1.40(x + 2) = 28.80$

c. Less expensive brand: 10 pounds;
More expensive brand: 12 pounds

9. a. Number of children's tickets: x
Number of adult tickets: $82 - x$

b. $2.50x + 4.00(82 - x) = 310$

c. 12 children's tickets; 70 adult tickets

11. a. Amount invested at 4%: x
Amount invested at 6%: $x + 4000$

b. $0.04x + 0.06(x + 4000) = \$920$

c. 4% investment: \$6800
6% investment: \$10,800

13. a. Amount invested at 6%: x
Amount invested at 4%: $42,000 - x$

b. $0.06x = 0.04(42,000 - x)$

c. 6% investment: \$16,800
4% investment: \$25,200

15. a. Amount invested at 5%: x
Amount invested at 6%: $8000 - x$

b. $0.05x + 0.06(8000 - x) = 430$

c. 5% investment: \$5000
6% investment: \$3000

17. a. Amount invested at 7%: x

b. $0.04(8000) + 0.07x = 0.05(8000 + x)$

c. \$4000

19. a. Number of quarts of 10% solution: x

b. $0.10x + 0.40(20) = 0.30(x + 20)$

c. 10 quarts

21. a. Number of ounces: x

b. $0.40x + 0.60(60 - x) = 0.50(60)$

c. 30 ounces

23. a. Liters of 30% solution: x

b. $0.30x + 0.12(40) = 0.20(x + 40)$

c. 32 liters

25. a. Liters of pure alcohol: x

b. $x + 0.45(12) = 0.60(x + 12)$

c. 4.5 liters

27. a. Cost for grading: x

b. $0.03(140,000) = x$

c. \$4200

29. a. Gallons of 15% solution: x

b. $0.15x + 0.60(80) = 0.55(x + 80)$

c. 10 gallons

31. a. Amount invested at 6%: x
Amount invested at 4%: $2x$

b. $0.06x + 0.04(2x) = 490$

c. 6% investment: \$4000
4% investment: \$8000

33. a. Length left: x
    b. $10.00 - 1.06 - 2.12 - 1.88 - 3(0.06) = x$
    c. 4.76 inches

35. a. Cost of 1990 model: x
      Cost of 1992 model: $x + 120$
    b. $x + x + 120 = 940$
    c. 1990 model: \$410
      1992 model: \$530

Review Exercises (page 46)

1. a. monomial; degree 3   **b.** trinomial; degree 2
2. a. binomial; degree 5   **b.** trinomial; degree 4
3. $\dfrac{1}{5}$ **4.** 7   **5. a.** 8   **b.** 13
6. a. -2 **b.** -14
7. a. $x + y - z$ **b.** $2x^2 - 2z^2 - x + 3y$
8. a. $3x - 3y + z$ **b.** $-2x - y - 6z$
9. a. $-2x^2 - 4y - z^2 - z$
    b. $-2x^2 + 2x - y^2 - y + 2z$
10. a. $2x - 5$ **b.** $-x^2 - 2x$
11. a. $2y^2 - 1$ **b.** $2y + 1$
12. a. $-z$ **b.** 2   **13.** $\{1\}$ **14.** $\{600\}$
15. $\left\{\dfrac{2}{3}\right\}$ **16.** $\{-5\}$ **17.** $\{5\}$ **18.** $\{8\}$
19. $\left\{\dfrac{4}{11}\right\}$ **20.** $\left\{-\dfrac{2}{5}\right\}$ **21.** $\{5\}$ **22.** $\{200\}$
23. $\{9\}$ **24.** $\{17\}$ **25.** $n = \dfrac{l - a + d}{d}$
26. a. $\dfrac{2s - k}{t}$ **27.** $R = \dfrac{S + 2\pi r}{2\pi}$ or $R = \dfrac{S}{2\pi} + r$
28. $F = \dfrac{9C + 160}{5}$ or $F = \dfrac{9C}{5} + 32$
29. a. Number of serves: n
    b. $0.26n = 52$
    c. 200 times
30. a. Total salary: x
    b. $x - 0.20x = 180$
    c. \$225
31. a. Amount invested at 5%: x
      Amount invested at 6%: $x + 1000$
    b. $0.05x + 0.06(x + 1000) = 324$
    c. 5% investment: \$2400
      6% investment: \$3400
32. a. Number of 29-cent stamps: x
      Number of 2-cent stamps: $x + 6$
    b. $0.29x + 0.02(x + 6) = 3.84$

    c. Number of 29-cent stamps: 12
      Number of 2-cent stamps: 18
33. a. Amount of 60% copper alloy: x
    b. $0.60x + 0.20(4 - x) = 0.35(4)$
    c. 1.5 pounds
34. a. Cost of renting car: x
    b. $x = 7(28) + 0.16(480)$
    c. \$272.80
35. a. Net price: x
    b. $24 - 0.15(24) = x$
    c. \$20.40

Cumulative Exercises (page 48)   **1.** $-2.3, 0, \dfrac{4}{3}$

2.   **3.** $x\left(\dfrac{1}{7}\right)$
4. $\dfrac{x + y}{3}$ **5.** -5 **6.** -1 **7.** 2   **8.** 0
9. 161   **10.** 7.7   **11.** 13   **12.** -4
13. $-3x^2$ **14.** $-2x^2 + 4xy - y^2$ **15.** $\left\{\dfrac{3}{2}\right\}$
16. $\{-8\}$ **17.** $\{93\}$ **18.** $\{6000\}$
19. $R_0 = \dfrac{R}{1 + at}$ **20.** $t = \dfrac{R - R_0}{R_0 a}$
21. Computer B: \$170
    Computer A: \$290
22. 240, 120, and 80 votes, respectively
23. 13-cent bolts: 6
    10-cent bolts: 18
24. 4% investment: \$2000
    5% investment: \$1600
25. 10 quarts

Exercise Set 3.1 (page 51)   **1.** $-14t^3$

3. $-40a^3b^3c$ **5.** $44x^3y^4z^2$ **7.** $6x^5y^5$
9. $-2r^6s^4t^2$ **11.** $3x^2y^6z^4$ **13.** $6r^3t^4$
15. $6x^4$ **17.** $6z^5$ **19.** x^6 **21.** x^4y^4
23. y^6z^3 **25.** $8x^3z^6$ **27.** $4x^2y^4z^2$
29. $-8x^3y^9z^3$ **31.** $x^4y^2 + x^3y^3$
33. $4x^2y^4z^2 - x^2y^2z^4$ **35.** $x^2y^2 - x^3y^4$
37. $4x^5y^3 + xy^2$ **39.** $8x^2y^2 - 3x^5y^2$
41. $x^3y^3 - x^4y^2$ **43.** $6r^3t^3 + 4r^2t^5$
45. $a^4b - a^3b^2 + a^2b^3$ **47.** $-2x^3y - x^3y^2 + xy^2$
49. $r^5t^2 + 2r^4t^4 - r^2t^5$ **51.** $a^3b^2 + 2a^2b^3$
53. $-a^2b^2$ **55.** $a^4 - a^3b + 2a^2b^2$
57. $a^3 + a^2b + b^3$ **59.** $2a^2b^2c$

Exercise Set 3.2 (page 54) **1.** $2 \cdot 2 \cdot 2$ **3.** $7 \cdot 7$
5. prime   **7.** $-2 \cdot 2 \cdot 3$ **9.** $2 \cdot 2 \cdot 2 \cdot 7$
11. $-2 \cdot 2 \cdot 2 \cdot 2 \cdot 3$ **13.** $2(x + 3)$ **15.** $4x(x + 2)$
17. $3x(x - y + 1)$ **19.** $6(4a^2 + 2a - 1)$
21. $2x(x^3 - 2x + 4)$ **23.** $3z^2(4z^2 + 5z - 3)$
25. $a(y^2 + by + b)$ **27.** $3mn(m - 2n + 4)$
29. $3ac(5ac - 4 + 2c^2)$ **31.** $(a + b)(a + 3)$
33. $(2x - y)(x + 3)$ **35.** $(2y - x)(a + b)$
37. $(x + 3)(x + 4)$ **39.** $4(x - 2)(x - 4)$
41. $(2x - 1)^2(x + 1)$ **43.** $-5x(x - 5)$
45. $2(x + 3)(3x - 1)$ **47.** $-4(x - 1)$
49. $-(r - 7)$ **51.** $-(b - 2a)$ **53.** $-2(x - 1)$
55. $-a(b + c)$ **57.** $-(-2x + 1)$
59. $-(-x + y - z)$ **61.** $x(y - 1)$ **63.** $y(x - 5)$
65. $a(a - b - c)$ **67.** $3a^2$ **69.** $a(2a - b - 2c)$

Exercise Set 3.3 (page 57) **1.** $x^2 - 9$
3. $n^2 + 10n + 16$ **5.** $r^2 + 3r - 10$
7. $y^2 - 7y + 6$ **9.** $2z^2 - 5z - 3$ **11.** $8r^2 + 2r - 3$
13. $4x^2 - a^2$ **15.** $3x^2 + 3x - 60$
17. $x^2 + 6x + 9$ **19.** $-3x^2 + 6x - 3$
21. $y^3 - y + 6$ **23.** $x^3 + 2x^2 - 21x + 18$
25. $x^3 - 7x + 6$ **27.** $z^3 - 7z - 6$
29. $6x^3 + x^2 - 8x + 6$ **31.** $2x^2 + 12x + 2$
33. $-2x^3 + 12x^2 - 11x$ **35.** $-8x^3 + 6x^2 + 6x$
37. $8x - 16$ **39.** $-4x^2 - 4x - 10$
41. $(x + a)(x^2 - ax + a^2)$
$\quad = x(x^2 - ax + a^2) + a(x^2 - ax + a^2)$
$\quad = (x^3 - ax^2 + a^2x) + (ax^2 - a^2x + a^3)$
$\quad = x^3 - ax^2 + a^2x + ax^2 - a^2x + a^3$
$\quad = x^3 + a^3$
43. Substituting 1 for x and 2 for y gives
$\quad (1 + 2)^2 \overset{?}{=} 1^2 + 2^2; \quad 9 \neq 5$
45. **a.** $x; \quad x + 2; \quad x + 4$
$\quad$ **b.** $18\pi x^2; \quad 18\pi(x + 2)^2; \quad 18\pi(x + 4)^2$
$\quad$ **c.** $54\pi x^2 + 216\pi x + 360\pi$

Exercise Set 3.4 (page 62) **1.** $(x + 3)(x + 2)$
3. $(y - 4)(y - 3)$ **5.** $(x - 3)(x + 2)$
7. $(y - 5)(y + 2)$ **9.** $(2x - 1)(x + 2)$
11. $(4x - 1)(x + 2)$ **13.** $(3x - 1)(x - 1)$
15. $(3x - 8)(3x + 1)$ **17.** $(5x - 3)(2x + 1)$
19. $(2x + 3)(2x + 3)$ or $(2x + 3)^2$
21. $(3x - a)(x - 2a)$ **23.** $(3xy + 1)(3xy + 1)$
25. $(x - 5)(x + 5)$ **27.** $(xy - 1)(xy + 1)$
29. $(y^2 - 3)(y^2 + 3)$ **31.** $(x - 2y)(x + 2y)$

33. $(2x - 5y)(2x + 5y)$ **35.** $(4xy - 1)(4xy + 1)$
37. $3(x + 2)(x + 2)$ or $3(x + 2)^2$
39. $2a(a - 5)(a + 1)$
41. $4(a - b)(a - b)$ or $4(a - b)^2$
43. $4y(x - 3)(x + 3)$ **45.** $x(4 + x)(3 - x)$
47. $x^2y^2(x - 1)(x + 1)$ **49.** $(y^2 + 1)(y^2 + 2)$
51. $(3x^2 + 1)(x^2 + 2)$ **53.** $(x^2 + 4)(x - 1)(x + 1)$
55. $(x - 2)(x + 2)(x - 1)(x + 1)$
57. $(2a^2 + 1)(a - 1)(a + 1)$ **59.** $(3a^2 + 1)(2a^2 - 5)$
61. $(x + 2y)(x - y)$ **63.** $(2x + y)(x + y)$
65. $2(3x - y)(x + y)$ **67.** $(x^2 + y^2)(x - y)(x + y)$
69. $(x^2 + y)(x^2 - 2y)$

Exercise Set 3.5 (page 65) **1.** $\{-2, 5\}$
3. $\left\{-\dfrac{5}{2}, 2\right\}$ **5.** $\left\{0, -\dfrac{1}{2}\right\}$ **7.** $\left\{6, -\dfrac{3}{2}\right\}$
9. $\left\{2, -\dfrac{1}{2}\right\}$ **11.** $\left\{\dfrac{5}{2}, -\dfrac{2}{3}\right\}$ **13.** $\{0, 3\}$
15. $\{0, 3\}$ **17.** $\{3, -3\}$ **19.** $\{3, -3\}$
21. $\left\{\dfrac{2}{3}, -\dfrac{2}{3}\right\}$ **23.** $\left\{\dfrac{3}{2}, -\dfrac{3}{2}\right\}$ **25.** $\{4, 1\}$
27. $\{7, -2\}$ **29.** $\{1\}$ **31.** $\left\{\dfrac{1}{2}, 1\right\}$
33. $\{3, -2\}$ **35.** $\{1, -6\}$ **37.** $\{1, -5\}$
39. $\left\{\dfrac{1}{2}, -3\right\}$ **41.** $\{6, -3\}$ **43.** $\{3\}$
45. $\{1, 4\}$ **47.** $\{3, -3\}$ **49.** $x^2 + x - 2 = 0$
51. $x^2 + 5x = 0$ **53.** $x^2 + 6x + 9 = 0$
55. $x^2 - ax - bx + ab = 0$ **57.** $x = \pm 2b$
59. $x = 4a, \quad x = -a$ **61.** $x = a, \quad x = b$
63. $x = -a, \quad x = -b/2$ **65.** $x = 2a/b, \quad x = -2a/b$

Exercise Set 3.6 (page 68)
1. **a.** Smaller positive number: x
$\qquad$ Larger positive number: $x + 3$
$\quad$ **b.** $x(x + 3) = 40$
$\quad$ **c.** 5 and 8
3. **a.** A negative integer: x
$\qquad$ Next consecutive integer: $x + 1$
$\quad$ **b.** $x^2 + (x + 1)^2 = 61$
$\quad$ **c.** -6 and -5
5. **a.** A positive integer: x
$\qquad$ Next consecutive integer: $x + 1$
$\qquad$ Next consecutive integer: $x + 2$
$\quad$ **b.** $x^2 + (x + 1)^2 + (x + 2)^2 = 149$
$\quad$ **c.** 6, 7, and 8

7. **a.** Width: x
   Length: $x + 2$
   b. $x(x + 2) = 63$
   c. Width: 7 meters; length: 9 meters

9. **a.** Length of altitude: x
   Length of base: $x - 3$
   b. $\frac{1}{2}x(x - 3) = 27$
   c. Altitude: 9 inches
   Base: 6 inches

11. **a.** Shorter side: x
    Longer side: $x + 2$
    b. $x^2 + (x + 2)^2 = 10^2$
    c. Shorter side: 6 centimeters
    Longer side: 8 centimeters

13. **a.** Time to reach 28 feet on the way down: t
    b. $28 = 64t - 16t^2$
    c. $3\frac{1}{2}$ seconds (reaches 28 feet on the way up in $\frac{1}{2}$ second)

15. **a.** Time to move 24 cm in a positive direction: t
    b. $24 = t^2 - 5t$
    c. 8 seconds

17. **a.** Width: x
    Length: $2x$
    b. $(x - 4)(2x - 4) = 48$
    c. Width: 8 inches; length: 16 inches

19. **a.** Width of border: x
    b. $2x(25 + x) + 50x = 310$
    c. 3 meters

21. **a.** Width of tray: x
    Length of tray: $x + 2$
    Height of tray: 2
    b. $2x(x + 2) = 160$
    c. Width: 8 centimeters
    Length: 10 centimeters
    Height: 2 centimeters

Exercise Set 3.7 (page 70) **1.** $(a + b)(x + 1)$
3. $(ax + 1)(x + a)$ 5. $(x + a)(x + y)$
7. $(3a - c)(b - d)$ 9. $(3x + y)(1 - 2x)$
11. $(a^2 + 2b^2)(a - 2b)$ 13. $(x + 2y)(x - 1)$
15. $(2a^2 - 1)(b + 3)$ 17. $(x^3 - 3)(y^2 + 1)$
19. $(x + 2)(x^2 + 4)$ 21. $(2x - 3)(x^2 + 1)$
23. $(x - 1)(x^2 + 1)$ 25. $(x + 2 - y)(x + 2 + y)$
27. $(x + 1 - y)(x + 1 + y)$
29. $(y - x + 1)(y + x - 1)$

31. $(2x + 1 - 2y)(2x + 1 + 2y)$
33. $(x - 1)(x^2 + x + 1)$
35. $(2x + y)(4x^2 - 2xy + y^2)$
37. $(a - 2b)(a^2 + 2ab + 4b^2)$
39. $(xy - 1)(x^2y^2 + xy + 1)$
41. $(3a + 4b)(9a^2 - 12ab + 16b^2)$
43. $(4ab - 1)(16a^2b^2 + 4ab + 1)$
45. $(2x - y)(x^2 - xy + y^2)$
47. $[(x + 1) - 1][(x + 1)^2 + (x + 1) + 1]$
    $= x(x^2 + 3x + 3)$
49. $[(x + 1) - (x - 1)][(x + 1)^2 + (x + 1)(x - 1)$
    $+ (x - 1)^2] = 2(3x^2 + 1)$
51. $ac - ad + bd - bc$
    $= (ac - ad) - (bc - bd)$
    $= a(c - d) - b(c - d)$
    $= (a - b)(c - d);$
    $ac - ad + bd - bc$
    $= (bd - ad) - (bc - ac)$
    $= (b - a)d - (b - a)c$
    $= (b - a)(d - c)$

Review Exercises (page 72)
1. **a.** $-6x^3y^4$ **b.** $-6x^2y^3z^3$
2. **a.** $-8x^6y^9z^3$ **b.** $x^3y^6 - 4x^6y^2$
3. **a.** $9x^4y^5$ **b.** $2x^4y^5$
4. **a.** $6x^3y^4z^2$ **b.** $6x^2y^4z^3$
5. **a.** $5x^3y^2 - x^4y^3$ **b.** $5x^3y^3 - 3x^3y^2$
6. **a.** $5x^2y^2 + 2x^3y$ **b.** $6x^2y^3$
7. **a.** $x^3y^2 - x^2y^3$ **b.** $-2x^2y^3 + 2xy^4$
8. **a.** $x^4y - x^3y^2 + x^2y^3$ **b.** $-x^4y^2 - x^2y^4 + xy^5$
9. **a.** $-3x - 15$ **b.** $x^2 + 5x$
10. **a.** $-y^2 + 6y$ **b.** $-2y^2 + 4y$
11. **a.** $4(3x^2 - 2x + 1)$ **b.** $x(x^2 - 3x - 1)$
12. **a.** $4y^2(y - 2)$ **b.** $2xy^2(2x^2 - x + 3)$
13. **a.** $-(y - 3x)$ **b.** $-(y - 2x - z)$
14. **a.** $-x(x - 2)$ **b.** $-3xy(2x - 1 + y)$
15. **a.** $(a + 2)(x - 1)$ **b.** $(x - y)(2a + b)$
16. **a.** $(x + 2y)(1 - x)$ **b.** $(x + y)(y + 1)$
17. **a.** $y^2 + y - 6$ **b.** $x^2 + 3x - 4$
18. **a.** $6x^2 - 13x - 5$ **b.** $12x^2 + 13x - 4$
19. **a.** $4x^2 - 4x + 1$ **b.** $9y^2 + 12y + 4$
20. **a.** $y^3 - y^2 - y + 1$ **b.** $2x^3 + 5x^2 - 7x + 2$
21. **a.** $x^3 + 2x^2 - x - 2$ **b.** $y^3 + y^2 - 4y - 4$
22. **a.** $-2x^2 - 2x - 2$ **b.** $-3y^2 + 12y - 27$
23. **a.** $(x - 7)(x + 5)$ **b.** $(y + 8)(y - 4)$
24. **a.** $(xy - 6)(xy + 6)$ **b.** $(a - 7b)(a + 7b)$

25. **a.** $(3y - 1)(y + 4)$ **b.** $x(x + 5)(x - 2)$
26. **a.** $9(x - 2)(x + 2)$ **b.** $3(2x - y)(2x + y)$
27. **a.** $(2x - y)(x + 2y)$ **b.** $(3x + y)(2x - y)$
28. **a.** $(5a + 6b)(3a + 2b)$ **b.** $6(2a - b)(a - b)$
29. **a.** $(x^2 + 3)(x - 1)(x + 1)$
    b. $(y^2 + 1)(y - 2)(y + 2)$
30. **a.** $(3x^2 - 1)(3x^2 + 1)$ **b.** $(4y^2 - 3)(4y^2 + 3)$
31. **a.** $\{0, 2\}$ **b.** $\{2, 3\}$
32. **a.** $\{-3, 5\}$ **b.** $\{-3, 2\}$
33. **a.** $\{2\}$ **b.** $\{1, 3\}$
34. **a.** $x^2 - 3x - 10 = 0$ **b.** $x^2 + 3x = 0$
35. Base: 9 inches
    Altitude: 4 inches
36. Width: 6 centimeters
    Length: 10 centimeters
37. 7, 8, and 9   **38.**   3 seconds
39. **a.** $(y + x)(2x + 1)$ **b.** $(y - 3)(x - 1)$
40. **a.** $(a - 2b)(x + y)$ **b.** $(x - 2y)(2a + b)$
41. **a.** $(2a - 1)(a - 2)(a + 2)$ **b.** $(a + 2)^2(a - 2)$
42. **a.** $(2y - 3 - 2x)(2y - 3 + 2x)$
    b. $(2y - 1 - x)(2y - 1 + x)$
43. **a.** $(y - 2x - 1)(y + 2x + 1)$
    b. $(x - y + 4)(x + y - 4)$
44. **a.** $(2x - y)(4x^2 + 2xy + y^2)$
    b. $(x + 4y)(x^2 - 4xy + 16y^2)$
45. **a.** $(3y + z)(9y^2 - 3yz + z^2)$
    b. $(x - 2a)(x^2 + 2ax + 4a^2)$
46. **a.** $(2xy - 5)(4x^2y^2 + 10xy + 25)$
    b. $(1 + 4xy)(1 - 4xy + 16x^2y^2)$

Cumulative Exercises (page 74) **1.** -8 **2.** 2
3. 28   **4.** -92 **5.** $-x^2 - 1$ **6.** $-2x - 4$
7.
   -5 0 5
8. $y - 3 \geq 0$ or $y \geq 3$ **9.** 8   **10.** 56
11. 3   **12.** $x = y$
13. **a.** 3   **b.** -2 **c.** -12 **14.** 12
15. $\{34\}$ **16.** $\{37, 600\}$ **17.** $\{-4, 3\}$
18. $\{-2, 2\}$ **19.** $R = 2r$, $R = -2r$
20. $R = r_1 + r_2$, $R = -r_1 - r_2$
21. 2,133,333.3 cubic yards   **22.** 7.27 inches
23. 27.29 inches   **24.** $96,154   **25.** 4 feet

Exercise Set 4.1 (page 80) **1.** $\dfrac{-1}{4}$ **3.** $\dfrac{3}{5}$ **5.** $\dfrac{2}{5}$
7. $\dfrac{-3}{7}$ **9.** $\dfrac{-2x}{y}$ **11.** $\dfrac{3x}{4y}$

13. $\dfrac{-(x + 1)}{x}$ or $\dfrac{-x - 1}{x}$
15. $\dfrac{-(x - y)}{y + 2}, \dfrac{-x + y}{y + 2}$, or $\dfrac{y - x}{y + 2}$ **17.** $\dfrac{4}{y - 3}$
19. $\dfrac{-1}{y - x}$ **21.** $\dfrac{2 - x}{x - 3}$ **23.** $\dfrac{-x - 1}{y - x}$
25. $\dfrac{x - 2}{y - x}$ **27.** $\dfrac{a - 1}{3a + b}$
29. Substituting 1 for x gives $-\dfrac{1 + 3}{2} \stackrel{?}{=} \dfrac{-1 + 3}{2}$; $-2 \neq 1$.
31. $\dfrac{2x^2}{y}$ **33.** $\dfrac{2r^2}{t}$ **35.** $\dfrac{-2}{cd^2}$ **37.** $\dfrac{1}{a^3c^2}$
39. $\dfrac{-1}{6p^2}$ **41.** $\dfrac{2r}{t}$ **43.** $\dfrac{2x + 3}{3}$ **45.** $\dfrac{3x - 1}{3}$
47. $-a^2 + 3a - 2$ **49.** $y + 7$ **51.** $\dfrac{5}{3}$
53. $\dfrac{a - b}{2}$ **55.** $\dfrac{6t + 6}{t - 1}$ **57.** $y - 2$ **59.** $\dfrac{-2}{y + 3}$
61. $\dfrac{-x - y}{x - y}$ **63.** $\dfrac{x - 4}{x + 1}$ **65.** $\dfrac{2y - 3}{y - 1}$
67. $\dfrac{x + 2y}{x + y}$ **69.** $\dfrac{x + y}{2}$ **71.** $\dfrac{x + y}{a + 2b}$
73. $\dfrac{4y^2 + 6y + 9}{2y + 3}$
75. Let $x = 1$ and $y = 1$: $\dfrac{2(1) + (1)}{1} \neq 2(1)$

Exercise Set 4.2 (page 84) **1.** $4a^2 + 2a + \dfrac{1}{2}$
3. $y^2 - 2 + \dfrac{3}{7y^2}$ **5.** $6rs - 5 + \dfrac{2}{rs}$
7. $4ax - 2x + \dfrac{1}{2}$ **9.** $-5m^3 + 3 - \dfrac{7}{5m^3}$
11. $8m^2 - 5 + \dfrac{7}{5m}$ **13.** $2y + 5 + \dfrac{2}{2y + 1}$
15. $2t - 1 - \dfrac{6}{2t - 1}$ **17.** $x^2 + 4x + 9 + \dfrac{19}{x - 2}$
19. $a^3 - 3a^2 + 6a - 16 + \dfrac{47}{a + 3}$
21. $4z^3 - 2z^2 + 3z + 1 + \dfrac{2}{2z + 1}$
23. $x^3 + 2x^2 + 4x + 8 + \dfrac{15}{x - 2}$
25. $x - 1 + \dfrac{-7x + 12}{x^2 - 2x + 7}$

27. $4a^2 - 9a + 31 + \dfrac{-104a + 32}{a^2 + 3a - 1}$

29. $t - 1 + \dfrac{-t^2 - 3t + 3}{t^3 - 2t^2 + t + 2}$ **31.** $k = -2$

Exercise Set 4.3 (page 88)

1. $\dfrac{6}{9}$ **3.** $\dfrac{-30}{14}$

5. $\dfrac{20}{5}$ **7.** $\dfrac{6}{18x}$ **9.** $\dfrac{-a^2b}{b^3}$ **11.** $\dfrac{xy^2}{xy}$

13. $\dfrac{3a + 3b}{a^2 - b^2}$ **15.** $\dfrac{3xy - 9x}{y^2 - y - 6}$ **17.** $\dfrac{-2x - 4}{x^2 + 3x + 2}$

19. 60   **21.** 120   **23.** 252   **25.** $6ab^2$

27. $24x^2y^2$ **29.** $a(a - b)^2$ **31.** $(a - b)(a + b)$

33. $(a + 4)(a + 1)^2$ **35.** $(x + 4)(x - 1)^2$

37. $x(x - 1)^3$ **39.** $4(a + 1)(a - 1)^2$

41. $x^3(x - 1)^2$ **43.** $\dfrac{4y}{6xy}$ and $\dfrac{1}{6xy}$

45. $\dfrac{9}{12y^2}$ and $\dfrac{8y}{12y^2}$ **47.** $\dfrac{1}{2(x + 1)}$ and $\dfrac{x + 1}{2(x + 1)}$

49. $\dfrac{3y + 6}{(y - 3)(y + 2)}$ and $\dfrac{2y - 6}{(y - 3)(y + 2)}$

51. $\dfrac{10y + 5}{3(y - 2)(2y + 1)}$ and $\dfrac{y - 2}{3(y - 2)(2y + 1)}$

53. $\dfrac{2}{a^2 - 1}$ and $\dfrac{3a + 3}{a^2 - 1}$

55. $\dfrac{a - 1}{(a - 4)(a - 1)^2}$ and $\dfrac{2a - 8}{(a - 4)(a - 1)^2}$

57. $\dfrac{3y^2 + 6y}{(y + 1)(y + 2)^2}$ and $\dfrac{y^2 + y}{(y + 1)(y + 2)^2}$

59. $\dfrac{4x^2 - 2xy}{(2x - y)^2(2x + y)}$ and $\dfrac{6x^2 + 3xy}{(2x - y)^2(2x + y)}$

61. $\dfrac{10y}{2(x + y)^2}$ and $\dfrac{3x + 3y}{2(x + y)^2}$

63. $\dfrac{1}{(x - 1)(x^2 + x + 1)}$ and $\dfrac{3x^2 + 3x + 3}{(x - 1)(x^2 + x + 1)}$

65. $\dfrac{4x}{(x + y)(x^2 - xy + y^2)}$ and $\dfrac{x^2y - xy^2 + y^3}{(x + y)(x^2 - xy + y^2)}$

67. $\dfrac{3x}{(x - y)(x - y)}$ and $\dfrac{-2x^2 + 2xy}{(x - y)(x - y)}$

69. $\dfrac{2}{2(x - 2y)}$ and $\dfrac{-3}{2(x - 2y)}$

or $\dfrac{-2}{2(2y - x)}$ and $\dfrac{3}{2(2y - x)}$

Exercise Set 4.4 (page 91)

1. $\dfrac{x - 3}{2}$ **3.** $\dfrac{a + b - c}{6}$

5. $\dfrac{2x - 1}{2y}$ **7.** $\dfrac{1 - 2x}{x + 2y}$ **9.** $\dfrac{6 - 2a}{a^2 - 2a + 1}$ **11.** $\dfrac{7x}{6}$

13. $\dfrac{-y}{15}$ **15.** $\dfrac{5x}{12}$ **17.** $\dfrac{7}{6}x$ **19.** $\dfrac{1}{12}y$

21. $\dfrac{3}{4}y$ **23.** $\dfrac{3xy + y - x}{xy}$ **25.** $\dfrac{3x - 4y}{6xy}$

27. $\dfrac{5y - 3x - 8}{(x + 1)(y - 1)}$ **29.** $\dfrac{4x^2 + x}{(3x + 2)(x - 1)}$

31. $\dfrac{-3y^2 + 3y}{(2y - 1)(y + 1)}$ **33.** $\dfrac{2x^2 + 8x + 7}{(x + 2)(x + 3)}$

35. $\dfrac{y^2 - 4y + 5}{(y + 1)(2y - 3)}$ **37.** $\dfrac{17}{6(x + 2)}$

39. $\dfrac{-4}{15(x - 2)}$ **41.** $\dfrac{4x - 2}{(x - 2)(x + 1)(x + 1)}$

43. $\dfrac{-6y - 4}{(y + 4)(y - 4)(y - 1)}$ **45.** $\dfrac{-x^2 - 4x - 1}{(x - 1)(x - 1)(x + 1)}$

47. $\dfrac{3y + 1}{y(y - 3)(y + 2)}$ **49.** $\dfrac{-x^2 - 7x + 2}{(x - 2)(x - 2)(x + 2)}$

51. $\dfrac{-1}{(z - 4)(z - 3)(z - 2)}$ **53.** $\dfrac{x^3 - 2x^2 + 2x - 2}{(x - 1)(x - 1)}$

55. $\dfrac{y^3 - 2y^2 - y}{(y - 1)(y + 1)}$ **57.** $\dfrac{x^3 + 2x^2 + 3x - 4}{(x + 1)(x + 1)(x - 1)}$

59. $\dfrac{x^2 + x + 1}{x + 2}$ **61.** $\dfrac{x^2 + 5x + 4}{x + 3}$

63. $\dfrac{c}{s} + \dfrac{s}{c} = \dfrac{c \cdot c}{c \cdot s} + \dfrac{s \cdot s}{c \cdot s}$ **65.** $c + \dfrac{s^2}{c} = \dfrac{c \cdot c}{c \cdot 1} + \dfrac{s^2}{c}$

$\qquad = \dfrac{c^2 + s^2}{cs} = \dfrac{1}{sc}$ $\qquad = \dfrac{c^2 + s^2}{c} = \dfrac{1}{c}$

67. $\dfrac{(c - 1)(c + 1)}{s^2} + 1 = \dfrac{c^2 - 1}{s^2} + \dfrac{s^2}{s^2}$

$\qquad = \dfrac{c^2 + s^2 - 1}{s^2}$

$\qquad = \dfrac{1 - 1}{s^2} = 0$

69. $\dfrac{s - c}{s + c} + \dfrac{2sc}{s^2 - c^2}$

$\qquad = \dfrac{(s - c)(s - c)}{(s - c)(s + c)} + \dfrac{(2sc)}{(s - c)(s + c)}$

$\qquad = \dfrac{s^2 - 2sc + c^2 + 2sc}{(s - c)(s + c)}$

$\qquad = \dfrac{s^2 + c^2}{s^2 - c^2} = \dfrac{1}{s^2 - c^2}$

Exercise Set 4.5 (page 95) 1. $\dfrac{2}{3}$ 3. $\dfrac{7}{10}$ 5. $\dfrac{10}{3}$

7. $\dfrac{1}{8x}$ 9. $\dfrac{25p}{n}$ 11. $\dfrac{-n}{2}$ 13. $\dfrac{2x^5}{7}$

15. $\dfrac{x^3y^3}{2}$ 17. $\dfrac{-x^3y^2z^2}{3}$ 19. $\dfrac{-b^2}{a}$

21. $\dfrac{3c}{35ab}$ 23. $\dfrac{5}{ab}$ 25. 5 27. $\dfrac{a(2a-1)}{a+4}$

29. $\dfrac{x+3}{x-5}$ 31. $\dfrac{x-7}{x-5}$ 33. $\dfrac{1}{5}x^2 - 3x$

35. $x^2 + \dfrac{2}{3}x + \dfrac{1}{9}$ 37. $y^2 - \dfrac{1}{2}y + \dfrac{1}{16}$ 39. $\dfrac{4}{3}$

41. $\dfrac{1}{ax^2y}$ 43. $\dfrac{20y}{3a}$ 45. $\dfrac{2}{9}$ 47. $\dfrac{a+1}{a-2}$

49. $\dfrac{x+2}{x^2-1}$ 51. $\dfrac{x^3-4x^2}{x+1}$ 53. $\dfrac{x+3}{6y}$

55. $3(x^2 - xy + y^2)$ 57. $(y-3)(x+2)$

59. $\dfrac{x+1}{x-1}$ 61. $\dfrac{4x+4}{x+2}$ 63. $\dfrac{x^2+xy+y^2}{2y}$

65. $\dfrac{3a-3}{2}$

Exercise Set 4.6 (page 98) 1. $\dfrac{3}{2}$ 3. $\dfrac{2}{21}$ 5. $\dfrac{a}{bc}$

7. $\dfrac{4y}{3}$ 9. $\dfrac{1}{5}$ 11. $\dfrac{1}{10}$ 13. $\dfrac{8}{13}$ 15. $\dfrac{11}{35}$

17. $\dfrac{7}{2(5a+1)}$ 19. x 21. $\dfrac{x}{x-1}$ 23. $\dfrac{y}{y+2}$

25. $\dfrac{y^2}{y^3+y^2-y-1}$ 27. $\dfrac{x^2y-x^2}{xy^2+y^2}$ 29. $\dfrac{a-2b}{a+2b}$

31. $\dfrac{a+6}{a-1}$ 33. 1 35. $\dfrac{2-y}{2y}$ 37. $\dfrac{3-y}{y}$

39. $\dfrac{\dfrac{(c+s)^2}{c-s} - \dfrac{1}{c-s}}{2cs}$

$$= \dfrac{\dfrac{c^2+2cs+s^2}{c-s} - \dfrac{2cs}{c-s}}{}$$

$$= \dfrac{\dfrac{c^2+s^2+2cs-2cs}{c-s}}{}$$

$$= \dfrac{1}{c-s}$$

41. $\dfrac{\dfrac{1}{s-c} + \dfrac{s-c}{s}}{\dfrac{s^2-c^2}{}}$

$$= \dfrac{\dfrac{1}{s-c}\cdot(s-c)(s+c)}{\dfrac{s}{(s-c)(s+c)}\cdot(s-c)(s+c)} + \dfrac{s-c}{s}$$

$$= \dfrac{s+c}{s} + \dfrac{s-c}{s}$$

$$= \dfrac{s+c+s-c}{s} = \dfrac{2s}{s} = 2$$

Exercise Set 4.7 (page 103) 1. $\left\{-\dfrac{27}{2}\right\}$ 3. $\{3\}$

5. $\{-30\}$ 7. $\{-7\}$ 9. $\varnothing$ 11. $\{13\}$

13. $\varnothing$ 15. $\{4\}$ 17. $\{-2\}$ 19. $\{4\}$

21. $\{40\}$ 23. $\left\{-2, \dfrac{3}{2}\right\}$

25. $\{-3, 1\}$ 27. $\left\{-\dfrac{10}{3}, 1\right\}$ 29. $r = \dfrac{S-a}{S}$

31. $t = \dfrac{2rs}{s-r}$ 33. $t = \dfrac{15c-15V}{c}$

35. $n = \dfrac{125b-50w}{w}$ 37. 66 inches   39. 132 feet

41. 120 ohms   43. $8\dfrac{3}{4}$ years;   15 years

45. 62.6° Fahrenheit   47. 15 sides

Exercise Set 4.8 (page 107)

1. **a.** Number of bricks laid in 40 hours: x

   b. $\dfrac{x}{450} = \dfrac{40}{3}$

   c. 6000 bricks

3. **a.** Number of pounds of tin to make 90 pounds of alloy: x

   b. $\dfrac{x}{2.5} = \dfrac{90}{12}$

   c. $18\dfrac{3}{4}$ pounds

5. **a.** Number addressed in 5 hours: N

   b. $\dfrac{N}{144} = \dfrac{5}{3}$

   c. 240 envelopes

7. $x = 5$, $y = 6$ 9. $x = 6$, $8 + x = 14$

11. **a.** Height of tree: h

   b. $\dfrac{h}{6.5} = \dfrac{39.4}{14.2}$

   c. Approximately 18 feet

13. **a.** Rate of auto: r
   Rate of plane: $r + 120$

   b. $\dfrac{1260}{r + 120} = \dfrac{420}{r}$

   c. Auto: 60 miles per hour
   Plane: 180 miles per hour

15. **a.** Time for second ship to reach first ship: t
   b. $20t + 5 = 30t$

   c. $\dfrac{1}{2}$ hour

17. **a.** Speed of man: s
   Speed of woman: $s + 20$

   b. $\dfrac{120}{s + 20} = \dfrac{80}{s}$

   c. Speed of man: 40 miles per hour
   Speed of woman: 60 miles per hour

19. **a.** Speed of current: s

   b. $\dfrac{63}{18 + r} - \dfrac{30}{18 - r} = 1$

   c. 3 miles per hour

21. **a.** Amount of honey: A

   b. $\dfrac{A}{\frac{5}{2}} = \dfrac{\frac{1}{3}}{\frac{3}{2}}$

   c. $\dfrac{5}{9}$ cup

23. **a.** Earnings in 52 weeks: E

   b. $\dfrac{E}{6200} = \dfrac{52}{20}$

   c. \$16,120

25. **a.** Rate to the city: r
   Rate from the city: $r + 10$

   b. $\dfrac{10}{r} + \dfrac{10}{r + 10} = \dfrac{5}{6}$

   c. 20 miles per hour; 30 miles per hour

Review Exercises (page 110) 1. a. $\dfrac{-1}{-(a-b)}$, $\dfrac{-1}{b-a}$,

$\dfrac{-1}{a-b}$, $-\dfrac{-1}{-(b-a)}$, $-\dfrac{1}{-(a-b)}$, $-\dfrac{1}{b-a}$

b. $\dfrac{1}{a-b}$ is a positive number if $a > b$ and a negative number if $a < b$.

2. $\dfrac{1}{a-1}$, $\dfrac{-1}{1-a}$ 3. **a.** $\dfrac{2x}{5y}$ **b.** $x - 2$

4. **a.** $-2x - 1$ **b.** $-\dfrac{1}{2}$

5. **a.** $6x - 3 + \dfrac{3}{2x}$ **b.** $2y + 1 - \dfrac{1}{3y}$

6. **a.** $y - 3 + \dfrac{10}{2y + 3}$ **b.** $bx^2 + 3x^2 + 3x + 5 + \dfrac{7}{x - 1}$

7. **a.** $x^2 + x + \dfrac{1}{x - 1}$ **b.** $2x^3 - 2x^2 + x - 1 - \dfrac{1}{x + 1}$

8. **a.** $x^3 + 2x^2 + 1$ **b.** $x^4 + x^3 + x^2 + x + 1$

9. **a.** $\dfrac{-18}{24}$ **b.** $\dfrac{x^2y}{2xy^2}$

10. **a.** $\dfrac{2x - 6y}{x^2 - 9y^2}$ **b.** $\dfrac{y - y^2}{y^2 - 4y + 3}$

11. **a.** $\dfrac{4x}{3}$ **b.** $\dfrac{-x - y}{4x}$

12. **a.** $\dfrac{8y - 15x + 7}{20xy}$ **b.** $\dfrac{3y + 4}{6y - 18}$

13. **a.** $\dfrac{2x + 21}{(x - 2)(x + 3)}$ **b.** $\dfrac{x - 2y + 3}{x^2 - 4y^2}$

14. **a.** $\dfrac{5x + 1}{(x^2 - 1)(x + 1)}$ **b.** $\dfrac{-6y - 4}{(y - 4)(y + 4)(y - 1)}$

15. **a.** $\dfrac{x^2}{3}$ **b.** $\dfrac{2}{y}$ 16. **a.** 1 **b.** $\dfrac{2y^2 - 2y}{y + 1}$

17. **a.** $\dfrac{5xy}{3}$ **b.** 1

18. **a.** $\dfrac{(y + 3)(y + 2)}{(y - 2)(y + 1)}$ **b.** $\dfrac{1}{1 - x}$ 19. $\dfrac{5x - 4y}{12}$

20. 4 21. $x^2 + 3x$ 22. $\dfrac{-x + 21}{(x + 3)(x + 3)(x - 3)}$

23. $\dfrac{2x + 3y}{(x + 3y)(x - 3y)}$ 24. $\dfrac{x^2 + x - 2}{x + 4}$

25. $\dfrac{-x^2 + 4x - 2}{(x - 1)(x + 1)}$ 26. $\dfrac{y}{y + 1}$

27. **a.** $\dfrac{5}{3}$ **b.** $\dfrac{2}{11}$ 28. **a.** $\dfrac{6x + 9}{3x - 2}$ **b.** $\dfrac{y^2 - 1}{y^2 + 1}$

29. **a.** $\dfrac{2x}{x^2 - 1}$ **b.** 10

30. **a.** $\dfrac{y^3 + y^2 - y - 1}{y^2}$ **b.** $\dfrac{(x^2 + 1)(x - 1)}{x(x - 2)}$

31. a. $\left\{\frac{1}{2}\right\}$ **b.** $\{12\}$ **32. a.** $\{4\}$ **b.** $\left\{\frac{-10}{7}\right\}$

33. a. $\left\{\frac{-4}{3}\right\}$ **b.** $\{-17\}$

34. a. $\left\{\frac{1}{8}, 4\right\}$ **b.** $\left\{\frac{1}{2}, 6\right\}$ **35.** $13\frac{3}{4}$ inches

36. Rate of car: 50 miles per hour
Rate of plane: 150 miles per hour

37. $2\frac{1}{2}$ hours **38.** 7 hits **39.** 20 miles per hour

40. 4 miles per hour **41.** 144 miles

42. 90 miles **43.** 17.1 square feet

44. 102 yards

Cumulative Exercises (page 113) 1. -12

2. -15 **3.** $2x - 5$ **4.** $-8b^3 - a^4b^4$

5. $-3x^2 + 9x + 9$ **6.** $3x + 2$ **7.** 30 **8.** 56

9. ⟨number line with closed dot at -5, open circle at 5⟩

10. $x^2 - 2x + 3 - \dfrac{5}{x + 2}$ **11.** $\dfrac{x^2 + 2}{(x - 3)(x - 1)(x + 2)}$

12. $\dfrac{a^2 - 4a + 1}{a^2 + a - 5}$ **13.** $\{8\}$ **14.** $\{8000\}$

15. $\left\{\frac{1}{2}, 3\right\}$ **16.** $\{-3, 6\}$ **17.** $\left\{\frac{2}{3}\right\}$ **18.** $\{0\}$

19. $t = \dfrac{A - P}{Pr}$ **20.** $h = \dfrac{S}{2\pi r} - r$ or $h = \dfrac{S - 2\pi r^2}{2\pi r}$

21. 725 students **22.** 60 liters

23. Width: 52 feet **24.** Short leg: 9 inches
Length: 104 feet Hypotenuse: 15 inches

25. 60 miles per hour

Exercise Set 5.1 (page 117) 1. x^5 3. a^8

5. a^6 **7.** x^6 **9.** x^3y^6 **11.** $a^4b^4c^8$

13. $-16x^4$ **15.** $4a^7b^6$ **17.** x^2 **19.** xy^2

21. $\dfrac{x^3}{y^6}$ **23.** $\dfrac{8x^3}{y^6}$ **25.** $\dfrac{-8x^3}{27y^6}$ **27.** $\dfrac{16}{x}$

29. $\dfrac{y^4}{x}$ **31.** x^4y **33.** $\dfrac{8x}{9y^2}$ **35.** $36y^2$

37. $\dfrac{x^2s^{14}}{y^2t^2}$ **39.** $\dfrac{-1}{x^3a^3b}$ **41.** $\dfrac{y + z}{x^4}$

43. Use 1 for x and 2 for y: $(1^2 + 2^2)^3 \stackrel{?}{=} 1^6 + 2^6$;
$125 \neq 1 + 64$.

45. x^{2n} **47.** x^{3n} **49.** x^{2n}

Exercise Set 5.2 (page 120) 1. $\dfrac{1}{2}$ 3. 3

5. $-\dfrac{1}{8}$ **7.** $\dfrac{1}{5}$ **9.** $\dfrac{5}{3}$ **11.** $\dfrac{9}{5}$ **13.** $\dfrac{82}{9}$

15. $\dfrac{3}{16}$ **17.** $\dfrac{x^2}{y^3}$ **19.** $\dfrac{1}{x^6y^3}$ **21.** $\dfrac{x^2}{y^6}$ **23.** $\dfrac{y^4}{x}$

25. x^4 **27.** $\dfrac{1}{x^6}$ **29.** $\dfrac{y}{x}$ **31.** $4x^5y^2$ **33.** $\dfrac{z^2}{y^2}$

35. $\dfrac{xy}{z}$ **37.** $\dfrac{z}{y^2}$ **39.** $\dfrac{x^2 + y^2}{x^2y^2}$ **41.** $\dfrac{x^2y^2 + 1}{xy}$

43. $\dfrac{1}{(x - y)^2}$ **45.** $\dfrac{y^2 - x^2}{xy}$ **47.** $1 - xy$

49. $x + y$

51. Substituting 1 for x and 2 for y gives
$(1 + 2)^{-2} \stackrel{?}{=} \dfrac{1}{1^2 + 2^2}$; $\dfrac{1}{9} \neq \dfrac{1}{5}$.

53. a^{n+4} **55.** a^{2-2n} **57.** $b^{-1}c^{-1}$ **59.** x^{-1}

Exercise Set 5.3 (page 124) 1. 2.85×10^2

3. 2.1×10 **5.** 8.372×10^6 **7.** 2.4×10^{-2}

9. 4.21×10^{-1} **11.** 4×10^{-6} **13.** 240

15. 687,000 **17.** 0.005 **19.** 0.0202

21. 12,270 **23.** 0.00235 **25.** 0.0005 **27.** 12.5

29. 0.00006 **31.** 10^{-5} or 0.00001,

33. 10^0 or 1 **35.** 6×10^{-3} or 0.006

37. 1.8×10^6 or 1,800,000 **39.** 72×10 or 720

41. 4×10^{-1} or 0.4 **43.** 8 **45.** 9.78×10^9

47. 7.22×10^{-7} **49.** 1.081×10^{10}

51. 3.5973×10^{-7} **53.** 4.1175×10^{-1}

55. 5.6968×10^9

57. a. 3×10^8 **b.** 1.18×10^{10} inches per second

59. 3×10^8 **61.** 1.5×10^{-5}

✓ Exercise Set 5.4 (page 128) 1. 3 3. 2

5. -2 **7.** 8 **9.** 27 **11.** 16 **13.** $\dfrac{1}{4}$

15. $\dfrac{1}{8}$ **17.** 9 **19.** 81 **21.** $x^{2/3}$ **23.** $x^{1/3}$

25. $a^{3/2}$ **27.** $\dfrac{1}{x^{1/2}}$ **29.** $a^{1/3}b^{1/2}$ **31.** $\dfrac{a^4}{b^2}$

33. $\dfrac{r^2}{t^3}$ **35.** $\dfrac{t^2}{z}$ **37.** $\dfrac{yz}{x}$ **39.** $x^{3/2} + x$

41. $x - x^{2/3}$ **43.** $x^{-1} + 1$ **45.** $t + 1$

47. $b + b^{1/4}$ **49.** $x^2 + 2x - 1$ **51.** $2x + x^{1/2} - 1$

53. $x - 4x^{1/2} + 4$ **55.** $x - x^{3/2} - 2x^2$

57. Use 1 for a and 1 for b: $(1 + 1)^{1/2} \stackrel{?}{=} 1^{1/2} + 1^{1/2}$;
$2^{1/2} \neq 1 + 1$.

59. $x^{3n/2}$ **61.** $x^{3n/2}$ **63.** $x^{5n/2}y^{(3m+2)/2}$

65. $x^{n/3}y^n$

Exercise Set 5.5 (page 132)   **1.** $7^{1/2}$ **3.** $(2x)^{1/3}$
5. $x^{1/3} - 3y^{1/2}$ **7.** $x^{1/3}y^{1/2}$ **9.** $\sqrt{3}$ **11.** $4\sqrt[3]{x}$
13. $\sqrt[4]{x-2}$ **15.** $3\sqrt[3]{xy}$ **17.** 3   **19.** 2
21. 3   **23.** 5   **25.** $\sqrt[3]{x^2}$ **27.** $3\sqrt[5]{x^3}$
29. $\sqrt{(x+2y)^3}$ **31.** $\dfrac{1}{\sqrt{y}}$ **33.** $\dfrac{1}{\sqrt[3]{x^2}}$ **35.** $\dfrac{3}{\sqrt[3]{y^2}}$
37. $x^{2/3}$ **39.** $(xy)^{2/3}$ **41.** $(xy^3)^{1/2}$ **43.** $\dfrac{1}{x^{1/2}}$
45. 3   **47.** -4 **49.** x **51.** x^2 **53.** $2y^2$
55. $-x^2y^3$ **57.** $\dfrac{2}{3}xy^4$ **59.** $\dfrac{-2}{5}x$ **61.** $2xy^2$
63. $2a^2b^3$ **65.** $\sqrt{3}$ **67.** $\sqrt{3}$ **69.** $\sqrt[3]{9}$
71. $\sqrt{x}$ **73.** $13 < \sqrt{173} < 14$
75. $7 < \sqrt[3]{408} < 8$ **77.** $-5 < \sqrt[3]{-87.3} < -4$
79. $3 < \sqrt[4]{130} < 4$ **81.**

$$\begin{array}{c} -\sqrt{7} \; -\sqrt{1} \quad\quad \sqrt{5} \; \sqrt{9} \\ \hline \quad\quad\quad 0 \quad\quad\quad 5 \end{array}$$

83.

$$\begin{array}{c} -\sqrt{20} \; -\sqrt{6} \quad \sqrt{1} \quad\quad 6 \\ \hline -5 \quad\quad 0 \quad\quad 5 \end{array}$$

85. Substitute a negative number such as -2 for a in the given equation and solve:
$$\sqrt{a^2} \overset{?}{=} a$$
$$\sqrt{(-2)^2} \overset{?}{=} -2$$
$$\sqrt{4} \overset{?}{=} -2$$
$$2 \neq -2$$

87. $2|x|$ **89.** $|x+1|$ **91.** $\dfrac{2}{|x+y|}$ $(x+y \neq 0)$

Exercise Set 5.6 (page 134)   **1.** 0.375   **3.** $-0.22\overline{2}$
5. 1.4   **7.** $-1.166\overline{6}$ **9.** 3.07   **11.** -2.53
13. 1.85   **15.** -4.18 **17.** 6.213   **19.** 8.414
21. 560.742   **23.** 7.368   **25.** 148.2   **27.** -29.9
29. 1127.1   **31.** 0.6   **33.** 5.2   **35.** 2.0
37. 1.9   **39.** Approximately 2.22 seconds
41. Approximately 16 feet

Exercise Set 5.7 (page 137)   **1.** $3\sqrt{2}$ **3.** $2\sqrt{5}$
5. $5\sqrt{3}$ **7.** x^2 **9.** $x\sqrt{x}$ **11.** $3x\sqrt{x}$
13. $2x^3\sqrt{2}$ **15.** $x\sqrt[4]{x}$ **17.** $xyz^2\sqrt[5]{x^2y^4z}$
19. $ab^2c^2\sqrt[6]{ac^3}$ **21.** $3abc\sqrt[7]{ab^2c^3}$ **23.** 6
25. x^3y **27.** 2   **29.** $10\sqrt{3}$ **31.** $100\sqrt{6}$
33. $\dfrac{\sqrt{5}}{5}$ **35.** $\dfrac{-\sqrt{2}}{2}$ **37.** $\dfrac{\sqrt{2x}}{2}$ **39.** $\dfrac{-\sqrt{xy}}{x}$
41. $\sqrt{x}$ **43.** $\dfrac{\sqrt{2xy}}{2x}$ **45.** $\dfrac{\sqrt[3]{x}}{x}$ **47.** $\dfrac{\sqrt[3]{18y^2}}{3y}$

49. $\dfrac{\sqrt[3]{2xy}}{2y}$ **51.** $\dfrac{\sqrt[5]{48x^2}}{2x}$ **53.** a^2b **55.** $7y\sqrt{2x}$
57. $\dfrac{2b}{a^2}\sqrt[3]{b}$ **59.** $\sqrt[5]{b}$ **61.** $\dfrac{1}{\sqrt{3}}$ **63.** $\dfrac{x}{\sqrt{xy}}$
65. Substitute two numbers such as 4 and 9 for a and b in the given equation and solve:
$$(\sqrt{a}+\sqrt{b})^2 \overset{?}{=} a+b$$
$$(\sqrt{4}+\sqrt{9})^2 \overset{?}{=} 4+9$$
$$(2+3)^2 \overset{?}{=} 13$$
$$25 \neq 13$$
67. $2(x-1)\sqrt{2(x-1)}$ **69.** $x(y-2)^2\sqrt{x(y-2)}$
71. $\dfrac{y-3}{xy^2}\sqrt{xy(y-3)}$ **73.** $x\sqrt[3]{4x^2-1}$
75. $\dfrac{(x-1)}{xy}\sqrt[3]{x^2y(x-1)}$ **77.** $\dfrac{1}{x^2}\sqrt{3x(x-1)}$

Exercise Set 5.8 (page 141)   **1.** $5\sqrt{7}$ **3.** $\sqrt{3}$
5. $9\sqrt{2x}$ **7.** $-6y\sqrt{x}$ **9.** $15\sqrt{2a}$ **11.** $5\sqrt[3]{2}$
13. $6 - 2\sqrt{5}$ **15.** $2\sqrt{3}+2\sqrt{5}$ **17.** $1 - \sqrt{5}$
19. $x-9$ **21.** $-4+\sqrt{6}$ **23.** $7-2\sqrt{10}$
25. $2(1+\sqrt{3})$ **27.** $6(\sqrt{3}+1)$ **29.** $4(1+\sqrt{y})$
31. $\sqrt{2}(1-\sqrt{3})$ **33.** $1+\sqrt{3}$ **35.** $1+\sqrt{2}$
37. $1-\sqrt{x}$ **39.** $x-y$ **41.** $2\sqrt{3}-2$
43. $\dfrac{2(\sqrt{7}+2)}{3}$ **45.** $\dfrac{x(\sqrt{x}+3)}{x-9}$ **47.** $\dfrac{\sqrt{6}}{2}$
49. $\dfrac{-1}{2(1+\sqrt{2})}$ **51.** $\dfrac{x-1}{3(\sqrt{x}+1)}$ **53.** $\dfrac{x-y}{x(\sqrt{x}+\sqrt{y})}$
55. $\dfrac{\sqrt{x+1}}{x+1}$ **57.** $\dfrac{-\sqrt{x^2+1}}{x(x^2+1)}$
59. $\dfrac{x-2}{\sqrt{x(x-1)}-\sqrt{x-1}+\sqrt{x-1}}$
61. $\dfrac{1}{2x+1+2\sqrt{x(x+1)}}$

Exercise Set 5.9 (page 145)   **1.** $2i$ **3.** $4i\sqrt{2}$
5. $6i\sqrt{2}$ **7.** $6i\sqrt{6}$ **9.** $40i$ **11.** $-4i\sqrt{3}$
13. $4+2i$ **15.** $2+15i\sqrt{2}$ **17.** $2+2i$
19. $5+5i$ **21.** $-2+i$ **23.** $-1-2i$
25. $8+i$ **27.** $13+13i$ **29.** $21-18i$
31. $3-4i$ **33.** $5+0i$ or 5   **35.** $\dfrac{-i}{3}$
37. $\dfrac{-1}{5}-\dfrac{3}{5}i$ **39.** $1+i$ **41.** $\dfrac{1}{2}-\dfrac{1}{2}i$
43. $\dfrac{12}{13}-\dfrac{5}{13}i$ **45.** $\dfrac{9}{34}+\dfrac{19}{34}i$ **47.** $4+2i$

49. $15 + 3i$ **51.** $-\dfrac{3}{2}i$ **53.** $\dfrac{3}{5} - \dfrac{4}{5}i$

55. $x \geqslant 5; \quad x < 5$

57. a. -1 **b.** 1 **c.** $-i$ **d.** -1

59. $5 + 4i$

Review Exercises (page 147)

1. a. $x^3 y^2$ **b.** $27x^6 y^3$

2. a. $\dfrac{1}{x^3 y}$ **b.** $\dfrac{y^6}{x^8}$ **3. a.** $\dfrac{11}{18}$ **b.** $\dfrac{x^2 + y^2}{xy}$

4. a. $\dfrac{2x}{4x^2 + 4x + 1}$ **b.** $\dfrac{(y^2 - x^2)(x - y)^2}{x^2 y^2}$

5. a. 2.3×10^{-11} **b.** 3.07×10^{11}

6. a. 0.0000349 **b.** 0.0075

7. a. 10^2 or 100 **b.** 8×10^1 or 80

8. a. 51.7 **b.** 6.2 **9. a.** 9 **b.** $\dfrac{1}{2}$

10. a. x^2 **b.** $x^2 y^3$

11. a. $x - x^{5/3}$ **b.** $y - y^0$ or $y - 1$

12. a. $x^{1/5}(x^{3/5})$ **b.** $y^{-1/2}(y^{-1/4})$

13. a. $\sqrt[3]{(1 - x^2)^2}$

  b. $\sqrt[3]{(1 - x^2)^{-2}}$ or $\dfrac{1}{\sqrt[3]{(1 - x^2)^2}}$

14. a. $(x^2 y)^{1/3}$ or $x^{2/3} y^{1/3}$ **b.** $(a + b)^{-2/3}$

15. a. $2y$ **b.** $-2xy^2$ **16. a.** $\dfrac{1}{2}x^2 y^3$ **b.** $\dfrac{1}{2}y$

17. a. 3.015 **b.** 3.341

18. a. 2.301 **b.** 3.359

19. a. 9.482 **b.** 63.571

20. a. 64.301 **b.** 47.591

21. a. $6\sqrt{5}$ **b.** $2xy\sqrt[4]{2y}$

22. a. $\dfrac{\sqrt{2}}{2}$ **b.** $\dfrac{\sqrt{3}}{3}$

23. a. $\dfrac{\sqrt{xy}}{y}$ **b.** $x\sqrt{3xy}$

24. a. $\dfrac{\sqrt[3]{4}}{2}$ **b.** $\dfrac{\sqrt[4]{54x^3}}{3x}$

25. a. $xy\sqrt[3]{x^2 y}$ **b.** xy

26. a. $2xy\sqrt[3]{y}$ **b.** $x\sqrt[5]{y^2}$

27. a. $\dfrac{3x}{2\sqrt{3x}}$ **b.** $\dfrac{2x}{y\sqrt{2x}}$

28. a. $\dfrac{6x}{\sqrt{2x}}$ **b.** $\dfrac{2x}{\sqrt{x}}$

29. a. $18\sqrt{3}$ **b.** $19\sqrt{2x}$

30. a. $3y\sqrt{2x}$ **b.** $4x\sqrt{3x}$

31. a. $3\sqrt{2} - 2\sqrt{3}$ **b.** $5\sqrt{2} - 5$

32. a. $12 - 7\sqrt{3}$ **b.** $x - 4$

33. a. $1 + 2\sqrt{2}$ **b.** $1 - \sqrt{2}$

34. a. $1 + \sqrt{xy}$ **b.** $1 - \sqrt{x}$

35. a. $\dfrac{\sqrt{x}}{2x}$ **b.** $\dfrac{10\sqrt{y}}{3y}$

36. a. $8 + 4\sqrt{3}$ **b.** $2\sqrt{5} - 4$

37. a. $\dfrac{y(\sqrt{y} + 3)}{y - 9}$ **b.** $\sqrt{x} - \sqrt{y}$

38. a. $\dfrac{13}{8 - 2\sqrt{3}}$ **b.** $\dfrac{x - 16}{x(\sqrt{x} - 4)}$

39. a. $4 + 6i$ **b.** $5 - 6i\sqrt{3}$

40. a. $6 - i$ **b.** $5 + 3i$

41. a. $7 + 17i$ **b.** $4 + 3i$

42. a. $\dfrac{-4i}{3}$ **b.** $1 - i$

43. a. $-4 + 6i$ **b.** $11 - 2i\sqrt{3}$

44. a. $\dfrac{2}{3}i$ **b.** $\dfrac{1}{3} - \dfrac{2\sqrt{2}}{3}i$

Cumulative Exercises (page 149) **1.** $2x^2 + 2x - 20$

2. $x - 4$ **3.** $-\dfrac{3}{2}$ **4.** $\dfrac{x^8}{y^6}$ **5.** 6

6. $\dfrac{2x}{(x - 2)(x - 1)^2}$ **7.** -9 **8.** $3xy\sqrt{y}$

9. -16 **10.** $-x^2 + 3x - 2$ **11.** $\dfrac{y + \sqrt{2y}}{y - 2}$

12. $\dfrac{1}{4} - \dfrac{\sqrt{3}}{4}i$ **13.** $x^2 + \dfrac{1}{x - 2}$

14. a.

  b.

15. $\left\{\dfrac{7}{4}\right\}$ **16.** $\{-3, 1\}$ **17.** $\left\{\dfrac{24}{5}\right\}$

18. $\left\{-\dfrac{2}{3}, 3\right\}$ **19.** $\{1, 9\}$ **20.** $\left\{\dfrac{44{,}000}{7}\right\}$

21. Christmas club: $221
Savings: $421
Checking: $842

22. $32,000 **23.** 2 seconds

24. $1.20 **25.** 240 seats

Exercise Set 6.1 (page 156) **1.** $\{10, -10\}$

3. $\left\{\dfrac{5}{3}, -\dfrac{5}{3}\right\}$ **5.** $\{\sqrt{7}, -\sqrt{7}\}$

7. $\{i\sqrt{6}, -i\sqrt{6}\}$ **9.** $\{\sqrt{6}, -\sqrt{6}\}$

11. $\left\{9\dfrac{i}{2}, -9\dfrac{i}{2}\right\}$ **13.** $\{5, -1\}$ **15.** $\left\{\dfrac{5}{2}, -\dfrac{3}{2}\right\}$

17. $\{-2 + i\sqrt{3}, -2 - i\sqrt{3}\}$

19. $\left\{\dfrac{1 + \sqrt{3}}{2}, \dfrac{1 - \sqrt{3}}{2}\right\}$ **21.** $\left\{-\dfrac{2}{9}, -\dfrac{4}{9}\right\}$

23. $\{1, 4\}$ **25.** $\left\{-\dfrac{2}{3}, -\dfrac{8}{3}\right\}$

27. $\left\{\dfrac{1 + i\sqrt{15}}{7}, \dfrac{1 - i\sqrt{15}}{7}\right\}$

29. $\left\{\dfrac{7 + 2i\sqrt{2}}{8}, \dfrac{7 - 2i\sqrt{2}}{8}\right\}$ **31.** $\{2, -6\}$

33. $\{1\}$ **35.** $\{-5, -4\}$ **37.** $\{1 + \sqrt{2}, 1 - \sqrt{2}\}$

39. $\left\{\dfrac{-3 + \sqrt{21}}{2}, \dfrac{-3 - \sqrt{21}}{2}\right\}$

41. $\left\{\dfrac{-2 + \sqrt{10}}{2}, \dfrac{-2 - \sqrt{10}}{2}\right\}$ **43.** $\left\{\dfrac{5}{2}, -1\right\}$

45. $\left\{\dfrac{1 + i\sqrt{11}}{2}, \dfrac{1 - i\sqrt{11}}{2}\right\}$

47. $\left\{\dfrac{-2 + i\sqrt{2}}{2}, \dfrac{-2 - i\sqrt{2}}{2}\right\}$ **49.** $\{\sqrt{a}, -\sqrt{a}\}$

51. $\left\{\sqrt{\dfrac{bc}{a}}, -\sqrt{\dfrac{bc}{a}}\right\}$ **53.** $\{a + 4, a - 4\}$

55. $\left\{\dfrac{3 - b}{a}, \dfrac{-3 - b}{a}\right\}$ **57.** 44.4 meters

59. 2.3 feet

61. 10 centimeters, 24 centimeters, 26 centimeters

63. $\{\sqrt{c^2 - a^2}, -\sqrt{c^2 - a^2}\}$

65. $\left\{-1 + \sqrt{\dfrac{A}{P}}, -1 - \sqrt{\dfrac{A}{P}}\right\}$ **67.** $y = \pm\dfrac{1}{3}\sqrt{9 - x^2}$

69. $y = \pm\dfrac{2}{3}\sqrt{x^2 - 9}$ **71.** (See page 157.)

Exercise Set 6.2 (page 161) 1. $\{4, 1\}$ **3.** $\{1, -4\}$

5. $\left\{\dfrac{3 + \sqrt{5}}{2}, \dfrac{3 - \sqrt{5}}{2}\right\}$ **7.** $\left\{\dfrac{5 + \sqrt{13}}{6}, \dfrac{5 - \sqrt{13}}{6}\right\}$

9. $\left\{\dfrac{3}{2}, -\dfrac{2}{3}\right\}$ **11.** $\{0, 5\}$ **13.** $\{i\sqrt{2}, -i\sqrt{2}\}$

15. $\left\{\dfrac{1 + i\sqrt{7}}{4}, \dfrac{1 - i\sqrt{7}}{4}\right\}$ **17.** $\left\{\dfrac{3 + \sqrt{13}}{2}, \dfrac{3 - \sqrt{13}}{2}\right\}$

19. $\left\{\dfrac{2 + \sqrt{7}}{3}, \dfrac{2 - \sqrt{7}}{3}\right\}$ **21.** $\left\{\dfrac{1 + i\sqrt{23}}{6}, \dfrac{1 - i\sqrt{23}}{6}\right\}$

23. $\left\{\dfrac{1 + i\sqrt{3}}{4}, \dfrac{1 - i\sqrt{3}}{4}\right\}$ **25.** 1; real and unequal

27. -16; imaginary and unequal   **29.** 0; one real

31. $x = 2k$; $x = -k$ **33.** $x = \dfrac{1 \pm \sqrt{1 - 4ac}}{2a}$

35. $x = -1 \pm \sqrt{1 + y}$ **37.** $x = \dfrac{-y \pm \sqrt{24 - 11y^2}}{6}$

39. $y = \dfrac{-x \pm \sqrt{8 - 11x^2}}{2}$ **41.** 29.2 miles per hour

43. a. 24.5 seconds   **b.** 1.2 seconds

Exercise Set 6.3 (page 164) 1. $\{64\}$ **3.** $\{-2\}$

5. $\left\{-\dfrac{1}{3}\right\}$ **7.** $\left\{2, -\dfrac{1}{2}\right\}$ **9.** $\{12\}$ **11.** $\{5\}$

13. $\{4\}$ **15.** $\{-27\}$ **17.** $\{17\}$ **19.** $\{5\}$

21. $\{0\}$ **23.** $\{4\}$ **25.** $\{1, 3\}$ **27.** $A = \pi r^2$

29. $S = \dfrac{1}{R^3}$ **31.** $t = \pm\sqrt{r^2 + s^2}$

33. $E = \pm\sqrt{\left(\dfrac{A - B}{C}\right)^2 - D}$ **35.** $A \geqslant 0$

37. $2\sqrt{10}$ centimeters   **39.** 4 feet   **41.** 18 miles

Exercise Set 6.4 (page 167) 1. $\{1, -1, 2, -2\}$

3. $\{1, -1, \sqrt{3}, -\sqrt{3}\}$ **5.** $\{\sqrt{2}/2, -\sqrt{2}/2, 3i, -3i\}$

7. $\{i, -i, \sqrt{3}i, -\sqrt{3}i\}$ **9.** $\{25\}$ **11.** $\varnothing$

13. $\{3, -3\}$ **15.** $\{\sqrt{10}, -\sqrt{10}\}$ **17.** $\{64, -8\}$

19. $\{64, -1\}$ **21.** $\{9, 36\}$ **23.** $\left\{\dfrac{1}{4}, 16\right\}$

25. $\left\{\dfrac{1}{4}, -\dfrac{1}{3}\right\}$ **27.** $\{626\}$ **29.** $\{9, 16\}$

31. $\{4, 81\}$ **33.** $\{6\}$

Review Exercises (page 168)

1. a. $\{5, -5\}$ **b.** $\left\{\dfrac{1}{3}i\sqrt{21}, -\dfrac{1}{3}i\sqrt{21}\right\}$

2. a. $\{2, -8\}$ **b.** $\{4 + \sqrt{15}, 4 - \sqrt{15}\}$

3. a. $\left\{\dfrac{1 + \sqrt{2}}{3}, \dfrac{1 - \sqrt{2}}{3}\right\}$

   b. $\left\{\dfrac{-2 + \sqrt{5}}{3}, \dfrac{-2 - \sqrt{5}}{3}\right\}$

4. a. $\left\{\dfrac{3 + i\sqrt{5}}{2}, \dfrac{3 - i\sqrt{5}}{2}\right\}$

   b. $\left\{\dfrac{-2 + i\sqrt{7}}{3}, \dfrac{-2 - i\sqrt{7}}{3}\right\}$

5. a. $\{2 + \sqrt{10}, 2 - \sqrt{10}\}$

   b. $\left\{\dfrac{-3 + \sqrt{33}}{4}, \dfrac{-3 - \sqrt{33}}{4}\right\}$

6. a. $\left\{\dfrac{-3 + \sqrt{21}}{2}, \dfrac{-3 - \sqrt{21}}{2}\right\}$

   b. $\left\{\dfrac{1 + \sqrt{13}}{3}, \dfrac{1 - \sqrt{13}}{3}\right\}$

7. **a.** $\left\{\dfrac{1 + i\sqrt{7}}{2}, \dfrac{1 - i\sqrt{7}}{2}\right\}$

   b. $\left\{-1 + i\sqrt{2}, -1 - i\sqrt{2}\right\}$

8. **a.** $\left\{\dfrac{1 + i\sqrt{5}}{2}, \dfrac{1 - i\sqrt{5}}{2}\right\}$

   b. $\left\{\dfrac{3 + i\sqrt{3}}{6}, \dfrac{3 - i\sqrt{3}}{6}\right\}$

9. **a.** $\{1, 2\}$ **b.** $\left\{\dfrac{3 + i\sqrt{19}}{2}, \dfrac{3 - i\sqrt{19}}{2}\right\}$

10. **a.** $\left\{\dfrac{3 + \sqrt{5}}{2}, \dfrac{3 - \sqrt{5}}{2}\right\}$ **b.** $\left\{1, -\dfrac{3}{2}\right\}$

11. **a.** $\left\{\dfrac{1 + i\sqrt{7}}{2}, \dfrac{1 - i\sqrt{7}}{2}\right\}$ **b.** $\{1 + i\sqrt{3}, 1 - i\sqrt{3}\}$

12. **a.** $\left\{\dfrac{-3 + i\sqrt{7}}{4}, \dfrac{-3 - i\sqrt{7}}{4}\right\}$

   b. $\left\{\dfrac{1 + i\sqrt{23}}{4}, \dfrac{1 - i\sqrt{23}}{4}\right\}$

13. 20 people   **14.** 120 members   **15.** $\{1, 4\}$

16. $\{8\}$ **17.** $t = \pm\sqrt{\dfrac{1 - p^2 s}{2}}$

18. $p = \pm 2\sqrt{R^2 - R}$ **19.** $\{2, -2, i, -i\}$

20. $\{16\}$ **21.** $\{16\}$ **22.** $\{2\}$ **23.** $\{9\}$

24. $\{12\}$

Cumulative Exercises (page 170) **1.** $4x^5 y^2 - 3x^3 y^4$

2. 16 **3.** $3\sqrt{y} - x\sqrt{3}$ **4.** $-24x^3 - 14x^2 + 17x$

5. $x^2 y^2 (2 - y)(2 + y)$ **6.** $-2x + 2x^{1/3}$

7. $3x^3 - 10x^2 + 17x - 12$

8. $(2x - 3y)(4x^2 + 6xy + 9y^2)$ **9.** $\dfrac{11}{25} + \dfrac{2}{25} i$

10. $\dfrac{x^2 - x - 2}{x(x - 1)}$ **11.** $5t^2 + 9t - 2$

12. $\dfrac{-3x^2 - 6x}{2x^3 - 8x}$ **13.** $-3xy^4$ **14.** $\dfrac{\sqrt[3]{6x}}{2x}$

15. $\left\{-2, \dfrac{7}{2}\right\}$ **16.** $\left\{\dfrac{3}{2}, 5\right\}$ **17.** $\{1 \pm i\sqrt{2}\}$

18. $\left\{\dfrac{5}{3} \pm i\sqrt{2}\right\}$ **19.** $d = \dfrac{C - s}{C}$ **20.** $Q = 2A^2 - 4$

21. 154 square centimeters

22. 20 tulips and 30 daffodils

23. 15 feet   **24.** 21.5 gallons

25. 32 miles per hour

Exercise Set 7.1 (page 173)

1. **a.** $(0, 7)$ **b.** $(2, 9)$ **c.** $(-2, 5)$

3. **a.** $\left(0, -\dfrac{3}{2}\right)$ **b.** $(2, 0)$ **c.** $\left(-5, -\dfrac{21}{4}\right)$

5. $(-3, -7), (0, -4), (3, -1)$

7. $(1, 1), \left(2, \dfrac{3}{4}\right), \left(3, \dfrac{3}{5}\right)$

9. $(1, 0), (2, \sqrt{3}), (3, 2\sqrt{2})$

11. $y = 6 - 2x; \{2, -2\}$

13. $y = \dfrac{x + 2}{x}; \{0, 2\}$ **15.** $y = \dfrac{4}{x - 1}; \left\{\dfrac{4}{3}, \dfrac{4}{7}\right\}$

17. $y = \dfrac{2}{x^2 - x - 4}; \left\{-1, -\dfrac{1}{2}\right\}$

19. $y = \dfrac{\pm\sqrt{x + 8}}{2}; \left\{\pm\dfrac{\sqrt{7}}{2}, \pm\dfrac{\sqrt{11}}{2}\right\}$

21. $y = \pm\dfrac{\sqrt{3x^2 - 4}}{2}; \left\{\pm\sqrt{2}, \pm\dfrac{\sqrt{23}}{2}\right\}$

23. $(-4, 1)$ **25.** $(-1, 3)$ **27.** $(3, 8)$ **29.** $\left(3, \dfrac{1}{8}\right)$

31. $k = \dfrac{7}{2}$

Exercise Set 7.2 (page 180)

1. **a.** High: 7°F;   low: −19°F

   b. Above 5°F from noon to 3 P.M.; below −5°F from midnight to 9 A.M. and from 7 P.M. to midnight

   c. 7 A.M.: −10°F; 2 P.M.: 6°F
   10 A.M. and 5 P.M.: 0°F
   6 A.M. and 10 P.M.: −12°F

   d. Between 3 A.M. and 6 A.M.: 8°F;
   between 9 A.M. and noon: 10°F;
   between 6 P.M. and 9 P.M.: 9°F

   e. Increased most rapidly: 9 A.M. to noon;
   decreased most rapidly: 6 P.M. to 9 P.M.

3. **a.** At 43 miles per hour: 28 miles per gallon

   b. 34 miles per gallon: at 47 miles per hour

   c. Best gas mileage: at 65 miles per hour. The graph seems to be leveling off for higher speeds; any improvement in mileage probably would not be appreciable, and mileage might in fact deteriorate.

   d. Road condition, weather conditions, traffic, weight in the car

5. **a.** 12 minutes

   b. First 38 minutes

   c. Approximately from 38 minutes to 55 minutes

7.

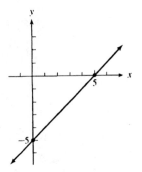

9.

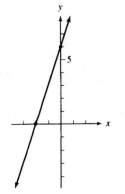

11.

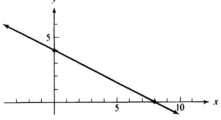

13.

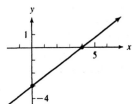

15.

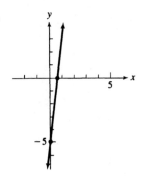

17.

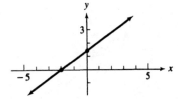

19.

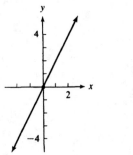

21.

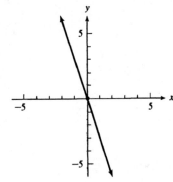

23.

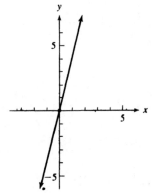

25.

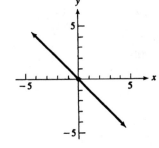

27.

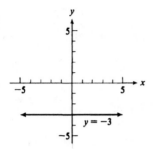

29.

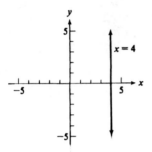

31.

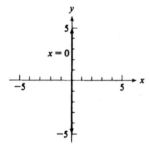

33. *I*   **35.** *I*

Exercise Set 7.3 (page 187)

1. Distance: 5;   slope: $\dfrac{4}{3}$

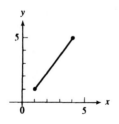

3. Distance: 13;   slope: $\dfrac{12}{5}$

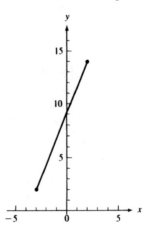

5. Distance: $\sqrt{5}$;   slope: $\dfrac{-1}{2}$

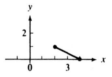

7. Distance: $\sqrt{61}$;   slope: $\dfrac{-5}{6}$

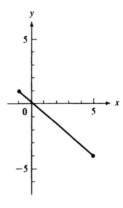

9. Distance: 5;   slope: 0

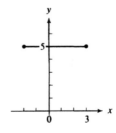

11. Distance: 10; slope: not defined

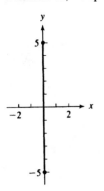

13. $15 + 9\sqrt{5}$

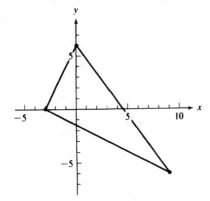

15. 48

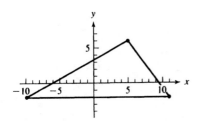

17. The slope of the segment with endpoints $(5, 4)$ and $(3, 0)$ is 2. The slope of the segment with endpoints $(-1, 8)$ and $(-4, 2)$ is 2. Therefore, the line segments are parallel.

19. Identify the given points as $A(0, -7)$, $B(8, -5)$, $C(5, 7)$, and $D(8, -5)$. Then the slopes of AB and CD are

$$\text{slope } AB = \frac{-7 - (-5)}{0 - (8)} = \frac{1}{4}$$

and

$$\text{slope } CD = \frac{7 - (-5)}{5 - 8} = -4$$

and

$$\left(\frac{1}{4}\right)(-4) = -1$$

21. a. 1   **b.** $\frac{1}{4}$ **23. a.** -6 **b.** 0

25. Identify the vertices as $A(0, 6)$, $B(9, -6)$, and $C(-3, 0)$. Then, by the distance formula, $(AB)^2 = 225$ and $(BC)^2 + (AC)^2 = 180 + 45 = 225$; the triangle is a right triangle.

27. Let the given points be $A(2, 4)$, $B(3, 8)$, $C(5, 1)$, and $D(4, -3)$. Since AB and CD have equal slopes $(m = 4)$ and BC and AD have equal slopes $(m = -7/2)$, there are two pairs of parallel sides. Hence, $ABCD$ is a parallelogram.

29. $k = -28$

Exercise Set 7.4 (page 193) 1. $2x - y + 5 = 0$
3. $x + y - 4 = 0$ **5.** $x - 2y + 6 = 0$
7. $3x + 2y - 1 = 0$ **9.** $y + 5 = 0$ **11.** $x + 3 = 0$
13. $x - 7y = -18$ **15.** $x - y = 2$
17. $2x - 5y = 14$ **19.** $4x - 3y = 12$
21. $y = -x + 3$; slope: -1; y-intercept: 3
23. $y = \frac{-3}{2}x + \frac{1}{2}$; slope: $\frac{-3}{2}$; y-intercept: $\frac{1}{2}$
25. $y = \frac{1}{3}x - \frac{2}{3}$; slope: $\frac{1}{3}$; y-intercept: $\frac{-2}{3}$
27. $y = \frac{8}{3}x$; slope: $\frac{8}{3}$; y-intercept: 0
29. $y = 0x - 2$; slope: 0; y-intercept: -2
31. $2x - 3y = 6$ **33.** $2x - y = -4$
35. $2x + y = -6$ **37.** $6x - 4y = -3$
39. $x - 2y = 0$

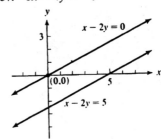

41. $2x + y = 0$

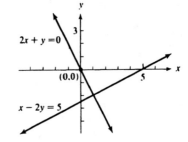

43. a. $y = x$ **b.** $y = -x$

45. $y = -\dfrac{b}{a}x + b$

47. $y = m(x - a)$

Exercise Set 7.5 (page 198)

1. a. $n = 6 + 2t$

b.

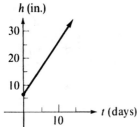

c. 48 inches or 4 feet

d. 33 days

3. a. $A = 250 - 15w$

b.

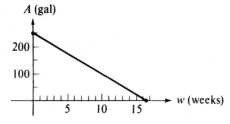

c. 130 gallons

d. 12 weeks

5. a. $t = 2 + \dfrac{n}{15}$

b.

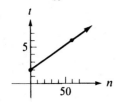

c. 6 hours

d. 90 houses

7. a. $C = 15w - 500$

b.

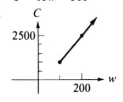

c. 1375 calories

d. 120 pounds

9. a. $0.60r + 0.80p = 4800$

b.

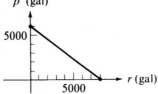

c. 4000 gallons

11. a. $I = 10,000 + 0.03s$

b.

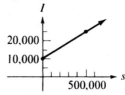

c. $25,000

d. $1,000,000

13. (Exercise 1) t-int.: negative; not meaningful
                        h-int.: 6 (initial height)

15. (Exercise 3) w-int.: $16.\overline{6}$ (weeks to empty tank)
                        A-int.: 250 (tank full)

17. (Exercise 5) n-int.: -30 (not meaningful)
                        t-int.: 2 (length of shift if no deliveries)

19. (Exercise 7) w-int.: $33.\overline{3}$ (no calorie intake; not
                        meaningful)
                        C-int.: -500 (not meaningful)

21. (Exercise 9) r-int.: 8000 (regular gas only)
                        p-int.: 6000 (premium gas only)

23. (Exercise 11) s-int.: (negative; not meaningful)
                         A-int.: $10,000 (basic salary only)

25. a.

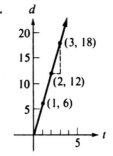

b. $\dfrac{\Delta d}{\Delta t} = \dfrac{(18 - 12) \text{ miles}}{(3 - 2) \text{ hours}} = 6$

c. Slope is the number of miles covered per hour.

27. **a.** $C = 80x + 5000$

b.

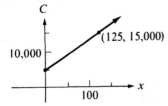

c. $m = 80$ dollars/bike is the cost of making each bike.

29. **a.** $k = 2.2p$

b.

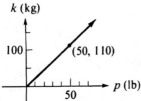

c. $m = 2.2$ kilograms/pound is the conversion factor from pounds to kilograms.

31. **a.** $d = 65t + 265$

b.

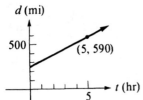

c. $m = 65$ miles/hour is their average speed.

7.

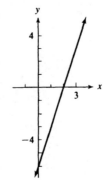

8.

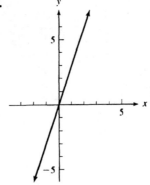

9.

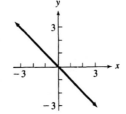

Review Exercises (page 201)

1. **a.** $(0, -2)$ **b.** $(6, 0)$ **c.** $(3, -1)$

2. $(2, 1), (4, 5),$ and $(6, 9)$

3. $y = \dfrac{3}{x - 2x^2} \left(x \neq 0, x \neq \dfrac{1}{2} \right)$ **4.** $y = \pm\dfrac{1}{3}\sqrt{x^2 - 4}$

5.

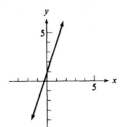

6.

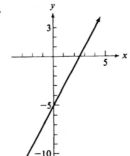

10.

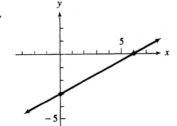

11.

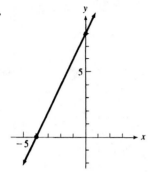

12.

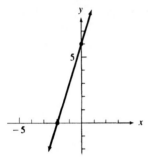

13.

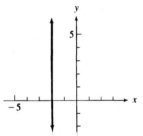

14.

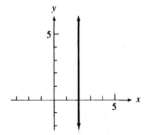

15. a. $\sqrt{178}$ **b.** $\dfrac{13}{3}$ **16. a.** $3\sqrt{5}$ **b.** -2

17. a. Slope of $P_1P_2 = 1$ and slope of $P_3P_4 = 1$; therefore, P_1P_2 and P_3P_4 are parallel.

b. Slope of $P_1P_2 = 1$ and slope of $P_1P_3 = -1$; since $1(-1) = -1$, the lines are perpendicular.

18. $2x - y - 1 = 0$ **19.** $x + 2y = 0$

20. a. $y = 3x - 4$ **b.** slope: 3; y-intercept: -4

21. a. $y = -\dfrac{2}{3}x + 2$ **b.** slope: $-\dfrac{2}{3}$; y-intercept: 2

22. $6x - y = 19$ **23.** $x - 4y = -12$

24. $2x - 5y = -10$

25. a. $C = 20x + 2000$

b.

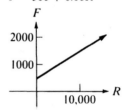

c. \$22,000

d. 400

26. a. $F = 500 + 0.10R$

b.

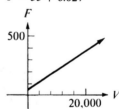

c. \$1700

27. a. $F = 35 + 0.02V$

b.

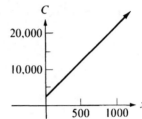

c. \$435

28. a. $R = 500 - 8t$

b.

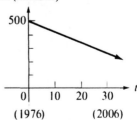

c. 308 million tons

d. Year 2038 $\left(62\dfrac{1}{2}\text{ years from }1976\right)$

29. a. $5A + 2C = 1000$

b.

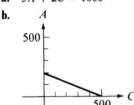

c. 200 tickets

d. *x*-int.: 500 (Only children's tickets are sold.)
y-int.: 200 (Only adults' tickets are sold.)

30. a. $W = 18x + 80$

b.

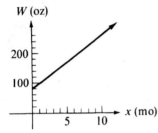

c. 242 ounces   or   15 pounds, 2 ounces

d. $3\frac{5}{9}$ months   or   3 months, 17 days

Cumulative Exercises (page 203) 1. $\dfrac{a^3b^3}{c^5}$ **2.** $\sqrt[3]{4}$

3. $\dfrac{y-2}{2(y+2)}$ **4.** -4 **5.** $\dfrac{1}{x+1}$ **6.** $\dfrac{-1}{x-1}$

7. $x = \dfrac{b+2}{a}$; $x = \dfrac{b-2}{a}$

8.

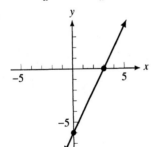

9. $1 + 3i\sqrt{3}$ **10.** $\dfrac{x^2}{y-x}$ **11.** $k \geqslant 0$

12. $2x + y = 7$ **13.** $\sqrt{3}(\sqrt{6} - 2\sqrt{2} + 1)$

14. $(3x - 2y - 2)(3x + 2y - 2)$ **15.** $\{8\}$

16. $\{-3, 2\}$ **17.** $\left\{\dfrac{3}{2}, 5\right\}$ **18.** $\{-6\}$ **19.** $\{82\}$

20. $\{1 \pm i\sqrt{2}\}$ **21.** $\$1000$ **22.** Width: 9 inches
Length: 12 inches

23. approximately $\$142{,}222$ **24.** 5 miles per hour

25. 600,000 copies

Exercise Set 8.1 (page 208)

1. a. $y = 6 - 2x$ **b.** function

3. a. $y = \dfrac{x-8}{2}$ **b.** function

5. a. $y = \dfrac{4}{x-2}$ **b.** function

7. a. $y = \dfrac{6}{x-4}$ **b.** function

9. a. $y = \pm\sqrt{8 - 2x^2}$ **b.** not a function

11. a. $y = \pm 2\sqrt{x^2 - 4}$ **b.** not a function

13. function   **15.** not a function

17. not a function   **19.** function

21. not a function   **23.** real numbers

25. real numbers, $x \neq 5$

27. real numbers, $x \neq -\dfrac{1}{2}$

29. real numbers, $x \geqslant -5$

31. real numbers, $1 \leqslant x < 2,$ $x > 2$

33. real numbers, $x \neq 1$ **35.** 9   **37.** $\underline{3}$

39. -6

41. a. $-2, 0, 5$ **b.** 2
   c. *x*-int.: -2 and 1;   *y*-int.: -2 **d.** 5   **e.** 3

43. a. $-1, 2$ **b.** 3 and $-\dfrac{3}{2}$
   c. *x*-int.: $-2, 2,$ and 4;   *y*-int.: 4
   d. $4; -5$ **e.** $0; 5$

45. a. $0, \dfrac{1}{2}, 0$

   b. $\dfrac{3}{4}$

   c. $-\dfrac{5\pi}{6}, -\dfrac{\pi}{6}, \dfrac{7\pi}{6}, \dfrac{11\pi}{6}$

   d. $1, -1$

   e. Maximum values at $-\dfrac{3\pi}{2}, \dfrac{\pi}{2}$;

   minimum values at $-\dfrac{\pi}{2}, \dfrac{3\pi}{2}$

47. a. $5a - 3$
   b. $5b - 3$
   c. $5a + 5b - 3$

49. a. $a^2 + 3a$
   b. $b^2 + 3b$
   c. $a^2 + 2ab + b^2 + 3a + 3b$

51. a. $3x + 3h - 4$

    b. $3h$

    c. 3

53. a. $x^2 + 2xh + h^2 - 3x - 3h + 5$

    b. $2xh + h^2 - 3h$

    c. $2x + h - 3$

55. a. $x^3 + 3x^2h + 3xh^2 + h^3 + 2x + 2h - 1$

    b. $3x^2h + 3xh^2 + h^3 + 2h$

    c. $3x^2 + 3xh + h^2 + 2$

57. -2 **59.** $1, 4$ **61.** $-2, 3$

63. a. $f(0) = 0;\ g(0) = 5$

    b. $0, -\dfrac{3}{2}$

    c. $\dfrac{5}{6}$

    d. $\dfrac{1}{2}, -5$

65. a. $f(0) = \sqrt{2};\ g(0) = -4$

    b. -2

    c. $\dfrac{4}{3}$

    d. 2

Exercise Set 8.2 (page 216)   **1.** 3 **3.** 200

5. 2 **7.** $\dfrac{32}{9}$ **9.** 264 **11.** $\dfrac{8}{3}$ **13.** 1400

15. 1600 feet   **17.** 120 kilograms/square centimeter

19. 6240 pounds/square foot   **21.** 55.9 centimeters

23. a. $\dfrac{24}{6^2} = \dfrac{y}{2^2}$ **b.** $\dfrac{8}{3}$

25. a. $56 \cdot 200 = y \cdot 8$ **b.** 1400

27. a. $\dfrac{400}{5^{-2}} = \dfrac{d}{10^2}$ **b.** 1600 feet

29. a. $15 \cdot 500 = P \cdot 62.5$

    b. 120 kilograms/square centimeter

31. a. $\dfrac{748.8}{12} = \dfrac{d}{100}$ **b.** 6240 pounds/square foot

33. a. $220 \cdot 65 = 256 \cdot l$

    b. Approximately 55.9 centimeters

35. $C = 10n + 5000;\ \$11,400$

37. $C = 52.5s;\ \$3150$

39. $P = 2w + \dfrac{6400}{w};$ 240 feet

41. $r = \dfrac{C}{2\pi};$ 7.48 meters (approx.)

43. $V = \dfrac{1}{4}\pi h^3;$ 785.4 cubic centimeters

45. $\dfrac{1}{4}$ of original illumination

47. 81% of original resistance

49. $D = \sqrt{625t^2 + (700 - 10t)^2};$ 1503 feet (approx.)

Exercise Set 8.3 (page 228)

1.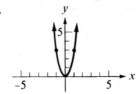

3.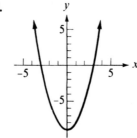

5.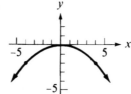

7.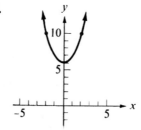

9.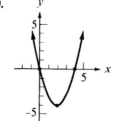

11.

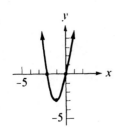

13.

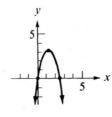

31.   Vertex: $\left(\dfrac{1}{4}, -\dfrac{23}{8}\right)$
y-int.: -3
x-int.: none

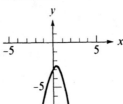

15. $(1, 1)$ **17.** $\left(\dfrac{5}{2}, -\dfrac{13}{4}\right)$

19. $\left(\dfrac{2}{3}, \dfrac{1}{9}\right)$ **21.** $(-4.5, 18.5)$

23.   Vertex: $\left(\dfrac{5}{2}, -\dfrac{9}{4}\right)$
y-int.: 4
x-int.: 1, 4

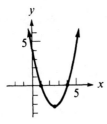

25.   Vertex: $\left(\dfrac{7}{4}, \dfrac{81}{8}\right)$
y-int.: 4
x-int.: $-\dfrac{1}{2}$, 4

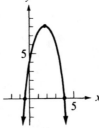

33.   Vertex: $(-1, -2)$
y-int.: -1
x-int.: -2.4, 0.4

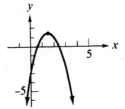

27.   Vertex: $(-0.5, -1.35)$
y-int.: -1.2
x-int.: -2, 1

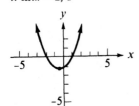

35.   Vertex: $\left(\dfrac{3}{2}, \dfrac{3}{2}\right)$
y-int.: -3
x-int.: 0.6, 2.4

29.   Vertex: $(-2, 3)$
y-int.: 7
x-int.: none

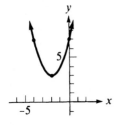

37.   a.   2 seconds, 64 feet
   b. d (ft)

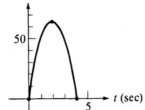

39. a. 625 square inches

b.

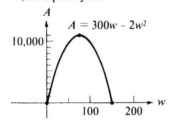

41. a. 11,250 square yards

b.

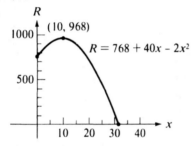

43. a. $44

b.

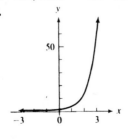

Many different answers besides those given here are possible for the following exercises.

45. $y = x^2 + 2$ and $y = 2x^2 + 2$

47. $y = x^2 + 2x - 5$ and $y = -2x^2 - x - 5$

49. $y = x^2 + x - 6$ and $y = -x^2 - x + 6$

Exercise Set 8.4 (page 236)   **1.**   1, 3, 9

3.   1, 10, 100   **5.** $\dfrac{1}{2}, 1, 2$ **7.** $\dfrac{1}{4}, \dfrac{1}{8}, \dfrac{1}{16}$

9. $27, \dfrac{1}{27}$ **11.**   0.14, 19.68   **13.**   0.83, 0.12

15.   6.70, 11.66   **17.**   11.04, 0.09

19.

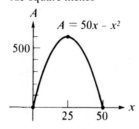

21.

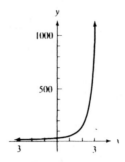

23.

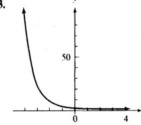

25.

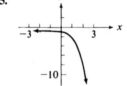

27.

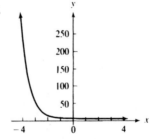

29.

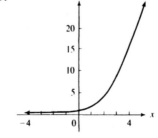

31.

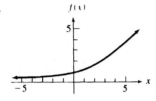

33.

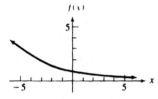

35. a. $P(t) = 300(2)^t$
   b. 76,800;   492
   c.

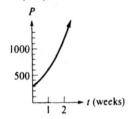

37. a. $P(t) = 20,000(2.5)^{t/6}$
   b. 36,840;   424,127
   c. P (thousands)

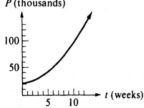

39. a. $P(t) = 250,000(0.75)^{t/2}$
   b. 162,379;   79,101
   c. P (thousands)

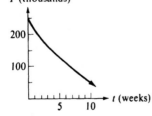

41. a. $L(d) = (0.85)^{d/4}$
   b. 44%;   16%
   c. L (%)

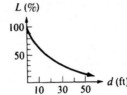

43.

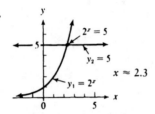

45. an increasing function for all $a > 1$ and a
   decreasing function for all $0 < a < 1$

Exercise Set 8.5 (page 241)

1. $\{(-2, -2), (2, 2)\}$; a function
3. $\{(3, 1), (3, 2), (4, 3)\}$; not a function
5. $\{(1, 1), (3, 2), (3, 3)\}$; not a function
7. a. $2y + 4x = 7$
   b.

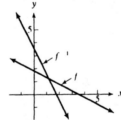

   c. a function

9. a. $y - 3x = 6$
   b.

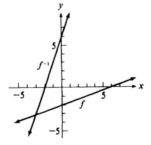

   c. a function

11. a. $x = y^2 - 4y$

b.

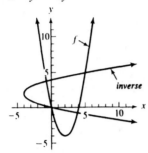

c. not a function

13. a. $x = \sqrt{4 + y^2}$

b.

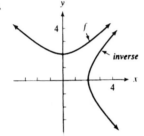

c. not a function

15. a. $x = |y|$

b.

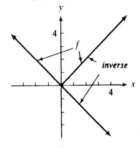

c. not a function

17.

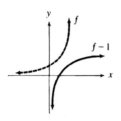

19.

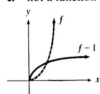

21.

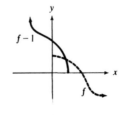

23. $f^{-1}: y = x;$ $f[f^{-1}(x)] = f[x] = x;$
$f^{-1}[f(x)] = f^{-1}[x] = x$

25. $f^{-1}: y = \dfrac{4 - x}{2};$

$$f[f^{-1}(x)] = f\left[\frac{4 - x}{2}\right] = -2\left[\frac{4 - x}{2}\right] + 4$$
$$= -4 + x + 4 = x;$$
$$f^{-1}[f(x)] = f^{-1}[-2x + 4] = 2 - \frac{1}{2}[-2x + 4]$$
$$= 2 + x - 2 = x$$

27. $f^{-1}: y = \dfrac{4x + 12}{3};$

$$f[f^{-1}(x)] = f\left[\frac{4x + 12}{3}\right] = \frac{3}{4}\left[\frac{4x + 12}{3}\right] - 3$$
$$= x + 3 - 3 = x;$$
$$f^{-1}[f(x)] = f^{-1}\left[\frac{3x - 12}{4}\right] = \frac{4}{3}\left[\frac{3x - 12}{4}\right] + 4$$
$$= x - 4 + 4 = x$$

Review Exercises (page 243)

1. a. $y = \dfrac{6 - 3x}{4}$

    b. function

    c. all real numbers

2. a. $y = \dfrac{2}{x - 5}$

    b. function

    c. all real numbers, $x \neq 5$

3. a. $y = \sqrt{x + 4}$

    b. function

    c. all real numbers, $x \geqslant -4$

4. a. $y = \pm\sqrt{2x^2 + 6}$

    b. not a function

5. function   **6.** not a function   **7.** not a function

8. function   **9. a.** 2   **b.** h

10. a. 10   **b.** $4x + 2h - 3$

11. a. 3 and 5

    b. 1 and 3

    c. x-intercepts: -3 and 4;
        y-intercept: 2

    d. maximum: 5 at $t = 2$

12. a. -2 and 3

    b. $-5, -\dfrac{1}{2}$, and 4

  c. x-intercepts: -4, -1, and 5; y-intercept: 3

  d. local minimum: -3 at $t = -2$; no absolute minimum

13. 1 and 6   **14.** 0 and $\dfrac{3}{2}$

15. **a.** $y = \dfrac{144}{t^2}$ **b.** $\dfrac{9}{4}$ **16.** **a.** $y = \dfrac{5s^2}{t}$ **b.** $\dfrac{45}{4}$

17. **a.** $s = \dfrac{7t^2}{4}$ **b.** 63 cm

18. **a.** $V = \dfrac{4T}{P}$ **b.** 32 cu units

19. **a.** $A = \dfrac{\sqrt{3}}{4}s^2$ **b.** $4\sqrt{3}$ sq cm

20. **a.** $A = \dfrac{1}{2}x\sqrt{144 - x^2}$ **b.** $16\sqrt{2}$ sq cm

21.

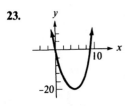

Vertex: $(0, 0)$
x- and y-int.: $(0, 0)$

22.

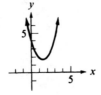

Vertex: $(0, -4)$
x-int.: -2, 2
y-int.: -4

23.

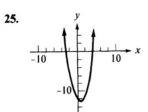

Vertex: $\left(\dfrac{9}{2}, -\dfrac{81}{4}\right)$

24.

Vertex: $(-1, 2)$
x-int.: -2, 0
y-int.: 0

25.

Vertex: $\left(\dfrac{1}{2}, -\dfrac{49}{4}\right)$
x-int.: -3, 4
y-int.: -12

26.

Vertex: $\left(\dfrac{1}{4}, -\dfrac{31}{8}\right)$
x-int.: none
y-int.: -4

27.

Vertex: $(1, 5)$
x-int.: $1 + \sqrt{5}$, $1 - \sqrt{5}$
y-int.: 4

28.

Vertex: $\left(\dfrac{3}{2}, \dfrac{7}{4}\right)$
x-int.: none
y-int.: 4

29. 42 trees per acre

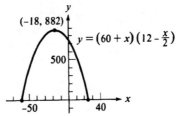

$(-18, 882)$

$y = (60 + x)\left(12 - \dfrac{x}{2}\right)$

30. \$35

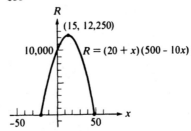

$(15, 12{,}250)$

$R = (20 + x)(500 - 10x)$

31. $\dfrac{1}{1000}, \dfrac{1}{10}, 1, 10, 1000$ **32.** $8, 2, 1, \dfrac{1}{2}, \dfrac{1}{8}$

33.

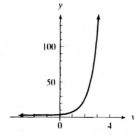

34.

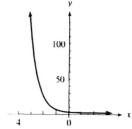

35. a and d   **36.** b and d

37.

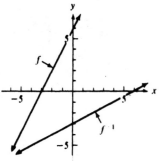

38.

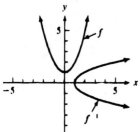

Cumulative Exercises (page 245) 1. $-3x - 1$

2. $-\dfrac{b}{at}$ **3.** $2(x - 3)(3x - 8)$

4. $(3a^2 + b)(9a^4 - 3a^2b + b^2)$

5. $\dfrac{-x^2 + 3x - 5}{(x - 3)(x - 1)(x + 2)}$ **6.** $\dfrac{-a^3}{2(a - 1)(a - 2)}$

7. $3t^2 + 6t + 5 + \dfrac{13}{t - 2}$ **8.** $(3x)^{1/4} + xy^{2/3}$

9. $l = \dfrac{A - 2a^2}{4w}$ **10.** $\{20\}$

11. $x = \dfrac{-k \pm \sqrt{k^2 - 4k + 16}}{2}$ **12.** $\left\{-\dfrac{1}{3}, \dfrac{1}{5}\right\}$

13.

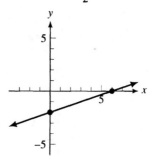

14.

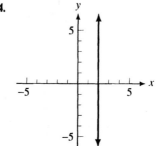

15. Use the distance formula:
One side: $\sqrt{(5 - 2)^2 + (-2 + 6)^2} = 5$;
Another side: $\sqrt{(1 - 5)^2 + (1 + 2)^2} = 5$
The two sides are equal. Hence, the triangle is isosceles.

16. $2x + 3y = 11$ **17.** $9x - 2y = 3$

18. $x - 3y = 10$ **19.** $2x + h = 3$

20.

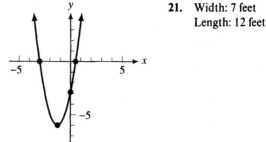

21. Width: 7 feet
Length: 12 feet

22. $1\dfrac{1}{2}$ and 3 inches   **23.** $1042.41

24. **a.** $W = 15n$ **b.**

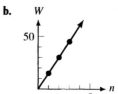

25. 400 square inches

Exercise Set 9.1 (page 249)   **1.** 2   **3.** 3   **5.** $\dfrac{1}{2}$

7. -1 **9.** 1   **11.** 2   **13.** -1

15. $\log_4 16 = 2$ **17.** $\log_3 27 = 3$ **19.** $\log_{1/2} \dfrac{1}{4} = 2$

21. $\log_8 \dfrac{1}{2} = -\dfrac{1}{3}$ **23.** $\log_{10} 100 = 2$

25. $\log_{10} 0.1 = -1$ **27** $2^6 = 64$ **29.** $3^2 = 9$

31. $\left(\dfrac{1}{3}\right)^{-2} = 9$ **33.** $10^3 = 1000$ **35.** $10^{-2} = 0.01$

37. 2   **39.** 2   **41.** 64   **43.** -3 **45.** 100

47. 4   **49.** 1   **51.** 0   **53.** 1   **55.** 0

57. $x > 9$ **59.**

61.

Exercise Set 9.2 (page 253)

1. $\log_b 2 + \log_b x$ **3.** $\log_b 3 + \log_b x + \log_b y$

5. $\log_b x - \log_b y$ **7.** $\log_b x + \log_b y - \log_b z$

9. $3 \log_b x$ **11.** $\dfrac{1}{2} \log_b x$ **13.** $\dfrac{2}{3} \log_b x$

15. $2 \log_b x + 3 \log_b y$ **17.** $\dfrac{1}{2} \log_b x + \log_b y - 2 \log_b z$

19. $\dfrac{1}{3} \log_{10} x + \dfrac{2}{3} \log_{10} y - \dfrac{1}{3} \log_{10} z$

21. $\dfrac{3}{2} \log_{10} x - \dfrac{1}{2} \log_{10} y$

23. $\log_{10} 2 + \log_{10} \pi + \dfrac{1}{2} \log_{10} l - \dfrac{1}{2} \log_{10} g$

25. $\dfrac{1}{2} \log_{10}(s - a) + \dfrac{1}{2} \log_{10}(s - b)$ **27.** 0.7781

29. -0.3980 **31.** 0.9542   **33.** 0.8751

35. -8.0970 **37.** 1.8751   **39.** $\log_b 4$

41. $\log_b 2$ **43.** $\log_b \dfrac{x^2}{y^3}$ **45.** $\log_b \dfrac{x^3 y}{z^2}$

47. $\log_{10} \dfrac{\sqrt{xy}}{z}$ **49.** $\log_b x^{-2}$ or $\log_b \dfrac{1}{x^2}$

51. $\{500\}$ **53.** $\{4\}$ **55.** $\{3\}$

57. Substitute arbitrary numbers, for example, 1 and 10, for x and y in the given equation.

$$\log_{10}(1 + 10) \overset{?}{=} \log_{10} 1 + \log_{10} 10$$
$$\log_{10} 11 \overset{?}{=} 0 + 1$$
$$\log_{10} 11 \neq 1$$

Since $\log_{10} 11 \neq 1$, $\log_{10}(x + y) \neq \log_{10} x + \log_{10} y$ for all $x, y > 0$.

59. Show that the left and right members of the equality reduce to the same quantity.

For the left side:
$$\log_b 4 + \log_b 8 = \log_b 2^2 + \log_b 2^3$$
$$= 2 \log_b 2 + 3 \log_b 2 = 5 \log_b 2$$

For the right side:
$$\log_b 64 - \log_b 2 = \log_b 2^6 - \log_b 2$$
$$= 6 \log_b 2 - \log_b 2 = 5 \log_b 2$$

61. For the left side:
$$2 \log_b 6 - \log_b 9 = \log_b 6^2 - \log_b 9$$
$$= \log_b 36 - \log_b 9 = \log_b \dfrac{36}{9} = \log_b 4$$

For the right side:
$$2 \log_b 2 = \log_b 2^2 = \log_b 4$$

63. For the left side:
$$\dfrac{1}{2} \log_b 12 - \dfrac{1}{2} \log_b 3 = \dfrac{1}{2}(\log_b 12 - \log_b 3)$$
$$= \dfrac{1}{2}\left(\log_b \dfrac{12}{3}\right) = \dfrac{1}{2}(\log_b 2^2) = \log_b 2$$

For the right side:
$$\dfrac{1}{3} \log_b 8 = \log_b 8^{1/3} = \log_b 2$$

Exercise Set 9.3 (page 261)   **1.** 2   **3.** -4

5. 0   **7.** 0.8280   **9.** 1.9227   **11.** 2.5011

13. $0.9101 - 1$ **15.** $0.9031 - 2$ **17.** 2.3945

19. 4.10   **21.** 36.7   **23.** 0.0642   **25.** 0.00718

27. 0.297   **29.** 0.0503   **31.** 0.00205   **33.** 7.52

35. 784   **37.** 0.357   **39.** 1.5373   **41.** 0.5655

43. 4.4817   **45.** 0.0907   **47.** 1.3610

49. 2.7726   **51.** $0.0837 - 1$ or -0.9163

53. 1.1735   **55.** 6.0496   **57.** 90.017   **59.** 2.83

61. 714.99   **63.** 2.99

Exercise Set 9.4 (page 265)

1. 2   **3.** −4   **5.** 1
7. 4   **9.** 1.7348   **11.** 3.3700   **13.** −1.1367
15. −0.15851   **17.** 41.687   **19.** 0.13490
21. 129.72   **23.** 0.58157   **25.** 25.704
27. 3.3113   **29.** 0.050119   **31.** 1.3610
33. 2.7726   **35.** 1.8563   **37.** 1.4918
39. 10.381   **41.** 0.30119   **43.** 0.67032
45. 4.1371   **47.** 1.8776   **49.** 0.074274
51. 5.39   **53.** 411.24   **55.** 5.13

10. a. $\{1\}$ **b.** $\{5\}$ **11. a.** −0.147   **b.** 3.26
12. a. 431   **b.** 0.0379   **13. a.** 17.2   **b.** 0.285
14. a. 2.29   **b.** 0.273
15. a. 1.95   **b.** −0.916
16. a. 2.08   **b.** 14.9   **17.** 0.114   **18.** 4.13
19. 0.453   **20.** 7.05   **21.** 4.61   **22.** 8.05
23. 4.53   **24.** 1.78   **25.** 2.46   **26.** 7.32
27. 0 milligrams; 3.9 milligrams   **28.** 461.6 lumens
29. 13.5 years   **30.** 1.7 seconds

Exercise Set 9.5 (page 269)

1. 0.693   **3.** 1.37
5. 3.83   **7.** 0.642   **9.** 3.81   **11.** −1.20
13. 0.977   **15.** −3.72   **17.** 0.768   **19.** −0.684
21. 0.828   **23.** 7.52   **25.** −2.97   **27.** 1.65
29. −3.07   **31.** 2.63   **33.** 2.89   **35.** 2.06
37. 2.81   **39.** 0.89   **41.** ±1.40   **43.** −2.10
45. $t = \dfrac{1}{k}\ln y$ **47.** $t = 2(\ln T - \ln R)$
49. $k = e^{T/T_0} - 10$
51. $\ln N = \dfrac{\log_{10} N}{\log_{10} e} \approx \dfrac{\log_{10} N}{0.43429} \approx 2.303 \log_{10} N$

Exercise Set 9.6 (page 271)

1. 9.60 inches of mercury
3. 1.91 miles   **5.** 3.34 miles
7. a. 19,960,000
   b. 25,349,000; 32,193,000; 40,884,000
9. 1.56%   **11.** 18.7 years   **13.** 12.1 grams
15. 99.3 volts   **17.** 2.77 seconds   **19.** 17.5%
21. 13.5%   **23.** $15,529.25; $16,035.68
25. 16 years

Review Exercises (page 273)

1. a. $\log_9 27 = \dfrac{3}{2}$ **b.** $\log_{4/9}\dfrac{2}{3} = \dfrac{1}{2}$
2. a. $5^4 = 625$ **b.** $10^{-4} = 0.0001$
3. a. 2   **b.** 8   **4. a.** 0.01   **b.** −1
5. a. 2   **b.** −1   **6. a.** 3   **b.** −3
7. a. $\log_b 3 + 2\log_b x + \log_b y$
   b. $\log_b y + \dfrac{1}{2}\log_b x - 2\log_b z$
8. a. 1.5562   **b.** 0.6276
9. a. $\log_b \dfrac{x^5}{y^2}$ **b.** $\log_b \sqrt[3]{\dfrac{xz^2}{y^4}}$

Cumulative Exercises (page 275)

1. $\dfrac{-bt^7}{a^5 c^4}$
2. $y^2 z^5 \sqrt[3]{5xy^2 z}$ **3.** $\dfrac{x+5}{(x+2)(3x-1)}$
4. $\dfrac{a^3}{-2a^2 + 6a - 4}$ **5.** $a^2 b(a^2 + b^2)(a-b)(a+b)$
6. $3t^2 + 6t + 5 + \dfrac{13}{t-2}$ **7.** $\dfrac{2\sqrt{x-1} - x}{x-2}$
8. $x = \dfrac{y \pm \sqrt{8 - y^2}}{2}$ **9.** 0   **10.** $(-2, 8)$
11. $3x - 2y = -8$ **12.** $\log_b\left(\dfrac{x^{1/2}}{y^2 z^3}\right)$
13. $\{\pm\sqrt{38}\}$ **14.** $\{0.3996\}$
15. $x = \dfrac{-k \pm \sqrt{k^2 - 8k + 32}}{4}$ **16.** $\left\{\dfrac{-1 \pm \sqrt{17}}{2}\right\}$

17.

18.

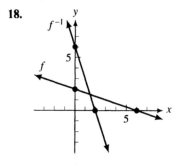

19.

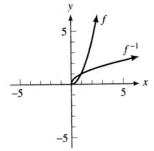

20.

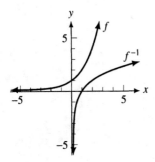

21. 10 inches   **22.** $x - 3y = 10$

23. approximately 14 lumens   **24.** 9 yards by 9 yards

25. approximately $7\frac{1}{2}$ years

Exercise Set 10.1 (page 282)

1. $\{(3, 2)\}$

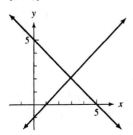

3. $\{(2, 1)\}$

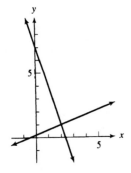

5. $\{(-5, 4)\}$

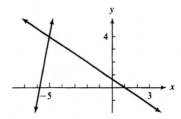

7. $\{(1, 2)\}$

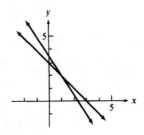

9. $\{(1, 0)\}$

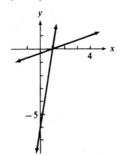

11. $\{(1, 2)\}$

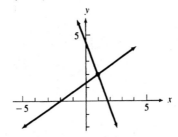

13. $\left\{\left(0, \frac{3}{2}\right)\right\}$

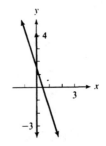

15. $\left\{\left(\frac{2}{3}, -1\right)\right\}$

17. $\{(1, 2)\}$

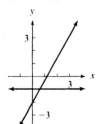

19. $\left\{\left(-\frac{19}{5}, -\frac{18}{5}\right)\right\}$

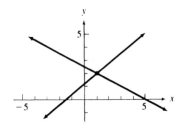

21. infinitely many solutions
23. $\varnothing$; no solutions   **25.** one solution
27. $\varnothing$; no solutions   **29.** one solution

31. one solution   **33.** $\left\{\left(\frac{1}{5}, \frac{1}{2}\right)\right\}$ **35.** $\{(-5, 3)\}$

37. $\left\{\left(\frac{1}{6}, \frac{1}{2}\right)\right\}$

Exercise Set 10.2 (page 286) **1.** $\{(1, 2, -1)\}$
3. $\{(2, -2, 0)\}$ **5.** $\{(2, 2, 1)\}$ **7.** $\{(3, -1, -1)\}$
9. $\{(1, -3, 4)\}$ **11.** $\{(0, -2, 3)\}$ **13.** $\{(4, -2, 2)\}$
15. $\{(1, 1, 0)\}$ **17.** $\left\{\left(\frac{1}{2}, -\frac{1}{2}, \frac{1}{3}\right)\right\}$

19. no unique solution   **21.** $\left\{\left(\frac{1}{2}, 0, 3\right)\right\}$
23. no unique solution   **25.** $\{(-1, 3, 0)\}$
27. no unique solution   **29.** $\left\{\left(\frac{1}{2}, \frac{1}{2}, 3\right)\right\}$
31. $\{(1, 1, 1)\}$ **33.** $\{(1, 2, -2)\}$

Exercise Set 10.3 (page 290) **1.** 1   **3.** -12
5. 2   **7.** 5   **9.** $\{(1, 1)\}$ **11.** $\{(2, 2)\}$
13. $\{(6, 4)\}$ **15.** inconsistent, $\varnothing$ **17.** $\{(4, 1)\}$
19. $\left\{\left(\frac{1}{a+b}, \frac{1}{a+b}\right)\right\}$ **21.** $\begin{vmatrix} a & a \\ b & b \end{vmatrix} = ab - ab = 0$

23. $\begin{vmatrix} a_1 & b_1 \\ a_2 & b_2 \end{vmatrix} = a_1 b_2 - a_2 b_1;$ $-\begin{vmatrix} b_1 & a_1 \\ b_2 & a_2 \end{vmatrix}$
$= -(b_1 a_2 - b_2 a_1) = -b_1 a_2 + b_2 a_1$
$= a_1 b_2 - a_2 b_1$

25. $\begin{vmatrix} ka & a \\ kb & b \end{vmatrix} = kab - kba = 0$

27. Since $D_x = \begin{vmatrix} c_1 & b_1 \\ c_2 & b_2 \end{vmatrix} = c_1 b_2 - c_2 b_1 = 0,$ then
$b_1 c_2 = b_2 c_1.$
Since $D_y = \begin{vmatrix} a_1 & c_1 \\ a_2 & c_2 \end{vmatrix} = a_1 c_2 - a_2 c_1 = 0,$ then
$a_1 c_2 = a_2 c_1.$
In the proportion $\frac{b_1 c_2}{a_1 c_2} = \frac{b_2 c_1}{a_2 c_1},$ if c_1 and c_2
are not both 0, then $\frac{b_1}{a_1} = \frac{b_2}{a_2},$ from which
$a_1 b_2 = a_2 b_1$ and $a_1 b_2 - a_2 b_1 = 0.$ Since
$D = \begin{vmatrix} a_1 & b_1 \\ a_2 & b_2 \end{vmatrix} = a_1 b_2 - a_2 b_1,$ it follows that $D = 0.$

Exercise Set 10.4 (page 294) **1.** 3   **3.** 9   **5.** 0
7. -1 **9.** -5 **11.** 0   **13.** x^3 **15.** 0
17. $-2ab^2$ **19.** $\{(1, 1, 1)\}$ **21.** $\{(1, 1, 0)\}$
23. $\{(1, -2, 3)\}$ **25.** $\{(3, -1, -2)\}$
27. no unique solution   **29.** $\left\{\left(1, -\frac{1}{3}, \frac{1}{2}\right)\right\}$
31. $\{(-5, 3, 2)\}$
33. Expanding about the elements of the third column of
the given determinant produces
$$a \begin{vmatrix} y & y \\ z & z \end{vmatrix} - b \begin{vmatrix} x & x \\ z & z \end{vmatrix} + c \begin{vmatrix} x & x \\ y & y \end{vmatrix} = 0 + 0 + 0 = 0$$

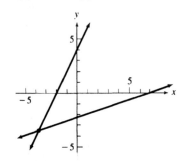

35. For the left side: $\begin{vmatrix} 1 & 2 & 3 \\ 4 & 5 & 6 \\ 0 & 0 & 1 \end{vmatrix} = 1\begin{vmatrix} 1 & 2 \\ 4 & 5 \end{vmatrix} = 5 - 8 = -3.$

For the right side:

$-\begin{vmatrix} 4 & 5 & 6 \\ 1 & 2 & 3 \\ 0 & 0 & 1 \end{vmatrix} = -1\begin{vmatrix} 4 & 5 \\ 1 & 2 \end{vmatrix} = -1(8 - 5) = -1(3) = -3.$

37. Expanding about the elements of the first row produces

$$x\begin{vmatrix} -1 & 1 \\ 3 & 1 \end{vmatrix} - y\begin{vmatrix} 4 & 1 \\ 2 & 1 \end{vmatrix} + 1\begin{vmatrix} 4 & -1 \\ 2 & 3 \end{vmatrix} = 0$$
$$-4x - 2y + 14 = 0$$

which is equivalent to

$$2x + y = 7$$

and is satisfied by $(4, -1)$ and $(2, 3)$.

Exercise Set 10.5 (page 300)   **1.** $\begin{bmatrix} 1 & -3 \\ 0 & 7 \end{bmatrix}$

3. $\begin{bmatrix} 2 & 6 \\ 4 & 0 \end{bmatrix}$ **5.** $\begin{bmatrix} 1 & -2 & 2 \\ 0 & 7 & -5 \\ 0 & 9 & -11 \end{bmatrix}$

7. $\begin{bmatrix} -1 & 4 & 3 \\ \frac{3}{2} & 0 & -\frac{5}{2} \\ \frac{3}{2} & 0 & \frac{3}{2} \end{bmatrix}$ **9.** $\begin{bmatrix} -2 & 1 & -3 \\ 0 & 4 & -6 \\ 0 & 0 & 5 \end{bmatrix}$

11. $\{(2,3)\}$ **13.** $\{(-2,1)\}$ **15.** $\{(3,-1)\}$

17. $\left\{\left(-\frac{7}{3}, \frac{17}{3}\right)\right\}$ **19.** $\{(1,2,2)\}$

21. $\left\{\left(2, -\frac{1}{2}, \frac{1}{2}\right)\right\}$ **23.** $\{(-3,1,-3)\}$

25. $\left\{\left(\frac{5}{4}, \frac{5}{2}, -\frac{1}{2}\right)\right\}$ **27.** $\{(5,1,3,2)\}$

29. $\{(3,-1,-2,0)\}$

Exercise Set 10.6 (page 303) One possible system of equations is shown for each exercise. Other systems that yield correct solutions are possible.

1. **a.** Larger number: x
Smaller number: y
b. $x - y = 6$
$x + y = 24$
c. Numbers are 15 and 9

3. **a.** One integer: x
Next consecutive integer: y

b. $x + 1 = y$
$\frac{1}{3}x + \frac{1}{2}y = 33$
c. Integers are 39 and 40

5. **a.** Number of adults: x
Number of children: y
b. $x + y = 82$
$1.50x + 0.85y = 93.10$
c. 36 adults and 46 children

7. **a.** Amount invested at 10%: x
Amount invested at 8%: y
b. $x + y = 2000$
$0.10x + 0.08y = 184$
c. $1200 at 10% and $800 at 8%

9. **a.** Number of first-class passengers: x
Number of tourist passengers: y
b. $x + y = 42$
$80x + 64y = 2880$
c. 12 first-class passengers and 30 tourist passengers

11. **a.** Rate of automobile: x
Rate of airplane: y
b. $x + 120 = y$
$\frac{420}{x} = \frac{1260}{y}$
c. Rate of automobile: 60 miles per hour
Rate of airplane: 180 miles per hour

13. **a.** One number: x
Second number: y
Third number: z
b. $x + y + z = 15$
$y = 2x$
$z = y$
c. The numbers are 3, 6, and 6

15. **a.** Number of nickels: x
Number of dimes: y
Number of quarters: z
b. $x + y + z = 85$
$0.05x + 0.10y + 0.25z = 6.25$
$x = 3y$
c. 60 nickels, 20 dimes, and 5 quarters

17. **a.** One side: x
Second side: y
Third side: z
b. $x + y + z = 155$
$x + 20 = y$
$z + 5 = y$
c. Side x: 40 inches; side y: 60 inches; and side z: 55 inches

19. **a.** Age of red wine: x
  b. Age of white wine: y
    1976: $y = 2x$
    1986: $y + 10 = (x + 10) + 4$
  c. $x = 4$ and $y = 8$;
    White wine: $1976 - 8 = 1968$
    Red wine: $1976 - 4 = 1972$

21. **a.** $C = 20 + 0.40x$
  b. $R = 1.20x$
  c. 25 records

23. $a(-1) + b(2) + 3 = 0$
  $a(-3) + b(0) + 3 = 0$
  $a = 1$ and $b = -1$

25. $a(-2) + b(0) + c(4) = 1$
  $a(6) + b(-1) + c(0) = 1$
  $a(0) + b(3) + c(0) = 1$
  $a = \dfrac{2}{9}$, $b = \dfrac{1}{3}$, and $c = \dfrac{13}{36}$

Review Exercises (page 306) **1.** $\left\{\left(\dfrac{1}{2}, \dfrac{7}{2}\right)\right\}$

2. $\{(1, 2)\}$ **3.** $\{(12, 0)\}$ **4.** $\left\{\left(\dfrac{1}{2}, \dfrac{3}{2}\right)\right\}$

5. unique solution   **6.** inconsistent
7. dependent   **8.** unique solution
9. $\{(2, 0, -1)\}$ **10.** $\{(2, 1, -1)\}$ **11.** $\{(2, -5, 3)\}$
12. $\left\{\left(\dfrac{4}{17}, -\dfrac{2}{17}, -\dfrac{84}{17}\right)\right\}$ **13.** $\{(-2, 1, 3)\}$
14. $\{(2, -1, 0)\}$ **15.** -13 **16.** 24
17. $\{(8, 1)\}$ **18.** $\{(-7, 4)\}$ **19.** $\{(1, 2)\}$
20. $\{(6, 0)\}$ **21.** -2 **22.** -19
23. $\{(1, 2, 3)\}$ **24.** $\{(2, -1, 3)\}$ **25.** $\{(1, 2, -1)\}$
26. $\{(1, 2, -1)\}$ **27.** $\{(3, -1)\}$ **28.** $\{(4, 0)\}$
29. $\{(4, 1)\}$ **30.** $\{(0, 3, -1)\}$ **31.** $\{(-1, 0, 2)\}$
32. $\{(1, 0, 0)\}$
33. **a.** Number of dimes: x
    Number of quarters: y
  b. $x - y = 25$
    $0.10x + 0.25y = 4.95$
  c. 32 dimes; 7 quarters
34. **a.** Number of first-class tickets: x
    Number of tourist tickets: y
  b. $x + y = 64$
    $280x + 160y = 12{,}160$
  c. 16 first-class tickets;
    48 tourist tickets

35. **a.** Amount invested at 10%: x
    Amount invested at 12%: y
  b. $x + y = 8000$
    $0.10x + 0.12y = 844$
  c. \$5800 invested at 10%;
    \$2200 invested at 12%
36. **a.** Amount invested at 14%: x
    Amount invested at 11%: y
  b. $x + y = 2400$
    $0.14x - 0.11y = 111$
  c. \$1500 invested at 14%;
    \$900 invested at 11%
37. **a.** Rate of automobile: x
    Rate of airplane: y
  b. $y - x = 180$
    $\dfrac{840}{y} = \dfrac{210}{x}$
  c. Rate of automobile: 60 miles per hour
    Rate of airplane: 240 miles per hour
38. **a.** Speed of one woman (slower): x
    Speed of second woman: y
  b. $y - x = 5$
    $\dfrac{200}{y} = \dfrac{180}{x}$
  c. Speed of first woman: 45 miles per hour
    Speed of second woman: 50 miles per hour
39. **a.** Length of shortest side: x
    Length of second side: y
    Length of longest side: z
  b. $x + y + z = 30$
    $y - x = 7$
    $z - y = 1$
  c. Lengths are 5 cm, 12 cm, and 13 cm
40. **a.** Measure of smallest angle: x
    Measure of second angle: y
    Measure of third angle: z
  b. $x + y + z = 180$
    $y - x = 20$
    $z = 3x$
  c. Measures are 32°, 52°, and 96°

Cumulative Exercises (page 308) **1.** -32
2. $3(xy)^{1/2} - yx^{2/3}$ **3.** $(x - 3)(x - 2)(2x - 1)$
4. a^3 **5.** -16 **6.** $6x^2 + 2x$
7. $\dfrac{-x + 6}{(x - 3)(x - 1)(x + 2)}$ **8.** $\dfrac{xy}{y^2 - x^2}$
9. $\left\{\dfrac{3 \pm i\sqrt{15}}{4}\right\}$ **10.** $l = \dfrac{3V - hc}{ah + bh}$

11. $t = -\ln\dfrac{k-y}{k}$ or $t = \ln\dfrac{k}{k-y}$

12. $k = l^{T/T_0} - 10$ **13.** $\{(8, -6)\}$

14. $\{(5, 1, -1)\}$ **15.** $2x + 3y = 11$

16. $9x - 2y = 3$ **17.** $4x + 2h - 1$

18.

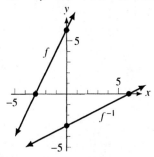

19.

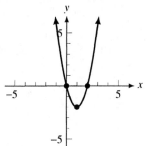

20.

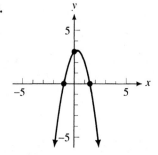

21. $34°$, $68°$, and $78°$

22. 144 miles   **23.** 5.26 centimeters   **24.** $35

25. 12 days

Exercise Set 11.1 (page 318)

1.

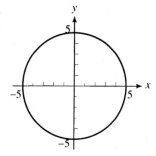

3.

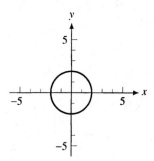

5.

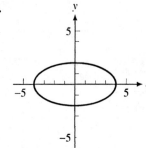

7.

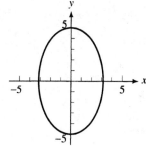

9.

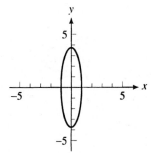

11.

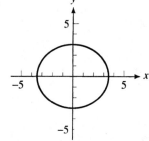

13.

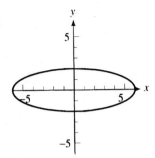

15.

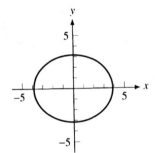

17.

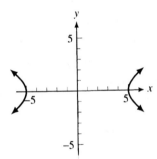

19.

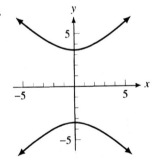

21.

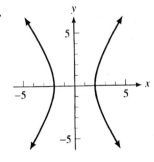

23.

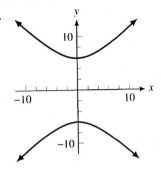

25.

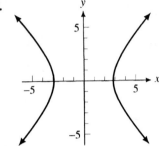

27.

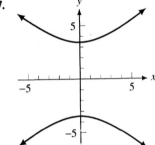

29. circle;   radius: 2

31. hyperbola; x-intercepts: $\pm\sqrt{8}$

33. ellipse; x-intercepts: $\pm\sqrt{3}$; y-intercepts: $\pm\sqrt{6}$

35. parabola;   vertex: $\left(0, -\dfrac{3}{2}\right)$, opens up

37. hyperbola; y-intercepts: $\pm\sqrt{6}$

39. parabola;   vertex: $(0, -4)$, opens up

41.

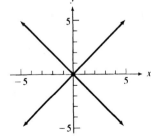

43.

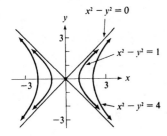

$x^2 - y^2 = 0$

$x^2 - y^2 = 1$

$x^2 - y^2 = 4$

Exercise Set 11.2 (page 321)

1. $\{(-1, -4), (5, 20)\}$

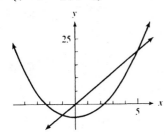

3. $\{(2, 3), (3, 2)\}$

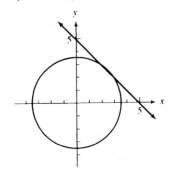

5. $\{(-3, 4), (4, -3)\}$

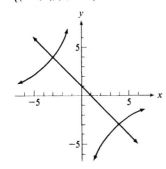

7. $\{(2, 2), (-2, -2)\}$

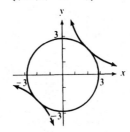

9. $\{(i\sqrt{7}, 4), (-i\sqrt{7}, 4)\}$

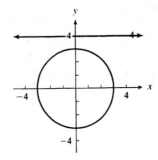

11. $\left\{ \left(\dfrac{-1 + \sqrt{13}}{2}, \dfrac{1 + \sqrt{13}}{2} \right), \left(\dfrac{-1 - \sqrt{13}}{2}, \dfrac{1 - \sqrt{13}}{2} \right) \right\}$

13. $\{(3, 1), (2, 0)\}$ **15.** $\{(-1, -3)\}$

17. 2; 3   **19.** length, 12 inches; width, 1 inch

21. **a.** Amount of investment: A
Rate of investment: r

    b. $rA = 32$
$(r - 0.005)(A + 200) = 35$

    c. \$800 invested at 4%

Exercise Set 11.3 (page 324)

1. $\{(1, 3), (-1, 3), (1, -3), (-1, -3)\}$

3. $\{(1, 2), (-1, 2), (1, -2), (-1, -2)\}$

5. $\{(3, \sqrt{2}), (-3, \sqrt{2}), (3, -\sqrt{2}), (-3, -\sqrt{2})\}$

7. $\{(2, 1), (-2, 1), (2, -1), (-2, -1)\}$

9. $\{(\sqrt{3}, 4), (-\sqrt{3}, 4), (\sqrt{3}, -4), (-\sqrt{3}, -4)\}$

11. $\{(2, -2), (-2, 2), (2i\sqrt{2}, i\sqrt{2}), (-2i\sqrt{2}, -i\sqrt{2})\}$

13. $\{(1, -1), (-1, 1), (i, i), (-i, -i)\}$

15. $\{(1, -2), (-1, 2), (2, -1), (-2, 1)\}$

17. $\{(3, 1), (-3, -1), (-2\sqrt{7}, \sqrt{7}), (2\sqrt{7}, \sqrt{7})\}$

19. $\left\{ \left(\dfrac{2\sqrt{3}}{3}, \dfrac{\sqrt{3}}{3} \right), \left(\dfrac{-2\sqrt{3}}{3}, -\dfrac{\sqrt{3}}{3} \right), (-6i, 4i), (6i, -4i) \right\}$

21. **a.** 1   **b.** 2   **c.** 4

Review Exercises (page 325)

1.

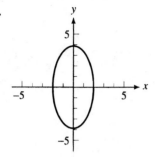

2.

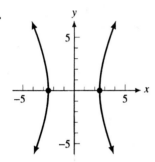

3.

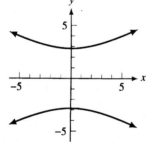

4.

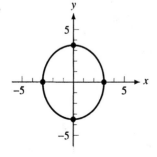

5.

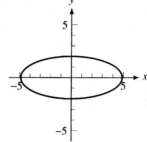

6.

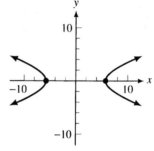

7.

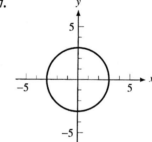

8.

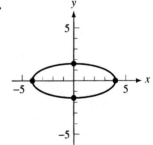

9.

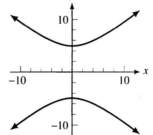

10.

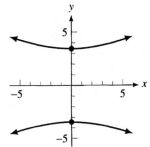

17.

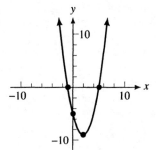

11. $\left\{\left(3,\dfrac{\sqrt{3}}{3}\right),\left(3,-\dfrac{\sqrt{3}}{3}\right)\right\}$ **12.** $\{(4i,-2),(-4i,-2)\}$

18.

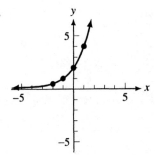

13. $\{(4,-13),(1,2)\}$ **14.** $\left\{\left(\dfrac{6}{7},-\dfrac{37}{7}\right),(2,-3)\right\}$

15. $\{(1,\sqrt{5}),(1,-\sqrt{5}),(-1,\sqrt{5}),(-1,-\sqrt{5})\}$

16. $\{(2,3),(2,-3),(-2,3),(-2,-3)\}$

17. $\left\{(1,-2),(-1,2),\left(2\sqrt{3},\dfrac{-\sqrt{3}}{3}\right),\left(-2\sqrt{3},\dfrac{1}{\sqrt{3}}\right)\right\}$

18. $\{(2,1),(-2,-1),(i,-2i),(-i,2i)\}$

19. Central ellipse;   **20.** Central hyperbola;
x-intercepts: $\pm\sqrt{24}$ vertices: $(0,\sqrt{12})$ and
y-intercepts: $\pm\sqrt{6}$ $(0,-\sqrt{12})$

19.

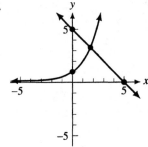

21. Central parabola;   **22.** Central parabola;
opens upward,   opens upward,
vertex: $(0,6)$ vertex: $\left(0,-\dfrac{9}{2}\right)$

23. Central hyperbola;   **24.** Central ellipse;
vertices: $(\sqrt{6},0)$ and   x-intercepts: $\pm\sqrt{2}$
$(-\sqrt{6},0)$ y-intercepts: $\pm\sqrt{12}$

25. Central circle;   **26.** Central hyperbola;
radius: $\sqrt{8}$ vertices: $(\sqrt{8},0)$ and
                                $(-\sqrt{8},0)$

20.

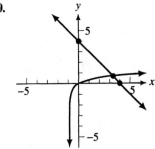

27. Width: 7 centimeters   **28.** Width: 2 centimeters
Length: 10 centimeters   Length: 7 centimeters

Cumulative Exercises (page 327) 1. $\dfrac{x^3-x^2-7x-2}{(x-3)(x+3)}$

2. $\dfrac{1}{x+4}$ **3.** $\dfrac{2x}{y}$ **4.** $-x\sqrt[3]{2y^2}$

5. $y=\pm\sqrt{\dfrac{3x-2}{6}}$ **6.** all real numbers; $x\neq 2,-2$

7. -2 and 7 **8.** $-3<x<3$ **9.** $\log_b\dfrac{x^{1/2}}{y^2z^3}$

10. $t=\dfrac{1}{k}\ln\dfrac{P-c}{P_0}$ **11.** $\{(-1,5)\}$

12. $\{(2,1),(7/4,7/4)\}$ **13.** $x=\dfrac{k\pm\sqrt{k^2-8}}{4}$

14. $2x-y=7$ **15.** $a=4,\ b=-4,\ c=-8$

16. $\{(2,-4,0)\}$

21. 45 miles

22. Approximately 48.6 centimeters

23. Approximately 94.6 pounds

24. 2.2 centimeters   **25.** 34.7 hours

Exercise Set 12.1 (page 331)

1. $x<2$

3. $x \leqslant 12$

5. $x > 3$

7. $x > 3$

9. $x < -6$

11. $x \geqslant -\dfrac{14}{3}$

13. $x > -11$

15. $x \geqslant 0$

17. $6 < x < 10$

19. $-2 < x \leqslant 3$

21. $-6 < x < -2$

23. $-2 < x \leqslant 3$

25. $-\dfrac{22}{3} < x < -4$

27. $7 \leqslant x < 7.9$

29. 94% or more
31. Between $-9.4°F$ and $28.4°F$
33. At least 22 points
35. When first month's salary greater than $1000
37. Between 79% and 100%

39.

41.

43.

Exercise Set 12.2 (page 335)

1.

3.

5.

7.

9.

11.

13.

15.

17.

19.

21. $(-5, 3]$ **23.** $[-1, 6]$ **25.** $[3, \infty)$
27. $(-\infty, 0]$
29. $\{x| -8 \leqslant x \leqslant 2\};$ $\{x| 3 < x \leqslant 7\}$

31. $\{x| -7 \leqslant x \leqslant -3\};$ $\{x| 0 < x \leqslant 4\}$

33. $\{x| -5 < x \leqslant -3\};$ $\{x| -2 < x \leqslant 0\};$
$\{x| 1 < x < 3\}$

35. $[-6, 4]$ **37.** disjoint   **39.** disjoint

Exercise Set 12.3 (page 338) 1. $\{5, -5\}$

3. $\{(13, -5)\}$ **5.** $\{(6, -7)\}$ **7.** $\left\{1, \dfrac{5}{3}\right\}$

9. $\left\{-\dfrac{3}{4}\right\}$ **11.** $\{(0, 3)\}$

13. $\{x| -2 < x < 2\}$ or $(-2, 2)$

15. $\{x| -7 \leqslant x \leqslant 1\}$ or $[-7, 1]$

17. $\{x| 1 < x < 4\}$ or $(1, 4)$

19. $\{x| -4 \leqslant x \leqslant 12\}$ or $[-4, 12]$

21. $\left\{ x \middle| -\dfrac{3}{2} < x < 2 \right\}$ or $\left(-\dfrac{3}{2}, 2 \right)$

23. $\left\{ x \middle| -\dfrac{13}{3} < x < \dfrac{11}{3} \right\}$ or $\left(-\dfrac{13}{3}, \dfrac{11}{3} \right)$

25. $\{x| x < -3\} \cup \{x| x > 3\}$ or $(-\infty, -3) \cup (3, +\infty)$

27. $\{x| x < -3\} \cup \{x| x > 7\}$ or $(-\infty, -3) \cup (7, \infty)$

29. $\{x| x \leqslant -2\} \cup \{x| x \geqslant 5\}$ or $(-\infty, -2] \cup [5, +\infty)$

31. $\left\{ x \middle| x < -\dfrac{4}{3} \right\} \cup \{x| x > 2\}$ or $\left(-\infty, \dfrac{4}{3} \right) \cup (2, +\infty)$

33. $\left\{ x \middle| x \geqslant \dfrac{13}{8} \right\} \cup \left\{ x \middle| x < -\dfrac{19}{14} \right\}$ or $\left(-\infty, -\dfrac{19}{4} \right) \cup \left(\dfrac{13}{8}, +\infty \right)$

35. $[-8, 6]$ **37.** $\left(-\infty, \dfrac{3}{2} \right) \cup \left(\dfrac{9}{2}, \infty \right)$ **39.** $\left\{ -\dfrac{2}{5} \right\}$

41. $\left[-\dfrac{5}{4}, \dfrac{7}{4} \right]$ **43.** $|y| = 3$ **45.** $|x - 5| = 3$

47. $|x - 7| < 4$

Exercise Set 12.4 (page 343)

1. $\{x| x < -1\} \cup \{x| x > 2\}$ or $(-\infty, -1) \cup (2, +\infty)$

3. $\{x| -3 < x < 4\}$ or $(-3, 4)$

5. $\{x| 0 \leqslant x \leqslant 2\}$ or $[0, 2]$

7. $\{x| x < 0\} \cup \{x| x > 5\}$ or $(-\infty, 0); (5, \infty)$

9. $\{x| x < -1\} \cup \{x| x > 4\}$ or $(-\infty, -1); (4, +\infty)$

11. $\{x| -2 \leqslant x \leqslant 3\}$ or $[-2, 3]$

13. $\{x| -5 \leqslant x \leqslant 3\}$ or $[-5, 3]$

15. $\{x| x < -3\} \cup \{x| x > 4\}$ or $(-\infty, -3); (4, \infty)$

17. $\{x| -\sqrt{5} < x < \sqrt{5}\}$ or $(-\sqrt{5}, \sqrt{5})$ **19.** $\varnothing$

21. $\{x| -3 < x < 2\}$ or $(-3, 2)$

23. $\left\{ x \middle| -\dfrac{8}{3} < x < -2 \right\}$ or $\left(-\dfrac{8}{3}, 2 \right)$

25. $\left\{ x \middle| x \leqslant -\dfrac{1}{2} \right\} \cup \{x| x > 0\}$ or $\left(-\infty, -\dfrac{1}{2} \right]; (0, +\infty)$

27. $\{x| x < 1\} \cup \{x \geqslant 2\}$ or $(-\infty, 1); [2, +\infty)$

29. $\{x| x < -1\} \cup \{x| 0 < x < 3\}$ or $(-\infty, -1); (0, 3)$

31. $\{x| x < 0\} \cup \{x| 2 < x \leqslant 4\}$ or $(-\infty, 0); (2, 4]$

33. $\{x| -3 < x < -2\} \cup \{x| 2 < x < 3\}$ or $(-3, -2); (2, 3)$

35. $(4, 16)$ **37.** $[0, 100) \cup (600, 700)$ **39.** $(10, 30)$

Exercise Set 12.5 (page 348)

1.

3.

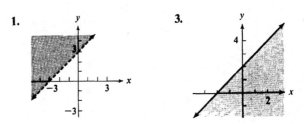

5.

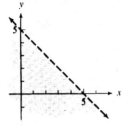

7.

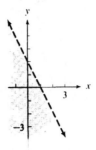

25.

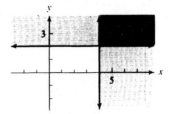

9.

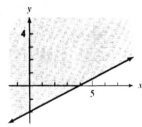

11.

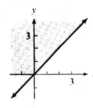

27.

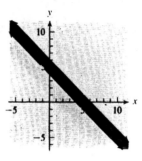

13.

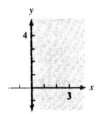

15.

29.

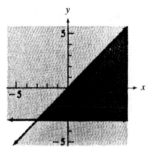

17.

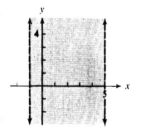

19.

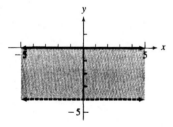

31.

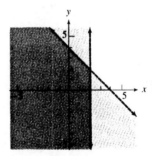

21.

23.

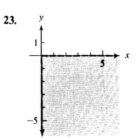

33.

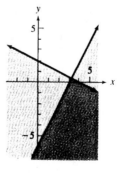

35.

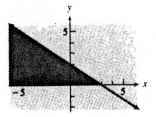

37.

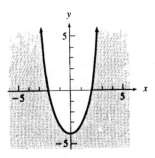

39.

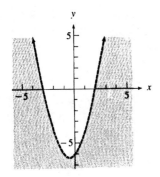

41.

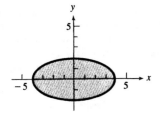

43.

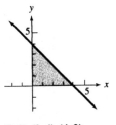

(0, 0), (0, 4), (4, 0)

45.

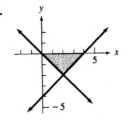

(0, 0), (4, 0), (2, −2)

47.

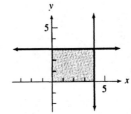

(0, 0), (0, 3), (4, 3), (4, 0)

49.

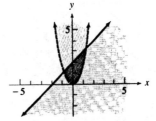

51.

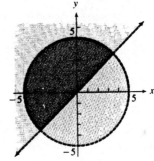

53.

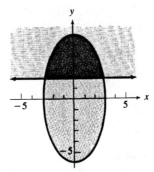

55.

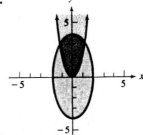

Review Exercises (page 350)

1. $x \leqslant 27$

2. $x \leqslant \dfrac{3}{2}$

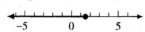

3. $2 < x \leqslant 5$

4. $1 < x < 3$

5. $x \geqslant 9$

6. $x > \dfrac{31}{32}$

7. Greater than or equal to 97   8. 500 miles

9.

10.

11.

12.

13.

14.

15.

16.

17. $(-\infty, -4]$ 18. $(3, \infty)$ 19. $(-5, 2]$

20. $[-4, 3]$ 21. $\{-4, 3\}$ 22. $\left\{-\dfrac{5}{4}, \dfrac{11}{4}\right\}$

23. $x \leqslant -8$ or $x \geqslant 2$

24. $-3 < x < 7$

25. $-3 < x < 4$

26. $x < -\dfrac{10}{3}$ or $x \geqslant 2$

27. $x < 0$ or $x > 9$

28. $-3 < x < -2$

29. $-4 \leqslant x \leqslant 2$

30. $x < -1$ or $x > 4$

31. $x \leqslant -1$ or $x > 3$

32. $x \leqslant -4$ or $x > -2$

33.

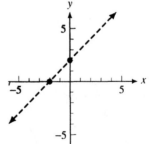

34.

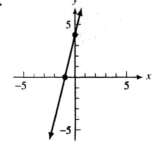

35.

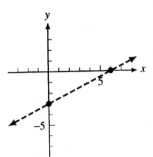

36.

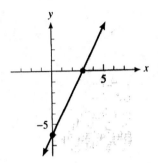

37.

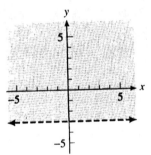

38.

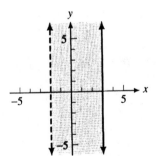

39.

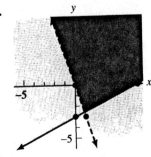

40.

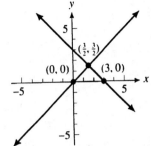

41.

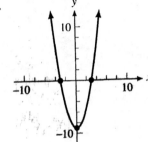

42.

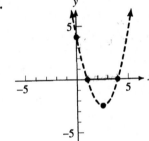

43.

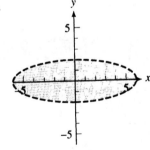

44.

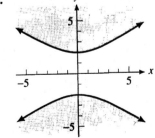

Cumulative Exercises (page 351) **1.** $3x^5y^6 - 3x^6y^{10}$

2. 8×10^3 **3.** $2yz^3\sqrt[4]{4x^3y^3}$

4. $-x^2(x+3)(x-2)$ **5.** $(2x-1)(x-1)(x+1)$

6. $\dfrac{x-4}{(x+2)(x-2)(x+4)}$

7. $\dfrac{x^3 - x^2 - 7x - 2}{(x-3)(x+3)}$ **8.** -6

9. $x > \dfrac{9}{5}$

10. $x \leqslant 0$ or $x \geqslant 3$

11. $\left\{(2,3), \left(\dfrac{146}{35}, \dfrac{48}{35}\right)\right\}$ **12.** $\{(-1,5)\}$

13. $-\dfrac{\sqrt{15}}{6} - \dfrac{\sqrt{3}}{3}i$ **14.** $\dfrac{-8x-1}{2x}$ **15.** $\left\{\dfrac{3 \pm \sqrt{3}}{4}\right\}$

16. $\{5,8\}$ **17.** $\left\{\dfrac{20}{3}\right\}$ **18.** $\left\{-\dfrac{3}{4} \pm \dfrac{\sqrt{15}}{4}i\right\}$

19. $\{4\}$ **20.** $\{-0.79\}$ **21.** $11x + 2y + 23 = 0$

22. 15 **23.** $S(x) = 4x^2$; $S(20) = 1600$

24. 1151 years

25. 20 crates to Boston, 25 to Chicago, and 10 to Los Angeles

Exercise Set 13.1 (page 355)

1. $-4, -3, -2, -1$ **3.** $-\dfrac{1}{2}, 1, \dfrac{7}{2}, 7$

5. $2, \dfrac{3}{2}, \dfrac{4}{3}, \dfrac{5}{4}$ **7.** $0, 1, 3, 6$ **9.** $-1, 1, -1, 1$

11. $1, 0, -\dfrac{1}{3}, \dfrac{1}{2}$ **13.** $1 + 4 + 9 + 16$

15. $3 + 4 + 5$ **17.** $2 + 6 + 12 + 20$

19. $-\dfrac{1}{2} + \dfrac{1}{4} - \dfrac{1}{8} + \dfrac{1}{16}$ **21.** $1 + 3 + 5 + \cdots$

23. $1 + \dfrac{1}{2} + \dfrac{1}{4} + \cdots$ **25.** $\sum\limits_{i=1}^{4} i$ **27.** $\sum\limits_{i=1}^{4} x^{2i-1}$

29. $\sum\limits_{i=1}^{5} i^2$ **31.** $\sum\limits_{i=1}^{\infty} \dfrac{i}{i+1}$ **33.** $\sum\limits_{i=1}^{\infty} \dfrac{i}{2i-1}$

35. $\sum\limits_{i=1}^{\infty} \dfrac{2^{i-1}}{i}$

Exercise Set 13.2 (page 360) **1.** $11, 15, 19$

3. $-9, -13, -17$ $s_n = 4n - 1$

$s_n = 3 - 4n$

5. $x+2, \quad x+3, \quad x+4$

$s_n = x + n - 1$

7. $x+5a, \quad x+7a, \quad x+9a$

$s_n = x + 2an - a$

9. $2x+7, \quad 2x+10, \quad 2x+13$

$s_n = 2x + 3n - 2$

11. $3x, 4x, 5x$ **13.** 31 **15.** $\dfrac{15}{2}$ **17.** -92

$s_n = nx$

19. $2; 3; 41$ **21.** twenty-eighth term

23. $1; 8$ **25.** 16 **27.** $9; 14; 19$ **29.** 63

31. 806 **33.** -6 **35.** 1938 **37.** 196 bricks

39. $2, 7, 12$ **41.** $\dfrac{14}{15}$

43. The first n odd natural numbers form an arithmetic sequence with $a = 1$ and $d = 2$. Hence, the sum of the first n odd natural numbers is

$$S_n = \dfrac{n}{2}[2a + (n-1)d] = \dfrac{n}{2}[2 + (n-1)2]$$

$$= \dfrac{n}{2}[2 + 2n - 2] = \dfrac{n}{2}[2n] = n^2$$

Exercise Set 13.3 (page 365) **1.** $128, 512, 2048$

$s_n = 2(4)^{n-1}$

3. $\dfrac{16}{3}, \dfrac{32}{3}, \dfrac{64}{3}$ **5.** $-\dfrac{1}{2}, \dfrac{1}{4}, -\dfrac{1}{8}$

$s_n = \dfrac{2}{3}(2)^{n-1}$ $s_n = 4\left(-\dfrac{1}{2}\right)^{n-1}$

7. $-\dfrac{x^2}{a^2}, \dfrac{x^3}{a^3}, -\dfrac{x^4}{a^4}$ **9.** 1536 **11.** $-243a^{20}$

$s_n = \dfrac{a}{x}\left(-\dfrac{x}{a}\right)^{n-1}$ **13.** 3 **15.** $3, 9$

17. 18 or -18 **19.** $16, 8, 4$ or $-16, 8, -4$

21. 1092 **23.** $\dfrac{31}{32}$ **25.** $\dfrac{364}{729}$

27.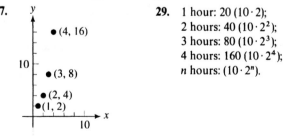

29. 1 hour: $20 \, (10 \cdot 2)$;
2 hours: $40 \, (10 \cdot 2^2)$;
3 hours: $80 \, (10 \cdot 2^3)$;
4 hours: $160 \, (10 \cdot 2^4)$;
n hours: $(10 \cdot 2^n)$.

Exercise Set 13.4 (page 370) **1.** 24

3. does not exist   **5.** $\dfrac{9}{20}$ **7.** $\dfrac{8}{49}$ **9.** 2

11. $\dfrac{1}{3}$ **13.** $\dfrac{31}{99}$ **15.** $\dfrac{2408}{999}$ **17.** $\dfrac{29}{225}$

19. \$220.80; \$222.55 **21.** 20 centimeters

23. 30 feet

25. After 2 years: $P(1 + r)(1 + r) = P(1 + r)^2$
after 3 years: $P(1 + r)^2(1 + r) = P(1 + r)^3$
after n years: $P(1 + r)^n$

Exercise Set 13.5 (page 374) **1.** $8\cdot7\cdot6\cdot5\cdot4\cdot3\cdot2\cdot1$
3. $2\cdot4\cdot3\cdot2\cdot1$ **5.** $6\cdot5\cdot4\cdot3\cdot2\cdot1$ **7.** 120

9. 72 **11.** 15 **13.** 28 **15.** $3!$ **17.** $\dfrac{6!}{2!}$

19. $\dfrac{8!}{5!}$ **21.** $n(n-1)(n-2)\cdot\cdots\cdot3\cdot2\cdot1$

23. $3n(3n-1)(3n-2)\cdot\cdots\cdot3\cdot2\cdot1$

25. $(n-2)(n-3)(n-4)\cdot\cdots\cdot3\cdot2\cdot1$

27. $x^5 + 15x^4 + 90x^3 + 270x^2 + 405x + 243$

29. $x^4 - 12x^3 + 54x^2 - 108x + 81$

31. $8x^2 - 6x^2y + \dfrac{3}{2}xy^2 - \dfrac{1}{8}y^3$

33. $\dfrac{1}{64}x^6 + \dfrac{3}{8}x^5 + \dfrac{15}{4}x^4 + 20x^3 + 60x^2 + 96x + 64$

35. $x^{20} + 20x^{19}y + \dfrac{20\cdot19}{2!}x^{18}y^2 + \dfrac{20\cdot19\cdot18}{3!}x^{17}y^3$

37. $a^{12} + 12a^{11}(-2b) + \dfrac{12\cdot11}{2!}a^{10}(-2b)^2$
$+ \dfrac{12\cdot11\cdot10}{3!}a^9(-2b)^3$

39. $x^{10} + 10x^9(-\sqrt{2}) + \dfrac{10\cdot9}{2!}x^8(-\sqrt{2})^2$
$+ \dfrac{10\cdot9\cdot8}{3!}x^7(-\sqrt{2})^3$

41. $-3003a^{10}b^5$ **43.** $3360x^6y^4$ **45.** $21x^{10}y^4$
47. $63a^5b^4$ **49.** 1.22 **51.** 0.92
53. **a.** $1^{-1} + (-1)(1^{-2})x + 1(1^{-3})x^2 + (-1)(1^{-4})x^3$ or
$1 - x + x^2 - x^3$
b. $1 - x + x^2 - x^3$ **c.** results are equal

Review Exercises (page 377) **1.** $1, \dfrac{3}{4}, \dfrac{5}{9}, \dfrac{7}{16}$

2. $1, -\dfrac{1}{2}, \dfrac{1}{3}, -\dfrac{1}{4}$ **3.** $2(1) + 3(2) + 4(3) + 5(4)$

4. $\dfrac{1}{2} + \dfrac{2}{5} + \dfrac{3}{10} + \cdots + \dfrac{i}{i^2 + 1}$ **5.** $4n + 1$ **6.** 94

7. 138 **8.** 68 **9.** $5\left(\dfrac{9}{5}\right)^{n-1}$ **10.** $-\dfrac{81}{8}$

11. $-\dfrac{26}{27}$ **12.** $\dfrac{121}{243}$ **13.** $\dfrac{1}{2}$ **14.** $-\dfrac{3}{7}$ **15.** $\dfrac{4}{9}$

16. $2\dfrac{7}{11}$ **17.** 56 **18.** $2n^3 - 6n^2 + 4n$

19. $x^{10} - 20x^9y + 180x^8y^2 - 960x^7y^3$

20. $-15{,}360x^3y^7$

Cumulative Exercises (page 378) **1.** $-6 + 4\sqrt{6}$

2. 0.2725 **3.** $y = \pm\sqrt{\dfrac{3x - 2}{6}}$ **4.** $\left\{\dfrac{17}{12}\right\}$

5. $\left\{\dfrac{3 \pm \sqrt{3}}{4}\right\}$ **6.** $\{5\}$

7. $\{(-2, -4), (2, 4), (-4, -2), (4, 2)\}$

8. $3 - \dfrac{5}{2} + \dfrac{7}{3} - \dfrac{9}{4} + \dfrac{11}{5}$ **9.** -182

10. $-5280x^4y^{21}$ **11.** $\left\{-4, \dfrac{3}{2}, -\dfrac{1}{3}\right\}$ **12.** $\left\{\dfrac{1}{2}\right\}$

13. $a^8b^3c^6$ **14.** $\dfrac{7}{13} + \dfrac{9}{13}i$ **15.** -4 and $\dfrac{3}{2}$

16.

17.

18.

19.

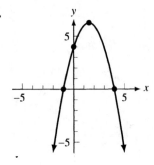

20.

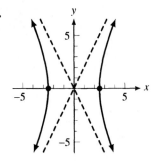

21. $a = -2$, $b = 5$, and $c = -3$

22. 13 meters by 16 meters

23. Approximately 6.93 seconds

24. 5304   **25.** 56 feet

Exercise Set Appendix A (page 382)

1. $x - 2$ $(x \neq 6)$ **3.** $x + 2$ $(x \neq -2)$

5. $x^3 - x^2 + \dfrac{-1}{x - 2}$ $(x \neq 2)$

7. $2x^2 - 2x + 3 + \dfrac{-8}{x + 1}$ $(x \neq -1)$

9. $2x^3 + 10x^2 + 50x + 249 + \dfrac{1251}{x - 5}$ $(x \neq 5)$

11. $x^2 + 2x - 3 + \dfrac{4}{x + 2}$ $(x \neq -2)$

13. $x^3 + x + 2 + \dfrac{3}{x - 2}$ $(x \neq 2)$

15. $x^4 + 2x^3 + 2x^2 + 4x + 4 + \dfrac{3}{x - 1}$ $(x \neq 1)$

17. $x^4 - x^3 + x^2 - 4x + 4 - \dfrac{5}{x + 1}$ $(x \neq -1)$

19. $x^5 + x^4 + 2x^3 + 2x^2 + 2x + 1 + \dfrac{1}{x - 1}$ $(x \neq 1)$

21. $x^4 + x^3 + x^2 + x + 1$ $(x \neq 1)$

23. $x^5 + x^4 + x^3 + x^2 + x + 1$ $(x \neq 1)$

Exercise Set Appendix B (page 387)

1. $74; -46$ **3.** $5; 44$

5.

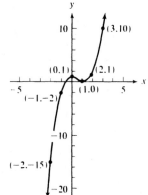

7.

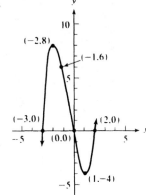

9.

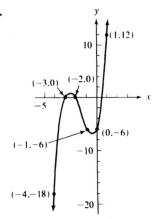

11.

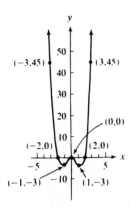

13. no   **15.** yes   **17.** -1 and -2

19. 0, 2, and 4

21.

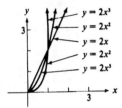

Exercise Set Appendix C (page 391) $x = -3$

3. $x = 2$, $x = -3$ **5.** $x = -2$, $x = 3$

7. Vertical asymptotes: $x = 3$, $x = -3$
  Horizontal asymptote: $y = 0$

9. Vertical asymptote: $x = \dfrac{1}{2}$

  Horizontal asymptote: $y = \dfrac{1}{2}$

11. Vertical asymptote: $x = -1$, $x = 4$
  Horizontal asymptote: $y = 2$

13. Horizontal asymptote: $y = 0$
  Vertical asymptote: $x = -3$

  y-intercept: $\dfrac{1}{3}$

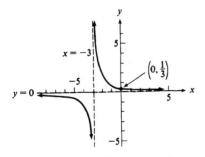

15. Horizontal asymptote: $y = 0$
  Vertical asymptote: $x = 4$, $x = -1$

  y-intercept: $-\dfrac{1}{2}$

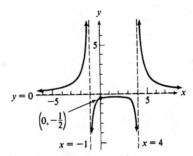

17. Horizontal asymptote: $y = 0$
  Vertical asymptotes: $x = 4$, $x = 1$

  y-intercept: $\dfrac{1}{2}$

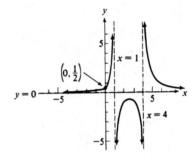

19. Horizontal asymptote: $y = 1$
  Vertical asymptote: $x = -3$
  Intercepts: $x = 0$, $y = 0$

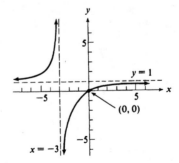

21. Horizontal asymptote: $y = 1$
Vertical asymptote: $x = -2$
y-intercept: $\dfrac{1}{2}$
x-intercept: -1

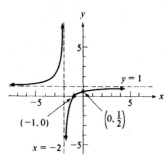

23. Horizontal asymptote: $y = 0$
Vertical asymptotes: $x = 2, \quad x = -2$
Intercepts: $(0, 0)$

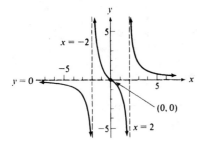

25. Horizontal asymptote: $y = 0$
Vertical asymptotes: $x = -1, \quad x = -4$
y-intercept: $-\dfrac{1}{2}$
x-intercept: 2

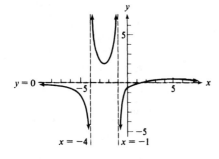

27.

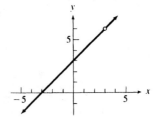

29.

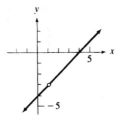

31.

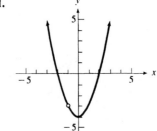

33.

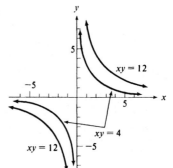

Index

Polynomial Functions

$$P(x) = (x - c)Q(x) + P(c)$$ Remainder theorem
If $P(c) = 0$, Factor theorem
then $x - c$ is a factor of $P(x)$

Conic Sections

Name of conic	Equation	Graph
Parabola	$y = ax^2 \quad (a \neq 0)$	$a < 0$ $a > 0$
Circle	$x^2 + y^2 = r^2$	
Ellipse a. Major axis on the x-axis b. Major axis on the y-axis	$\dfrac{x^2}{a^2} + \dfrac{y^2}{b^2} = 1$ $Ax^2 + By^2 = C$ $A \neq B$ A, B, C have like signs.	$a > b$ $b > a$ a. b.
Hyperbola a. Transverse axis on the x-axis b. Transverse axis on the y-axis	a. $\dfrac{x^2}{a^2} - \dfrac{y^2}{b^2} = 1$ b. $\dfrac{y^2}{a^2} - \dfrac{x^2}{b^2} = 1$ $Ax^2 + By^2 = C$ A and B, have opposite signs. $C \neq 0$.	a. b.

Systems of Linear Equations

A system of the form
$$a_1 x + b_1 y = c_1$$
$$a_2 x + b_2 y = c_2$$

has one and only one solution if
$$\frac{a_1}{a_2} \neq \frac{b_1}{b_2}$$

has no solution if
$$\frac{a_1}{a_2} = \frac{b_1}{b_2} \neq \frac{c_1}{c_2}$$

and has an infinite number of solutions if
$$\frac{a_1}{a_2} = \frac{b_1}{b_2} = \frac{c_1}{c_2}$$

Determinants

$$\begin{vmatrix} a_1 & b_1 \\ a_2 & b_2 \end{vmatrix} = a_1 b_2 - a_2 b_1$$

Cramer's rule for $a_1 x + b_1 y = c_1$
$$a_2 x + b_2 y = c_2$$

$$x = \frac{D_x}{D} = \frac{\begin{vmatrix} c_1 & b_1 \\ c_2 & b_2 \end{vmatrix}}{\begin{vmatrix} a_1 & b_1 \\ a_2 & b_2 \end{vmatrix}} \qquad y = \frac{D_y}{D} = \frac{\begin{vmatrix} a_1 & c_1 \\ a_2 & c_2 \end{vmatrix}}{\begin{vmatrix} a_1 & b_1 \\ a_2 & b_2 \end{vmatrix}}$$

$$\begin{vmatrix} a_1 & b_1 & c_1 \\ a_2 & b_2 & c_2 \\ a_3 & b_3 & c_3 \end{vmatrix} = a_1 \begin{vmatrix} b_2 & c_2 \\ b_3 & c_3 \end{vmatrix} - b_1 \begin{vmatrix} a_2 & c_2 \\ a_3 & c_3 \end{vmatrix} + c_1 \begin{vmatrix} a_2 & b_2 \\ a_3 & b_3 \end{vmatrix}$$

Cramer's rule for a linear system of three equations in three variables:

$$x = \frac{D_x}{D} \qquad y = \frac{D_y}{D} \qquad z = \frac{D_z}{D}$$

Matrices

A matrix can be written as a row-equivalent matrix by:

1. Multiplying the entries of any row by a nonzero real number

2. Interchanging two rows

3. Multiplying the entries of any row by a real number and adding the results to the corresponding elements of another row

Equations and Inequalities Involving Absolute Values

1. $|ax - b| = c$ $(c \geqslant 0)$

   is equivalent to $ax - b = c$ or $-(ax - b) = c$

2. $|ax - b| < c$

   is equivalent to $-c < ax - b < c$

3. $|ax - b| > c$

   is equivalent to $ax - b > c$ or $-(ax - b) > c$

Sequences and Series

First term a, number of terms r, nth term s_n, sum of n terms S_n

Arithmetic progression with common difference d:
$$s_n = a + (n - 1)d$$
$$S_n = \frac{n}{2}(a + s_n) = \frac{n}{2}[2a + (n - 1)d]$$

Geometric progression with common ratio r ($r \neq 1$):
$$s_n = ar^{n-1} \qquad S^n = \frac{a - ar^n}{1 - r} = \frac{a - rs_n}{1 - r}$$

Infinite geometric progression with $|r| < 1$:
$$S_\infty = \frac{a}{1 - r}$$

Binomial expansion:
$$(a + b)^n = a^n + \frac{n}{1!}a^{n-1}b + \frac{n(n - 1)}{2!}a^{n-2}b^2$$
$$+ \frac{n(n - 1)(n - 2)}{3!}a^{n-3}b^3 + \cdots$$

where $1! = 1$, $2! = 2 \cdot 1$, $3! = 3 \cdot 2 \cdot 1$,   etc.

Rational Functions

The graph of $y = \dfrac{P(x)}{Q(x)}$

has a vertical asymptote $x = a$
for each value a at which $Q(x) = 0$ and $P(x) \neq 0$

If ax^n is the term of highest degree of $P(x)$ and bx^n is the term of highest degree of $Q(x)$, the graph of $y = \dfrac{P(x)}{Q(x)}$ has a horizontal asymptote:

at $y = 0$ if $n < m$ at $y = \dfrac{a}{b}$ if $n = m$